About Pearson

Pearson is the world's learning company, with presence across 70 countries worldwide. Our unique insights and world-class expertise comes from a long history of working closely with renowned teachers, authors and thought leaders, as a result of which, we have emerged as the preferred choice for millions of teachers and learners across the world.

We believe learning opens up opportunities, creates fulfilling careers and hence better lives. We hence collaborate with the best of minds to deliver you class-leading products, spread across the Higher Education and Test Preparation spectrum.

Superior learning experience and improved outcomes are at the heart of everything we do. This product is the result of one such effort.

Your feedback plays a critical role in the evolution of our products and you can contact us - reachus@pearson.com. *We look forward to it.*

TRISHNA'S

PEARSON FOUNDATION

BIOLOGY

CLASS

9

TRISHNA'S

PEARSON FOUNDATION

BIOLOGY

CLASS 9

Eighth Edition

Pearson

Photo Credits

Chapter 1 Opener: Christoph Burgstedt / Shutterstock
Chapter 2 Opener: Kurteev Gennadii / Shutterstock
Chapter 3 Opener: Piyachok Thawornmat / 123RF
Chapter 4 Opener: Vlad61 / Shutterstock
Chapter 5 Opener: Illustration Forest / Shutterstock
Chapter 6 Opener: Stephen Mcsweeny / Shutterstock
Chapter 7 Opener: Les Scholz / Shutterstock

ISBN 978-93-713-6158-3

First Impression
Second Impression, 2026

Published by Pearson India Education Services Pvt. Ltd, CIN: U72200TN2005PTC057128.

Head Office: 1st Floor, Berger Tower, Plot No. C-001A/2, Sector 16B, Noida - 201 301, Uttar Pradesh, India.
Registered Office: 6th Floor, Tower A, Unit A and B, International Tech Park, CapitaLand, Chennai, 200 Feet Radial Road, Zamin Pallavaram, Old Pallavaram, Chennai – 600117, Tamil Nadu India
Website: in.pearson.com, Email: companysecretary.india@pearson.com

Compositor: Satish Kumar Shrivastava
Printed in India by: Rahul Print O Pack

Brief Contents

Contents

Preface

"If you have a great ambition, take as big a step as possible in the direction of fulfilling it. The step may only be a tiny one, but trust that it may be the largest one possible for now."

Mildred McAfee

Pearson Foundation Biology Series has been created keeping in mind the learner's ambition to excel in a competitive examination like NEET and other Biology Olympiads. The series can be used in addition to the books studied in school to attain that extra edge required to strengthen the concepts and prepare well for future endeavours.

Why Start Early with Pearson Foundation Series

Classes VI to X are the base years of a learner's academic life. In these years learner explore their interests and determine the goals they wish to attain. *Pearson Foundation Biology* series is filled with interactive learning that not only nurtures a learner's interest in science and mathematics but also strengthens their concepts.

The series uses real-life examples and application-based problems to teach theoretical concepts. The objective of this series is to help learners cultivate an analytical mind.

Most of the lessons to be learnt are introduced to the learners in the books for class VI. As they get promoted to higher classes, new topics are added to these lessons. This additive method helps the learners' span their learning over four standards, from VI–X. Thus, learners are not overwhelmed by the introduction of completely new lessons every time they are promoted to a new class.

While their learning is being spanned across five years, so is their ability to resolve doubts for further conceptual clarity. For instance, they can use concepts learnt in class VI to solve questions in class VII. If, in case, they get stuck while answering a question, the learners can infer for themselves that they might be lacking in conceptual clarity. They can then approach their teachers, requesting them to explain the concept once again. This helps the learner to clarify their concepts while revising the lessons previously learnt.

Since classes VI–X are deemed to be a student's formative years, we, at Pearson, aim to provide a foundation level course which serves more than just a standard curriculum.

Here is how it makes a difference to a learner's overall learning ...

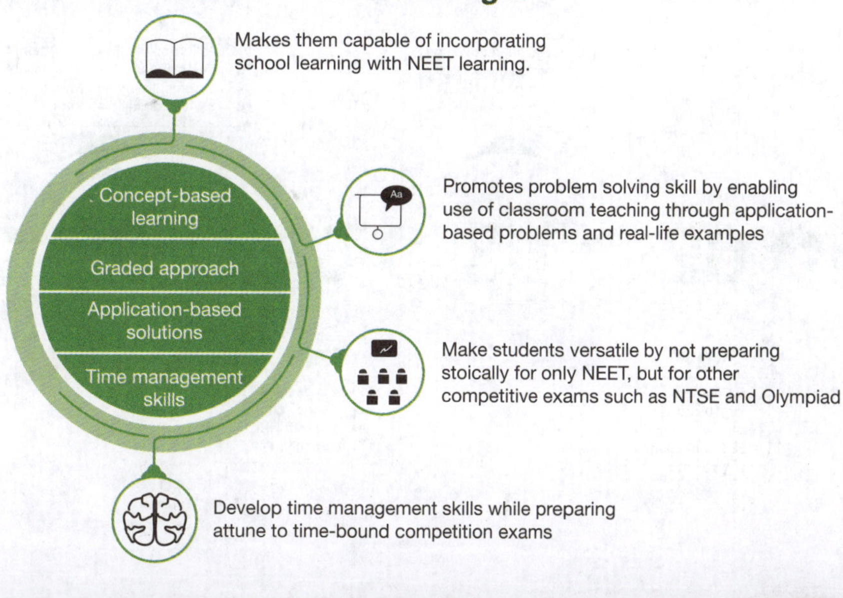

Other Uses of the Series

Instead of limiting themselves to NEET, a learner can also use this series to prepare for several other competitive examinations such as NSTSE, National and International Olympiads, BITSAT, etc. This series offers a level of concept learning that empowers learners to handle the challenging nature of questions posed in these examinations. Moreover, this will also allow the learners to have an early insight into their key strengths as well as improvement areas and help them work on themselves.

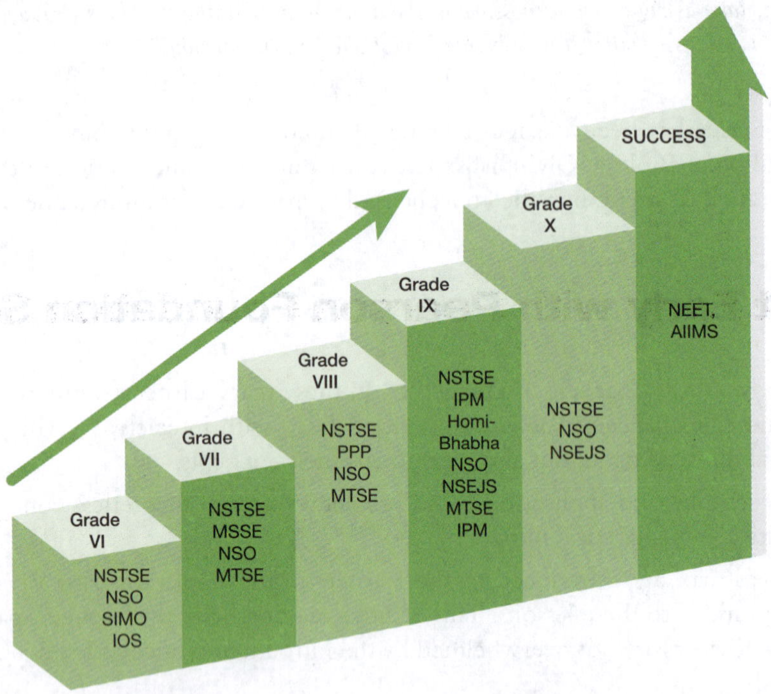

[IMO: International Mathematics Olympiad; NSO: National Science Olympiad, IOS: International Olympiad of Science, NSTSE: National Level Science Talent Search Examination, MTSE: Maharashtra Talent Search Examination, RMO: Regional Mathematical Olympiad, PPP: Pravinya Pradnya Prabhutva, NSEJS: National Standard Examination in Junior Science, IIT: Indian Institute of Technology, IISc: Indian Institute of Science, NIT: National Institute of Technology.]

Highlights of the Series

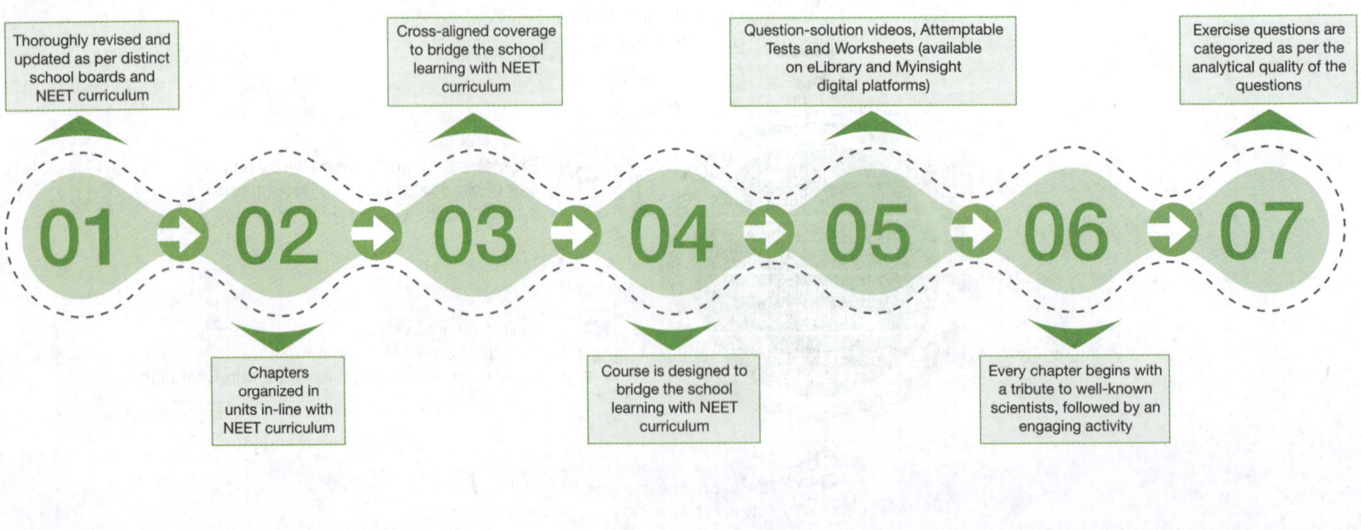

Pearson Foundation Biology series provides a perfect blend of learning through theory and practice questions with a fusion of school and NEET curriculum. It is imperative to note that this series would be as profound as you want it to be. Therefore, to get maximum benefit from this book, we recommend following the given study plan.

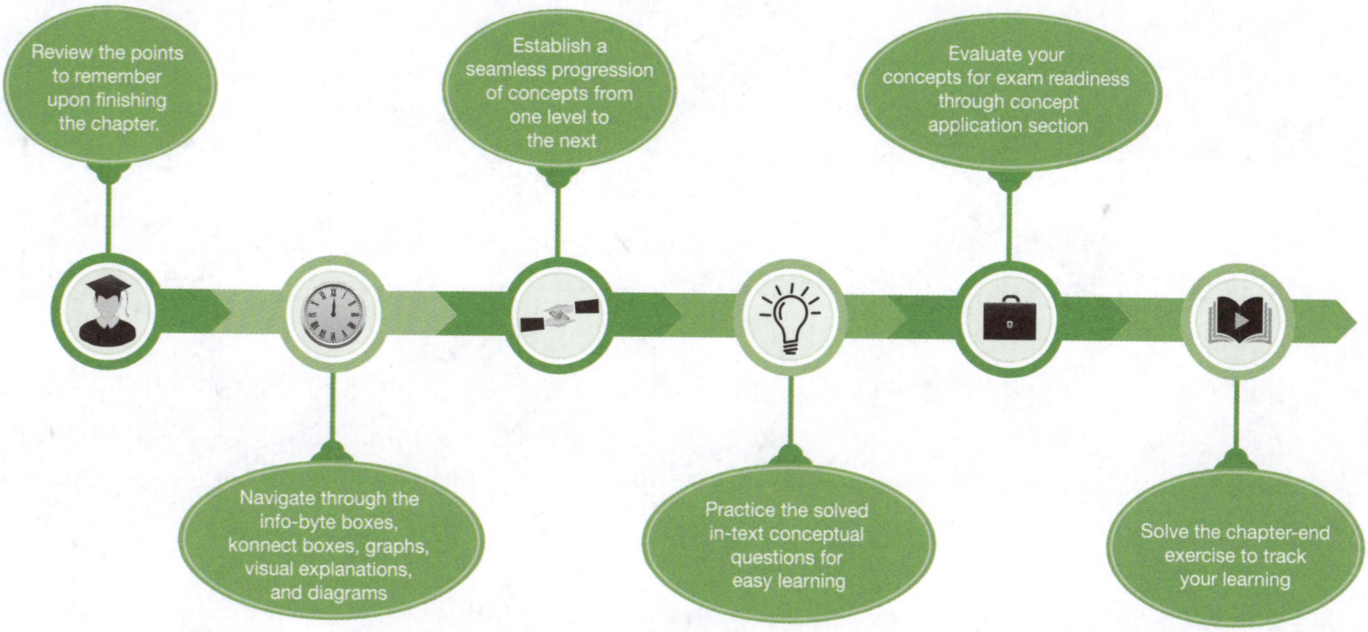

To provide a graded learning approach, the exercise part of each chapter is categorized by using four icons for question tagging. The question categorization helps the learners assess their own problem-solving and analytical skills and motivates them to improve to reach their objectives.

The following icons are used to categorize the questions with specific meanings:

Real-life situations question:

Analytical questions:

Conceptual questions:

Value-based questions:

With this refined and well-tuned course from Pearson, students will become more confident when they enter the competitive world for actual NEET preparation. The effort put in today will transform into a valuable asset, contributing to success in future competitive examinations.

Chapter Insights

Remember

Before beginning this chapter, you should be able to:

- Define interrelationship among various living organisms and their environment
- Define the importance of biodiversity
- List the different layers of earth

Remember section will help them to memorize and review the previous learning on a particular topic

Key points will help the students to identify the essential points in a chapter

Key Ideas

After completing this chapter, you should be able to:

- Define ecosystem and appreciate the interrelationships among the various living organisms and their environment.
- Classify the different types of natural resources on the basis of their need, availability and

Scientific Crypt

A Tribute to Rudolf Virchow (1821–1902)

Rudolf Virchow (1821-1902) is regarded as the '*Father of Modern Pathology*' in the scientific community. He was more than just a pathologist; he was a brilliant biologist, physician, and anthropologist who introduced the world to ground-breaking ideas that changed the way we think about biology and disease.

His seminal contribution was the cell theory, in which he boldly proposed '*omnis cellula e cellula*,' which means that every cell derives from another existing cell. This theory challenged the widely held concept of spontaneous generation at the time, laying the groundwork for cell biology and modern medicine.

Virchow deftly linked cellular abnormalities to diseases, paving the way for medical science to develop targeted treatments and therapies for a variety of ailments. His insights emphasized the importance of studying cells in understanding disease mechanisms, illuminating the path to unravelling the mysteries of life's smallest units.

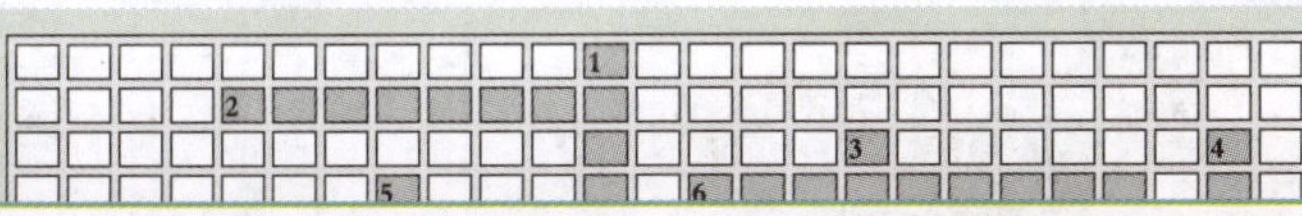

Scientific Crypt provides information about well-known scientists related to the chapter. The engaging activity is also given in the form of a crossword to keep the learners interested.

INTRODUCTION

Living organisms live in different environments. They possess different organs performing various functions. All these organisms are made up of basic building blocks, called cells, which have some common properties. These blocks are called **cells**. The cells are the smallest structural and functional units of life which are responsible for keeping an organism alive and functional. The study of cells with the subcellular components and their functions is known as **cytology or cell biology**.

Introduction section helps to lay the foundation of the following chapter and leads the way for further learning

Concepts are explained in a well-structured and lucid manner

Cell Theory

In 1838, Matthias Jakob Schleiden, a German botanist was the first to assert that cells are the bui plants. In 1839, another German physiologist, Theodor Schwann stated that cells are the fundament Their discoveries led to the formulation of the 'Cell Theory'. However, the cell theory failed to cells arise.

In 1855, Rudolf Virchow, a German physician and anthropologist, stated in Latin '*Omnis cellula e c* that new cells come from the pre-existing cells.

Konnect

- A ribonucleoprotein (RNP) is a complex of ribonucleic acid and RNA-binding protein.
- The two subunits of a ribosome are assigned values known as Svedberg Value, denoted by S.

Konnect boxes are some add-on information of related topic

Info bytes are interesting trivia and facts that engage young minds and keep the grey cells ticking!

Info Bytes!

The size of a cell is usually determined by its diameter and not by the length.

Quick Recap

✔ **Bryophytes can thrive only in moist places. Give reason.**

Bryophytes do not possess roots. The rhizoids of the thallus fix the plant to the substratum. They absorb water and minerals from the ground or from the atmosphere. Therefore, they require moist surface. Presence of water is essential for swimming the male gametes to the female reproductive structure for fertilization. The sporophyte produces spores which on germination give rise to the filamentous form called protonema. This also requires a moist surface.

✔ **Pteridophytes are the first vascular plants in plant kingdom. Give some reasons for the dominance of vascular plants over non-vascular plants on the earth.**

Possession of strong roots which can penetrate

✔ **How does the mutualistic association of mycorrhiza with plant roots benefit both the plant and the fungus?**

Mycorrhizal associations provide a win-win situation. Plants, through their association with mycorrhiza, get enhanced access to essential minerals and nutrients from the soil, which the fungus is adept at absorbing. In return, the fungus receives carbohydrates and sugars produced by the plant through photosynthesis. This partnership not only enhances growth and reproduction for both but also increases their resilience to environmental stresses.

✔ **How do mechanical tissues in vascular plants enable them to attain greater heights compared to non-vascular plants?**

Quick Recap section will help to review all important concepts, discussed in that particular chapter

Each section contains detailed diagrams, images, real life microscopic views for better understanding and conceptual clarity.

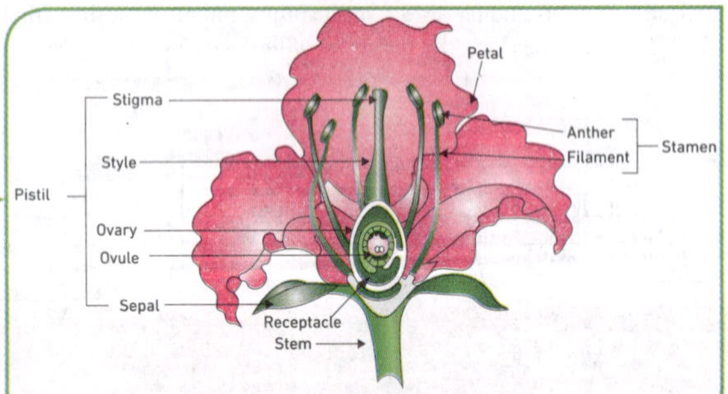

Figure 3.36 Parts of a flower

POINTS TO REMEMBER

✔ Different living organisms show wide range of variations in form, functioning and behaviour. This is known as biological diversity.

✔ The study of principles and procedures of classification of living organisms is called taxonomy.

✔ Taxonomic hierarchy involves the arrangement of organisms into various taxonomic groups in definite order.

✔ In a scientific name, first term is called genus

✔ Whittaker proposed the five-kingdom classification for the living organisms based on three basic distinguishing features: structure of cell, cellular organization and mode of nutrition.

✔ Plants which bear flowers come under phanerogamae and plants which do not bear flowers come under cryptogamae.

✔ Cryptogams are divided into thallophytes, bryophytes and Pteridophytes.

Points to remember summarises the concepts and topics presented in each chapter

CLASSROOM WING

Practice Questions

Very Short Answer Type Questions

Direction for Questions from 1 to 6:
Fill in the blanks.

1. In India, due to the ________ population and limited cultivable land, there's an emphasis on sustainable agricultural practices.

9. Which of the following is derived from animal faeces and plant wastes?
(a) Pesticides (b) Compost
(c) Manure (d) Insecticides

10. What is irrigation primarily concerned with?
...y of controlled amount of nutrients
...y of controlled amount of sunlight

Short Answer Type Questions

17. What is the significance of crop rotation in agricultur...
18. Describe the importance of animal husbandry in su... tainable agriculture.
19. Name the different methods that are employed ... crop variety improvement.

Essay Type Questions

46. Draw the flow chart involving the different stages of farming and the steps involved in each.
47. Draw a flow chart of different fish production cultures.

Different typologies of questions have been included in the *Classroom Wing* which help students to develop the problem-solving skill

Competition Wing has been integrated chapter-wise in the exercise part to prepare students for various competitive examinations.

COMPETITION WING

Practice Questions

Level 1: Apply your Concepts

Direction for Questions from 1 to 10:
Fill in the blanks.

1. The crops which are grown from June to October are

2.

(c) Because it requires less land than monoculture.
(d) To minimize water usage.

12. Crop variety improvement primarily aims to:
...ase the size of farmland.
...ify the plants genetically for improved resis-

Graded as per complexity: Level 1; Level 2; and Level 3

Level 2: Review your Concepts

36. National office of animal health works to provid... farmers with different range of vaccines to prot... health and welfare of their cattle. Why is it nec... to give vaccine to cattle?
37. Ramesh found that there is difference in prod... of milk by their cow and the dairy cow. What... be the reason behind this?

Level 3: Assess Your Concepts

76. How does the intake of zinc impact immunity of a person?
77. Vitamin C invariably enhances the immunity in the body. What is the effect of vitamin C? Explain.
78. The disease AIDS results in the drastic decrease in the immunity of the affected person. Explain the mechanism involved.
79. It is highly recommended to breast feed the new born babies as soon as they are born. Justify.
80. Antibiotics destroy the bacterial cells in the host body...

77. Vitamin C invariably enhances the immunity in the body. What is the effect of vitamin C? Explain.
78. The disease AIDS results in the drastic decrease in the immunity of the affected person. Explain the mechanism involved.
79. It is highly recommended to brea... babies as soon as they are born. J...
80. Antibiotics destroy the bacterial ... without causing harm to the hos...

67. Excessive use of antibiotics leads to deficiency disorders. Why?
68. The first line of defence in the immune system is provided by skin. Discuss.
69. The life of an infant is saved from three diseases. Identify the vaccines and diseases.
70. Give an account on hypersensitivity or allergic reaction.
71. No vaccination is possible for AIDS. Give reason.

The icons are used for categorisation of the questions in Classroom Wing and Competition Wing

NEET SPECIAL WING

Practice Questions

Multiple-Answer Type Questions

Questions number 1 to 5 are multiple-choice questions. Each question has FOUR options (a), (b), (c), and (d). ONE OR MORE THAN ONE of these four option(s) is/are the correct answer(s).

1. Identify diseases that are spread by female mosquito bite:
   (a) Chikungunya
   (b) Cholera

3. The diseases that are caused by protozoa:
   (a) Sleeping sickness
   (b) Malaria

Comprehension-Based Questions

A. Read the paragraph given below and answer the questions number 6 to 11:

Immunity provides our body with physiological mechanisms which enables our body to identify foreign substances and eliminate them from the system. It achieves this without causing any harm to the body's own tissues

NEET Special Wing is curated specifically for targeted preparation of NEET examination

Hints and Explanations

CLASSROOM WING

Very Short Answer Type Questions

19. The connective tissue is specialized for connecting various tissues and organs.
20. Meristematic tissues are known for their active cell division throughout the plant's life.
21. The vascular tissue system in plants is responsible for the transport of nutrients and water.
22. Epithelial is a type of tissue in animals, specifically humans, and is not found in plants.
23. The epithelial tissue acts as a thin and continuous protective sheet of cells in the human body.
24. The muscular tissue forms muscles in the body which are responsible for movement.
25. Cells of permanent tissue in plants take up a specific role and lose their division capability.

46. False; Sclerenchyma consists of dead cells.
47. False; Epithelial cells are not supplied with blood vessels
48. False; Xylem helps in conduction of water and minera salts from roots to leaves.
49. False; Minute openings present in the epidermis o leaves are called stomata.
50. False; Nails, horns, claws and hoofs are developed from epidermis.
51. False; Platelets help in clotting of blood.

Short Answer Type Questions

56. Jute—phloem fibres.
    Rose wood—secondary xylem.
    Hard shells of fruits—sclereids of phloem.
    Cork—parenchymatous cells in cortex

Hints and Explanations for key questions of classroom wing, competition wing and NEET special wing along with highlights on the common mistakes that students usually make in the examinations

COMPETITION WING

Level 1: Apply your Concepts

1. Sandy soil consists of larger particles, loamy soil has a mixture of particle sizes, and clayey soil is characterized by fine, compact particles.
   Hence, the correct option is (c).
2. The ozonosphere or ozone layer absorbs most of the sun's harmful ultraviolet radiation. Depletion of this layer results in increased harmful ultraviolet radiations reaching the Earth's surface.
   Hence, the correct option is (c).
3. Plants, being primary producers, rely on abiotic factors like water and sunlight for photosynthesis. A scarcity of these factors would result in stunted plant growth, which

77. Through photosynthesis and absorption from soil
78. During day time water from different sources like pond, lake, river, sea, well, etc., gets evaporated and

NEET SPECIAL WING

Multiple-Answer Type Questions

1. Apical meristems are found in the growing tips of roots and shoots and help in increasing the length of the plant.
2. Chondrocytes are the cells present in cartilage, Osteocytes are the cells of bones, Adipocyte is the fat containing cell of adipose tissue whereas Sclerenchyma is the dead tissue of the plant made up of cell walls.
3. The areolar tissue mainly consists of transparent, sticky and jellylike matrix. All the three types of fibres are present in the matrix of areolar connective tissue. The cells and fibres are irregularly scattered in the matrix crossing each other in all directions.
4. Dense connective tissue is a tough band of fibrous connective tissue. It has large amounts of fibres in the matrix with relatively less proportion of ground substance. The fibres form the major part of the tissue.

10. In the synapse chemical substance called as neurotransmitters are present which help in the passage of the impulse from one neuron to another.
11. Match the following:

    Sensory neurons receive the sensations from the sensory organs and transmit it to the CNS.
    (i) (c)

    Central nervous system consists of the brain and the spinal cord.
    (ii) (d)

    Motor neurons transmit the impulses from the brain to the motor regions and help in movement and locomotion.
    (iii) (a)

    Interneurons form connections between neurons and help in the transmission of messages and conduction of nerve impulses.

CHAPTER 4: WORKSHEET

Objective Questions

Answer the following questions in one word.

1. The animals belonging to this phylae lack tissues.
2. Animals in this group do not possess a coelom. All the diploblastic animals come under this group.
3. The animals of this phylum were the first completely terrestrial vertebrates to originate on earth.
4. This is the only phylum (besides Cnidaria) which contains animals without mesoderm germ layer in their embryos.
5. This phylum is made up of animals in which notochord is not replaced by the vertebral column even in the adult stage of life.

Subjective Questions

1. Someone told me that the animals belonging to platyhelminths phylum do not possess skeleton. Is this true? List some of the features of this phylum.
2. Members of the Animal Kingdom can be broadly classified into two types. What are the characteristics of these types?
3. Is roundworm a coelomate animal? Why?
4. How does zygote develop in some arthropods like scorpion?
5. How does reproduction happen in vertebrates?

DW

DW: Downloadable worksheets supplementing textual exercises for hand-on learning

AI Assessments ×

________ is where parents are selected carefully to produce young ones having desired characters.

- ○ Artificial breeding
- ○ Selective breeding
- ○ Artificial hybridization
- ○ DNA cloning

Questions 1 of 4 Next

AT

AT: Attemptable Tests for assessing understanding of concepts and getting a clear picture of your exam readiness

57. In the following line diagram showing taxonomic hierarchy of plants, identify the missing taxonomic unit.

Division ⟶ Class ⟶ Family

(a) Order (b) Family
(c) Species (d) Phylum

Video icon: Audio and visual learning to difficult questions for effective learning and retention

Bridge Course

Pearson Foundation, Biology Class 9 book comes with a specially designed Bridge Course Supplement. This is not just an add-on—it is your transition support system, guiding you to move from the familiar school ways of learning towards the result-driven world of test-prep.

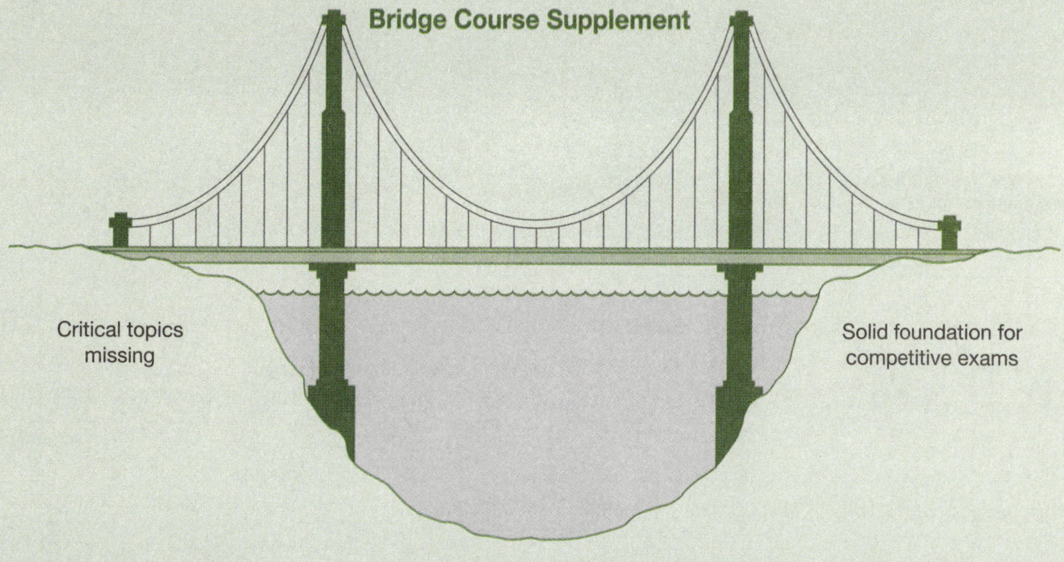

In recent years, many boards have deleted specific chapters and topics from their Class 9 and 10 syllabi to lighten the academic load. While this helps in the school cycle, some of these very topics are critical building blocks for exams like IIT-JEE and NEET. The Bridge Course carefully reintroduces these concepts so you don't face gaps later. It is like priming yourself on a treadmill before starting a race—you build stamina and rhythm before stepping into the real competition.

Why It Matters?

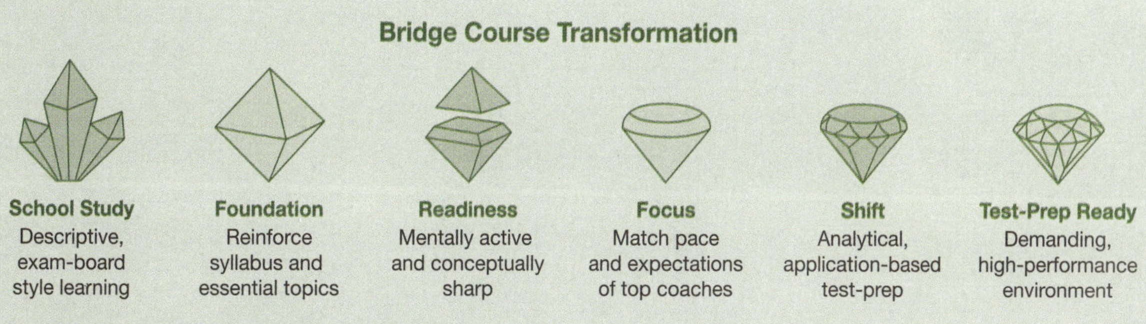

- **Foundation Strengthening:** Reinforces both the prescribed syllabus and deleted-but-essential topics that reappear in competitive exams.
- **Primed Readiness:** Keeps you mentally active and conceptually sharp so the rigour of the coaching ecosystem in the coming months doesn't feel overwhelming.
- **Result-Oriented Focus:** Prepares you to match the pace and expectations of star coaches and top learning centres, where students are expected to be 'race-ready' from Day 1.
- **Shift in Approach:** Guides you from descriptive, exam-board style study to analytical, application-based test-prep learning.
- **Confidence Bridge:** Ensures a smoother leap from the security of school study habits into the demanding, high-performance environment of competitive preparation.

In short, the Bridge Course is your warm-up lap—keeping you flexible, alert, and conditioned for the intense training and performance-driven coaching classrooms that await you. It makes sure you are not just board-exam ready, but also test-prep ready.

CHAPTER

1

Cell—Fundamental Unit of Life

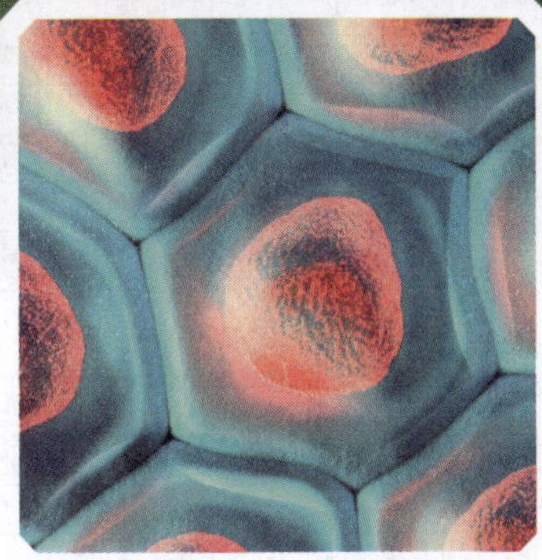

Key Ideas

After completing this chapter, you should be able to:

- Discuss the structure of a cell in plants and animals
- Explain the structures and functions of various cell organelles

Remember

Before beginning this chapter, you should be able to:

- Define the basic structure of cell and its components
- Relate the basic functions of major cell organelles
- Describe the processes of mitosis and meiosis

Scientific Crypt

A Tribute to Rudolf Virchow (1821–1902)

Rudolf Virchow (1821-1902) is regarded as the '*Father of Modern Pathology*' in the scientific community. He was more than just a pathologist; he was a brilliant biologist, physician, and anthropologist who introduced the world to ground-breaking ideas that changed the way we think about biology and disease.

His seminal contribution was the cell theory, in which he boldly proposed '*omnis cellula e cellula*,' which means that every cell derives from another existing cell. This theory challenged the widely held concept of spontaneous generation at the time, laying the groundwork for cell biology and modern medicine.

Virchow deftly linked cellular abnormalities to diseases, paving the way for medical science to develop targeted treatments and therapies for a variety of ailments. His insights emphasized the importance of studying cells in understanding disease mechanisms, illuminating the path to unravelling the mysteries of life's smallest units.

Crossword

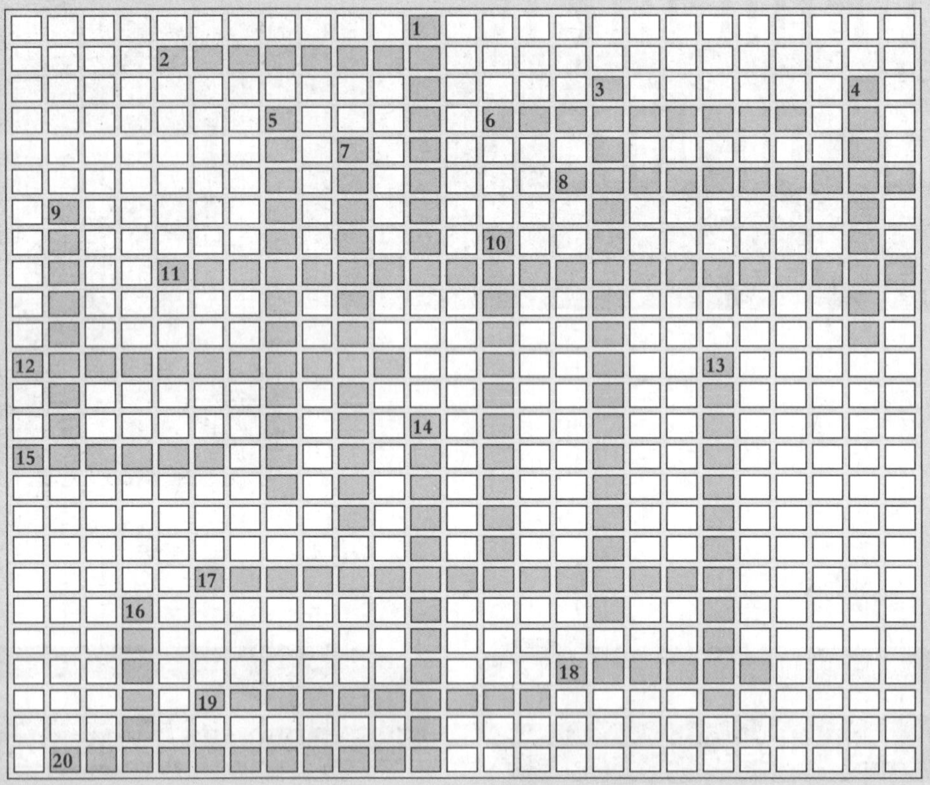

Across

2. Study of cells with the subcellular components and their functions
6. Small ribonucleoprotein particles
8. Bacteria with thin and flexible spiral shape is called
11. Non-living, non-membrane-bound materials in the cytoplasm are called_____
12. The model proposed by Singer and Nicolson to describe the structure of cell membrane
15. Matrix found inside chloroplast
17. Particle movement against concentration gradient using energy
18. Substance which helps in cell adhesion and binds the cell walls of the adjacent cells
19. Purkinje discovered component of the cell
20. Another term for cell drinking

Down

1. Organelles which contain several digestive enzymes
3. An optical instrument that consists of two convex lenses of short focal lengths
4. Flattened sac-like structures which are parallelly arranged in the endoplasmic reticulum
5. Cytoplasmic strands which facilitate the transport of proteins and other materials between the cells
7. Scientist who stated that 'new cells arise from pre-existing ones'
9. Membrane of vacuole
10. Powerhouse of the cell
13. Cellular macromolecule uptake process_____
14. Protein strands found in centrioles
16. _____make cell wall impermeable

INTRODUCTION

Living organisms live in different environments. They possess different organs performing various functions. All these organisms are made up of basic building blocks, called cells, which have some common properties. These blocks are called **cells**. The cells are the smallest structural and functional units of life which are responsible for keeping an organism alive and functional. The study of cells with the subcellular components and their functions is known as **cytology or cell biology**.

Invention of the Microscope

Cells are microscopic entities which are not visible to naked eyes. Invention of microscope was a milestone towards learning the intricate details of the internal arrangement of the cell.

The earliest simple types of magnification instruments were magnifying glasses which were used for probing tiny insects. But, it was Anton van Leeuwenhoek (1632–1723), a Dutch draper and scientist (one of the founders of microscopy), who in the late 17th century became the first man to make and use a real microscope.

Info Bytes!

An adult body of human contains approximately 100 trillion cells.

Work of Antonie van Leeuwenhoek

Antonie van Leeuwenhoek took inspiration from the glasses used by drapers to examine the quality of cloth. He explored new methods for polishing tiny lenses himself, which gave the finest and most exceptional magnifications at the time. These lenses led to the building of his microscopes, considered the first workable ones.

Fundamentally, all his microscopes comprised single biconvex lens which had considerable magnifying ability.

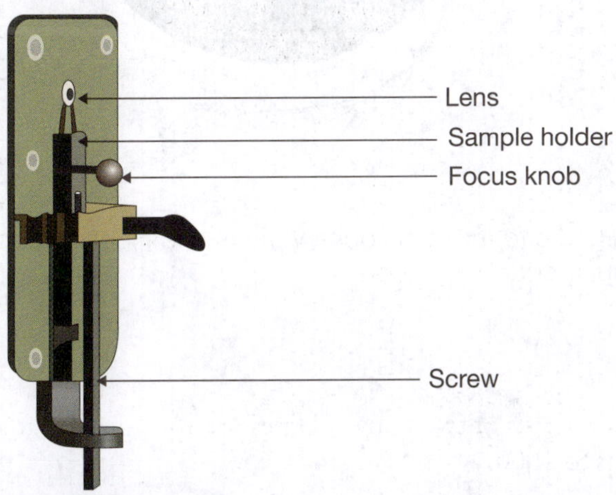

Figure 1.1 Leeuwenhoek's simple microscope

Info Bytes!

Antonie van Leeuwenhoek is the Father of Microbiology.

As shown in above figure, in his microscope, the eye was placed close to the lens and the object was mounted on needle-like screw on the opposite side of the lens.

Table 1.1 A brief timeline of milestones in the invention of microscope

Timeline/Year	Inventor/s	Features
1590	Zacharias Jansen and his father Hans	Mounted two lenses in a tube; the first compound microscope
1609	Galileo Galilei	Constructed a compound microscope with a convex and a concave lens
1674	Anton van Leeuwenhoek	Constructed an extremely simple instrument, using a single lens mounted on a tiny hole in a brass plate that makes up the body of the instrument

Discovery of the Cell

The Englishman Robert Hooke (1635–1703) was an architect and scientist, published his book *Micrographia* in 1665 and used the word 'cell' for the first time to describe the basic unit of life. His most famous observations were made in his study of thin slices of cork, describing the 'cells' he observed. Hooke had been examining the cell walls in cork tissue.

In actuality, he coined the term 'cells' for the box-like compartments of cork.

Info Bytes!

The term 'cell' is derived from Latin word "cellula" meaning small room.

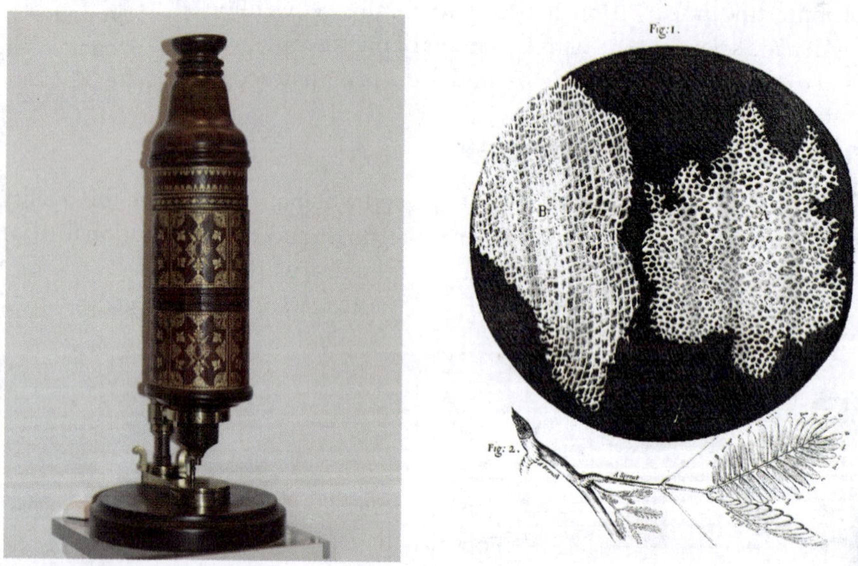

Figure 1.2 Microscope used by Robert Hooke to make his observations and Hooke's observations of cellular structure of cork

Compound Microscope

A compound microscope is an optical instrument that consists of two convex lenses of short focal lengths. The compound microscope can magnify the image of a tiny object up to 1000.

Principle of Compound Microscope

A compound microscope works on the principle that when a tiny object is placed just beyond the focus of the objective lens, a virtual, inverted and highly magnified image of the object is formed at the least distance of distinct vision from the eye held close to the eye piece.

Electron Microscope

An electron microscope is a type of microscope that uses electron beams to illuminate a specimen/object and create a magnified image. It magnifies to over 2,00,000 times the magnification of an ordinary compound microscope.

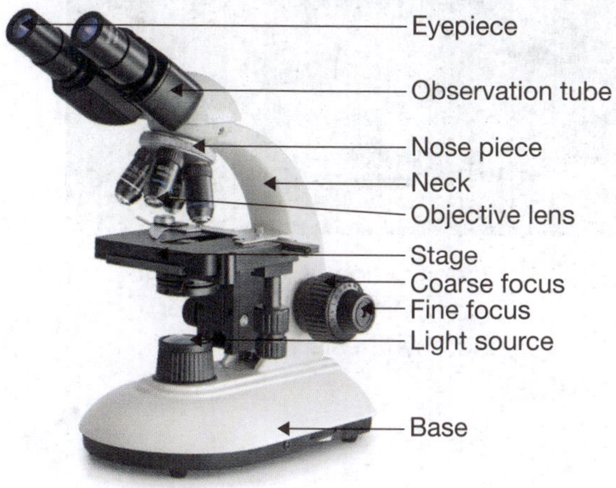

Figure 1.3 Compound microscope

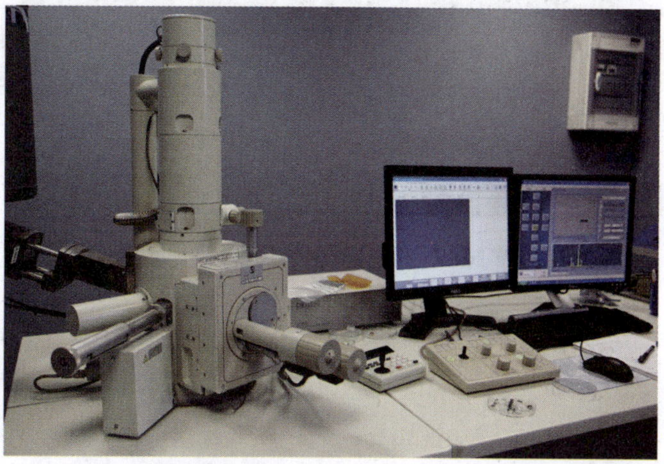

Figure 1.4 Electron microscope

Table 1.2 Contributors to the study of cells

Scientist	Contribution
Zacharias Janssen (1590)	Invented the first compound microscope.
Robert Hooke (1665)	Discovered dead cells from cork.
Leeuwenhoek (1674)	First observed living cells of bacteria, sperm and protozoa.
Robert Brown (1831)	Demonstrated the presence of nucleus in the cells.
Johannes Purkinje (1839)	Named the fluid content of the cells as protoplasm.
S. J. Singer and G. L. Nicolson	Fluid mosaic model of plasma membrane.
Camillo Golgi	Discovery of Golgi complex.
George Emil Palade	Observation of ribosomes in animal cell.
Carl Benda	Coined the term 'mitochondria'.

Cell Theory

In 1838, Matthias Jakob Schleiden, a German botanist was the first to assert that cells are the building blocks of all plants. In 1839, another German physiologist, Theodor Schwann stated that cells are the fundamental units of animals. Their discoveries led to the formulation of the 'Cell Theory'. However, the cell theory failed to explain how new cells arise.

In 1855, Rudolf Virchow, a German physician and anthropologist, stated in Latin '*Omnis cellula e cellula*' which means that new cells come from the pre-existing cells.

Figure 1.5 Cellular structure of a leaf under microscope

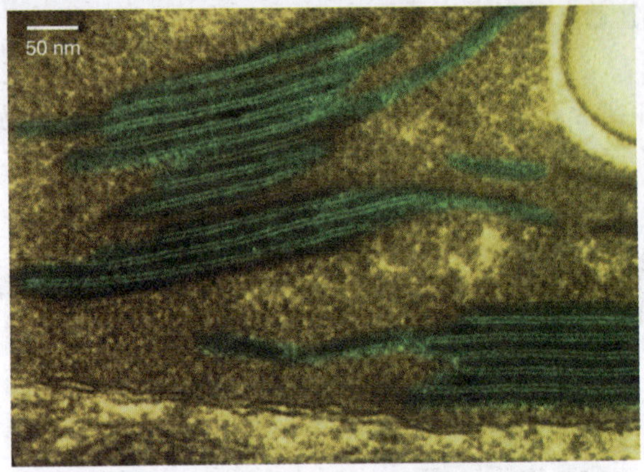

Figure 1.6 Magnification of leaf cells showing chloroplast which is site for photosynthesis

The three main postulates of cell theory are as follows:

1. All living organisms are made of cells.
2. Cell is the fundamental and basic unit of living organisms.
3. All cells arise from pre-existing cells.

Explanation of Cell Theory

Let us take example of a rose plant to understand the postulates of the Cell Theory.

Cells are the structural unit of life: Take any part of a rose plant and examine it under a microscope, we will observe cells as the structural units of organization.

Cells are the functional unit of life: In rose plant, food is prepared through the process of photosynthesis that occurs in the cells of the leaves. Absorption of water and minerals from the soil is done by the cells present in the roots which are specialized to do so. Hence, any function in the body of a living organism is essentially due to the activity of the cells.

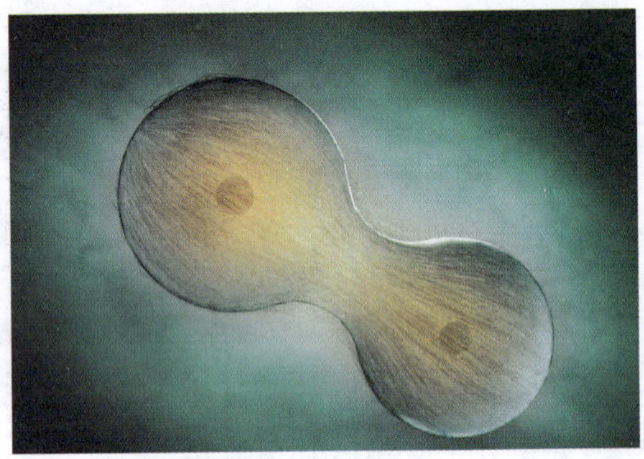

Figure 1.7 Division of a pre-existing cell leads to formation of new cells

***Omnis cellula e cellula (All cells arise from pre-existing cells.)*:** Most of the cells of the rose plant continuously die and are replaced by new cells which are formed as the products of cell division. Hence, all new cells arise from division of already existing cells.

Important takeaways from Cell Theory are as follows:

- All organisms are composed of cells.
- Cell is the structural and functional unit of life.
- Every organism starts its life as a single cell.
- No cell arises spontaneously and develops into an organism. All cells arise from the pre-existing cells.
- All the cells are basically alike in chemical composition and metabolic activities.
- The functions of an organism as a whole correspond to the functions carried out by its cells.

Morphology and Internal Structure of a Typical Cell

The various aspects of the cell, such as size, shape and the structure constitute the morphology of a cell. The sizes and shapes of cells vary depending on the complexity of the organism. However, the basic structure of a typical cell is more or less same for all the organisms.

Unicellular and Multicellular Organisms

Based on the number of cells present, organisms are classified into unicellular and multicellular life forms. Simple organisms may be unicellular, consisting of just one cell, while more complex organisms are multicellular, that is, composed of more than one cell.

Unicellular Organisms

A unicellular organism is an organism that consists of one cell only. All life processes, such as reproduction, nutrition, digestion, excretion, control and coordination occur inside one cell. They are generally microscopic and cannot be seen with the naked eye.

Unicellular organisms can belong to either prokaryotic or eukaryotic forms of life. Eukaryotes are unique because they can be unicellular or multicellular. Eukaryotes have a nucleus where the DNA is stored, mitochondria, which is responsible for energy generation, and other organelles carry out different functions. On the other hand, prokaryotes consist of a single cell with no membrane-bound organelles and nucleus. DNA exists freely in the cytoplasm. In such cases, the organism also has to adapt to other ways of carrying out various cellular functions, such as reproduction, nutrition, waste excretion, circulation, etc., since it does not have any specialized organelles.

Examples of unicellular organisms: Bacteria, *Amoeba*, *Paramecium*, Yeast, etc.

Multicellular Organisms

A multicellular organism is an organism that consists of more than one cell. These organisms are characterized by division of labour, that is, various functions of an organism are carried out by different groups of cells. A particular function is carried out by a specialized group of cells at a particular location.

Multicellular organisms assign biological responsibilities/functions, such as digestion, circulation, respiration, circulation, sexual reproduction, etc., to specific organ systems such as the digestive system, respiratory system, circulatory system, reproductive system, etc. These organ systems comprise various different organs that work together to perform specific tasks. Further, these organs are composed of various types of cells that are responsible for doing their specific functions. For example, rod and cone cells of the eye have photoreceptors that help in absorbing light, whereas neurons are cells of the nervous system that have axons to carry nerve impulses.

Examples of multicellular organisms: Human beings, mango plant, banyan tree, cat, dog, etc.

Table 1.3 Comparison between unicellular and multicellular organisms

Feature	Unicellular organism	Multicellular organism
Cell number	One	Many
Function	Performed by one cell	Different cells perform different functions
Division of labour	Absent	Present
Life span	Shorter	Longer

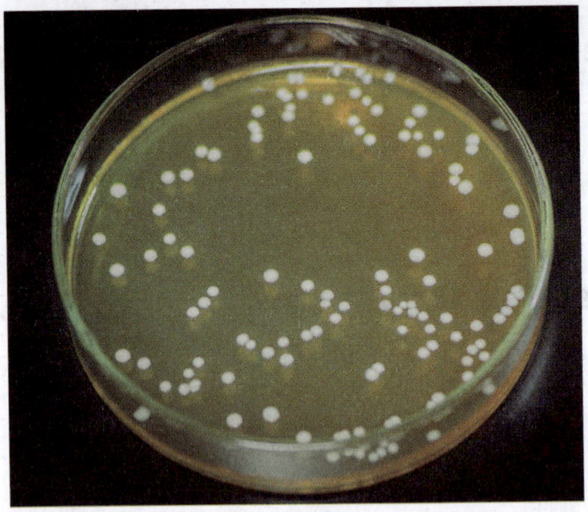

> **Konnect**
>
> A colony is a cluster of identical unicellular organisms living together. The difference between a multicellular organism and a colony is that individual one-celled organisms from a colony can survive on their own after being separated while cells from a multicellular organism cannot.

Figure 1.8 Bacterial colonies present on media; each colony is an association of identical bacterial cells

Cell Size

Cells are usually small in size and can be seen with the help of microscopes. There are two main reasons because of which cells are small in size.

1. For a cell to function efficiently, small size results in quick and rapid communication and transfer of substances between the different components of the cell as well as between the cells and their surroundings.
2. Small size presents larger surface area/volume ratio.

Surface Area/Volume Ratio

Imagine a cube with each of its side measuring 30 μm. The total surface area of the cube becomes 30 μm × 30 μm × 6, which is, 5400 sq. μm. Now, cut the cube into 27 equal smaller cubes by reducing the length of its each side to 10 μm. The total surface area of these 27 smaller cubes becomes 10 μm × 10 μm × 6 × 27, which is, 16,200 sq. μm. In both the cases, volume of the cubes remains the same. However, the total area of the smaller cubes is double that of the original one.

> **Info Bytes!**
>
> - **The smallest cell**—*Mycoplasma galliseptium* (0.1 μm), which is an organism intermediate between virus and bacteria.
> - **Largest cell**—Egg of Ostrich (18cm long).
> - **Longest cell**—Nerve cell which has axon of 3m length (giraffe).
> - In human body, the spermatozoon is the smallest cell and ovum is the largest cell. Nerve cell is the longest cell with an axon of 1m length.

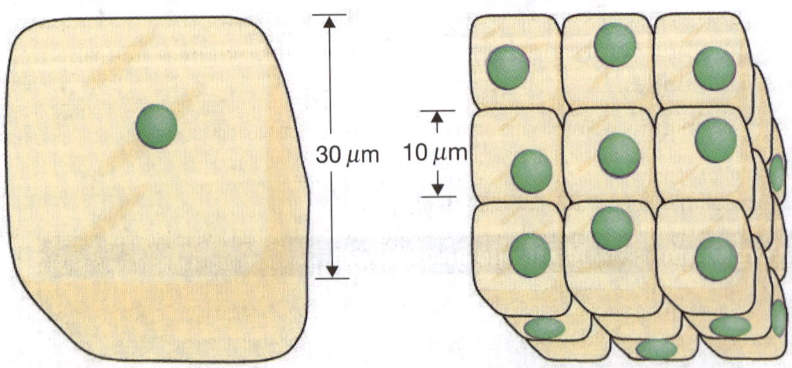

Surface area of one large cube = 5400 μm^2

Total surface area of 27 small cubes = 16,200 μm^2

Figure 1.9 Illustration of surface area-to-volume ratio

The larger surface area/volume ratio is helpful in following ways. It facilitates:

- Greater diffusion of the substances.
- Easy repair of damaged cells.
- Easy passage of nutrients into the cell.
- Convenient exit of metabolic wastes from the inside of the cell to the outside of the cell.
- Easy exchange of respiratory gases, i.e., oxygen into the cell and carbon dioxide out of the cell.

Cell Shape

Cells vary significantly in shape. The shape of the cell is related to the function it performs.

RBCs (red blood cells) of human beings are **bi-concave** so as to provide the greater surface area for diffusion of gases and for easy passage through the capillaries. WBCs (white blood cells), on the other hand, are irregular in shape and they change their shapes. This helps them to squeeze out through narrow capillary walls and hence, they can make their way to the site of injury for defence. In this way, they act as scavengers.

Nerve cells are **long and branched** to facilitate the conduction of impulses from one region to the other. Muscle cells are **elongated and contractile** because they help in movement.

The conducting cells in plants are **elongated and tubular** to suit their need to transport water and minerals in plants.

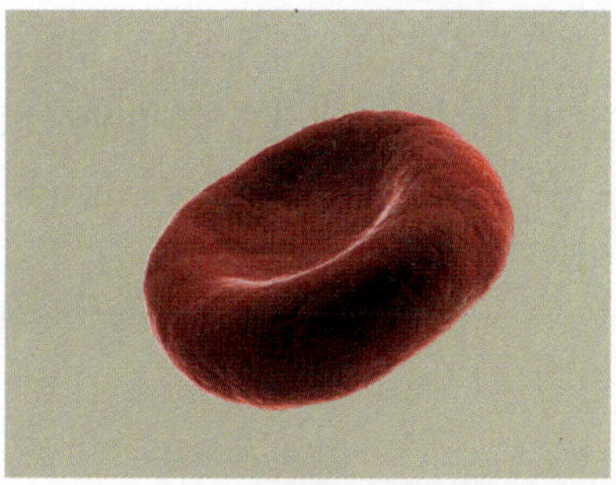

RBC

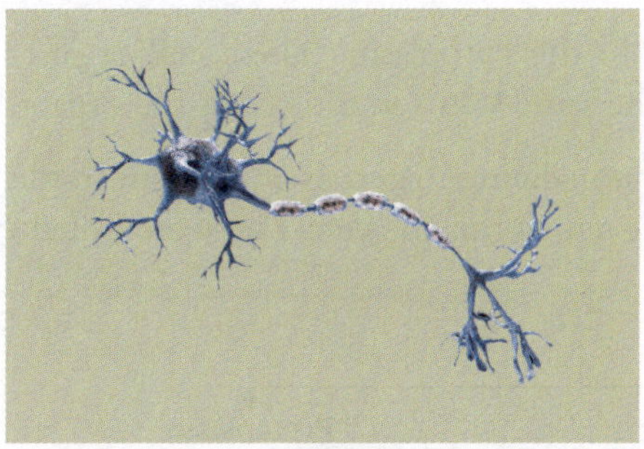

Neuron

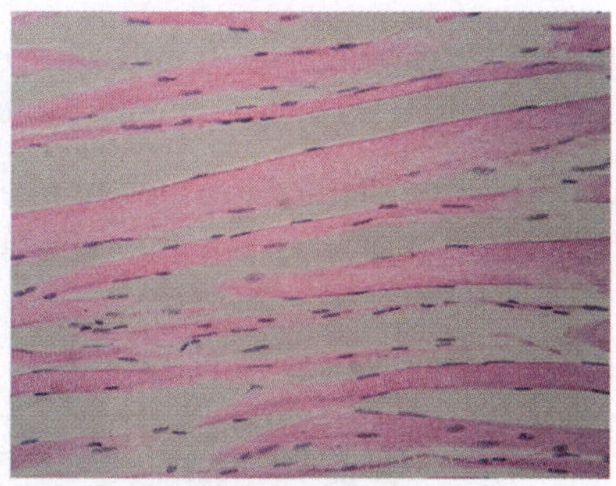

Muscle Cells

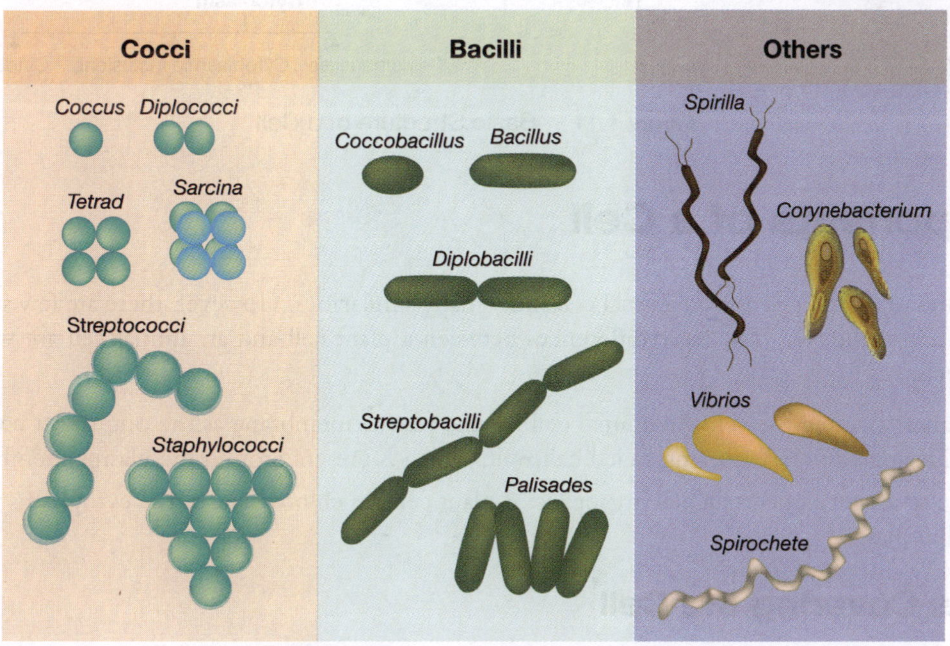

Figure 1.10 Various shapes of cells

Bacterial cells also vary greatly in shape. Following are the major shapes in which bacteria are found.

1. Coccus: The cocci (singular: coccus) are spherical or oval bacteria.
2. Rod or bacillus: Bacilli (singular: bacillus) are rod-shaped bacteria.
3. Spiral: Bacteria in any one of the following spiral shapes.
   a. *Vibrio*: Comma-shaped bacteria
   b. *Spirillum*: Bacteria with thick and rigid spiral
   c. *Spirochete*: Bacteria with thin and flexible spiral

Info Bytes!

The size of a cell is usually determined by its diameter and not by the length.

Structure of a Typical Cell

Although the living cells show wide variations in the parameters such as size, shape and structural features, a typical cell shows some common characteristic features.

A cell is bound by membranes which give shape to the cell. An animal cell is bound by a single membrane, called plasma membrane or cell membrane. A plant cell is bound by another covering, called cell wall, in addition to plasma membrane.

The plasma membrane encloses the protoplasm. Protoplasm contains **nucleus and cytoplasm**. Nucleus is the most important structure found in the cell and it controls all the activities of the cell. Cytoplasm is a jelly-like substance found within the cell, surrounding the nucleus. Within the cytoplasm, there are tiny membrane-bound living structures called **cell organelles**.

The cell organelles are found floating in the cytoplasm. These cell organelles are responsible for specific functions within the cell. The cell organelles have the same status in the cell as the organs have in the body of the organism.

In addition to the cell organelles, many non-living materials are present inside the cytoplasm. These are not membrane bound and do not carry out any metabolic activity in the cell. These are called **cytoplasmic inclusions**.

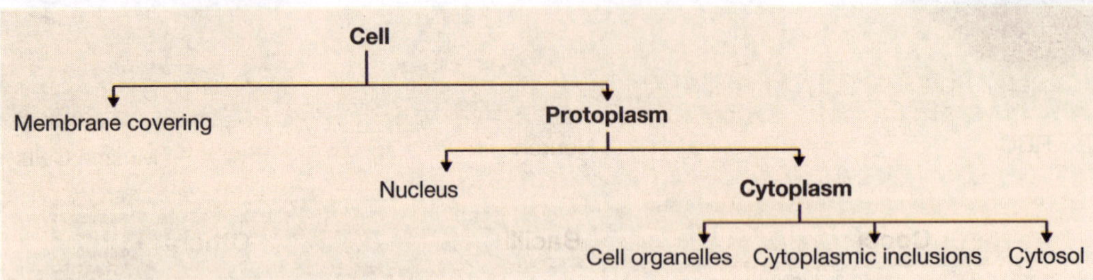

Figure 1.11 Basic Structure of a Cell

Components of a Cell

The typical structures of a plant cell and an animal cell show many similarities. However, there are few striking differences between the structure of the two. The basic differences between a plant cell and an animal cell are with respect to the following two aspects:

1. The membranes covering the cell: An animal cell has the plasma membrane as the outermost covering of the cell. A plant cell has an additional covering called cell wall, which is present around the plasma membrane.
2. The presence or absence of certain cell organelles: A plant cell has chloroplasts in the cytoplasm, whereas an animal cell lacks chloroplast.

Membranes Covering the Cell

An animal cell is covered by only one membrane which is plasma membrane or cell membrane. A plant cell is covered by two membranes—Plasma membrane and cell wall.

Cell Membrane

Structure

The cell membrane is a living semi-permeable (partially or selectively permeable) membrane. It is elastic, delicate and flexible. It is made of lipids and proteins.

Location

The cell membrane is the outer covering of the cell, enclosing the cytoplasm and nucleus. In plant cells, it is present between the cytoplasm and the cell wall.

Functions

Cell membrane gives shape to the cell. It as acts a mechanical barrier and protects the cell from injury. It regulates the movement of various materials into and out of the cell, also It maintains a constant environment inside the cell, called homeostasis.

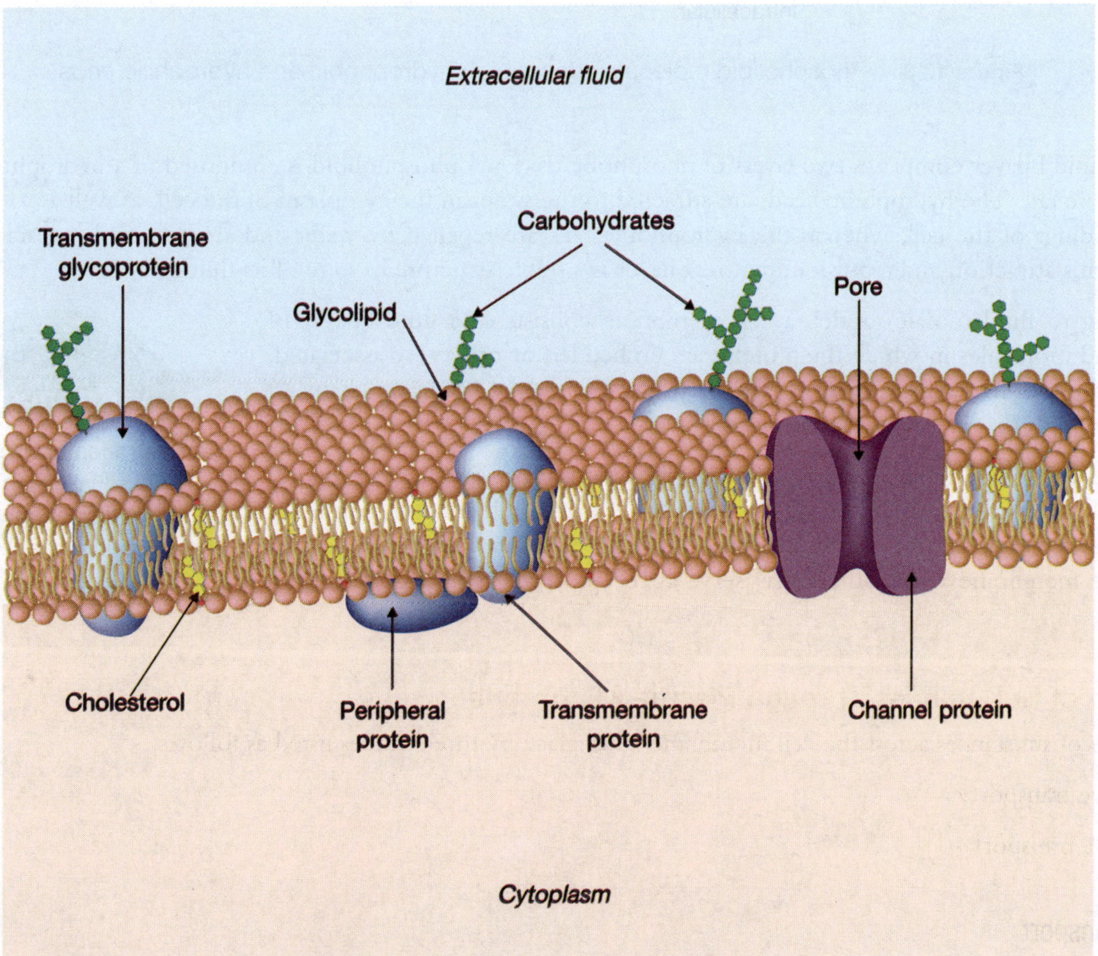

Figure 1.12 Structure of cell membrane

Fluid Mosaic Model

The fluid mosaic model was first proposed by S. J. Singer and G. L. Nicolson in 1972 to account for the structure of cell membranes. This model describes that plasma membrane is composed of a phospholipid bilayer with various protein molecules floating within it.

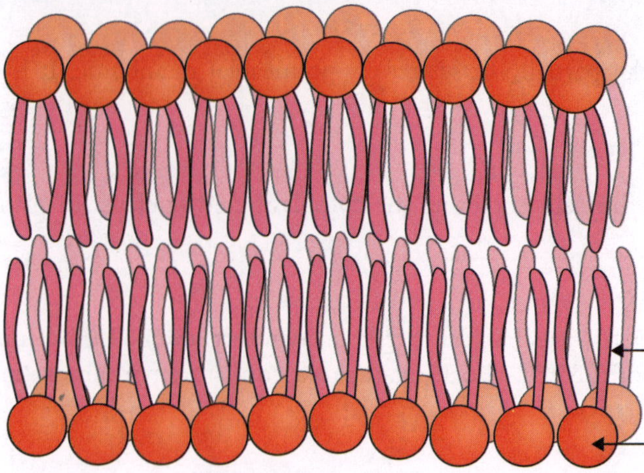

Figure 1.13 Phospholipid molecules describing hydrophobic and hydrophilic ends

A phospholipid bilayer comprises two layers of phospholipids. Each phospholipid is composed of a hydrophilic head and a hydrophobic tail. The hydrophilic heads are attracted to the water in the cytoplasm of the cell, as well as to the water in the surroundings of the cell, whereas the hydrophobic tails are repelled by water and are attracted to each other. It is because of this attraction and repulsion that the bilayer is a stable structure in spite of its fluidity.

According to fluid mosaic model, a cell membrane consists of a fluid bilayer of phospholipid molecules in which the proteins are embedded or otherwise associated, much like the tiles in a mosaic picture. The fluidity is due to the fatty acid chains of the phospholipids that are in constant motion.

> **Konnect**
>
> Concentration gradient refers to the gradual change in the concentration of solutes present in a solution across two regions.

The model is called mosaic is due to the changing position of associated proteins. This complex structure allows the membrane to perform multiple functions. For example, certain proteins may act as channels allowing particular molecules to pass through the membrane while others may serve as receptors allowing recognition of the cell.

Transport of Substances Through Plasma Membrane

The passage of substances across the cell membrane takes place by three modes listed as follows:

1. Passive transport
2. Active transport

Passive Transport

Passive transport is a mode of transport which takes place without the expenditure of energy. It takes place either by diffusion or osmosis.

Diffusion: Diffusion is the process in which movement of molecules takes place from a region of their higher concentration to a region of lower concentration till the concentrations become equal on both the sides. This is generally applicable for the movement of gaseous and liquid substances. The taking in of carbon dioxide from the air and release of oxygen into the air by the plants during the process of photosynthesis takes place by diffusion. The taking in of oxygen into the blood from lungs and the release of carbon dioxide from the blood into the lungs also takes place by diffusion.

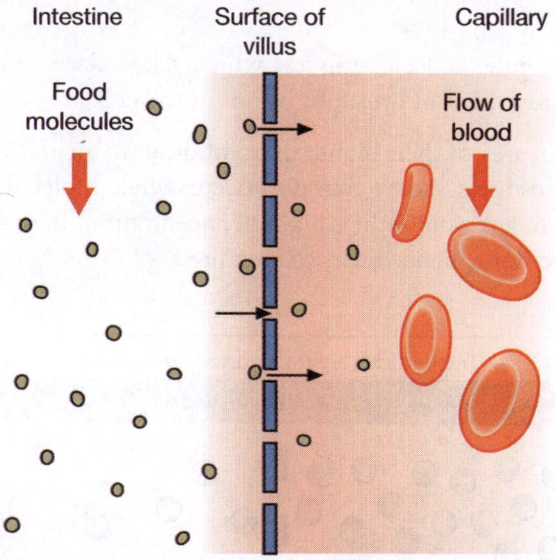

Figure 1.14 Absorption of food molecules into blood by diffusion

Diffusion is significant to biological systems because of the following reasons.

- It helps in uniform distribution of substances in the cytoplasm.
- It assists in exchange of gases which is critical to processes, such as respiration, photosynthesis, etc.
- In flowering plants, it helps in attracting insects for pollination by spreading the scented chemicals from the flowers.
- With the help of diffusion, nutrient chemicals get absorbed into the cells in the intestine of the digestive system.

Osmosis: The movement of the solvent (water) molecules from a solution of their higher concentration to a solution of lower concentration through a semi-permeable membrane is known as osmosis. The process of osmosis in living systems is affected by the external environment. If a cell is in an environment of a hypertonic solution (solution of low-water concentration), the movement of water molecules takes place from the cell into the outside solution. This process is called exosmosis or plasmolysis. This leads to shrinkage of the cell. If a cell is placed in a hypotonic solution (solution of high-water concentration), the movement of water molecules takes place from the outside solution into the cell. This process is called endosmosis. This results in swelling of the cell. If the cell is placed in an isotonic solution (same concentration of water inside and outside of the cell), no osmosis takes place in either direction.

Osmosis is significant to biological systems because of the following reasons:

- It helps in absorption of water by the roots from the soil.
- It helps in closing and opening of stomata on the leaves.
- It assists in cell-to-cell movement of water.

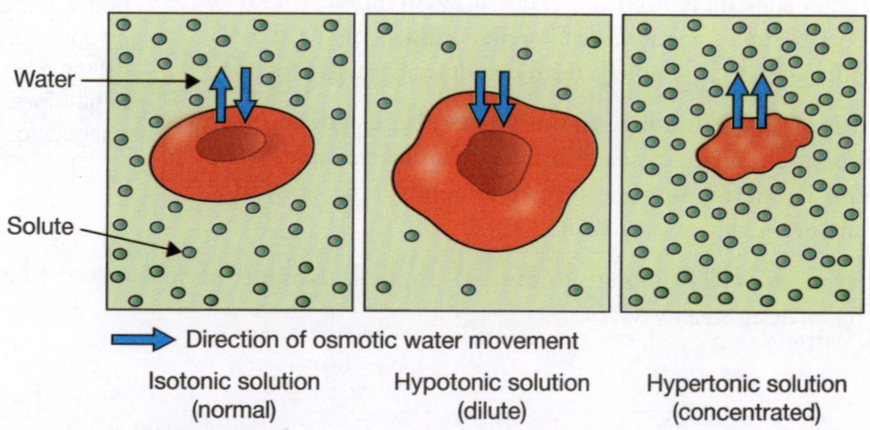

Figure 1.15 Illustration of osmosis in red blood cell

Active Transport

Active transport is the movement of ions and electrolytes, which takes place across the membrane by using energy produced by the cell. For example, movement of ions into or out of the cell.

In general, molecules move from an area of their higher concentration to an area of their lower concentration without the expense of energy by diffusion or osmosis. Active transport occurs when molecules move across a cell membrane from a region of their lower concentration to a region of their higher concentration. In order to get molecules move against the concentration gradient, work must be done, hence energy is required.

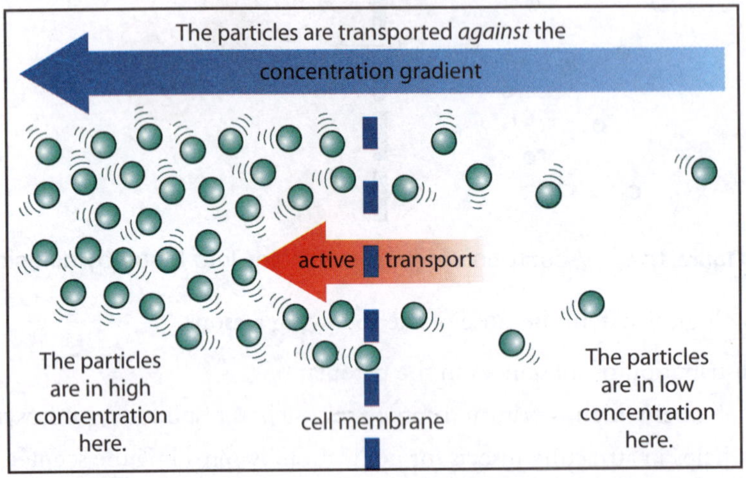

Figure 1.16 Active transport of molecules across a cell membrane

Bulk Transport

Bulk transport includes transport of large substances or large quantities of smaller substances. Large molecules as well as larger particles, generally cross the membrane in bulk by mechanisms that involve packaging in vesicles. It takes place by using the energy produced by the cell. There are two such processes namely, exocytosis and endocytosis.

- **Exocytosis:** The process by which materials move from inside to outside of the cell is known as exocytosis. This is useful in releasing out of the secretory and excretory materials from the cell. For example, release of the proteins and other materials formed in the cell to outside the cell.
- **Endocytosis:** The process by which materials move into the cell by engulfing of the food and other substances from the external environment is known as endocytosis. For example, engulfing of foreign substances, dead cells, pathogens, etc. Endocytosis is an umbrella term that describes two processes:
  - ***Phagocytosis***: It means 'cell eating'. In this process, large particles, such as cells or macromolecules, are taken in by a cell. For example, when microorganisms invade the human body, neutrophils (type of WBCs) will engulf and eventually destroy them.
  - ***Pinocytosis***: It means 'cell drinking'. In this process, bulk transport of fluid matter takes place across the cell membranes by forming small vesicles.

Info Bytes!

Phagosome is a membrane-bound vesicle formed in a cell by an inward folding of the cell membrane to hold and engulf foreign particles by phagocytosis.

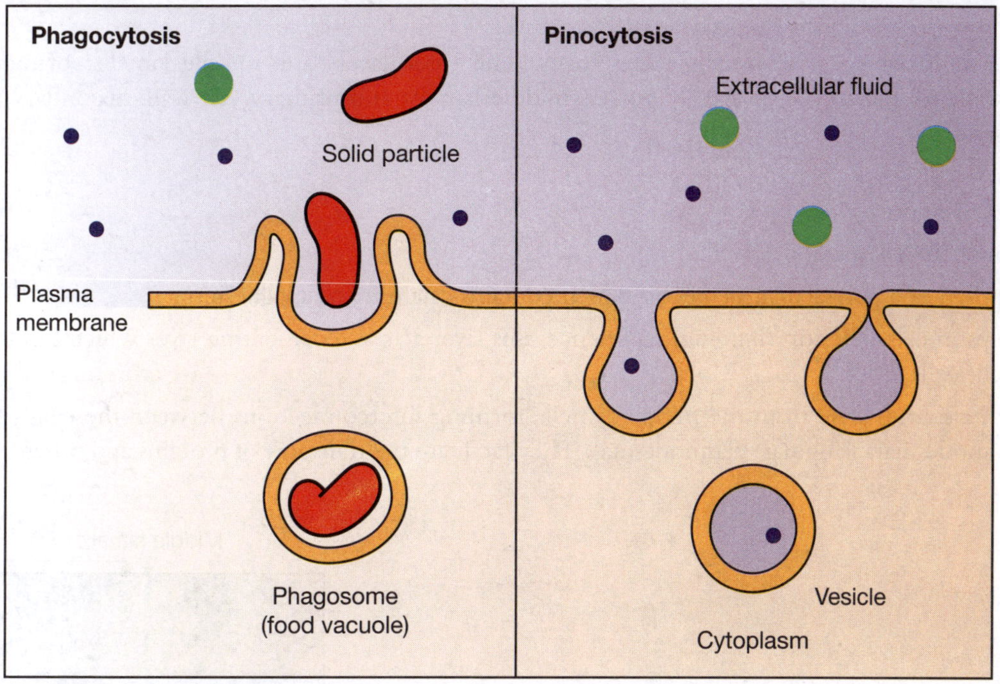

Figure 1.17 Illustration of phagocytosis and pinocytosis

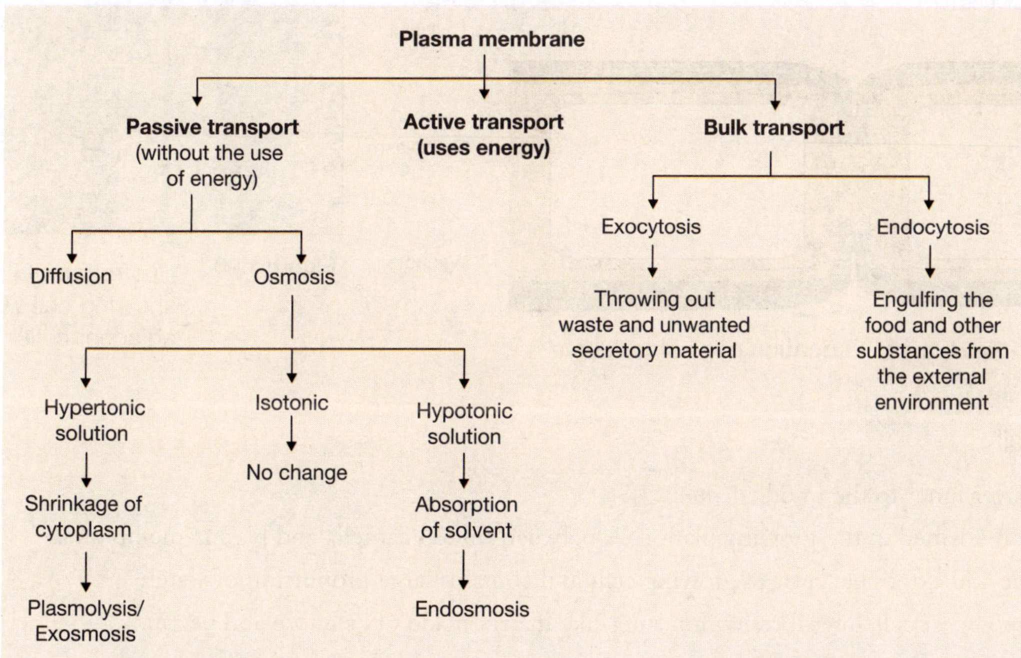

Figure 1.18 Types of transport processes across plasma membrane

Cell Wall

Cell wall is present in plant cells, bacteria and fungi. The protective semi-transparent membrane surrounding the plasma membrane is known as cell wall. The cell wall is always associated with the cell membrane. The composition of cell wall is variable depending on the type of organisms. In most of the plants, cell wall is generally made up of a fibrous polysaccharide (complex carbohydrate) called cellulose. In fungi, it is generally made up of chitin. Cell wall is freely permeable and allows substances in the form of solution to enter and leave the cell without hindrance.

Structure

The cell wall is multilayered with usually three layers. The three layers are: middle lamella, primary cell wall and secondary cell wall. All plant cells invariably possess middle lamella and primary cell wall. Secondary cell wall may or may not be present.

Middle Lamella

- It is the outermost layer of cell wall.
- It is composed of a polysaccharide pectin which contains calcium and magnesium.
- Pectin helps in cell adhesion (binding) and hence, this layer acts as a cementing layer which binds the cell walls of the adjacent cells.
- Cytoplasmic strands arise from the middle lamella forming interconnections between the cells. These strands are called plasmodesmata (singular: plasmodesma). They facilitate the transport of proteins and other materials between the cells.

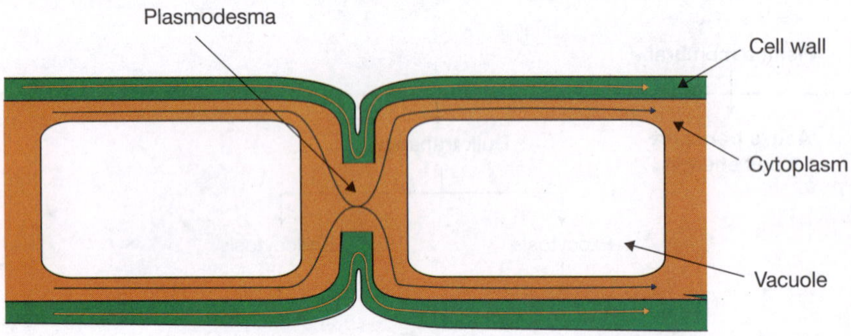

Figure 1.19 Location of plasmodesma

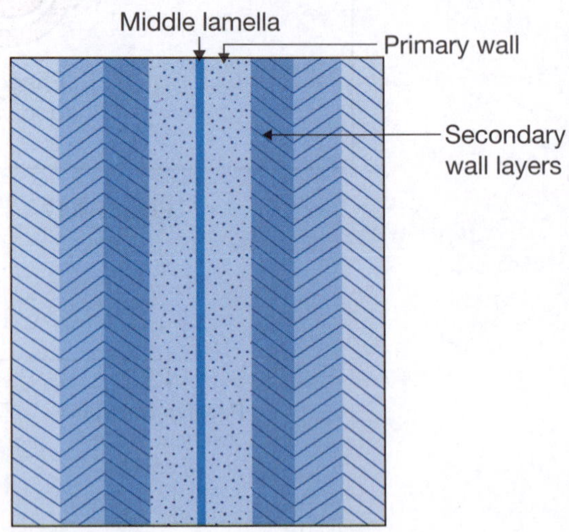

Figure 1.20 Illustration of LS of plant cell showing cell walls of two adjacent cells

Primary Cell Wall

- It is the layer inner to the middle lamella.
- It is mainly formed in the growing plant cells between middle lamella and plasma membrane.
- It is elastic and extensible layer of growing cells and contains large proportion of water.
- It is composed of cellulose fibres within a gel-like matrix made of cellulose and pectin.
- It provides strength and flexibility required to allow the growth of cells.

Secondary Cell Wall

- It is a tough and rigid layer formed after the cell reaches maturity.
- It is formed inside the primary cell wall by the deposition of materials over the existing surface.
- The composition of secondary cell walls is variable.
- In some cases, a substance called lignin may be deposited on the secondary walls of some cells. This process is known as lignification.
- In some regions, the deposition of a substance called suberin on the walls makes the walls impermeable to water.

Functions

- Cell wall provides a framework and definite shape to the cell.
- It gives rigidity and support to the tissues in plants.
- Cell wall gives mechanical strength to the cell to facilitate the plant to support its long and tall body.
- It helps in balancing and maintaining osmotic pressure and prevents bursting of cells.
- It protects protoplasm against infections.
- It helps in the transport of water and minerals over long distances.

Protoplasm

Protoplasm is the colourless material containing the living content of the cell. The living content includes nucleus and cytoplasm. Various cell organelles are found floating in the cytoplasm. These organelles are responsible for carrying out various cellular activities. Substances called cytoplasmic inclusions are also present in it.

Nucleus

Nucleus is a large spherical body. It is generally located in the centre of the cell. Most of the cells contain a single nucleus. Such condition is called uninucleate condition. In multinucleate condition, the cell contains more than one nucleus. For example, muscle cells and cells in fungi. Multinucleate cells are produced under special cases in which nuclear division occurs without cytokinesis.

The nucleus is made up of the following four components:

1. Nuclear membrane
2. Nuclear sap or Nucleoplasm
3. Nucleolus
4. Chromatin material

Nuclear Membrane

- The nuclear membrane is double layered with space between the outer and inner membranes.
- It separates the nucleus from the cytoplasm.
- It is made up of lipids and proteins.
- It has minute nuclear pores which allow for the exchange of material between cytoplasm and nucleus.

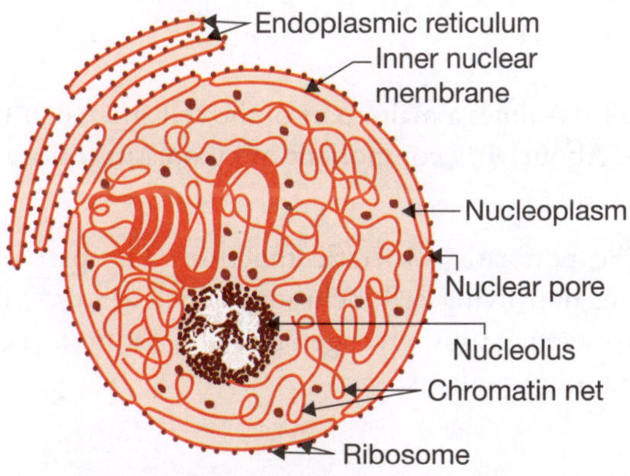

Figure 1.21 Illustration of nucleus

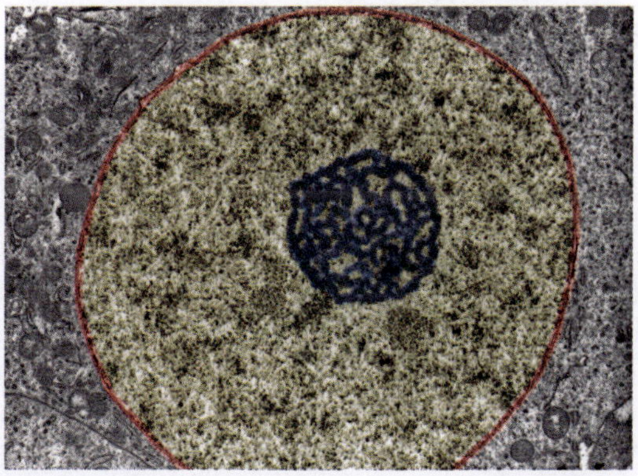

Figure 1.22 Electron micrograph showing the ultrastructure of a nucleus (gold) with a very prominent nucleolus (blue) and a remarkable nuclear envelope (red)

Nucleoplasm

- It is transparent, dense and ground substance of the nucleus.
- Two nuclear structures called chromatin fibres and nucleoli are suspended in it.
- It is surrounded by the nuclear membrane.

Info Bytes!

Ribosomes are the site for protein synthesis.

Nucleolus

- It is a spherical body found inside the nucleoplasm.
- It may be one or more in number.
- It is not surrounded by a membrane.
- It is rich in proteins and RNA (ribonucleic acid) molecules.
- It is a site for the formation of ribosomes. Hence, nucleoli are known as the ribosome factories.

Chromatin Material

- The nucleus contains fine thread-like structures called chromatin fibres.
- Chromatin fibre is composed of the genetic material called DNA (deoxyribonucleic acid).
- DNA stores and transmits all the hereditary information from one generation to the next.
- During cell division, the chromatin fibres get condensed into thick ribbon-like structures called chromosomes.
- Chromosomes contain the hereditary material, that is DNA. The fragments of DNA present in the chromosomes are called genes. These genes are the fundamental, physical and functional units of heredity.

Functions of Nucleus

The nucleus is the main controlling centre of the cell. It plays a major role in cell division. All the cells undergo cell division to form new cells. The cell division is basically of two types—Mitosis or mitotic cell division and meiosis or meiotic cell division.

Mitosis or mitotic cell division takes place in the somatic cells. Somatic cells are the cells which are not concerned with sexual reproduction. This cell division is mainly responsible for the growth of the organism.

Meiosis is the type of cell division which occurs in the reproductive cells or germ cells. This is the type of cell division which is involved in the formation of male and female gametes in the higher organisms. This cell division is responsible for the transmission of heredity characters from one generation to the next. The nucleus controls the metabolic activities that take place in the cell which are controlled by enzymes. The synthesis and regulation of these enzymes is controlled by the nucleus.

Cytoplasm

Cytoplasm is a living, colourless, semi-liquid, homogeneous substance. It occupies a major part of the cell and is constantly moving. It is limited on the outside of the cell by the cell membrane. About 90% component of cytoplasm is water and the remaining are amino acids, vitamins, enzymes, fats and carbohydrates.

It contains many specialized, living cell organelles. Each organelle performs a specific function. The part of the cytoplasm excluding the cell organelles is called cytosol. It also contains non-living cell inclusions which are also known as ergastic bodies. The cell inclusions include reserve food material like starch grains, glycogen granules, fat droplets, etc., and excretory or secretory products, such as oils, alkaloids, tannins, resins, gums, latex, etc.

The various cell organelles are:

- Mitochondria
- Endoplasmic reticulum
- Ribosomes
- Golgi body
- Lysosomes
- Centrosome and centriole
- Plastids
- Vacuoles
- Peroxisomes

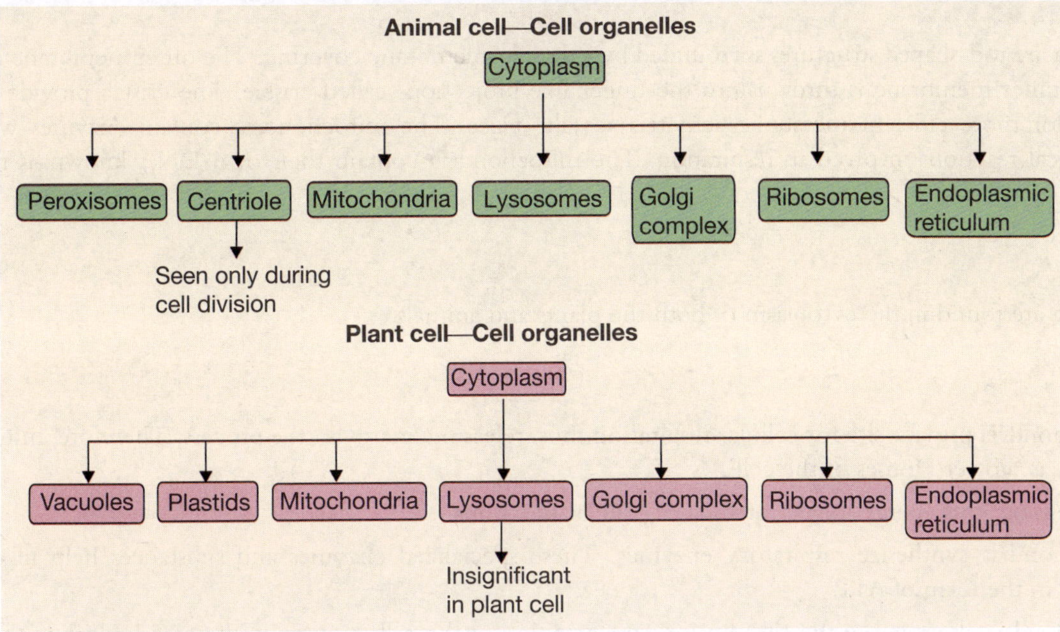

Figure 1.23 Difference in composition of plant and animal cells' cytoplasm

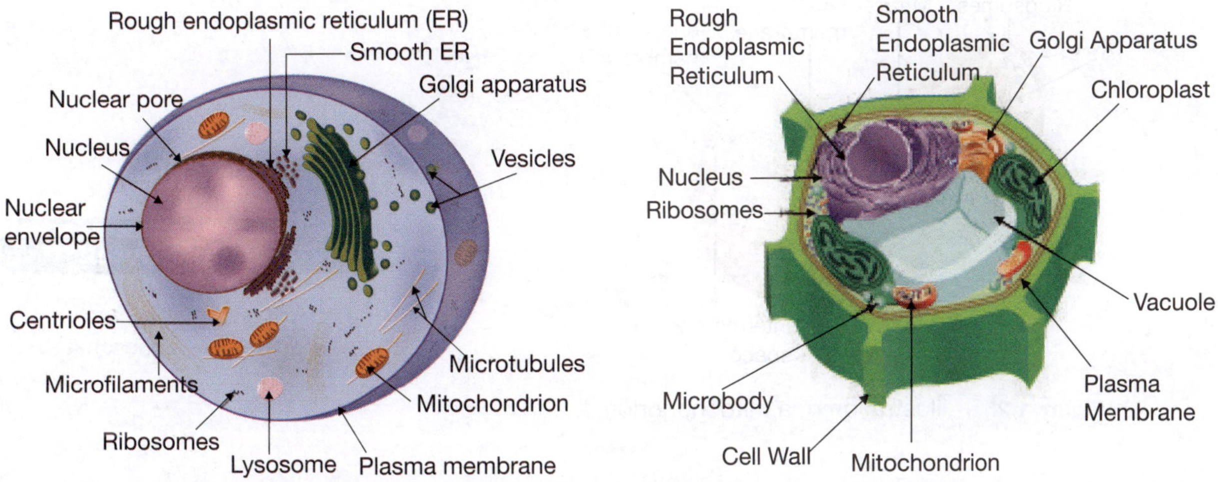

Figure 1.24 Structures of typical animal (left) and plant (right) cells

Cell Organelles

Highly evolved organisms have to perform a great deal of biochemical exercises in order to support life by well-maintained composition of their constituents. To that end, cells of eukaryotes comprise various subcellular components which are delegated specific roles for proper functioning of the cells. These subcellular constituents are called cell organelles. In this section, we shall discuss some major cell organelles.

Mitochondria

Mitochondria (singular: mitochondrion) were first observed by Kölliker. However, it was Benda in 1898 who named them so. Mitochondria are present in all aerobic eukaryotic organisms.

Structure

Mitochondria are rod-shaped structures surrounded by a double-membrane covering. The outer membrane is smooth and porous. The inner membrane is thrown into the finger-like projections called cristae. The cristae provide the increased surface area for more efficient metabolic activities to take place. The mitochondria contain enzymes which catalyze the biochemical reactions involved in respiration. The mitochondria contain their own DNA known as mitochondrial DNA.

Location

Mitochondria are found in the cytoplasm of both the plants and animals.

Function

- Mitochondria provide site for cellular respiration thus, releasing energy in the process. Therefore, mitochondria are known as 'Power Houses of the cell'.
- The cells use this energy for performing of cellular functions.
- Mitochondria synthesize respiratory enzymes. These specialized enzymes and substances help in generation of energy in the form of ATP.
- Mitochondria also regulate the calcium ion concentration in the cells by storing them and releasing them as per the need.

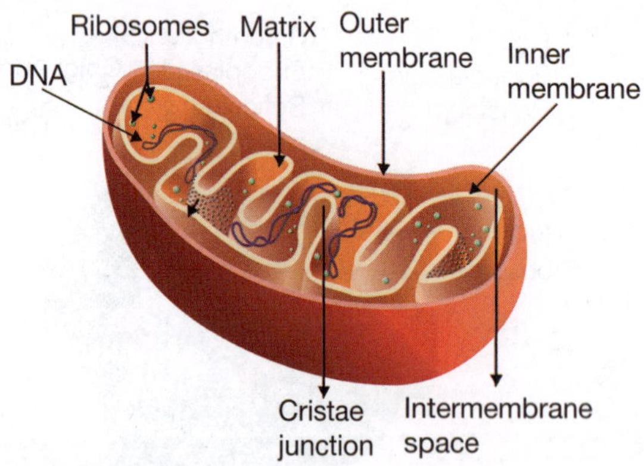

Figure 1.25 Illustration of a mitochondrion

Info Bytes!

ATP is an acronym for 'adenosine triphosphate'.

Endoplasmic Reticulum

Endoplasmic reticulum (ER) is a complex network of membranes which is continuous with the nuclear envelope.

The ER was first observed with light microscopy by Garnier in 1897, who coined them 'ergastoplasm'. With electron microscopy, the detailed components were first seen in 1945. Later, the word 'reticulum', meaning 'network' was given by Porter in 1953 to describe network of membranes.

Structure

Endoplasmic reticulum is a large network of fluid-filled interconnecting tubules. These are tubular double-walled membranes. The spaces are filled with a fluid called endoplasmic matrix. It is made up of three types of structures namely cisternae, vesicles and tubules. The vesicles are sac-like structures. Cisternae are flattened sac-like structures which are parallelly arranged. The tubules are irregularly lobed structures.

ER is of two types—Rough ER and smooth ER. The ER which possesses ribosomes has rough surface and hence, is called rough ER. The ER which does not possess ribosomes has smooth surface and hence, is called smooth ER. Smooth ER is mainly composed of tubules and vesicles while rough ER is mainly composed of cisternae and tubules.

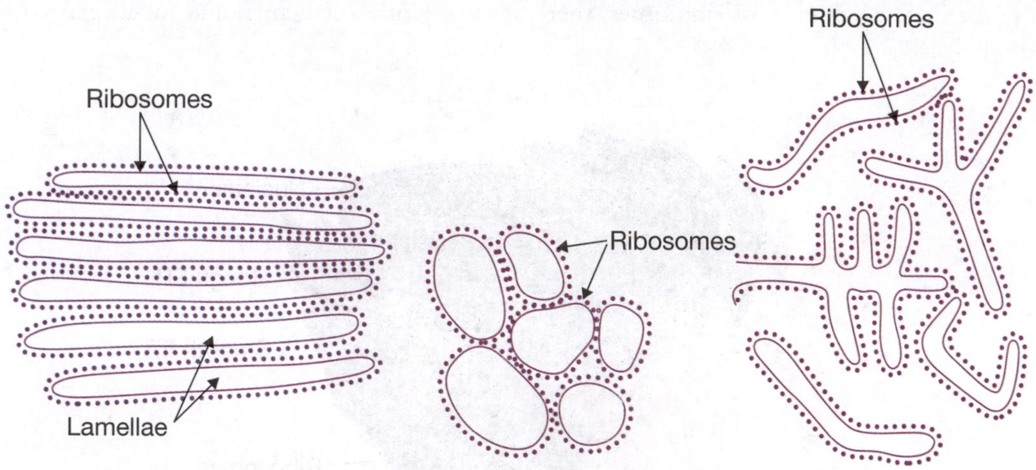

Figure 1.26 Parts of endoplasmic reticulum (starting from the left: cisternae, vesicles, tubules)

Location

- They are found in the cytoplasm of both plants and animals.
- They are continuous with the plasma membrane on the outside and the nuclear membrane on the inside.

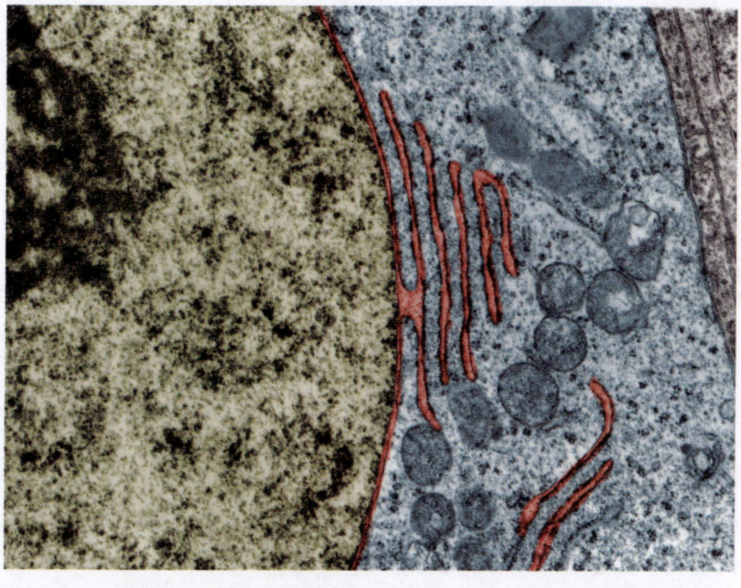

Figure 1.27 Electron micrograph showing continuity between nuclear envelope and cistern of rough endoplasmic reticulum (red), nucleus (gold) and cytoplasm (blue)

> **Konnect**
>
> Sphaerosomes are found only in plant cells and are also known as plant lysosomes, because they contain hydrolytic enzymes.

Functions

- Endoplasmic Reticulum (ER) provides a supportive framework for the cell.
- Endoplasmic Reticulum (ER) provides larger surface area for the metabolic processes to take place.
- It forms an intracellular transport system for the cell.
- Rough ER is responsible for synthesis and transport of proteins.
- Smooth is responsible for synthesis of lipids.
- Smooth ER of liver cells detoxifies many drugs and unwanted substances entering our body.

Apart from the presence or absence of ribosomes, there are many other structural and functional variations between smooth ER and rough ER.

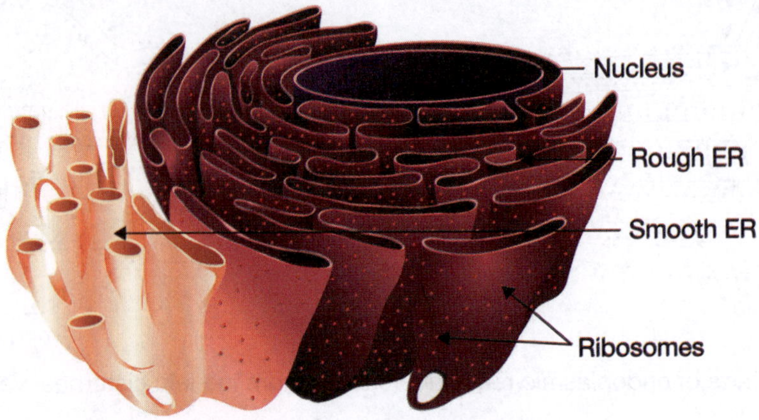

Figure 1.28 Illustration of endoplasmic reticulum

Table 1.4 Differences between smooth ER and rough ER

Smooth ER (SER)	Rough ER (RER)
Do not possess ribosomes.	Ribosomes are present and attached to cytoplasmic surface.
Formed from vesicles and tubules.	Formed from cisternae and few tubules.
Peripherally located and connected with plasma membrane.	Present deep in the cytoplasm and connected to nuclear membrane.
Help in the formation of sphaerosomes in plant cells.	Help in the formation of lysosomes along with Golgi complex.
Mainly concerned with the synthesis of fats in the cells of adipose tissue.	Mainly concerned with the formation of proteins.

Ribosomes

Ribosomes are small ribonucleoprotein particles. They were first observed by the cell biologist George Emil Palade, using an electron microscope. The term 'ribosome' was proposed by scientist Richard B. Roberts in the late 1950s.

Structure

They occur as small granules. They are single-walled dense, spherical bodies. Each ribosome is made up of two subunits, one is smaller subunit and the another one is larger subunit. Each subunit is made up of ribonucleic acid (RNA) and proteins called ribonucleoproteins.

Location

- Ribosomes are found attached to the rough ER and in free form in the cytoplasm of the cell.
- The ribosomes are synthesized in the nucleolus inside the nucleus. After synthesis, they move out through the nuclear pores of the nuclear membrane into the cytoplasm.

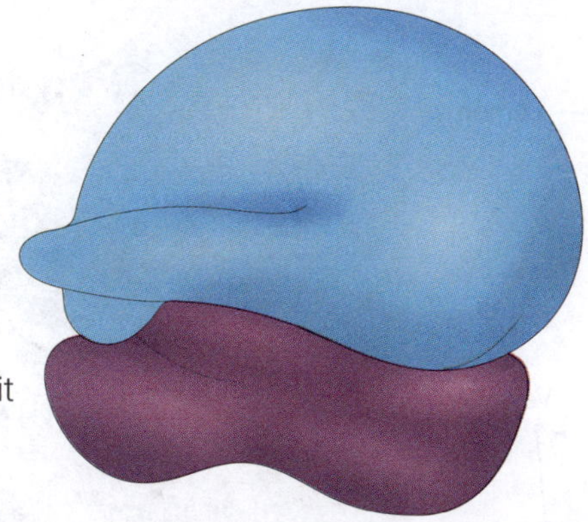

Figure 1.29 Illustration of structure of ribosome

Konnect

- A ribonucleoprotein (RNP) is a complex of ribonucleic acid and RNA-binding protein.
- The two subunits of a ribosome are assigned values known as Svedberg Value, denoted by S.

Functions

- Ribosomes are involved in the process of protein synthesis.
- They provide site for the synthesis of proteins and hence are called protein factories of the cell.

Table 1.5 Differences in prokaryotic and eukaryotic ribosomes

Parameter	Prokaryotic cell (70 S)	Eukaryotic cell (80 S)
Small subunit	30 S	40 S
Large subunit	50 S	60 S

Golgi Complex or Golgi Apparatus

Golgi apparatus was one of the first organelles to be observed in detail. It was discovered in 1898 by Camillo Golgi (Italian physician) and was named after him. Golgi apparatus is a membranous structure that originates from smooth ER. It is also formed of cisternae, vacuoles and vesicles.

Golgi complex has a convex, forming face (cis) and a concave, maturing face (trans). The forming face receives vesicles from ER and maturing face secretes vesicles.

Info Bytes!

Polysome is a cluster of ribosome associated together to synthesize proteins.

Structure

- Stacks of flattened double-walled membrane sacs.
- Fluid is present between both the membranes.
- Sacs are called cisternae.
- Cisternae are packed one above the other.
- They consist of tubules, vesicles and vacuoles.
- These are absent in RBC of mammals and sieve tubes (transporting cells) of plant cells.
- These are known as dictyosomes in a plant cell.

Location

- In the cytoplasm of the animal and plant cell.
- They are linked with the membrane of the ER.

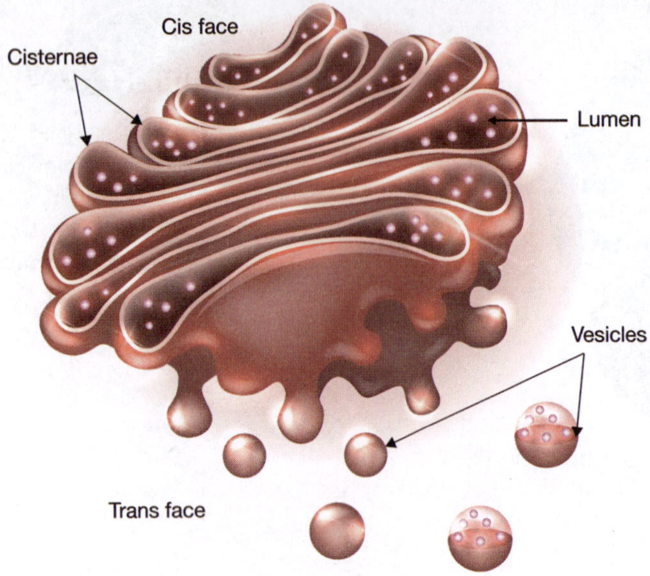

Figure 1.30 Illustration of Golgi apparatus

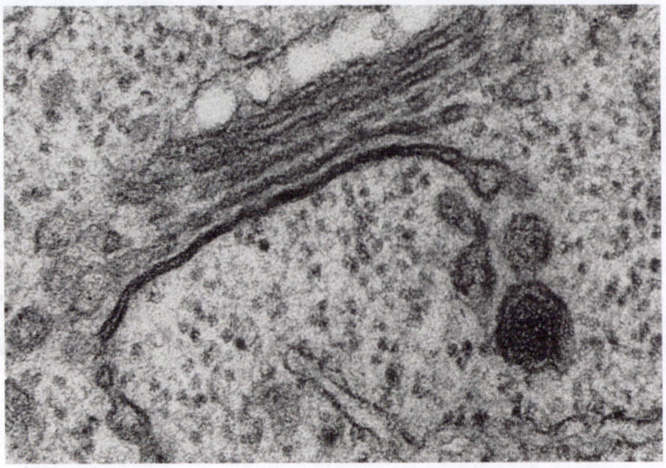

Figure 1.31 Electron micrograph showing stacks of cisternae of the Golgi complex and secretory granules

Functions

- Golgi apparatus is chiefly concerned with the secretion of enzymes and other substances.
- It transports the synthesized substances from the cell to the outside of the cell.
- It is involved in the formation of lysosomes, cell wall and plasma membrane.
- It produces vacuoles which contain cellular secretions. For example, enzymes, proteins, cellulose, melanin pigment, lactoprotein (milk protein), etc.

Lysosomes

Lysosomes are electron microscopic sac-like entities found in the cytoplasm of eukaryotic plant cells. They were discovered and named by Belgian biologist Christian de Duve. They contain several digestive enzymes. Some of the enzymes of lysosomes are synthesized by rough ER and are brought to the lysosomes through Golgi apparatus.

Structure

Lysosomes are membranous sacs budded off from the Golgi body. They are surrounded by a single membrane and contain digestive enzymes.

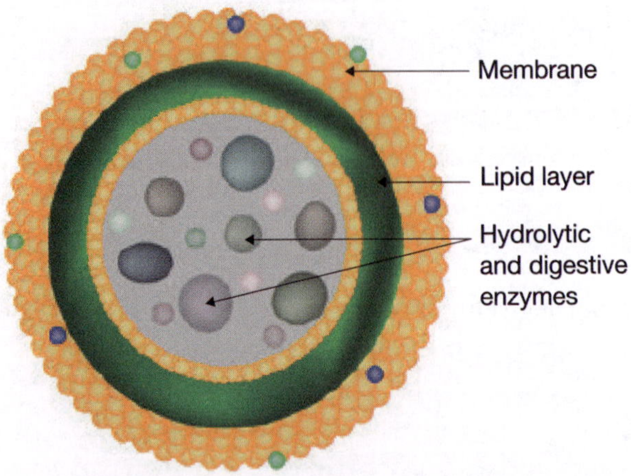

Figure 1.32 Illustration of structure of lysosome

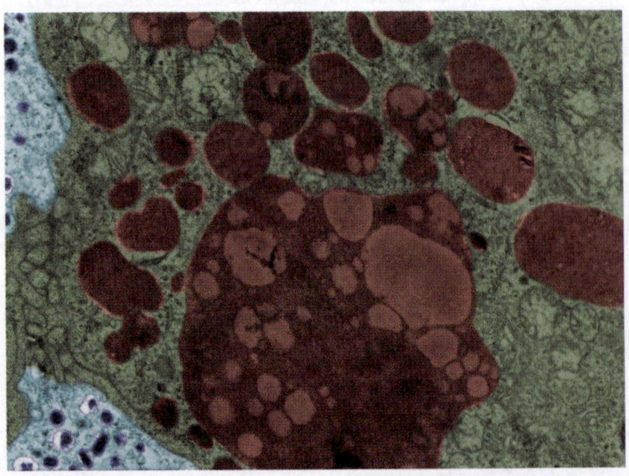

Figure 1.33 Electron micrograph showing many lysosomes (red). At the left is a noradrenaline cell (blue)

Location

- They are located in the cytoplasm of all animal cells and the cells of few lower plants, such as fungi and yeast.

Functions

- They serve as the intracellular digestive system and are called digestive bags of the cell.
- Lysosomes participate in the digestion of food material.
- Under diseased condition or when the cell gets old or damaged, lysosomes burst, and the enzymes digest their own cells. Hence, they are also known as the 'suicidal bags' of the cell.
- They destroy bacteria or any other foreign bodies entering the cell.

Info Bytes!

Lysosomes help sperm to enter ovum as lysosomal enzymes present inside the sperm cells digest the limiting membrane of the ovum.

Centrosome and Centriole

The term centrosome is a combination of two words Latin *centrum* 'centre' + Greek *sōma* 'body'. The role of a centrosome is to organize microtubules and provide structure for the cell, as well as assist to pull chromatids apart during cell division.

A centriole is a cylindrical cellular organelle, found in animal cells only. All centrioles are made of protein strands called microtubules. A centriole is typically made up of nine sets of short microtubule triplets, arranged in a cylinder.

During cell division, two centrioles come together with some special proteins and form the centrosome.

Structure

Centrosome is a small structure consisting of granule-like structures called centrioles. Centrioles are hollow and cylindrical structures made up of microtubules.

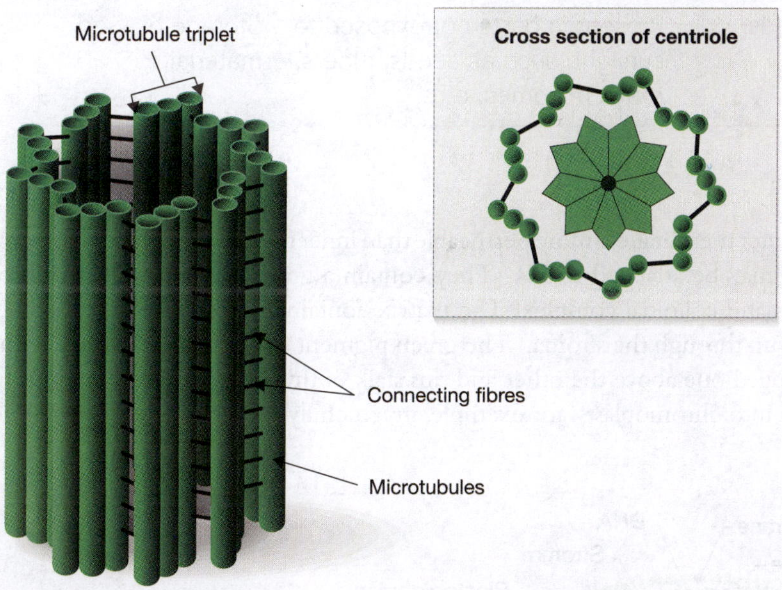

Figure 1.34 Cross section of centriole and nine triplet microtubules

Info Bytes!

Centrioles are absent in flowering plants and most fungi, but they are present in the male gametes of bryophytes and seedless vascular plants.

Location

- They are located close to the nucleus.
- They are present only in animal cells.
- In plant cells, there are polar caps instead of centrioles.

Functions

- Centrosome initiates and regulates cell division in animal cells.
- During cell division, the centrioles move to the poles of the cell.
- They develop many spindle fibres with the help of the asters. An aster is a cellular structure shaped like a star, formed around each centrosome during cell division in an animal cell.

Plastids

They are double-membrane structures found exclusively in a plant cell. Plastids contain pigments, like starch and oil drops. Based on their colour, they are categorized into three types, listed as follows:

1. Leucoplasts
2. Chromoplasts
3. Chloroplasts

Table 1.6 Types of plastids

Type of plastids	Structure	Location	Function
Chloroplasts	Contain green pigment called chlorophyll.	Present in parts of plant exposed to light.	Photosynthesis
Chromoplasts	Contain fat-soluble red, orange and yellow pigments, such as carotenoids.	Present in flowers and fruits and are responsible for their colours. They can change from one form to another.	Impart colours to fruits and flowers.
Leucoplasts	Colourless plastids. Do not possess pigments.	Present in parts not exposed to sunlight, such as seeds, tubers, roots, rhizomes, etc.	Storage of food material.

Structure

It is a double-membrane structure in which the outer membrane is more permeable than inner membrane. The inner membrane possesses more proteins. The outer membrane may be attached to ER. They contain a green pigment called chlorophyll. The matrix or stroma is a semi-fluid, colourless and colloidal complex. The matrix contains DNA and RNA. Membrane-bound, flat sac-like structures called thylakoids run through the stroma. The green pigment chlorophyll is located within the thylakoid membrane. These thylakoids are arranged one above the other and this stalk of thylakoids is called granum (plural: grana). In some cases, chloroplasts may change into chromoplasts, for example, green chilly is converted into red chilly due to conversion chloroplast into chromoplast.

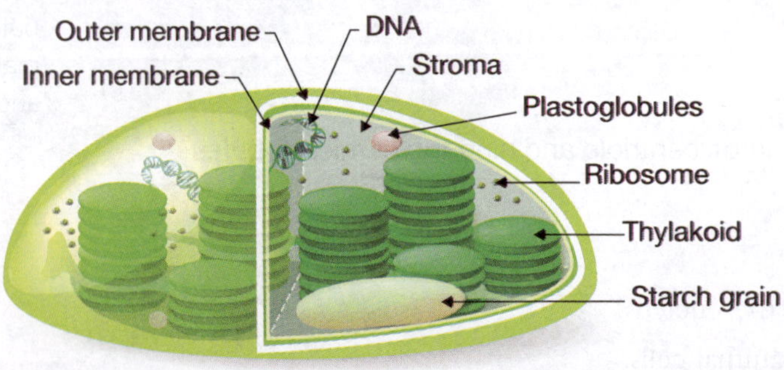

Figure 1.35 Illustration of a chloroplast

Location

- They are present in the cytoplasm of green algae and higher plants.

Function

- Chloroplasts are the site for photosynthesis.
- Leucoplasts store the reserve food in the form of oil droplets or starch grains.
- Chromoplasts assist in pollination and dispersal of fruits by attracting pollinating agents towards bright colours.

Vacuoles

Vacuoles are membrane-bound organelles which are present in all plant and fungal cells. Vacuoles are enclosed compartments which are filled with water containing inorganic and organic molecules. Dujardin coined the term 'vacuole'.

Structure

Vacuoles are the single-membrane bound storage sac-like structures. Membrane of vacuoles is called tonoplast.

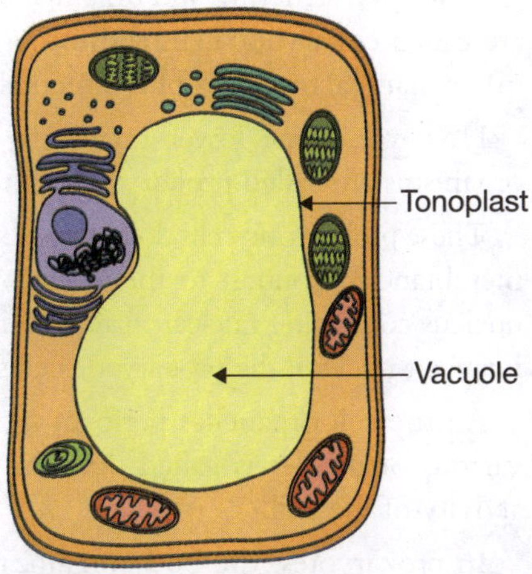

Figure 1.36 Illustration of vacuole in a plant cell

Location

- In plant cells, they are large and occupy almost 90% of the cell.
- They are small or even absent in animal cells.

Functions

- They store dissolved material, such as amino acids, sugars, various organic acids and some proteins. In single-celled organisms, for example, *Amoeba*, they store the food material ingested by the organism.
- They provide turgidity and rigidity to the cell.
- They help to maintain the osmotic pressure of the cell.

Peroxisomes

A peroxisome is a type of organelle known as a microbody, found in eukaryotic cells. They are involved in the catabolism of fatty acids. Peroxisomes were identified as organelles by the Belgian cytologist Christian de Duve.

Structure

Peroxisomes are small spherical organelles bounded by a single membrane. The inner contents are finely granular. Sometimes a crystalline core is visible at the centre which contains a protein called catalase enzyme.

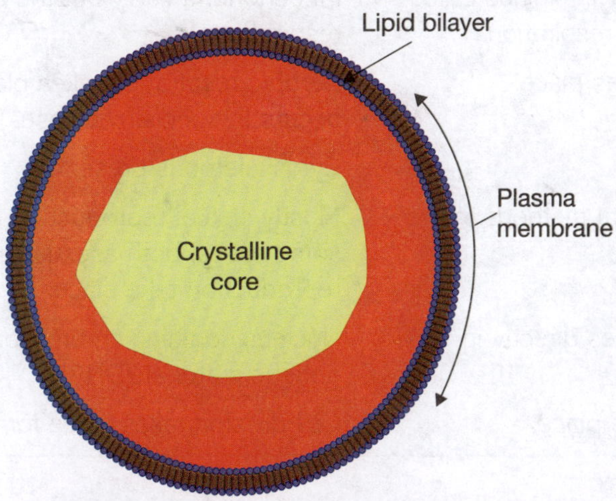

Figure 1.37 Illustration of a peroxisome

Location

- They are found in the cytoplasm of animal cells.
- They are mostly located in the liver and kidney cells.

Function

- They are specialized in detoxification of toxic substances from the cell.

Structure of Cell in Relation to Complexity of Body Organization

The detailed structure and organization of a typical cell pertain to the higher organisms, such as plants and animals. These are called eukaryotic cells and the organisms are called eukaryotes, for example, all plants and animals; lower organisms other than bacteria and blue-green algae.

However, some lower organisms possess primitive cells. These primitive cells are called prokaryotic cells and the organisms are called prokaryotes. For example, bacteria and blue-green algae.

These prokaryotic cells do not possess a well-defined or true nucleus, i.e., the nuclear material is not enclosed within a nuclear membrane in contrast to the eukaryotic cells in which the nucleus has a double-layered nuclear membrane. The primitive nucleus containing nuclear material lying free in the cytoplasm is called nucleoid. In addition to the possession of indistinct or incipient nucleus, the prokaryotic cell shows many characteristics which are quite distinct from the eukaryotic cells.

All the cell organelles perform specific function in the cell. This kind of distribution of various functions among the various organelles is called **division of labour**. All the functions of the organelles together constitute the metabolic activity of the cell.

In prokaryotes, the body organization is simple and the prokaryotic cell shows many characteristics which are quite distinct from the eukaryotic cells.

Table 1.7 Differences between prokaryotic cell and eukaryotic cell

Prokaryotic cell	Eukaryotic cell
These cells are under developed and have sizes from 1 to 10 μM.	These cells are well-developed and have sizes ranging from 5 to 100 μM.
Indistinct nucleoid with a single chromosome.	Nucleus is distinct with more than one chromosome.
Membrane-bound cell organelles are absent.	Membrane-bound cell organelles are present.
Nucleolus is absent.	Nucleolus is present.
Mitochondria are absent.	Mitochondria are present.
Cell membrane consists of infoldings called mesosomes. They help in respiration.	Mitochondria carry out the function of cellular respiration.
Anaerobic respiration takes place.	Aerobic respiration takes place (anaerobic respiration occurs in specialized cases).
Cytoskeleton is absent.	Cytoskeleton is present.
Reproduction is by asexual methods in the organisms.	Mostly sexual reproduction takes place. In some cases, both asexual and sexual modes of reproduction take place.
Genetic material (DNA) lies directly in cytoplasm.	Nucleus contains chromosomes which bear the genetic material (DNA).
Usually, cell division takes place.	Cell division takes place for growth and reproduction.

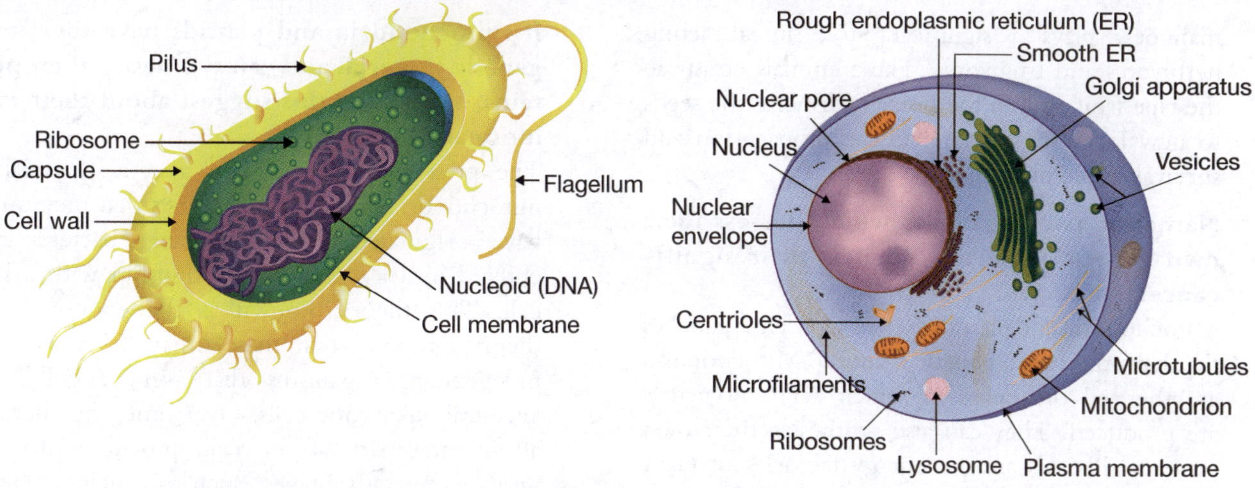

Figure 1.38 Structures of typical prokaryotic (left) and eukaryotic (right) cells

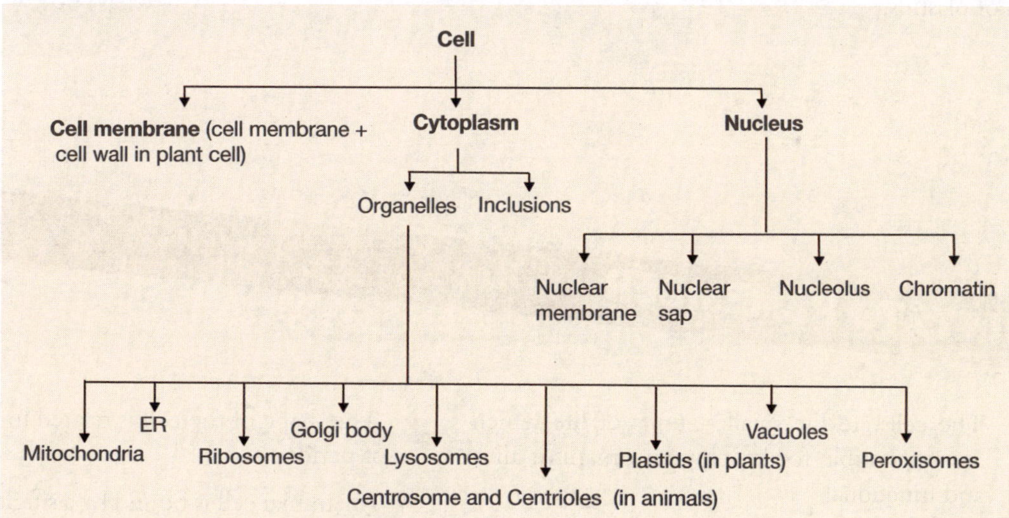

Figure 1.39 Subcellular components

Quick Recap

✔ **Explain the role of flexibility of plasma membrane in the activity of the cell.**

- Plasma membrane is selectively permeable to ions and organic molecules, and regulates the movement of substances in and out the cell.
- Plasma membrane is made up of bilayered phospholipids embedded within proteins. In the lipid layer, cholesterol molecules are present. The presence of these cholesterol molecules in the lipid layer helps to prevent the membrane from splitting apart.

✔ **How does the presence of cholesterol molecules in the lipid layer of the plasma membrane benefit the overall structure and function of the membrane?**

The cholesterol molecules in the lipid layer of the plasma membrane play a crucial role in maintaining its fluidity. They prevent fatty acid chains of phospholipids from packing too closely together, which helps maintain the flexibility of the membrane. This flexibility is essential for various cellular processes, including membrane fusion, vesicle formation, and the function of membrane-bound proteins. Additionally, cholesterol helps stabilize the membrane and prevents it from splitting apart.

✔ **Why is the conversion of chloroplasts into chromoplasts significant for the survival and reproduction of certain plants?**

The conversion of chloroplasts to chromoplasts, which results in a change of colour in fruits like mangoes, plays a significant role in attracting herbivores and frugivores. These animals consume the ripe fruit and, in the process, disperse the seeds to new locations, assisting in the propagation and survival of the plant species.

✔ **Name the two organelles which possess their own genetic material. What is their significance?**

Mitochondria and plastids are the two cell organelles that have their own genetic material. Mitochondria are the cell organelles in which ATP molecules are produced. They can also synthesize their own proteins. Plastids are the energy factories of plant cells where chloroplasts convert solar energy into chemical energy. Photosynthesis is the major function of plastids.

✔ **If mitochondria and plastids have their own genetic material and can synthesize their proteins, what does this suggest about their evolutionary history?**

The presence of their own genetic material in mitochondria and plastids suggests that they might have originated from free-living bacteria that entered into a symbiotic relationship with a host cell. This theory, known as the endosymbiotic theory, proposes that these organelles were once independent organisms that were engulfed by ancestral eukaryotic cells. Over time, they became an integral part of the cell, providing the cell with certain advantages, such as efficient energy production in the case of mitochondria and photosynthesis in the case of chloroplasts.

POINTS TO REMEMBER

- ✔ The cells are the smallest units of life which are responsible for keeping an organism alive and functional.
- ✔ Robert Hooke coined the term 'cells' for the box-like compartments of cork.
- ✔ A compound microscope is an optical instrument that consists of two convex lenses of short focal lengths.
- ✔ No cell arises spontaneously and develops into an organism. All cells arise from the pre-existing cells.
- ✔ Simple organisms may be unicellular, consisting of just one cell, while more complex organisms are multicellular, that is, composed of more than one cell.
- ✔ The shape of the cell is related to the function it performs.
- ✔ An animal cell is bound by a single membrane, called plasma membrane or cell membrane. A plant cell is bound by another covering, called cell wall in addition to plasma membrane.
- ✔ Eukaryotic cells comprise various subcellular components which are delegated specific roles for proper functioning of the cells.
- ✔ All the functions of all the organelles together constitute the metabolic activity of the cell.
- ✔ The detailed structure and organization of a typical cell pertains to the higher organisms, such as plants and animals.

CLASSROOM WING

Practice Questions

Very Short Answer Type Questions

Direction for Questions from 1 to 14:
Fill in the blanks in each question.

1. The folds of plasma membrane in bacterial cells are known as ______.

2. The part of the cytoplasm excluding the organelles is called ________.

3. Homeostasis in the cell is maintained by ______.

4. Genes are made up of complex chemical substance known as ________.

5. Energy stored in mitochondria is in the form of ________.

6. Membrane covering the vacuole is known as ____________.

7. Metabolism of fats in the cell takes place by ___________.

8. Groups of ribosomes in the cell are known as ___________.

9. The cell organelles which contain hydrolytic enzyme is ________.

10. In liver cells, the smooth endoplasmic reticulum produces enzymes that help in ________.

11. The cell organelles that release oxygen are ________.

12. The cell organelle which is found abundant in glandular cells is ________.

13. Plastids present in flowers and fruits are called ________.

14. ________ are considered as kitchen of the cell.

Direction for Questions from 15 to 29:
For each of the following questions four choices have been provided. Select the correct alternatives.

15. 'Master control of the cell' or 'cell brain' is ________.

(a) mitochondria (b) ribosomes
(c) nucleus (d) plastids

16. The cell wall is not involved in ________.

(a) absorption (b) secretion
(c) osmoregulation (d) translocation

17. In certain fungi, many nuclei are present in their single large body. This is known as ________ condition.

(a) syncytium (b) multicellular
(c) coenocytic (d) unicellular

18. What happens to the cell when it is placed in salt solution?

(a) Bursts (b) Shrinks
(c) Swells (d) No effect

19. Identify the protein factories of the cell.

(a) Lysosomes (b) Chloroplasts
(c) Mitochondria (d) Ribosomes

20. Identify the incorrect match.

(a) Vesicles—Golgi complex
(b) Grana—chloroplast
(c) Ribosomes—mitochondria
(d) Chromosomes—nucleus

21. The stack of thylakoids of chloroplast is called __________.

(a) matrix (b) granum
(c) stroma (d) oxysomes

22. The solution filled in vacuole is called ________.

(a) nuclear sap (b) cytoplasm
(c) cell sap (d) latex

23. The cell organelle which helps in the synthesis of fats in adipose tissue is ________.

(a) smooth endoplasmic reticulum
(b) rough endoplasmic reticulum

(c) mitochondria
(d) adipocytes

24. Synthesis of ATP in mitochondria takes place in/on ________.
(a) matrix
(b) cristae
(c) outer membrane
(d) between membrane

25. The energy currency of the cell is ________.
(a) mitochondria (b) ATP
(c) FAD (d) glucose

26. The colourless proteinaceous matrix of chloroplast is ________.
(a) grana (b) cytoplasm
(c) thylakoids (d) stroma

27. Mature erythrocytes cannot utilize glucose because they lack ________.
(a) enzymes (b) Golgi complex
(c) mitochondria (d) nucleus

28. In which of the following cases, conversion of leucoplasts to chloroplasts is observed?
(i) Tubers of radish
(ii) Potato tubers
(iii) Ovary of tomato
(iv) Maize kernels
(a) (i) and (ii) (b) (ii) and (iii)
(c) (i) and (iv) (d) (ii) and (iv)

29. What happens if lysosomes get ruptured in the cell?
(a) Cell dies
(b) Cell swells
(c) Cell shrinks
(d) No change

Direction for Questions 30 and 31: Match the entries of Column 1 with those of Column 2.

30.

Column 1	Column 2
A. Plasma membrane	(i) Respiration
B. Chloroplast	(ii) Maintenance of osmotic pressure
C. Mitochondria	(iii) Semi-permeable membrane
D. Genes	(iv) Photosynthesis
E. Vacuoles	(v) Transfer of hereditary information

31.

Column 1	Column 2
A. Cell theory	(i) Disposal of wastes from the cell
B. Plasmolysis	(ii) Conduction of nerve impulses
C. Nerve cell	(iii) Packing and forwarding
D. Exocytosis	(iv) Schleiden and Schwann
E. Golgi complex	(v) Shrinking of cell

Direction for Questions from 32 to 41: Write True or False.

32. All animal cells contain cell wall.
33. Cell wall is made up of proteins.
34. All cells arise from pre-existing cells.
35. Blue green algae is a eukaryote.
36. Centrosome is present in animal cell.
37. Golgi complex are otherwise known as dictyosomes.
38. Mitochondria regulate cell functioning.
39. Synthesis of proteins is carried out by rough endoplasmic reticulum.
40. All plastids have pigments.
41. Single chromosome is present in prokaryotes.

Short Answer Type Questions

42. Define phagocytosis.
43. Explain the structure of plasma membrane. What are its major functions?
44. What is nucleolus? Explain its function.
45. Explain the structure of a bacterial cell.
46. Define cell and justify that division of labour as seen within the cell.

47. Distinguish between exocytosis and endocytosis.

48. Differentiate between chromosome and chromatin network.

49. How does the structure of a cell pertain to higher organisms like plants and animals?

50. Why is the shape of a cell important in relation to its function?

51. Define autolysis. Name the cell organelle involved in it.

52. Differentiate between centrosome and centrioles.

53. Where do you find vaccuoles? Give their functions.

54. What are mesosomes? Where do you find them? Mention their functions.

55. Give two statements of the modern form of cell theory.

56. Define Autolysis. Name the cell organelle involved in it.

Essay Type Questions

57. Define the following:

(a) Diffusion (b) Osmosis

(c) Plasmolysis (d) Imbibition

(e) Protoplasm

58. Mention the functions of the following organelles:

(a) Endoplasmic reticulum

(b) Golgi complex

(c) Mitochondria

59. Explain the structures of:

(a) Mitochondria

(b) Chloroplasts

60. What are the different kinds of plastids? Mention their location and function.

COMPETITION WING

Practice Questions

Level 1: Apply your Concepts

Direction for Questions from 1 to 13:
Fill in the blanks in each question.

1. Robert Hooke named the compartments he observed in cork as ________.
2. A ____________ is an optical instrument that uses two convex lenses for magnification.
3. The metabolic activity of the cell is a result of functions of all the ____________.
4. Robert Hooke's observation of 'cells' in cork was not of living cells but of ____________ structures that once contained living cells.
5. While all cells arise from pre-existing cells, the initial spark of life remains a scientific ____________.
6. Eukaryotic cells have a defined nucleus surrounded by a ____________.
7. Cell theory was proposed by ________ and ________.
8. Nucleus was discovered by ________.
9. The smallest cell is ________.
10. When bean seed is dropped in salt solution ________ process occurs.
11. Single chromosome is present in ________.
12. Functional segments of DNA are called ________.
13. Mitosis takes place in somatic cells and ________ takes place in ________ cells.

Direction for Questions from 14 to 23:
For each of the following questions four choices have been provided. Select the correct alternatives.

14. Which of the following is NOT bound by a cell wall?
    (a) Fungus (b) Bacteria
    (c) Animal cell (d) Plant cell
15. The concept that no cell arises spontaneously but from pre-existing cells is summarized by which statement?
    (a) Theory of Evolution
    (b) Law of Segregation
    (c) Cell Theory
    (d) Central Dogma
16. If an organism's shape of its cells is tailored specifically for fast movement through fluid, which shape might it have?
    (a) Square (b) Spherical
    (c) Star-shaped (d) Streamlined
17. Considering that the shape of a cell is related to its function, which type of cell is likely to have pseudopods?
    (a) Muscle cells (b) Red blood cells
    (c) Amoeba (d) Nerve cells
18. Which statement about the plasma membrane of animal cells is FALSE?
    (a) It is a lipid bilayer.
    (b) It is selectively permeable.
    (c) It provides rigid support to the cell.
    (d) It contains embedded proteins.
19. If the compound microscope didn't employ two convex lenses, its magnification capability would be ____________.
    (a) doubled (b) halved
    (c) unaffected (d) non-existent
20. The cell wall in plant cell is made up of
    (a) cellulose (b) proteins
    (c) lipids (d) minerals

21. Leucoplasts are present in
(a) roots (b) stem
(c) leaves (d) flowers

22. Tonoplast is the membrane surrounds the
(a) nucleus (b) vaccuole
(c) plastids (d) lysosomes

23. The colourless proteinacious matrix of chloroplast is
(a) grana (b) cytoplasm
(c) matrix (d) stroma

Assertions and Reasons

Direction for Questions from 24 to 32:

Choose the correct option.

(a) Both A and R are true and R is the correct explanation for A.
(b) Both A and R are true, but R is not the correct explanation for A.
(c) A is true and R is false.
(d) A is false and R is true.

24. **Assertion (A):** Eukaryotic cells are more complex than prokaryotic cells.
Reason (R): Eukaryotic cells contain various subcellular components which have specific roles.

25. **Assertion (A):** Animal cells lack a rigid cell wall.
Reason (R): Animal cells need flexibility for movement and interactions.

26. **Assertion (A):** Human RBCs lack nucleus.
Reason (R): RBCs perform the function of transportation of food materials.

27. **Assertion (A):** Endocytosis takes place only in animal cells.
Reason (R): Animal cell does not possess cell wall.

28. **Assertion (A):** Phagocytosis is the intake of solid material by the cell through cell membrane.
Reason (R): Phagocytosis leads to the formation of food vacuole.

29. **Assertion (A):** Smooth endoplasmic reticulum is associated with synthesis of lipids.
Reason (R): Smooth endoplasmic reticulum possesses ribosomes.

30. **Assertion (A):** Lysosomal enzymes work best at acidic pH.
Reason (R): Lysosomes contain as many as 40 kinds of hydrolytic enzymes.

31. **Assertion (A):** Energy is stored in mitochondria in the form of ATP.
Reason (R): Mitochondria possess DNA.

32. **Assertion (A):** Chromoplasts do not help in photosynthesis.
Reason (R): Chromoplasts contain green-coloured pigment.

Direction for Questions from 33 to 38:

Write the missing correlated terms.

33. Plastids : Pigments :: Mitochondria : ________

34. Protein synthesis : Ribosomes :: Homeostasis: ________

35. _____ : Nucleus :: Robert Hooke: Cell

36. Endocytosis : Engulfing food :: _____ : Disposal of wastes

37. Thylakoid : Chloroplast :: ________ : Mitochondria

38. Somatic cells : Mitosis :: ________ : Meiosis.

Level 2: Review your Concepts

39. There is no relation between the size of an animal and the size of cell. Justify your answer.

40. When does the plant lose stiffness and droop?

41. Why is nucleus considered as the most important part of the cell?

42. Cell is the fundamental unit of life. Do you agree with the statement? Give reason.

43. Plasma membrane has fluid-mosaic model. Justify your statement.

44. Complete the following table:

	Made up of lipid bilayer	Gives shape to the cell
Golgi complex		
	Extends from the nuclear membrane	
	Fluid-filled or solid-filled spaces covered by tonoplast	

45. Well-defined nucleus is absent in prokaryotes. Justify your statement.

46. Why do you consider RBC as living cell though it lacks nucleus?

47. Viruses are living organisms without cells. Give reason.

48. Cells without nuclei cannot survive for a longer period. Give reason.

49. Plasmids help in survival of bacteria. Give reason.

50. Explain the biological principle involved in the storage of jams and pickles by adding excess sugar and salt, respectively.

51. After washing clothes for a long time, the skin on the fingers appears to shrink. Give reason.

52. Identify the odd one among the following and justify that.

(a) Bacteria; Insect; Earthworm; Hydra

(b) Polythene; Egg membrane; Cell membrane; Onion peel

(c) Nucleus; Chromosomes; Genes; Lysosomes

(d) Cellulose; Hemicellulose; Suberin; Protein

53. How might the presence of multiple subcellular components in eukaryotic cells contribute to the complex functioning of higher organisms?

54. Lysosomes are called by different names such as suicidal bags of the cell, cells waste disposal system or demolition squads. Justify.

55. The inner membrane of mitochondria possesses finger-like projections. Give reason.

56. More number of mitochondria are found in actively dividing cells. Give reason.

57. Identify the odd one among the following and justify. Chloroplast; Mitochondria; Leucoplast; Chromoplast

58. Mitochondria and plastids are known as semi-autonomous organelles of the cell. Give reason.

59. When a bottle stopper and onion peel are placed in water for some time, then cut into slices, what observation is seen under a microscope?

60. Dried raisins or dates are placed in normal water first and later in concentrated salt solution. Discuss the changes taking place in them.

61. 'Mitochondria are the power houses of the cell'. Discuss.

62. Why is plasma membrane known as the semi permeable membrane?

63. Which parts of the cell carry out the following activities?

(i) Liberation of energy.

(ii) Transmission of hereditary characters from parents to offspring.

(iii) Maintains osmotic pressure.

(iv) Controls cell activities.

(v) Produces enzymes for digestion.

(vi) Acts as a semi-permeable membrane.

(vii) Site of protein synthesis.

(viii) Helps in photosynthesis.

(ix) Secretory organs of cell.

(x) Initiates and regulates cell division in animal cells.

Direction for Questions from 64 to 67:
Give scientific reasons for the following.

64. Bacterial cell is prokaryotic cell.

65. The slowly moving fluid inside the cell is cytosol.

66. Lysosomes remove the organic debris.

67. Plastids are the energy factories of the plant cell.

Level 3: Assess Your Concepts

68. Potatoes are generally brown in colour. But, we find some green areas on potatoes. Give reason.
69. What happens when *Rhoeo* leaf is placed in boiling water and later transferred to strong sugar solution?
70. Why is salt added to the vegetables with high water content before cooking?
71. Kidney beans are soaked overnight before cooking.
    (a) What is the observation you find after soaking?
    (b) Name the phenomenon involved in the above observation. Explain the reason.
    (c) Do you find the same change when a raw egg is placed in water? Justify that.
72. In an experiment, red blood cells of humans and cells of thin onion peel are kept in water separately. What observations do you find? Why?
73. Few dried apricots are placed in beaker 'A' and beaker 'B' for some time. It is found that they shrank in beaker 'A' and became swollen in beaker 'B'. What conclusions can you draw regarding the nature of liquids in beakers 'A' and 'B'? Give justification.
74. Discuss the importance and implications of the statement, 'No cell arises spontaneously and develops into an organism. All cells arise from pre-existing cells.'
75. Why lysosomes are also called 'suicide bag' of cells?

AT

NEET SPECIAL WING

Practice Questions

Multiple-Answer Type Questions

Questions number 1 to 5 are multiple-choice questions. Each question has FOUR options (a), (b), (c), and (d). ONE OR MORE THAN ONE of these four option(s) is/are the correct answer(s).

1. Which among the following is not a non-membrane bound organelle found only in animal cell?
(a) Centriole
(b) Endoplasmic reticulum
(c) Peroxisome
(d) Glyoxisome

2. Pinocytosis is different from phagocytosis in that
(a) It means cell eating
(b) It means cell drinking
(c) Bulk transport of fluid takes place
(d) Neutrophils are involved

3. Which among the following are functions of the vacuole?
(a) Providing turgidity
(b) Storage of materials
(c) Detoxifying toxic substances
(d) Maintaining osmotic pressure

4. Which of the following is an incorrect statement?
(a) Virus is acellular
(b) In animates are made up of cells
(c) Rudolf Virchow said all plants are made up of cells
(d) Smooth muscles are spindle shaped cells

5. Which of the following is the part of the endomembrane system?
(a) Peroxisome
(b) Lysosome
(c) Vacuole
(d) Endoplasmic reticulum

Comprehension-Based Questions

A. Read the paragraph given below and answer the questions number 6 to 11, more than one option can be the answer to the questions:

Just like diffusion, osmosis is a passive process which takes place without the expenditure of energy. In osmosis movement of water molecules takes place from higher concentration to lower concentration across a semi permeable membrane. This movement continues until an equilibrium is achieved on both the sides of the membrane. Cells in presence of different types of solutions based on concentration will show different osmotic movements. The three different types of solutions based on concentration are- Isotonic, hypertonic and hypotonic solution. Isotonic solutions are those which have the same concentration of solutes both inside and outside the cell. In this case no net movement is seen and the shape and size of the cell is retained. Hypertonic solutions are those which show a higher solute concentration outside the cell then inside. In this case when cells are subjected to these solutions the cells usually show exosmosis and the cells shrink or shrivel up. Hypotonic solutions are those in which the concentration of solutes is higher inside the cell than outside. In these solutions cells swell or burst. Animal cells and plant cells show differential reaction to these solutions on account of plant cells having cell wall which gives them extra resilience.

6. Osmosis is
(a) Diffusion of solute
(b) Diffusion of solvent
(c) imbibition of solute
(d) evaporation of solvent

7. Which of the following is not involved in protein synthesis in cells?
(a) RER
(b) SER
(c) Free Ribosome
(d) Lysosome

8. Choose correct statements from the following regarding cell membrane.
   (a) Fluid mosaic model was proposed by Singer and Nicholson
   (b) Carbohydrates make up 90% of the cell membrane
   (c) Lipids are arranged in a bilayer with their polar heads pointing to the outer parts
   (d) Heads are hydrophilic and the tails are hydrophobic in nature.

9. Which of the following cells have the ability to divide and give rise to new cells?
   (a) RBC (b) Nerve cell
   (c) Muscle cell (d) Skin cells

10. For which of the following does cell theory holds true
   (a) Virus (b) Fungus
   (c) Bacteria (d) Algae

11. Using the data given in the previous paragraph, match the following.

Column – A	Column – B
(i) Freshwater fish is placed in seawater	(a) Swelling
(ii) Seawater fish is placed in freshwater	(b) Shrinking or shrivelling
(iii) Grapes are placed in hypotonic solution	(c) Endosmosis followed by swelling and death
(iv) Grapes are placed in hypertonic solution	(d) Imbibition
(v) Swelling of wooden doors during monsoon	(e) Exosmosis followed by shrivelling and death

B. Read the paragraph given below and answer the questions number 12 to 17:

Cell is the basic unit of living organisms. A basic plant cell consists of an outer boundary called plasma membrane and is selectively permeable. It is a phospholipid bilayer with protein molecules. The passage of substances through the plasma membrane can take place via three modes that is- passive transport, active transport and bulk transport. Cell wall is the outermost protective layer surrounding the plant cell. It is made up of three layers- middle lamella, primary cell wall and secondary cell wall. Inside the cell is a colourless material containing the living content of the cell. Various cell organelles are embedded in the cytoplasm and this includes nucleus. The nucleus contains the genetic material and is the main control centre of the cell. Organelles like mitochondria, ribosomes, endoplasmic reticulum perform various functions like energy production, protein generation, protein transportation, etc. Plant cells also consists of chloroplast which perform the function of photosynthesis.

12. Plasmodesmata arise from which layer of cell wall?
   (a) Middle lamella
   (b) Primary cell wall
   (c) Secondary cell wall
   (d) Both a and b

13. The site known as ribosome factories
   (a) Nucleus
   (b) Nucleolus
   (c) Cytoplasm
   (d) Mitochondria

14. Which among the following is an important role of mitochondria?
   (a) Regulation of calcium ion concentration in the cell
   (b) Kitchen of the cell
   (c) Terminator of the cell
   (d) Scavenger of the cell

15. Endoplasmic reticulum is made up of
   (a) Cristae and cisternae
   (b) Vesicles and cisternae
   (c) Cisternae, vesicles and tubules
   (d) Vesicles, cristae and tubules

16. Golgi body in plant cells are called
   (a) Cisternae (b) Dictyosomes
   (c) Tonoplast (d) Cristae

17. Using the data given in the previous paragraph, match the following.

Column – A	Column – B
(i) Suberin	(a) Deposition on secondary walls
(ii) Pectin	(b) Cell adhesion
(iii) Lignin	(c) Nuclear division without cytokinesis
(iv) Multinucleate cells	(d) Cell wall becomes impermeable to water
(v) Cytosol	(e) Cytoplasm without organelles

Answer Keys

Crossword

Across

2. Cytology 6. Ribosome 8. Spirochetes 11. Cytoplasmic inclusions
12. Fluid Mosaic 15. Stroma 17. Active Transport 18. Pectin 19. Protoplasm
20. Pinocytosis

Down

1. Lysosomes 3. Compound Microscope 4. Cisternae 5. Plasmodesmata
7. Rudolf Virchow 9. Tonoplast 10. Mitochondria 13. Phagocytosis 14. Microtubules
16. Lignin

Classroom Wing

Very Short Answer Type Questions

1. Mesosomes 2. Cytosol 3. Plasma membrane 4. DNA
5. Adenosine triphosphate 6. Tonoplast 7. Golgi complex 8. Polysomes
9. Lysosomes 10. Detoxification 11. Chloroplasts 12. Golgi complex 13. Leucoplasts
14. Chloroplasts 15. (c) 16. (d) 17. (c) 18. (c)
19. (d) 20. (c) 21. (b) 22. (c) 23. (a)
24. (a) 25. (b) 26. (c) 27. (c) 28. (a)
29. (b) 30. A-c; B-d; C-a; D-e; E-b 31. A-d; B-e; C-b; D-a; E-c
32. False 33. False 34. True 35. False 36. True
37. True 38. False 39. True 40. False 41. True

Competition Wing

Level 1: Apply your Concepts

1. Cells 2. Compound microscope 3. Organelles 4. Dead
5. Mystery 6. Nuclear envelope 7. Scheiden and Schwann 8. Robert Brown.
9. *Mycoplasma galliseptium* 10. Plasmolysis 11. Prokaryotic cell 12. Genes
13. Meiosis, germ 14. (c) 15. (c) 16. (d) 17. (c)
18. (c) 19. (b) 20. (a) 21. (a) 22. (c)
23. (d) 24. (a) 25. (a) 26. (b) 27. (a)
28. (a) 29. (c) 30. (b) 31. (b) 32. (d)
33. ATP 34. Plasma membrane 35. Robert Brown 36. Exocytosis 37. Cristae
38. Germ cells

NEET Special Wing

Multiple-Answer Type Questions

1. (b, c, d) 2. (b, c) 3. (a, b, d) 4. (b, c) 5. (b, c, d)

Comprehension-Based Questions

6. (d) 7. (b, d) 8. (a, c, d) 9. (a, c, d) 10. (a)

11. (i) → (e); (ii) → (c); (iii) → (a); (iv) → (b); (v) → (d)

12. (a) 13. (b) 14. (a) 15. (c) 16. (b)

17. (i) → (d); (ii) → (b); (iii) → (a); (iv) → (c); (v) → (e)

Hints and Explanations

CLASSROOM WING

Short Answer Type Questions

42. The intake of solid material by evagination of the cell membrane on the periphery, later forming food vacuole is known as phagocytosis (cell eating).

43. It is an elastic, delicate and flexible membrane.

This membrane is made up of lipoproteins. It contains lipid bilayer having integrated protein molecules. It encloses the nucleus andcytoplasm.

This membrane is a semi-permeable membrane or selectively permeable membrane. It gives shape to the cell. This membrane regulates the movement of molecules in and out of the cell.

44. The small round body located inside the nucleus is called nucleolus. Nucleolus acts as the site for the synthesis of ribosomes. These ribosomes take part in protein synthesis.

45. Bacterial cell is a prokaryotic cell. Nucleus is not enveloped by a nuclear membrane.
    - It contains a single chromosome with DNA. Nucleolus is absent.
    - It does not possess membrane bound cell organelles. Mitochondria are absent.
    - The cell membrane consists of infoldings called mesosomes which help in respiration.

46. Cell is defined as the basic structural, functional and hereditary unit of all living organisms.

In a cell, different cell organelles perform different functions. For example, mitochondria carry out cellular respiration. Golgi complex performs secretory function. ER carries out protein and lipid synthesis. Nucleus controls all these activities and is responsible for the transmission of hereditary characters. Thus, division of labour is seen within a single cell.

47.

Exocytosis	Endocytosis
The movement of materials from inside to outside the cell.	Movement of materials into the cell by engulfing of the food and other substances from the external environment.
This is useful in throwing out the secretory and excretory materials.	This is useful in the engulfing of foreign substances, bacteria and pathogens.
This takes place in both plant and animal cells.	This takes place only in animal cell.

48.

Chromatin network	Chromosome
Fine thread-like network of chromatin material.	Short, thick distinct structures with two arms separated by centromere.
Present in the nucleus of a cell at all stages.	Seen in the nucleus at the time of cell division.

49. The detailed structure and organization of a cell is especially relevant to higher organisms such as plants and animals because their survival, growth, and reproduction depend on the specialized functions of the numerous cell types they contain.

50. The shape of a cell is closely related to its function, as it can enhance or enable specific processes. For instance, a flat shape can maximize surface area for absorption, while a streamlined shape allows for efficient movement through fluids.

51. Autolysis is the process of removal of worn out cellular organelles and all the organic debris from the cell. When the cell gets old or damaged, this process takes place. Lysosomes are the organelles involved, as they burst and enzymes are produced which digest their own cells.

52. Centrosomes are structures within the cell nearby to the nucleus. They are made up of two centrioles. Centrosomes are the centre for microtubule organization. Centrioles are small set of microtubules which are found in pairs. They move to the opposite poles during cell division by forming spindle fibres. Centrioles also have basal bodies which help in formation of cilia and flagella.

53. Large fluid-filled spaces in cell sap of plant cell are known as vacuoles.
   - Vacuoles are filled with cell sap in which pigments, minerals and waste products are collected.
   - The cell sap maintains its concentration by absorbing sufficient water from cytoplasm.
   - Vacuoles provide turgidity and rigidity to the sells by means of the cell sap concentration.

54. Mesosomes are circular or finger-like invaginations or infoldings of plasma membrane that appear in prokaryotic cells (e.g., bacteria).
   - Increases the surface area of cell membrane.
   - Helps in DNA replication and cell division and also contain co-enzymes associated with cell respiration.

55. Statements of cell theory are
   - Cell is the structural, functional and hereditary unit of life. All vital functions of an organism occur within cells.
   - All the cells arise from pre-existing cells.

56. • Autolysis is the process of removal of worn out cellular organelles and all the organic debris from the cell. When the cell gets old or damaged, this process takes place. Lysosomes are the organelles involved, as they burst and enzymes are produced which digest their own cells.
   - Hence, they are also called 'Suicide Bags' of the cell.

Essay Type Questions

57. (a) Diffusion is the process in which movement of molecules takes place from higher concentration to lower concentration till the concentrations become equal.

   (b) The movement of solvent (water) molecules from a solution of lower concentration to a solution of higher concentration through a semi-permeable membrane is known as osmosis.

   (c) If a cell is in an environment of a hypertonic solution (solution of higher concentration), the movement of molecules takes place from the cell into the solution. This process is called exosmosis or plasmolysis. This leads to shrinkage of the cell.

   (d) If a cell is placed in a hypotonic solution (solution of lower concentration), the movement of solvent molecules takes place from the solution into the cell. This process is called endosmosis or imbibition. This results in swelling of the cell.

   (e) Protoplasm is the colourless material containing the living content of the cell which includes nucleus and cytoplasm.

58. (a) • Endoplasmic reticulum (ER) forms the intercellular transport system of cell. Rough ER is involved in the synthesis and transport of proteins.
   - Smooth ER performs the function of synthesis of lipids.
   - ER provides larger surface area for the metabolic processes to take place.
   - Proteins and lipids synthesized in this organelle serve the purpose of synthesis of plasma membrane for the newly formed cells during cell division.

   (b) • Proteins built in the ER are collected by vesicles, pass through cytoplasm and empty in cisternae.
   - They are the secretory organs of the cell and help in the formation of the cell wall and plasma membrane.
   - Complex sugars are made from simple sugars in Golgi complex.
   - It helps in the formation of lysosomes

   (c) • Oxidation of carbohydrates and fats takes place in mitochondria with the help of enzymes, to release energy.
   - The energy is stored in mitochondria in the form of ATP molecules.
   - Mitochondria regulate the calcium ion concentration in the cells by storing them and releasing them as per the need.
   - The mitochondrial DNA helps to produce many proteins or enzymes for functional purpose.

59. (a) • Mitochondria is rod-shaped double membrane structure.
   - Outer membrane is smooth and inner membrane is folded and is selectively permeable.
   - A large number of finger-like structures formed as a result of folding of inner membrane are present called cristae.
   - Cristae bear small bat-shaped structures called elementary particles or oxysomes which are rich in enzymes.
   - Cristae provide large surface area for efficient functioning.
   - Inner cavity is filled with proteinaceous gel-like matrix.

- They contain their own DNA known as mitochondrial DNA.

(b)
- Chloroplast is a double-membrane structure in which the outer membrane is more permeable than inner membrane.
- The inner membrane possesses more proteins.
- The outer membrane may be attached to ER.
- The chloroplast contains a ground substance known as matrix or stroma which is a semifluid, colourless and colloidal complex.
- Stroma contains DNA and RNA.
- Membrane bound, flat sac-like structures called thylakoids run through the stroma.
- These thylakoids are arranged one above the other and this stalk of thylakoids is called grana.
- The grana contain chlorophyll and other pigments and are capable of trapping the solar energy.

Type of plastids	Structure	Location	Function
Chloroplasts	Contain green pigment called chlorophyll.	Present in plant parts exposed to light.	Photosynthesis
Chromoplasts	Contain fat-soluble red, orange and yellow pigments such as carotenoids.	Present in flowers and fruits and are responsible for their colours. They can change from one form to the other.	Impart colours to fruits and flowers.
Leucoplasts	Colourless plastids. Do not possess pigments.	Present in parts not exposed to sunlight such as seeds, tubers, roots, rhizomes, etc.	Storage of food material.

COMPETITION WING

Level 1: Apply your Concepts

14. While fungi, bacteria, and plant cells have a cell wall, animal cells only have a plasma membrane.
Hence, the correct option is (c).

15. One of the fundamental principles of the Cell Theory is that all cells come from pre-existing cells.
Hence, the correct option is (c).

16. A streamlined shape reduces resistance and allows for faster movement through a fluid.
Hence, the correct option is (d).

17. Amoeba uses pseudopods for movement and capturing food, and its shape is constantly changing.
Hence, the correct option is (c).

18. The plasma membrane is flexible, not rigid. The rigidity in plant cells is provided by the cell wall.
Hence, the correct option is (c).

19. A compound microscope uses two convex lenses (objective and eyepiece) to magnify an image. Without one, its magnification would be significantly reduced.
Hence, the correct option is (b).

24. Eukaryotic cells are indeed more complex and this complexity is due to their various subcellular components or organelles, which have specific roles.
Hence, the correct option is (a).

25. Animal cells indeed lack a rigid cell wall, which gives them the flexibility they need for movement and various cell-cell interactions.
Hence, the correct option is (a).

26. The function of RBC in human body is transport of materials.
    - If nucleus would have been there in the RBC, it would have occupied more space resulting in the obstruction of flow.
    - Flow in the transportation of the material would be difficult.

Hence, the correct option is (b).

27. In case of an animal cell, plasma membrane is the outermost covering. Therefore, it is in direct contact with the external environment.
    - Hence, endocytosis takes place where the cell engulfs food and other substances.
    - A plant cell has a cell wall as the outermost covering.
    - Plasma membrane is not in contact with the external environment. Hence, endocytosis is not observed.

Hence, the correct option is (a).

28. Phagocytosis is known as cell-eating or intake of solid food material from outer media by the cell. This leads to the formation of large vesicles, which are formed by the membrane evagination on the periphery to engulf the solid particle. This leads to the formation of food vacuole. Reason supports the assertion.
Hence, the correct option is (a).

29. Smooth endoplasmic reticulum is associated with the synthesis of lipids. It lacks ribosomes and does not help in protein synthesis. Assertion is correct, but reason is incorrect.
Hence, the correct option is (c).

30. Lysosomes are cell organelles which contain many kinds of powerful digestive (hydrolytic) enzymes. These are made up of acidic hydrolases. Lysosomal enzymes are capable of breaking down wide variety of molecules, they work best acidic PHS. These enzymes are inactive as long as the membrane is intact or does not come in contact with other cellular structures. Both assertion and reason are correct, but reason does not support.
Hence, the correct option is (b).

31. Oxidation of carbohydrate takes place in mitochondria. This results in release of energy which is stored in the form of ATP. Mitochondria possesses DNA. But this is not the reason for the given assertion.
Hence, the correct option is (b).

32. Plastids are pigment-containing organelles found in plant cell only. Chromoplasts are a type of plastids which contain many types of coloured pigments. These cells are present in flower and fruits which impart colouration. These plastids do not contain chlorophyll, but contain xanthophyll, carotene, etc., As chlorophyll is absent, chromoplast will not help in photosynthesis. Assertion and reason, both are incorrect.
Hence, the correct option is (d).

33. Plastids : Pigments :: Mitochondria : ATP

34. Protein synthesis : Ribosomes :: Homeostasis : Plasma membrane

35. Robert Brown: Nucleus :: Robert Hook : Cell

36. Endocytosis : Engulfing food :: Exocytosis :Disposal of wastes

37. Thylakoid : Chloroplast :: Cristae : Mitochondria

38. Somatic cells : Mitosis :: Germ cells : Meiosis.

Level 2: Review your Concepts

39. The size of the cell does not increase in proportion to the size of an organism. As the organism grows in size, the number of cells increases. The size of an animal cannot be estimated by the size of the cell it possesses.

40. Cell absorbs water and swells when plants are watered. Cell wall is tough and hard as it prevents excess swelling of cell. The cell becomes slightly stretched and turgid. When there is no water, cell shrinks and no pressure is exerted on cell wall. Plant loses stiffness and droops.

41. Nucleus is the most important part of the cell. It regulates and coordinates various life processes of the cell. It plays an important role in cell division. It contains factors (genes) which determine heredity.

42. Yes. Cell is the basic unit of life. Life of every organism begins from a single cell.
    - In unicellular organism, life completes in a single cell itself and in multicellular organisms, all cells of the body are formed from single cell zygote.
    - The activities of an organism is the sum total of all the activities performed by its components.
    - Groups of cells that have similar structure and function constitute a tissue. Group of tissues aggregate together to form organ. Group of organs combine to form the organ system and in turn various organ systems assemble together to form an individual.

    Cells → tissues → organs → organ systems → organisms

43. Plasma membrane has fluid mosaic model.
    - Plasma membrane contains bimolecular lipid layer, the surface of which is interrupted by proteins.
    - The molecular arrangement of plasma membrane resembles moving sea of lipids in the central region covered by different types of proteins which resemble to mosaic arrangement, hence the model is known as fluid mosaic model.
    - Lipids act as fluid and the solid proteins act as mosaic arrangement above lipids.
    - This model helps in retaining its semi-permeability.

44.

Plasma membrane	Made up of lipid bilayer.	Gives shape to the cell.
Golgi complex	Made up of cisternae and vesicles.	Secretory function.
Endoplasmic reticulum	Extends from the nuclear membrane.	Synthesis of proteins and fats.
Vacuoles	Fluid filled or solid filled spaces covered by tonoplast.	Storage of food.

45. Prokaryotes are primitive cells, they do not have well-defined nucleus and nuclear membrane.

    A single chromosomal, circular, double stranded DNA molecule is located in a region called nucleoid which helps in transmitting the genetic material.

46. Mammalian RBCs lack nucleus which is an adaptation to carry more haemoglobin and therefore help in transportation of gases.

    The cells maintain their biconcave shape to carry more oxygen.

    The oxygen molecule gets oxidized to produce energy which is required by the cell to perform various metabolic activities. Hence, erythrocytes are considered as living cells.

47. Viruses are the only living organisms without cells.
    - They contain genetic material (DNA and RNA) enclosed in a protein capsule.
    - They do not have membrane bounded cell organelles.
    - They do not have self-metabolism.

48. Nucleus is the most important organelle in the cell.
    - It contains DNA (genetic material) which is responsible for controlling and directing all the activities of the cell.
    - The nucleolus within the nucleus is the site for RNA synthesis as well as DNA replication.
    - Protein synthesis which takes place by ribosomes is also formed by the nucleus.
    - As nuclei are serving major roles in the survival of the cell, cell dies or cannot survive for a longer period without nuclei.

49. Plasmids are small circular piece of DNA found in bacteria.

    They replicate by themselves during cell division and are stable for long periods. They contain antibiotic resistance genes, which produce proteins that protect the bacteria from harmful drugs.

Thus, they help in survival of the organisms.

50. Addition of excess sugar and salt to jams and pickles leads to the excess concentration of solutions in them.

Any microorganism which enters the foodmaterials possesses cell sap of lower concentration.

As a result, the cells of the microorganisms undergo exosmosis which ultimately results in their death.

Since microorganisms cannot grow in them, they can be preserved for long time without getting spoiled.

51. The soap or detergent solution has higher concentration than the cell sap of the cells of skin.

When the skin lies in contact with the soap solution for a long time, exosmosis takes place in the skin for some time. Hence, the skin shrinks.

52. (a) Bacteria are prokaryotes while others are eukaryotes.

(b) Polythene is not a semi-permeable membrane while others are semi-permeable membranes.

(c) Lysosomes are not related to heredity while others help in heredity.

(d) Proteins are not the components of cell wall while others are.

53. The presence of multiple subcellular components or organelles in eukaryotic cells allows for compartmentalization of various biochemical processes. This ensures efficiency, minimizes conflicting interactions, and enables multifaceted cellular functions, contributing to the complexity of higher organisms.

54. Organic waste results from metabolic processes and is broken down by lysosomes via autolysis, serving as the cell's waste disposal system. Lysosomes digest food and damaged cells. They're known as "suicidal bags" when they burst and digest their own contents. They also act as "demolition squads" by destroying foreign bodies in the cell.

55. The inner membrane of mitochondria contains large number of finger-like structures. These folding are known as cristae. Cristae increase the surface area of the inner membrane. Thus, more area is provided for the metabolic reactions to take place for cellular respiration.

56. More number of mitochondria are found in actively dividing cells than matured cells.

- Cell division is the process which requires more amount of energy.
- The cells that divide actively require more amount of energy for cell division.
- Mitochondrion is the only cell organelle which helps in generating energy in the form of ATP molecules by oxidation of glucose.
- Hence, more number of mitochondria are found in actively dividing cells than matured cells.

57. Mitochondria. All others are different types of same cell organelles, i.e., plastids. Mitochondria are other cell organelles.

58. Mitochondria and plastids are the cell organelles which possess their own DNA. The DNA provides information for the purpose of synthesis of proteins. These proteins are utilized for the activities of cellular respiration and photosynthesis.

59.
- When a bottle stopper is soaked sliced and observed under a microscope only empty (hollow) boxes are observed.
- But when onion peel is observed under microscope, cells with nucleus are seen.
- This shows the difference between living and non-living cells.
- Bottle stopper is composed of dead tissue and onion peel is composed of living tissue.

60.
- When dried raisins or dates are placed in water, they swell.
- As plasma membrane is a selectively permeable membrane, it absorbs water and swells.
- This process is known as "Imbibition"
- When they are placed in salt solution, since the concentration of solvent to more in the solution, the water from raisins comes out into salt solution where the cell shrinks.
- This process is known as "Plasmolysis"

61. Mitochondria contains enzymes which help in oxidation of carbohydrates and fat molecules.

Carbohydrates and fats are used to produce ATP molecules.

ATP molecules are energy rich molecules.

Energy rich molecules (ATP) are formed and stored in mitochondria. Hence they are known as Power houses of the cell.

62. Plasma membrane or cell membrane is known as semi permeable membrane as it allows only few substances to enter into the cell by the process of Osmosis.

63. (i) Liberation of energy – Mitochondria.

(ii) Transmission of hereditary characters – Genes.

(iii) Maintains osmotic pressure – Vacuole.

(iv) Controls cell activities – Nucleus.

(v) Produces enzymes for digestion – Lysosomes.

(vi) Acts as semipermeable membrane – Plasma membrane or cell membrane.

(vii) Site of protein synthesis – Ribosomes.

(viii) Helps in photosynthesis – (Plastids) chloroplasts contain chlorophyll and help in photosynthesis.

(ix) Secretory organs of cell – Golgi complex.

(x) Initiates and regulates cell division in animal cells – Centrosome.

64. Bacterial cell does not have membrane bound organelles. Mitochondria and plastids are absent and chlorophyll is present in vesicles. Nucleus is absent but nuclear material is present in cytoplasm (DNA present) with single chromosome. Hence it is considered as a prokaryotic cell.

65. The jelly like substance which is constantly and slowly moving between the plasma membrane and the nucleus is cytoplasm. It is a site for cellular reactions. Part of the cytoplasm excluding the cell organelles is called cytosol. It stores vital substances like glucose, vitamins etc.,

66. Lysosomes secrete digestive enzymes and are capable of digesting and breaking down all organic matter. It serves as the waste disposal system in the cell. Hence lysosomes are considered to remove the organic debris.

67. One of the major type of plastid is chloroplast present in the green parts of the plant. It has the ability to trap solar energy and convert it into chemical energy by the process called photosynthesis. Thus, these chloroplasts synthesise starch and hence are known as the energy factories of plants.

Level 3: Assess Your Concepts

68. Potato tubers are underground stem modifications which store starch.

When potato tubers are exposed to light, leucoplasts are converted into chloroplasts, hence show green colour.

69. When *Rhoeo* leaf is placed in boiling water, the cells are killed.

As the cells are destroyed, shrinking does not occur. Plasmolysis does not take place.

Movement of molecules takes place in living cells and not in dead cells.

70. When salt is added to a vegetable, the water that is present inside the cell's cytoplasm will move out by the process of osmosis.

Once water comes out of the cells, the cell shrinks and can be easily cooked and made soft.

71. (a) On soaking overnight, kidney beans become swollen.

(b) Endosmosis. The cells of the kidney beans are covered by a porous cell wall and a plasma membrane. Water enters the cells of the kidney beans as the cell sap has higher concentration. Thus, endosmosis takes place and the beans become swollen and palatable after cooking.

(c) A raw egg does not swell if kept in water as the material of the shell is impermeable to water.

72. The cell initially swells because of endosmosis as the concentration of cell sap is greater than that of the external environment.

In case of onion peel, the cell wall prevents the entry of water after some time. Hence, it does not burst.

However, RBC bursts due to the absence of cell wall and such protective mechanism.

73. The beaker 'A' should contain a higher concentrated solution and hence, exosmosis takes place.

Due to this, the apricots shrink. The beaker 'B' should contain a lower concentrated solution or water and endosmosis takes place.

Due to this, the apricots become swollen.

74. The assertion that no cell arises spontaneously, and all cells come from pre-existing ones revolutionized our understanding of life. This foundation of cell theory negates spontaneous generation, asserting that life cannot just appear from non-life under present-day conditions. This principle implies continuity of life, linking all living organisms to a shared origin. Furthermore, it accentuates the importance of reproduction at cellular and organismal levels. This understanding aids in areas ranging from developmental biology to medicine, where cell growth and differentiation are pivotal. Additionally, this knowledge counters the previous belief that diseased states could emerge spontaneously, aiding medical advancements. Lastly, the interconnection of all life through cell lineage reinforces the intricate web of life on Earth, highlighting the evolutionary interdependence and shared history of all living entities.

75. Lysosomes are tiny, spherical structures which contain many digestive enzymes. If any kind of disturbances are caused to cell structure and its organization, lysosomes burst releasing their enzymes. These enzymes are capable of digesting their own cell. Therefore, lysosomes are called suicide bag of cells.

NEET SPECIAL WING

Multiple-Answer Type Questions

1. Peroxisomes, Glyoxysomes and endoplasmic reticulum are all membrane bound organelles found in eukaryotic cells whereas centrioles are the only non-membrane bound organelle found exclusively in animal cells.
2. Phagocytosis means 'cell eating'. In this process, large particles are taken in by a cell. For example, when microorganisms invade the human body, neutrophils will engulf and destroy them. On the other hand, Pinocytosis means 'cell drinking'. In this process, bulk transport of fluid matter takes place across the cell membranes by forming small vesicles.
3. The functions of vacuoles include- providing turgidity, storage of materials and maintaining osmotic pressure
4. Non living things are not made of cells and it was a botanist named Schleiden who said that all plants are made up of cells.
5. The endomembrane system is the membranous system of the eukaryotic cells . They work together to modify, package and transport lipids and proteins in the cell. They include- Lysosome, Vacuole and Endoplasmic reticulum

Comprehension-Based Questions

A.

6. In osmosis diffusion of solvent takes place from high concentration area to low concentration area across the cell membrane which is semipermeable.
7. Rough endoplasmic reticulum and free ribosomes are involved in protein synthesis within the cells.
8. The fluid mosaic model was proposed by Singer and Nicholson. A phospholipid bilayer comprises two layers of phospholipids. Each phospholipid is composed of a hydrophilic head and a hydrophobic tail. The hydrophilic heads are attracted to the water in the cytoplasm of the cell, as well as to the water in the surroundings of the cell, whereas the hydrophobic tails are repelled by water and are attracted to each other. It is because of this attraction and repulsion that the bilayer is a stable structure in spite of its fluidity.
9. Nerve cells once they reach maturity lose the ability to divide and give rise to new cells. This is the reason why head injuries can lead to paralysis or even death. All the other cells have the ability to divide.
10. Viruses are acellular hence cell theory that proposes that all organisms are made up of cells does not apply to them.
11. Match the following:

    When freshwater fish is placed in salt water / sea water the cells are facing hypertonic solution which results in water escaping the cells via exosmosis. This causes the cells to shrivel up and the fish ultimately dies.

    (i) (e)

    When seawater fish is placed in freshwater the cells are exposed to hypotonic solution, as a result of endosmosis the water molecules will move from the solution inside the cells where it is present in lower concentration. This causes the fishes to swell and subsequent death occurs.

    (ii) (c)

    Grapes when placed in hypotonic solution, water will enter the cells via endosmosis and the grapes will swell further.

    (iii) (a)

    Grapes when placed in hypertonic solution, water will exit the cells vis exosmosis and the grapes will shrivel up.

    (iv) (b)

    Wooden doors are made up of dead plant cells containing cell walls. Cell walls are freely permeable and when they are exposed to moisture in the air during monsoons, the cell walls imbibe the water and this results in swelling of the wooden doors.

    (v) (d)

B.

12. Cytoplasmic strands arise from the middle lamella forming interconnections between the cells. These strands are called plasmodesmata and they facilitate the transport of proteins and other materials between the cells.
13. Nucleolus is rich in proteins and RNA (ribonucleic acid) molecules. It is a site for the formation of

ribosomes. Hence, nucleoli are known as the ribosome factories.

14. Mitochondria regulate the calcium ion concentration in the cells by storing them and releasing them as per the need.

15. Endoplasmic reticulum is made up of three types of structures namely cisternae, vesicles and tubules. The vesicles are sac-like structures. Cisternae are flattened sac-like structures which are parallelly arranged. The tubules are irregularly lobed structures.

16. Golgi body is known as Dictyosomes in the plant cells as they are very scattered in contrast to animal cells where they are stacked together.

17. Match the following:
In some regions of the cell wall, the deposition of a substance called suberin on the walls makes the walls impermeable to water.
(i) (d)

Pectin helps in cell adhesion and hence, this layer acts as a cementing layer which binds the cell walls of the adjacent cells.
(ii) (b)

A substance called lignin may be deposited on the secondary walls of some cells. This process is known as lignification.
(iii) (a)

When nuclear division takes place without cytoplasmic division, multinucleated cells are produced.
(iv) (c)

Cytoplasm which excludes the organelles is called cytosol.
(v) (e)

CHAPTER

2

Tissues

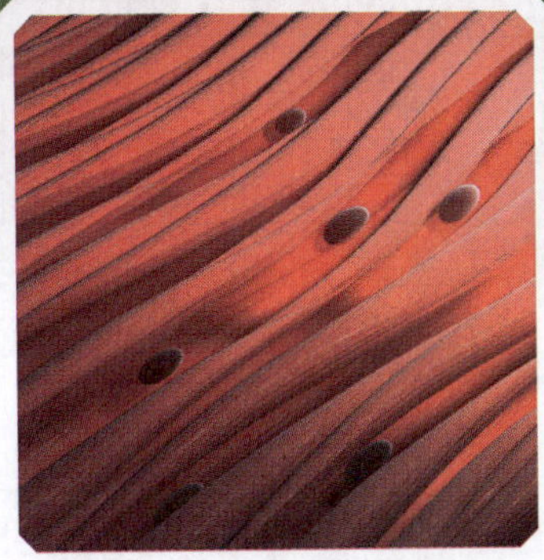

Key Ideas

After completing this chapter, you should be able to:

- Interpret organizational hierarchy in higher organisms
- Describe the structure and function of plant tissues
- Explain the structure and function of animal tissues

Remember

Before beginning this chapter, you should be able to:

- Define different types of plant and animal tissues
- Describe the basic structure and functions of important tissues

Scientific Crypt

A Tribute to Theodore Schwann (1810-1882)

A German physiologist, is regarded as one of the primary architects of the cell theory in the annals of biological science. This seminal theory, which holds that the cell is the fundamental structural and functional unit of all living organisms, has become a cornerstone in tissue research. '*Microscopical Researches into the Accordance in the Structure and Growth of Animals and Plants*' (1839), his seminal work, is a treasure trove of insights, revealing the existence of cells in animals and thus establishing a profound parallel between animal and plant tissues.

Other than his ground-breaking contributions to cell theory, he also dabbled in enzymology, discovering the digestive enzyme 'pepsin' and researching the fermentation process. He delved into the intricate realms of animal physiology, providing a plethora of insights that paved the way for subsequent biological breakthroughs.

Though he did not receive significant awards or honours during his lifetime, his monumental contributions were recognized posthumously, and his legacy is still celebrated by biologists and scholars worldwide. Theodore Schwann's discoveries have provided generations of scientists with the foundational knowledge they need to investigate and comprehend the myriad mysteries of life at the cellular level, propelling the scientific exploration of biology forward.

Crossword

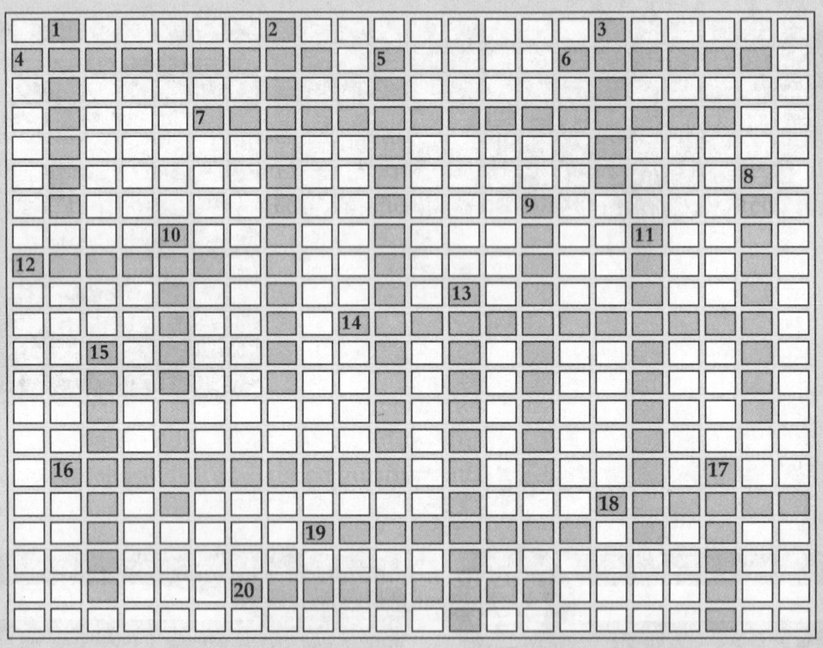

Across

4. Desert plants contain modified epidermal cells forming fine outgrowths called
6. Tissue which connects muscle to bone
7. Tissues which increase the height of the plant
12. The waterproof substance present in the cell wall of dead tissues which is responsible for the hardening of cells
14. Neurons which form connections between others and help in the transmission of messages and conduction of nerve impulses.
16. Unspecialized plant tissues which form the bulk of the plant body
18. Tissue system in plants which forms a protective layer over the entire plant body
19. Epithelial cells found in oviduct
20. Type of dead tissue which consists of hard and strongly lignified stone cells

Down

1. Loose connective tissue which holds various organs in place
2. Fibrous membrane covering the cartilage
3. The special thickening present between the cells of collenchyma
5. The only living cells in xylem tissue
8. Canal through which blood vessels and nerves pass in the bone tissue
9. Tissue containing air spaces and providing buoyancy to the aquatic plant
10. Elongated, cylindrical, thin-walled cells with perforated ends for transportation of food
11. Type of plants in which cuticle is absent
13. Tissues in which the cells divide actively throughout the life of the plant
15. Plant tissues which have lost the ability to divide further
17. Spindle-shaped muscle cells

INTRODUCTION

Cells are the basic building blocks of all the living organisms. All metabolic activities take place in the cells. In unicellular organisms such as Amoeba, Paramecium, all activities are performed by a single cell. However, in multicellular organisms, all the cells are not alike. The specific tasks are performed by groups of similar cells. Such groups of cells are termed as tissues. The term 'tissue' originates from the French word 'Tisser' which means 'something woven'. The study of tissues is known as histology. The cells of plants and animals constantly divide, re-divide and acquire a variety of shapes and structures for the specific function that they perform. In course of their development they become specialized. This process is called cell differentiation. During the process of cell differentiation, the unspecialized cells become specialized to perform some specific functions. In this process, they lose the ability to perform other functions. The various functions are distributed among the various types of tissues. Thus, cell differentiation resulting in the formation of tissues leads to division of labour.

Organizational Hierarchy in Higher Organisms

Similar cells which together perform a specific function form a tissue. Several tissues performing a specific function together form an organ. Many organs acting together to perform a specific life process form an organ system. All the organ systems together form the organism.

Cells ⟶ Tissues ⟶ Organs ⟶ Organ systems ⟶ Organism

The formation of different kinds of tissues in plants and animals eventually results in body organization, with the various systems performing various activities required for life.

Konnect

The process by which a cell becomes specialized in order to perform a specific function in course of time is known as cell differentiation.

Tissues in Plants

Though the formation of tissues and body organization are the characteristic features of all the higher organisms, the plants and animals show large variation in the type of tissues and hence, in the body organization. Based on various aspects, plant tissues are divided into various categories. Based on their ability to divide, the plant tissues are classified into two types, namely

1. Meristematic tissue
2. Permanent tissue

Meristematic Tissue or Meristems

Meristematic tissues or simply meristems, are tissues in which the cells divide actively throughout the life of the plant. Their structure and types are discussed below.

Structure

The cells are small and usually cuboid in shape. The cell walls are thin and nuclei are large. Vacuoles are almost absent. The cells are tightly packed with almost no intercellular spaces. The cells actively undergo cell division and form new cells. The new cells that are produced transform into mature permanent cells.

Classification

Based on the location, the meristematic tissue is categorized into three types. They are as follows.

1. Apical meristems
2. Cambium or lateral meristems
3. Intercalary meristems

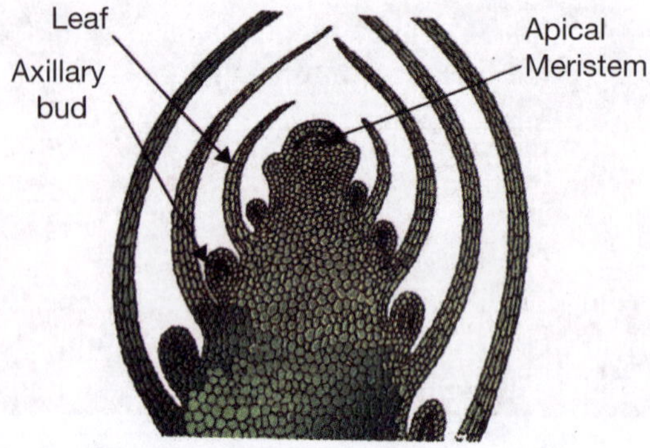

Figure 2.1 Illustration of a stem tip showing apical meristem

Table 2.1 Comparison between different types of meristematic tissues

Type of meristems	Apical meristems	Intercalary meristems	Lateral meristems (Cambium)
Location	At the apices (growing tips) of root, stem and branches.	At the base of the leaves and at the nodal region of twigs.	Present at the lateral axis parallel to the periphery of the stem or root (below the outer layers of stems and roots).
Function	Increase in height of the plant (length of roots and stems) by the active division of cells.	Remain active only for short period. Rapid stem elongation; the tissue at the base of leaves allows the regrowth of the leaves, when they are damaged.	Increase in girth or width (diameter) of the plant by active division.

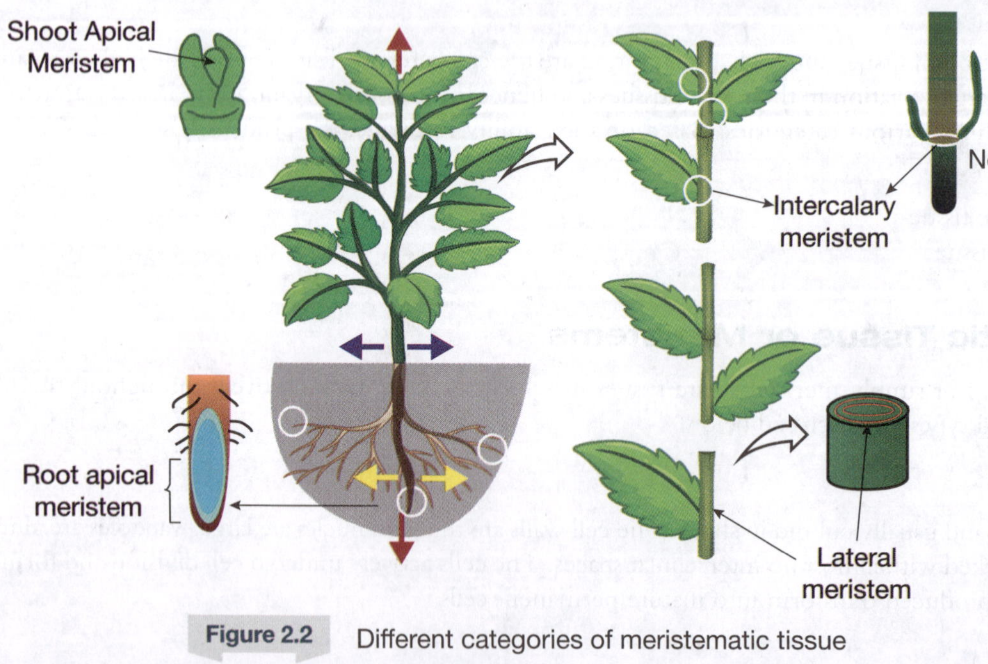

Figure 2.2 Different categories of meristematic tissue

Permanent Tissue

The cells of this tissue have lost their ability to multiply. They take up a specific role and lose their ability to divide further. As a result, they form a permanent tissue and thus perform some permanent function. They are of various sizes, shapes and other characteristics to make them suitable for the specific functions.

Permanent tissues are classified into two types.

1. Simple permanent tissues
2. Complex permanent tissues

Konnect

The giant sequoia trees, with their massive girths, owe their size largely to their extensive permanent tissues.

Simple Permanent Tissue

These simple tissues are each made up of one type of cells. Based on their functions, the simple permanent tissues are further differentiated into following three types:

1. Parenchyma
2. Collenchyma
3. Sclerenchyma

Parenchyma (para, beside + enchyma, in-filling)

Structure: The tissue is made up of living cells which are large and unspecialized. They have thin cell walls. They are loosely packed with large intercellular spaces.

Location: This tissue is found in the soft parts of stems and roots of the plant, and forms the bulk tissue of the plant body.

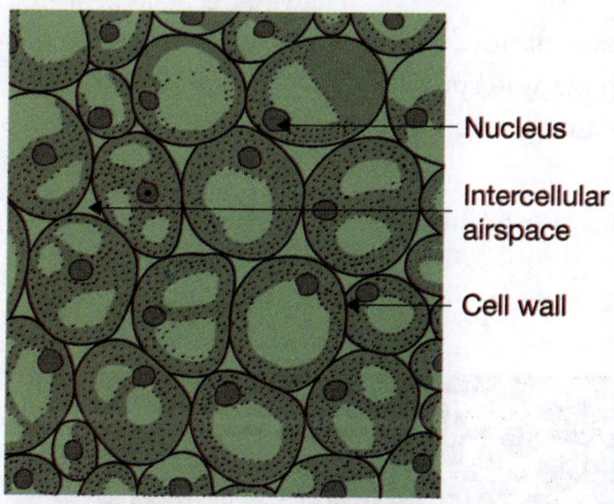

Figure 2.3 Illustration of parenchyma

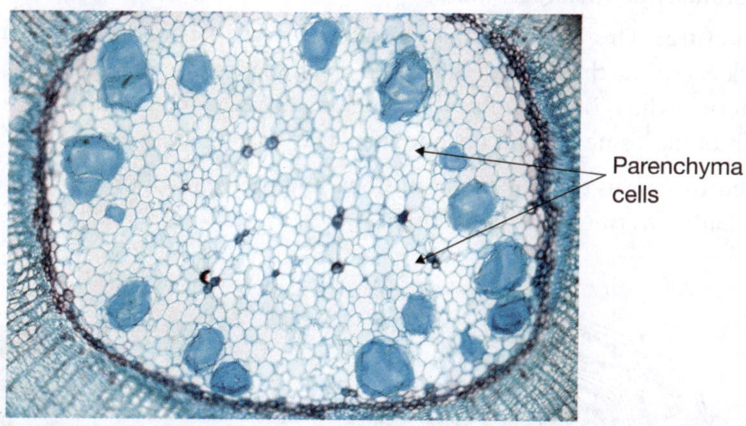

Figure 2.4 Light microscopic view of parenchyma

Functions: Parenchyma stores food and also provides temporary support to the plant. Some of these tissues, particularly those found in the leaves, contain chlorophyll and perform photosynthesis. This type of parenchyma tissue is known as **chlorenchyma** (Chloros = green). In aquatic plants, large air spaces are present in the parenchyma tissue to give buoyancy to the plant and help them to float. This type of parenchyma is called **aerenchyma**.

Collenchyma (Collen = glue)

Structure: This tissue is made up of living cells which may be circular or oval or polygonal in shape. Cells are elongated which are thickened at the corners due to the deposition of cellulose and pectin. There are very little intercellular spaces. Few chloroplasts may be present in the cells of this tissue.

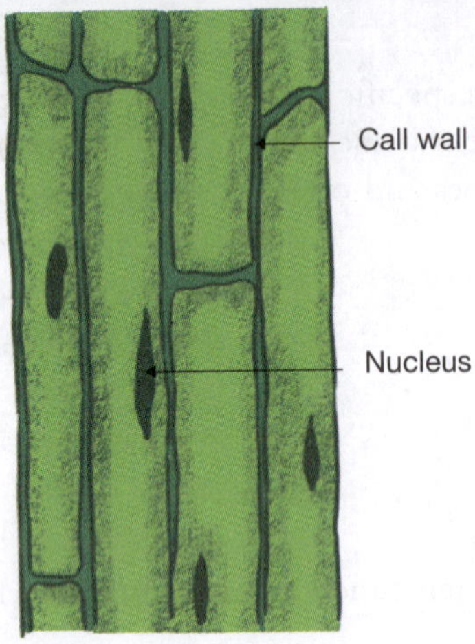

Figure 2.5 Illustration of collenchyma

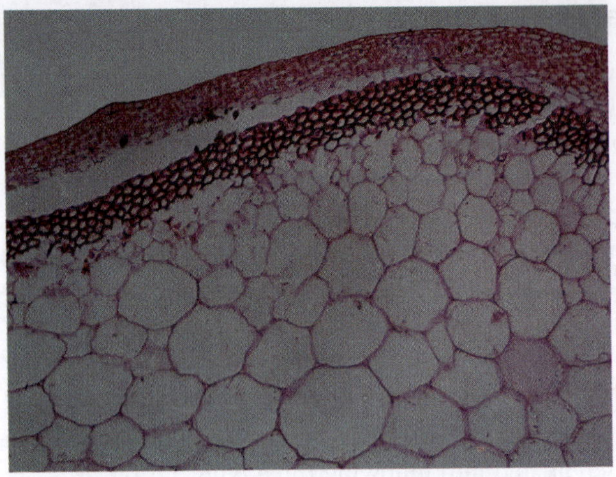

Figure 2.6 Cross-section of stem collenchyma

Location: The tissue is found in leaf stalks and below the outer protective layer of the stems and leaves.

Function: It provides mechanical support to the young plants and twigs. This tissue also provides flexibility and tensile strength to the branches and facilitates easy bending of the plant.

Konnect

A pear feels gritty when it is chewed because pear fruit contains sclerenchyma tissue composed of sclereid cells which harden the tissue.

Sclerenchyma (Scleros = hard)

Structure: This tissue is made up of dead cells. It is composed of long, narrow and thick cells. The thickness of the cells is due to deposition of lignin which is a waterproof material, which is responsible for hardening of walls. Intercellular spaces are absent. The walls of this tissue contain oblique thin areas, called pits.

Location: This tissue is found in stems and the veins of the leaves. It is also found in the hard covering of seeds and nuts.

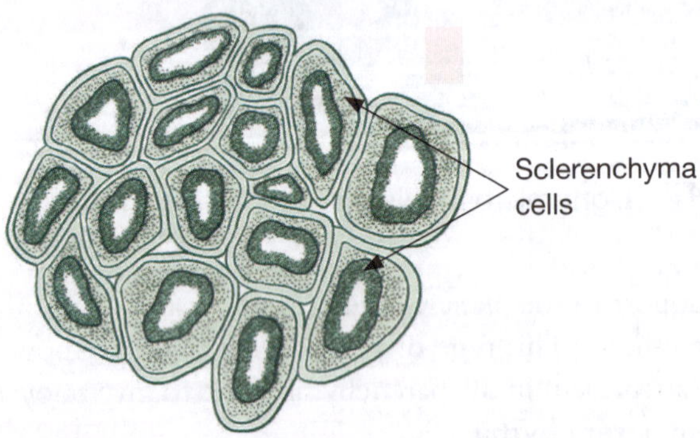

Figure 2.7 Illustration of sclerenchyma

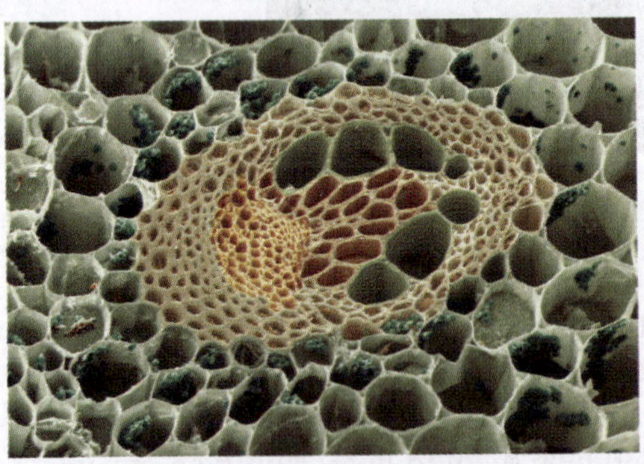

Figure 2.8 Cross-section of a stem of a Buttercup, showing vascular bundle embedded in parenchyma cells (yellow). At the outer edge of the vascular bundle is sclerenchyma tissue

Function: This tissue provides strength and mechanical support to various parts of the plant.

Types of Sclerenchyma

Fibres

- They are pointed, needle-like structures.
- They occur in groups or sheets or cylinders in various parts of plant body.
- It is a supporting tissue present below the outer layers of stems and roots.
  For example, jute and coir (husk of coconut).

Sclereids

- Very thick walled, hard and strongly lignified cells called stone cells or grit cells.
- Occur singly or in groups in stems, fruits and seeds.
  For example, hard grit of pear fruit.

Figure 2.9 Illustration of horizontal cross-section of sclereids

Complex Permanent Tissue

These tissues are made up of more than one type of cells. All these cells work together to perform a common function. The complex tissue basically carries out the function of conduction of substances through the plants. Hence, this tissue is also called vascular tissue or conducting tissue. The tissue which is concerned with the conduction of water and minerals from the roots to the other parts of the plant is called xylem. The tissue which is concerned with the conduction of food materials from the leaves to the other parts of the plant is called phloem. Usually, in higher plants, xylem and phloem occur together in the roots, stems and leaves. These are called vascular bundles.

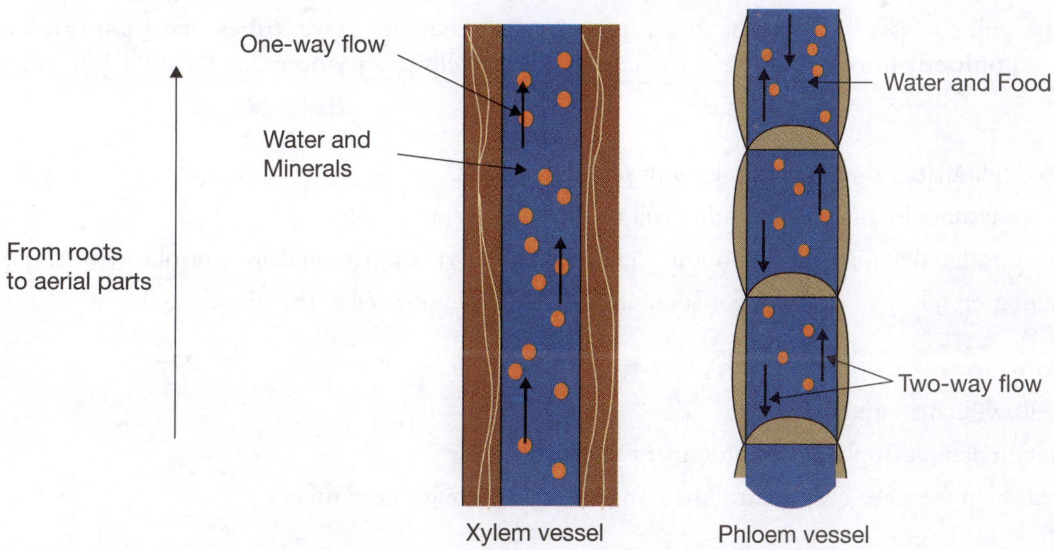

Figure 2.10 Conduction through xylem and phloem

Xylem

Structure: Cells are thick-walled. The xylem tissue consists of four types of cells. They are **tracheids, vessels, xylem parenchyma** and **xylem fibres**.

Tracheids

- They are non-living elongated cells with tapering ends.
- Cell wall is highly thickened with lignin.
- These are network of hollow connected cells through which water can pass.

Info Bytes!

The word 'xylem' is derived from the Greek word 'xylon' meaning 'wood'.

Xylem Vessels

- They are non-living cylindrical tube-like cells.
- They are placed one above another.
- Vessels are made up of lignin.
- Lignin makes the cell walls rigid and long-lasting.
- Vessels are interconnected through the perforations in their common walls.

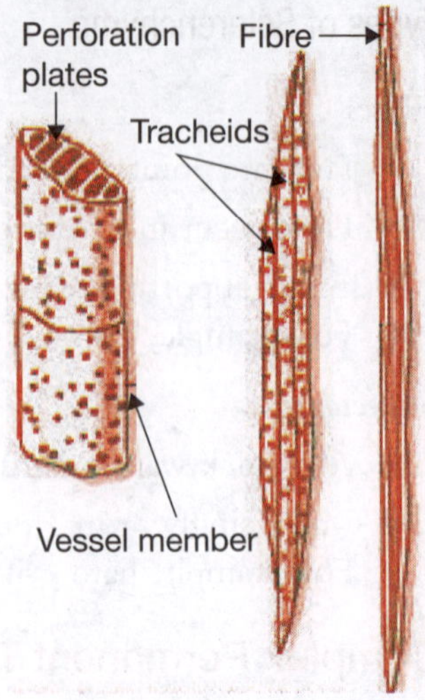

Figure 2.11 Different types of cells of xylem tissue

Xylem Parenchyma

- It contains living cells.
- Cell walls made up of cellulose.
- This helps in the sideways conduction of water and minerals.

Xylem Fibres

- They are non-living, thick-walled cells.
- They provide mechanical energy.

Functions: The lignin in xylem vessels helps in holding the trees up. Tracheids help to transport water and minerals from the soil to the leaves for the manufacture of food. Xylem tissue carries out the upward conduction of water and minerals from the roots to the other parts of the plant. Older xylem forms the wood and gradually loses the ability of transportation.

Phloem

Structure: The phloem tissue consists of four types of cells. They are **sieve tubes, companion cells, phloem parenchyma** and **phloem fibres**. All the phloem cells are living cells except those that form the phloem fibre.

Sieve Tubes

- Elongated, cylindrical, thin-walled cells with perforated ends.
- Matured sieve tubes lose nuclei and other cell organelles except vacuoles.
- They are considered living cells without nuclei as the nuclei of companion cells control the functional activities.
- Perforations (pores) help in easy transportation of substances from one cell to the adjacent cells.

Companion Cells

- Living cells, which are smaller in size.
- Cells contain dense cytoplasm and prominent nuclei.
- These cells help the sieve cells control the transportation through sieve tubes.

Phloem Parenchyma

- Contains living cells having thin cell walls made up of cellulose.
- Forms packing tissue in connecting different cells
- Helps in storage of starch and other organic substances, such as latex, resins, etc.
- Helps in the sideways conduction of water.

Phloem Fibres

- Elongated tapering dead cells found in stem.
- The cell walls are thickened and give the mechanical support.

Info Bytes!

The world's oldest living tree, a bristlecone pine named Methuselah, is over 4,800 years old. It owes its longevity to its meristems that have been dividing for millennia.

Function: Phloem tissue provides downward transportation of prepared food material (starch) from leaves to various parts of the plant. This process to transport of food in plants is called translocation.

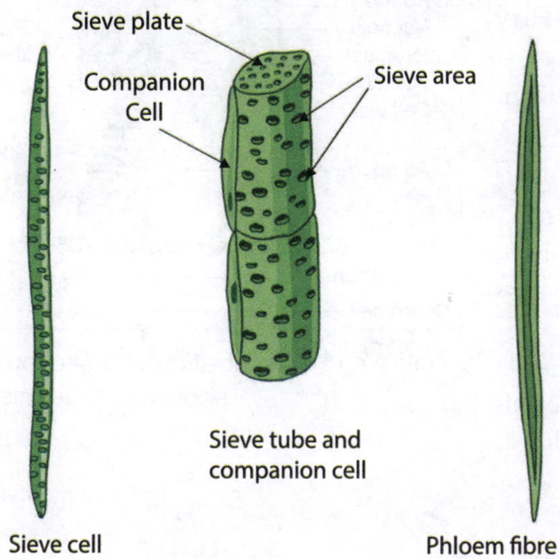

Figure 2.12 Different types of cells of phloem tissue

> **Info Bytes!**
> In plants, phloem tends to be closer to the bottom part of the leaves. Hence, we often find insects feeding on the bottom side of the leaves.

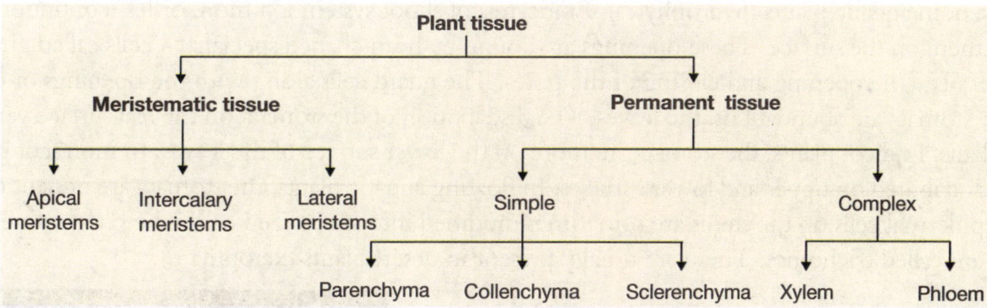

Figure 2.13 Classification of plant tissue

Tissue Systems in Plants

Based on the structures and functions, various types of tissues (both meristematic and permanent) in the internal structure of plant are categorized into three different kinds of tissue systems in a plant body.

1. Dermal or Epidermal tissue system
2. Ground tissue system
3. Vascular tissue system

Dermal Tissue System

All the parts of the plant, such as root, stem, leaves, flowers, fruits, etc., are covered by a layer of cells. This layer is protective in function and hence called dermal tissue (derma means skin). In plants, the dermal tissue performs the same function as skin in humans. The nature and composition of dermal tissue is variable and depends upon the nature and age of the plant. In all young plants, all the parts of the plant are covered by a single layer of cells, called epidermis. The small herbaceous plants with green stems are called non-woody plants. In non-woody plants, the structure of epidermis is simple. In woody plants, the epidermis undergoes transformation as the plant grows older. Thus, the structure of epidermis becomes complex. Also, the stems become brown coloured.

Epidermis in Non-woody Plants

Structure

- The cells of epidermis vary in shape and size. They are usually irregular in shape.
- The cells possess large central vacuole and thin peripheral cytoplasm.
- The cells are arranged very close to each other without any intercellular spaces.
- The epidermis of the aerial parts of the plant (shoot system) is slightly different from that of the roots which are not exposed out.
- In leaves, there are two layers of epidermis: one on upper surface (dorsal side) called upper epidermis and one on lower surface (ventral side) called lower epidermis.

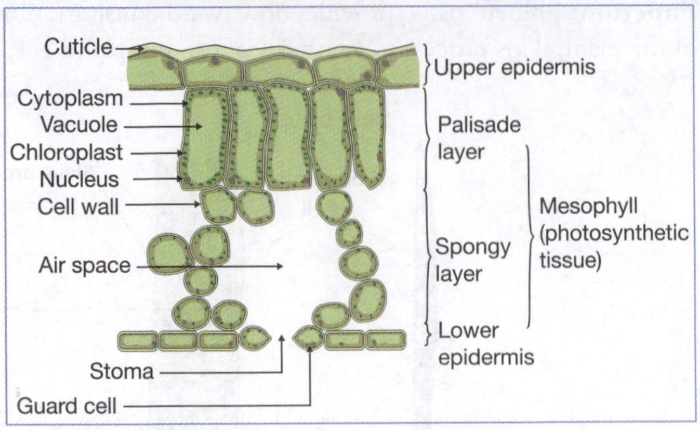

Figure 2.14 Illustration of a section through typical leaf showing epidermis

Epidermis in Shoot System

The epidermis is usually covered by a thin transparent layer of specialized wax-coated cells. This layer is called cuticle which contains contain a waxy substance called cutin. This cutin is secreted by the epidermal cells and it makes the cuticle a waterproof layer. Cuticle is absent in aquatic plants (hydrophytes). Epidermis of shoot system is a more or less continuous layer with small openings here and there on the surface. These openings are bound by bean-shaped specialized cells called guard cells on either sides. These cells regulate the opening and closing of the pores. The guard cells along with the openings or pores are together called stomata. The stomata are abundant on the leaves. The distribution of the stomata on the leaf surface varies depending on the nature of the plants. In dicot plants, the stomata are more on the lower surface of the leaves. In monocot plants, the stomata are almost equally distributed on upper and lower surfaces. In floating aquatic plants, the stomata are present only on the upper epidermis. Some epidermal cells on the stems are sometimes modified into specialized cells which form fine outgrowths from the surface. These are called trichomes. These are usually present in desert plants (xerophytes).

Figure 2.15 Macro close up of trichomes on female *Cannabis indica* plant leaf

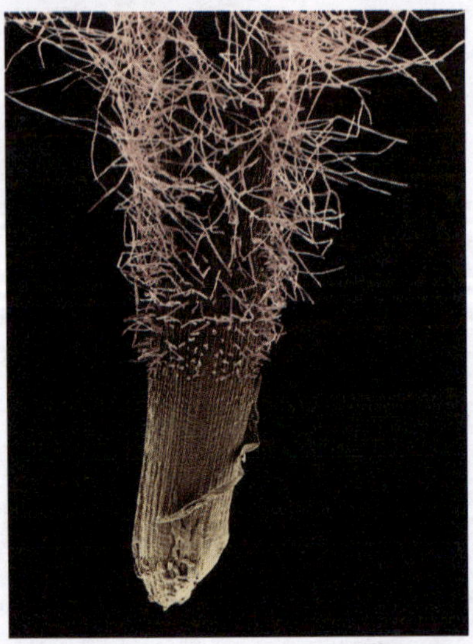

Figure 2.16 Electron micrograph of wheat root hair

Epidermis in Root System

In the roots, small, thin, unicellular hair-like structures grow from the epidermal cells. These are called root hair. Cuticle and stomata are absent in root system.

Functions

Epidermis forms the boundary between the plant and the external environment. Stomata in epidermis facilitate the exchange of gases (oxygen and carbon dioxide) during photosynthesis and respiration. They also help in the important process of transpiration which is the loss of excess of water from the plant in the form of water vapour. Cuticle on epidermis reduces water loss by transpiration in times of water scarcity. Epidermis protects the plant from mechanical injury. It also protects the plants from infections by preventing the entry of pathogenic fungi into the plant tissues. In roots, the main function of epidermis is the absorption of water and minerals. The root hair increase the surface area for more efficient absorption. The trichomes help in preventing loss of water and also protect the plant from excess sunlight. These are more significant in desert plants.

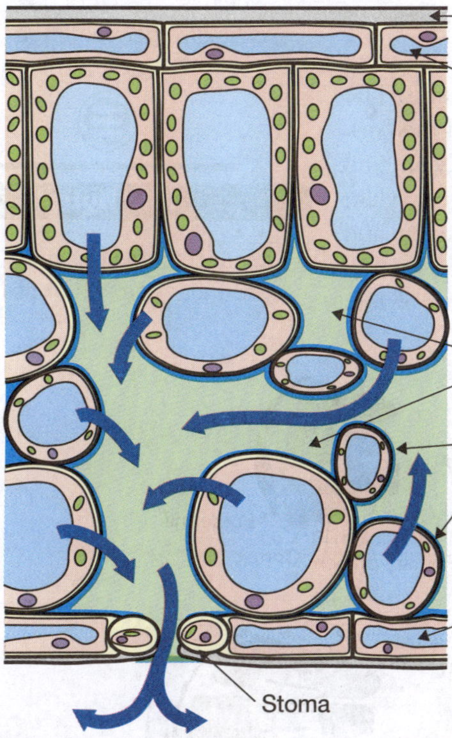

Figure 2.17 Diagram showing diffusion of water in leaf epidermis

Info Bytes!

Cactus spines are actually modified dermal tissues. They offer protection and also shade the plant's surface, reducing water loss.

Info Bytes!

Mosses and liverworts do not have leaves.

Epidermis in Woody Plants

The small, non-woody herbaceous plants retain the epidermis as such even when the plant grows older. But, in the woody plants, the epidermis is replaced by another tissue layer as the plants grow older and become big trees in course of time. The woody plants usually possess a layer of lateral meristematic tissue below the epidermis of stems and roots. This is known as cork cambium or phellogen. The cells of cork cambium undergo a series of mitotic cell divisions followed by cell differentiation to form a layer of cells called periderm. That means, the epidermis in stems and roots of young plants is replaced by a multilayered periderm. Structure of periderm is complex as it possesses layers of different kinds of cells. The outermost layer of periderm is called cork which has commercial importance.

Structure of Cork

- The cells are more or less cuboidal.
- They are tightly packed without any intercellular spaces.
- The cells become dead due to the deposition of a substance called suberin in the cell walls. This makes cork impermeable to water.
- Some breaks appear in the cork tissue which looks like rised openings. These are called lenticels.

Info Bytes!

Flowering plants are divided into two groups: monocots (one cotyledon) and dicots (two cotyledons).

Functions of Cork

- Cork provides protection to the plant from the invasion of parasites.
- Cork prevents loss of water from the plant.
- Lenticels in cork help in the exchange of gases during photosynthesis and respiration.
- Lenticels also facilitate transpiration in big trees.

Secondary Growth in Plants

The width of a plant is called secondary growth and it arises from the secondary/lateral meristems in stems. As with apical meristems, lateral meristems are regions of high cell division activity, the cells they make grow outward.

The lateral meristems that produce secondary growth are called cambiums. The two important ones for secondary growth are the vascular cambium and the cork cambium. The vascular cambium produces more xylem and phloem. Xylem and phloem that come from the vascular cambium replace the original (primary) xylem and phloem, and add to the girth of the plant, they are called secondary xylem and secondary phloem. On its interior, vascular cambium adds secondary xylem and on its exterior, it adds secondary phloem. In trees, the layers of secondary xylem form wood and layers of the secondary phloem form bark.

Info Bytes!

The thickest known bark in the plant kingdom belongs to the African baobab tree, which is a result of its extensive dermal tissue.

Info Bytes!

Monocots do not show secondary growth of tissues.

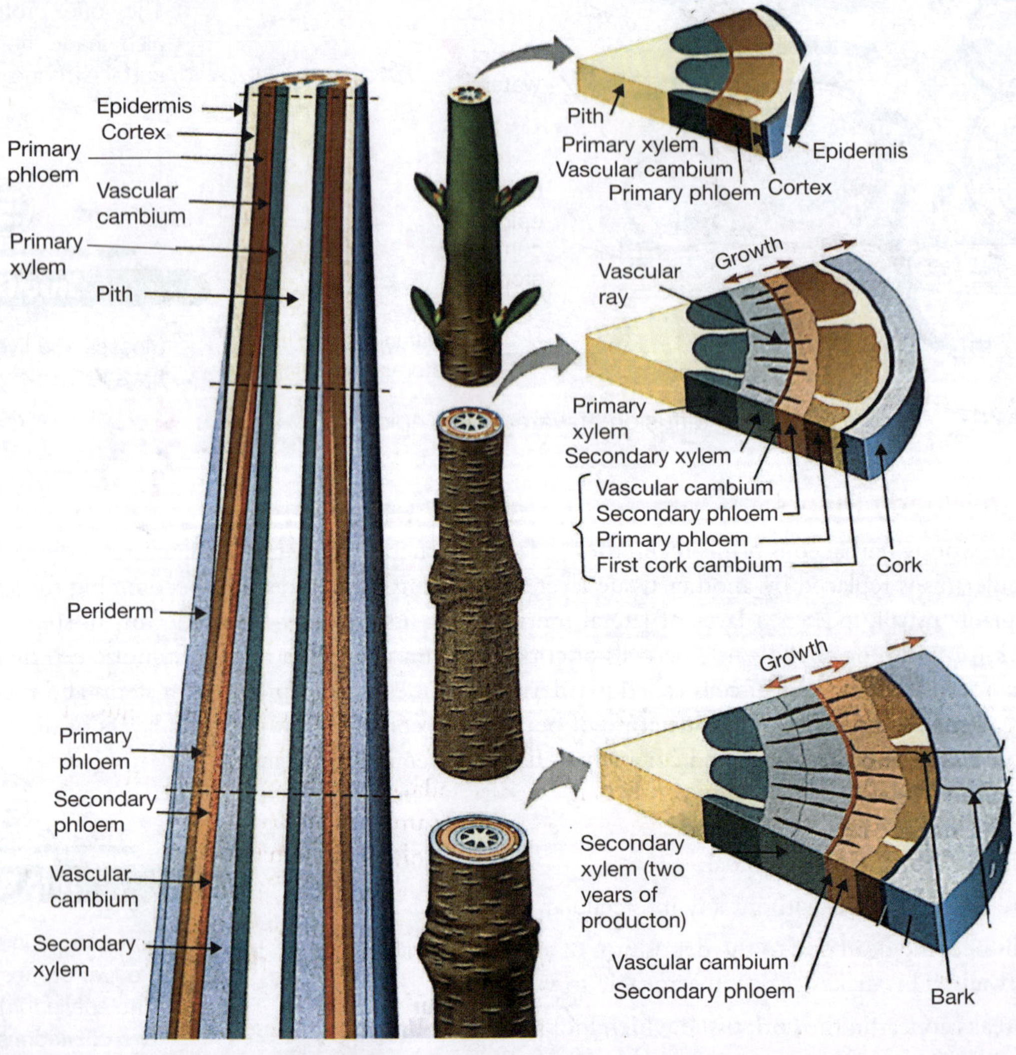

Figure 2.18 Secondary growth in shoot

Ground Tissue System

This tissue system is located below the dermal tissue, forming. This tissue system forms the main bulk of the plant body. The composition of ground tissue is variable as it depends on the parts of the plant in which it is located. In leaves, the ground tissue is located between upper epidermis and lower epidermis. It is totally composed of parenchyma tissue which is rich in chloroplasts. This is called mesophyll. It is mainly concerned with the function of manufacture and storage of food (photosynthesis). In stems and roots, the region beneath the epidermis is occupied by the tissues of ground tissue system. The ground tissue in stems and roots is usually heterogeneous, as it is made up of all the three types of simple permanent tissues that is parenchyma, collenchyma and sclerenchyma. It performs variable functions of all the three types of tissues. In roots, it is mostly supportive in function.

Vascular Tissue System

The vascular tissue system is present below the ground tissue system. It lies towards the central region of all the parts of the plant. This is composed of the conducting tissues namely, xylem and phloem. Xylem and phloem together constitute a vascular bundle.

In most of the plants, in stems and roots, a layer of lateral meristematic tissue is present between xylem and phloem. This layer is called vascular cambium. The vascular cambium undergoes repeated mitotic divisions and forms secondary xylem to the inside and secondary phloem to the outside.

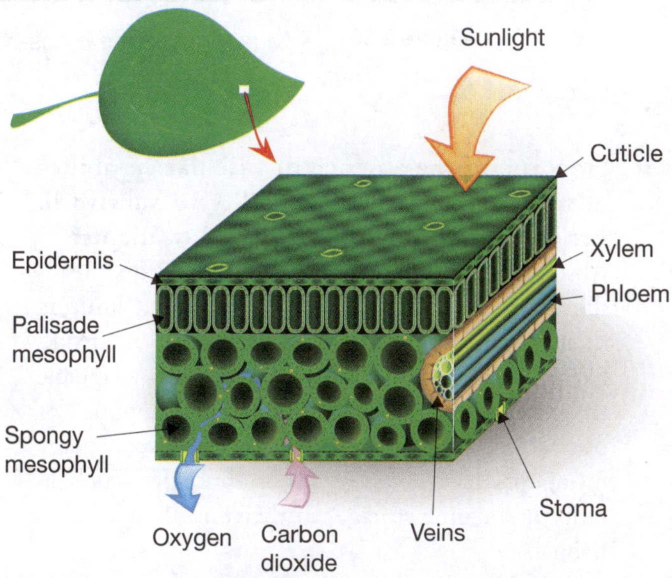

Figure 2.19 Tissue of leaf

This results in the growth in the girth (diameter) of the stems and roots. In woody plants, the growth of secondary xylem in stems is enormous and forms wood. As the wood grows older, the tissue loses the capacity to conduct water. The formation of wood is a significant event in the growth of the plant. It is because of the high commercial value attributed to wood. In fact, the term xylem is originated from the word 'xylo' which means wood. That means, xylem tissue is the wood-forming tissue. The nature and quality of wood depend on the age of the plant. The older is the tree, the greater is the quality of the wood.

The formation of wood depends on environmental factors and varies from one season to the other. The spring season is the favourable season for the growth of the plants. Therefore, during this season, the plant is in need of large amount of water and minerals. Hence, the xylem vessels possess large cavities. This wood is called spring wood. It is light in colour. The autumn season is generally less favourable for the growth of plants. Therefore, during this season, the plant is in need of lesser amount of water and minerals. Hence, the xylem vessels possess small cavities. This wood is called autumn wood. It is dark in colour. The two types of wood are formed every year and they appear as concentric rings of light and dark circles, when the horizontal cross section of stem is observed. These concentric rings are called annual rings. The age of the plant can be determined by the number of annual rings present.

Konnect

A tree's rings can help point us in the right direction. If we're in the northern hemisphere, the rings of the tree grow slightly thicker on the southern side since it receives more light. In the southern hemisphere, the opposite is true, with rings being thicker on the northern side.

Figure 2.20 Annual rings in the cross-section of stem

Info Bytes!

The tallest trees, like the coastal redwoods, rely on their xylem to transport water from the ground to heights over 300 feet.

Quick Recap

✔ **How might the absence of vascular cambium in monocots affect their ability to survive in various environments compared to dicots?**
Absence of vascular cambium in monocots means they can't undergo secondary growth, limiting their ability to produce thick stems or trunks like many dicots. This makes them less adaptable to environments requiring structural support or protection against herbivores. However, many monocots have evolved other strategies, such as bulb or rhizome storage, to thrive in their specific habitats.

✔ **If a dicot plant loses a part of its bark, will it still exhibit secondary growth? Why or why not?**
Yes, a dicot plant can still exhibit secondary growth even if it loses a part of its bark. The vascular cambium, which is responsible for secondary growth, is located deeper within the stem, between the xylem and phloem. As long as the vascular cambium remains intact, the plant will continue to produce secondary tissues.

Tissues in Animals

Animals have a greater complexity of body organization when compared to plants. The main characteristic difference between the animal and plant tissues is that animal bodies are mostly composed of living tissues. Depending on the location and functions of the tissues in the human body, the tissues are categorized into four types. They are listed as follows:

1. Epithelial tissue
2. Connective tissue
3. Muscular tissue
4. Nervous tissue

Info Bytes!

The human body is made up of approximately 37.2 trillion cells. But all of these cells aren't the same; they organize into over 200 different types of tissues.

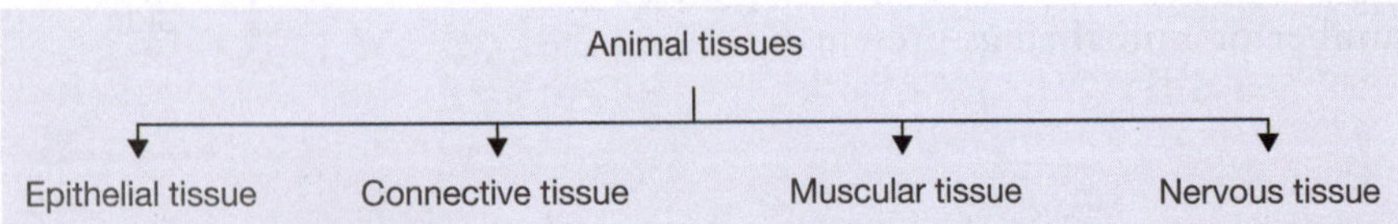

Figure 2.21 Classification of animal tissues

Epithelial Tissue

It is a thin and protective sheet of cells which is continuous.

Structure

The epithelial cells are either flat or cuboidal or columnar in shape. They are tightly packed and form continuous sheets. They have a small amount of cementing material between them and almost no intercellular spaces. The tissue lacks blood or lymph supply. The tissue is supplied by nerves. It is attached to the underlying tissues by a basement membrane made up of collagen fibres. If the epithelial tissue is made up of only one type of cells in a single layer, it is called simple epithelial tissue. If the epithelial tissue is made up of more than one type of cells arranged in multiple layers, it is called complex or stratified epithelium.

Info Bytes!

Collagen makes up about 30% of the total protein in our body.

Location

Epithelial tissue is found on outer covering of the entire body. It lines all cavities, such as that of the mouth, nose, throat, stomach, intestines, oesophagus, trachea and lungs. It also covers most organs and cavities within the body, including the blood vessels, outermost layer of the skin and the lining of the mouth, nose, lungs stomach, kidney tubules, etc.

Function

The epithelial tissue is protective, excretory and sensory in function. The cells of epithelial tissue are capable of cell division and regeneration throughout life.

Types of Epithelial Tissue

Based on the structure and function of the cells, the simple epithelial tissue is categorized into six types. The complex epithelial tissue is otherwise known as stratified epithelial tissue. Apart from these, there is another category of special epithelial tissue which is called pseudostratified epithelial tissue. Types of epithelial tissue are listed as follows:

- Squamous epithelium
- Cuboidal epithelium
- Columnar epithelium
- Glandular epithelium
- Ciliated epithelium
- Sensory epithelium
- Stratified epithelium
- Pseudostratified epithelium

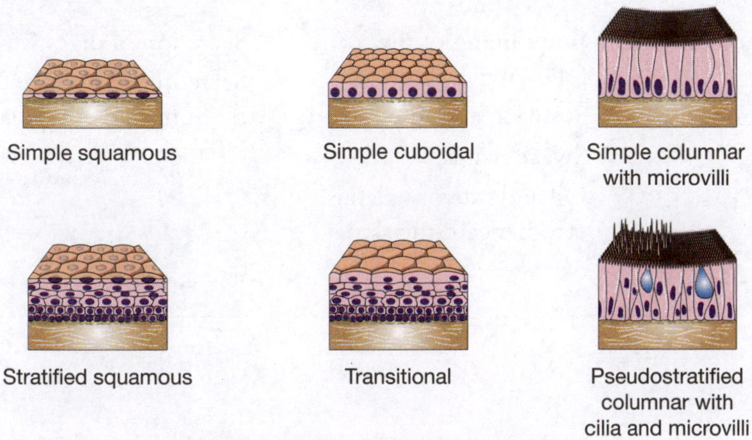

Figure 2.22 Types of epithelium

Info Bytes!

The human body sheds millions of epithelial cells each day, totalling about 9 lbs of skin cells in a year.

Info Bytes!

Every time you get a tan, it's your epithelial cells responding to the sun's UV rays.

Table 2.2 Comparative study of different types of epithelial tissues

Type of tissue	Structural features	Location	Function
Squamous epithelium or pavement epithelium 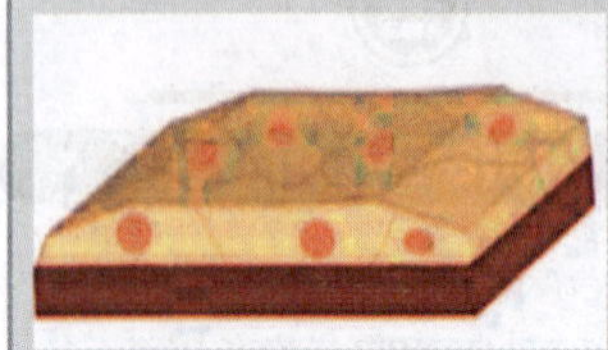	Cells are thin, flat and hexagonal. Cells possess nucleus Cells are arranged edge-to-edge thus forming a lining. Cells give appearance of pavement, hence known as pavement epithelium.	Skin Lining the following organs: Alveoli of lungs, Blood vessels and heart, Mouth, Oesophagus	Filtration and transportation of substances by the process of osmosis and diffusion Protection for the underlying parts from mechanical injury and invasion of germs Keeping the parts moist
Cuboidal epithelium 	Cells are long and broad giving cube-like appearance. Nucleus is centrally located in the cells	Lining of the following organs: Kidney tubules, Ducts of salivary glands and thyroid gland, Ovaries, Parts of eyes	Absorption of useful substances from glomerular filtrate (urine). Secretion of saliva.
Columnar epithelium 	Cells are longer Look like columns or pillars The cells are vertically arranged. Nucleus is centrally located in the cells.	Lining of the following organs: Digestive tract and Intestine	Secretion of digestive enzymes. Absorption of nutrients from digested food. Mechanical support in lining of kidney tubules and ducts of the salivary glands.
Ciliated epithelium 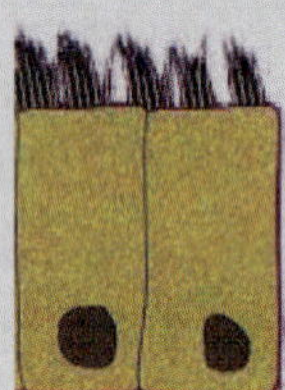	Columnar cells having numerous hair-like projections called cilia present on the outer free surface of cells.	Lining of the following organs: Trachea (wind pipe), Kidney tubules, Oviducts	Clearing the respiratory tract by pushing mucus and air forward Filtration.
Glandular epithelium 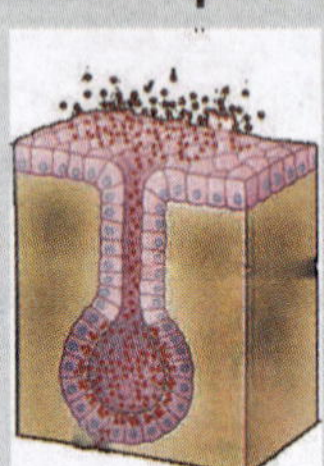	Specialized columnar epithelial cells Cells fold inwards to form glands.	Inner lining of the following organs: Stomach and intestine, Sweat glands, Oil and mucous glands, etc., beneath the skin.	Secretion of digestive juices. Secretion of sweat and oil from skin at regular intervals.

(*Continued*)

Table 2.2 *(Continued)*

Type of tissue	Structural features	Location	Function
Sensory epithelium 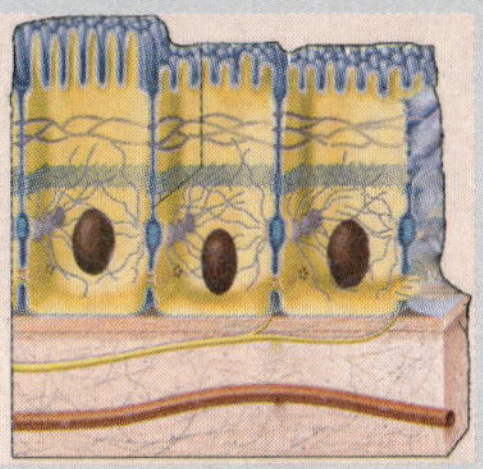	Some modified epithelial cells help in receiving external stimuli. Cells possess nerve endings to perceive stimulus.	Outer layer of the following organs: Skin, Taste buds of tongue, Retina of eye, Nasal passages, Hair cells of inner ear, etc.	Reception of stimulus from external environment
Stratified epithelium 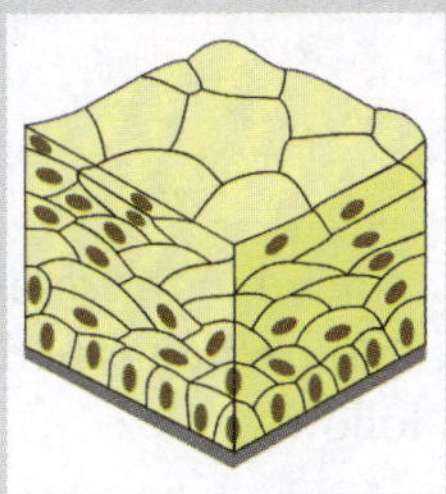	Different types of epithelial cells are present in layers. They are made up of same or different types of epithelial cells. The cells are arranged in layers (strata), i.e., one on top the other. It can be either stratified squamous epithelium or stratified columnar epithelium.	Epidermis of skin Lining of the following organs: Urinary bladder, Vagina, Tongue, Mouth cavity	Protection to organs which are subjected to continuous wear and tear.
Pseudostratified epithelium 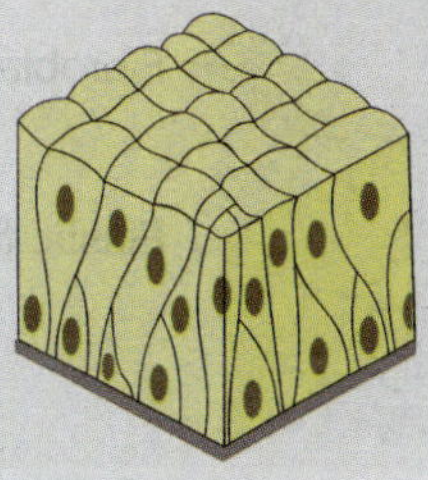	Columnar, ciliated cells arranged in a single layer Appearance of many layered structures due to the arrangement of nuclei at different levels.	Inner lining of the following organs: Trachea Bronchi in lungs.	Protection to respective organs in which it is present

Connective Tissue

It is the most abundant tissue found in human body. This tissue is specialized for connecting various tissues and organs. It also keeps the organs in their proper position by filling the space between the organs. It provides the structural framework. The tissue consists of three components, namely

1. A non-living intercellular substance called ground substance
2. The fibres made up of proteins
3. The living cells

> **Info Bytes!**
>
> Vitamin E improves the production of collagen, repairs and strengthens the connective tissue

The fibres along with the ground substance is called intercellular or extracellular matrix. The cells are embedded in the matrix. The fibres are basically made up of proteins and are of three types. They are:

1. **Collagen fibres:** They are made up of collagen proteins and consist of bundles of fibrils.
2. **Elastic fibres:** They are made up of elastin protein and are stretchable.

3. **Reticular fibres:** They are made up of reticulin protein and form a network or mesh.

The cells are of various types. They usually produce the material of the ground substance (matrix) and fibres. The tissue is categorized into three types based upon the nature of the matrix. They are:

1. Connective tissue proper
2. Skeletal connective tissue or supportive connective tissue
3. Fluid connective tissue

Connective Tissue Proper

In this tissue, the matrix is less rigid. This serves for packing and binding most of the organs. It is classified into two types based on the type of fibres and distribution of fibres in the matrix. They are:

1. Loose Connective Tissue
2. Dense Connective Tissue

Loose Connective Tissue

This tissue consists of semi-fluid matrix with lesser proportion of fibres. The cells and fibre are scattered in the semi-fluid matrix. This tissue consists of collagen and elastin fibres. Collagen fibres impart good tensile strength to the tissue. Elastin fibres provide elasticity to the tissue. Loose connective tissues are of two types, they are listed as follows.

1. Areolar Tissue
2. Adipose Tissue

Areolar Tissue

Structure: The areolar tissue mainly consists of transparent, sticky and jelly-like matrix. All the three types of fibres are present in the matrix of areolar connective tissue. The cells and fibres are irregularly scattered in the matrix crossing each other in all directions.

Location: Areolar connective tissue is mainly present beneath the epithelial tissue of the skin. It surrounds the blood vessels, nerve bundles, muscles and organs. It fills the space inside the internal organs.

Functions: It binds the skin to the underlying muscles of the body. It provides support for the organs and it also provides elasticity and strength. This tissue serves the purpose of holding various organs in place and in normal shape. It is considered as the packing tissue.

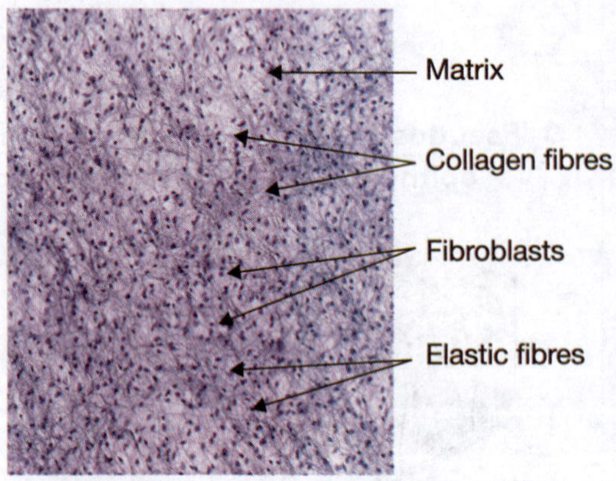

Figure 2.23 Areolar connective tissue at medium magnification

Adipose Tissue

Structure: The adipose tissue mainly consists of transparent, sticky and jelly-like matrix. The matrix consists of collagen and elastin fibres. Tissue contains less fibres with more number of cells. The cells are called adipocytes. These are specialized for storage of triglycerides, more commonly referred to as fats. Nucleus is pushed towards the periphery in the cells The cells contain a small amount of cytoplasm. Large part of the cell is occupied by fat globules.

Location:

- Below the skin.
- Around internal organs.
- More generally, it is found at the same locations throughout the body as areolar connective tissue.

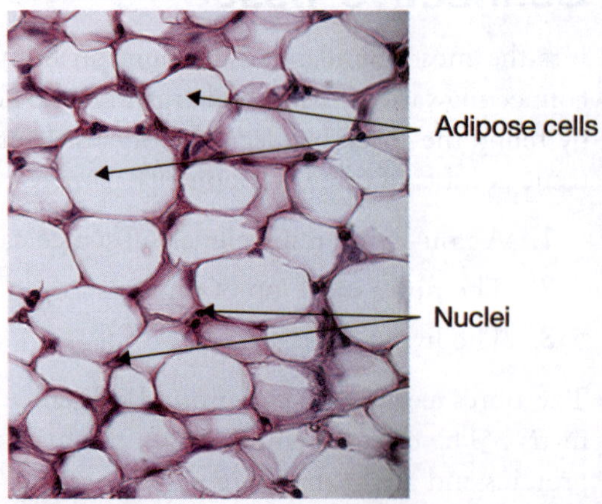

Figure 2.24 Light micrograph of adipose tissue

- Specific examples of the locations of adipose tissue include:
  - Subcutaneous layer deep to the skin
  - Around the heart
  - Around the kidneys
  - Yellow marrow of the long bones
  - Padding around the joints
  - Inside the eye-socket, posterior to the eyeball

***Functions*:** Adipose tissue acts as an insulating layer, helping to reduce heat loss through the skin. It also has a protective function, providing mechanical protection (padding). It provides support around some of the major organs, such as kidneys. Adipose tissue is also a means of energy storage. Food that is excess to requirements is converted into fat and stored within adipose tissue in the body.

Dense Connective Tissue

It is a tough band of fibrous connective tissue. It has large amounts of fibres in the matrix with relatively less proportion of ground substance. The fibres form the major part of the tissue. The fibres are mainly composed of collagen. The fibre-forming cells, called fibroblasts are present in rows in between the collagen fibres. These fibroblasts generate the fibres. These tissues are also of two types, they are:

1. Tendon
2. Ligament

Tendon

***Structure and Location*:** This tissue is made up of white, tough non-elastic collagen fibres and has limited flexibility. Tendons can have several shapes ranging from wide and flat, ribbon and fan shaped. Tendons can be found throughout the body from legs to hands. They connect the muscles to bones.

***Function*:** This tissue helps in the movement of bones.

Ligament

***Structure and Location*:** They are dense, regular connective tissue bundles made of collagen fibres. These fibres are very strong, flexible and resistant to damage. Collagen fibres are usually arranged in parallel bundles. They are elastic in nature and establish connection between two bones.

***Functions*:** Ligaments allow controlled movement of joints. They reinforce (strengthen) joint integrity and strength. They connect bone to bone.

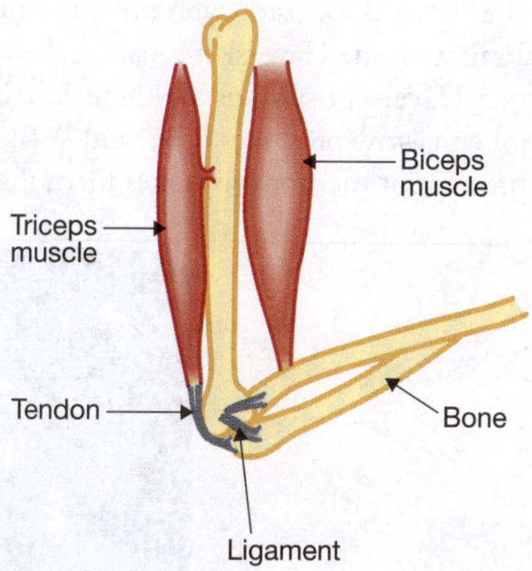

Figure 2.25 Illustration of tendon and ligament in human arm

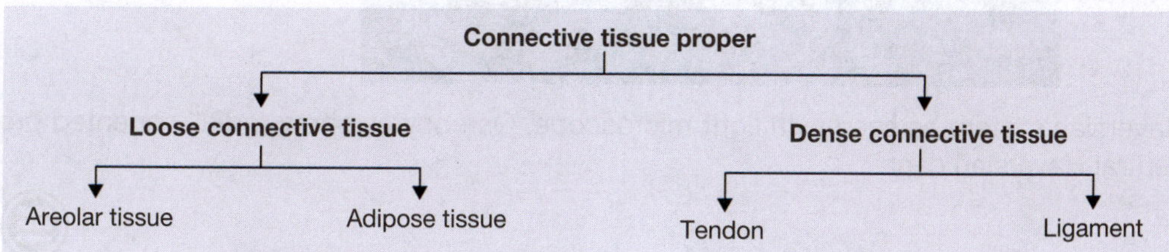

Figure 2.26 Classification of connective tissue proper

Skeletal Connective Tissue

It comprises strong and durable tissues, which serve as supportive structures for the other type of tissues. This tissue mainly forms the endoskeleton of the organisms. This tissue forms the rigid framework which supports the body and provides protection for all vital organs. It helps the body to maintain posture and to carry out movements and locomotion. Depending on the composition and characteristics, this tissue is classified into following two types:

1. Bone **2.** Cartilage

Bone

Structure and Location: Bone is hard, porous, rigid and non-flexible mineralized connective tissue. The solid matrix is mainly made up of inorganic materials. These materials include salts of calcium and magnesium. Calcium phosphate is the mineral present in maximum proportion. These salts impart hardness to bone. It also contains some amount of collagen protein. The protein imparts strength to the bone. This matrix is therefore called mineralized matrix.

The collagen fibres are distributed in the matrix. These are closely embedded as the amount of ground substance is less and fibres are more. These fibres impart elasticity to bone. This matrix and collagen fibres are generated by the cells called osteoblasts. These osteoblasts are present in the outer covering of the bone known as periosteum. This layer is supplied by blood vessels and nerves. After the formation of matrix and fibres from the osteoblasts, these cells lose some cell organelles and become hard and small. These cells remain inactive and are called osteocytes. The matrix is arranged in the form of concentric rings called lamellae. The osteocytes are present in fluid-filled spaces in the matrix. These spaces are called lacunae. From these lacunae, some projections arise which are called canaliculi. These canaliculi form the connections between the osteocytes.

The osteocytes arranged in the lamellae of the matrix form a continuous channel in the centre. This is called Haversian canal. Blood vessels and nerves pass through this canal and hence forms the communication network between the bones. The network of osteocytes present embedded in the lamellae in the mineralized matrix connected by canaliculi, formed along with the Haversian canal is called Haversian system. This Haversian system is the functional unit of the bones. Many such Haversian systems are there in a bone. Long bones consist of a special type of tissue are called bone marrow. Red bone marrow produces RBC and WBC. Yellow bone marrow is composed of adipose tissue. The bone tissue is distributed throughout the body as bones form the structural framework of the body.

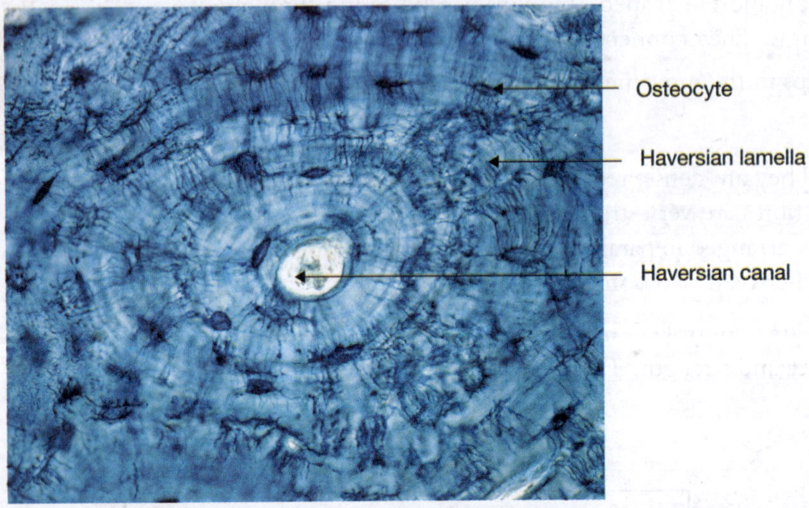

Figure 2.27 Haversian system as seen with light microscope. Osteocytes show radially oriented processed around central Haversian canal

Functions:

Bones aid in protection of internal organs. They form the framework of the body thus providing shape to the body. They also help in movement and locomotion. They are storage sites for calcium and phosphate. Hence, they maintain calcium levels in the blood. Bone marrow is responsible for the production of blood corpuscles.

Info Bytes!

Cartilage grows quicker than bone.

Cartilage

Structure: It is a tough and slightly elastic tissue which imparts flexibility to the respective organs. Cartilage is a semi-transparent and non-porous tissue. Matrix is dense and rubbery and composed of proteins and calcium salts. White collagen fibres are distributed in the form of delicate network. Cells, called chondrocytes, are embedded in this network. Blood vessels are absent in the matrix. Cartilage is usually covered by a tough and fibrous membrane called perichondrium. The perichondrium is supplied with blood vessels and nerves. Cartilage is capable of rapid and continuous growth.

Location: Tip of nose, pinna of the ear, rings of the trachea, ends of long bones, lower ends of ribs.

Functions: It provides support and flexibility.

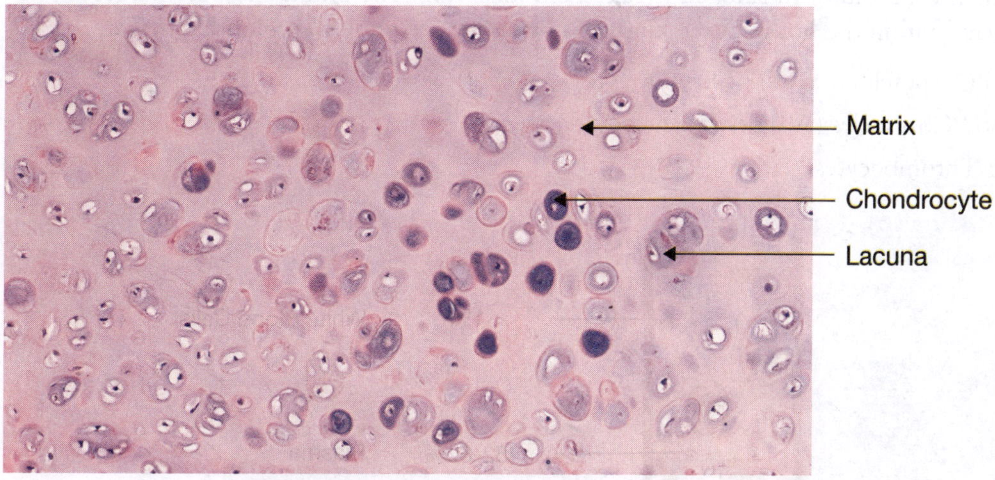

Figure 2.28 Cross-section of cartilage tissue

There are three types of cartilage in human body—Hyaline, fibrous and elastic.

Hyaline cartilage is flexible and elastic. It is bluish-white in colour. The cells are mainly spherical and occupy the entire lacuna. It is the most abundant type of cartilage. It exists in human adults at the ends of the ribs, and in the nose, larynx, trachea and bronchi. **Fibrous cartilage** is a tough, strong tissue found predominantly in the intervertebral disks and at the insertions of ligaments and tendons. **Elastic cartilage** is yellow in appearance. It is more flexible than the other two types because it contains elastic fibres in addition to collagen. It is present in the external ear, the auditory tube of the middle ear and the epiglottis.

Info Bytes!

A hyaline substance is the one with a glassy appearance. This term is derived from Greek 'hyalinos', meaning 'of glass'.

Table 2.3 Comparative study of three types of cartilage

Parameter	Hyaline	Fibrous	Elastic
Appearance	Bluish, translucent	Whitish, opaque	Yellowish, opaque
Flexibility	Flexible	Firm	Highly flexible
Perichondrium	Present	Absent	Present
Fibres	Fewer, thin white	Abundant, white	Abundant, yellow

Fluid Connective Tissue

The tissue consists of fluid matrix. The fibres are totally absent in the matrix. The matrix is in the form of liquid which is called plasma. The cells are found floating in the plasma and are called corpuscles. The material of the matrix is not secreted by the cells present in the tissue. Depending on the composition, this tissue is classified into two types listed as follows:

1. Blood **2.** Lymph

> **Info Bytes!**
>
> Cartilage has no nerves, hence it is insensitive.

Blood

Structure and Location: It is a bright-red fluid connective tissue. Blood is a slightly alkaline fluid with a pH value of 7.4 at normal temperature (25°C). The fluid matrix, that is, plasma is a straw-coloured liquid. The plasma consists of 90% water. The other components are proteins and salts. The various proteins present in plasma are albumins, globulins, fibrinogen and prothrombin. The blood plasma which is devoid of fibrinogen is called blood serum. The blood circulates in blood vessels, i.e., arteries, veins and capillaries within the body. Three kinds of corpuscles are present in blood. They are:

1. Red Blood Corpuscles (RBCs) or Erythrocytes
2. White Blood Corpuscles (WBCs) or Leucocytes
3. Platelets or Thrombocytes

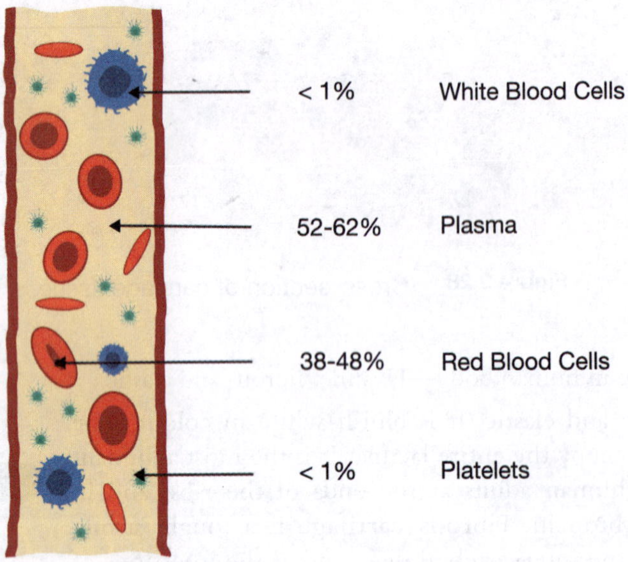

Figure 2.29 Composition of blood

Functions: It helps in distribution of heat, thus maintaining the body temperature. Transportation of various materials, such as hormones to the target tissues. Maintaining the balance of electrolytes. Protection of body from infections by the WBCs, transport of oxygen to the tissues by RBCs Helps in clotting of blood at the time of injury with the help of platelets. The protein albumin helps to maintain the osmotic pressure of the blood. The protein fibrinogen helps in clotting of the blood. The protein globulin (some) acts as antibodies.

Lymph

Structure and Location: It is a colourless fluid. It is the plasma that oozes out of the blood vessels. The composition of plasma in lymph is variable since it is constantly exchanging the materials from the blood. It contains WBCs. Lymphocytes are the type of WBCs abundantly found in lymph. Lymph does not contain RBCs and platelets. It is located in the nodes, spleen, tonsils, adenoids and thymus.

Functions: Lymph transports nutrients that may have got filtered out of the blood capillaries back into the heart. It brings back the carbon dioxide and nitrogenous wastes from tissue fluid to the blood. Since, it is loaded with WBCs (lymphocytes), it protects the body against infections. It forms the immune system of the body.

Table 2.4 Comparitive study of characteristic features of different types of corpuscles

Type of Corpuscles	RBC	WBC	Platelets
Other name	Erythrocytes	Leukocytes	Thrombocytes
Abundance in blood	Most abundant cells in human body constituting 40% blood volume.	WBCs make up 1% of blood volume in human body.	The ratio of platelets to RBCs in healthy humans ranges from 1:10 to 1:20.
Nature of cells	Living cells	Living cells	Cell fragments with no nucleus
Size and shape	Flexible, disc shaped	Flexible, irregular shaped	Biconvex or lens shaped.
Internal structure	Nucleus absent (anucleated cells)	Possess distinct nucleus.	Nucleus absent (anucleated cells)
Constituents	Contain an iron-containing protein called **haemoglobin** which imparts red colour to the blood.	No pigments. Hence, colourless	Haemoglobin absent
Formation	Formed in red bone marrow. In embryonic stage, they are also formed in spleen.	Formed in red bone marrow and spleen	Formed in red bone marrow
Life span	120 days	Variable	About 8–10 days.
Function	Exchange of gases during respiration.	Protect the body from infections.	Clotting of blood and prevents excess loss of blood in times of injury
Types	No	Lymphocytes Monocytes Basophils Eosinophils Neutrophils	No
	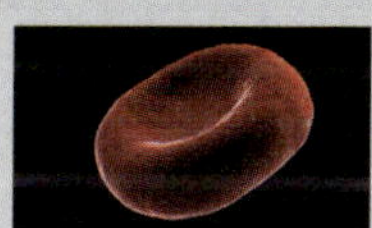	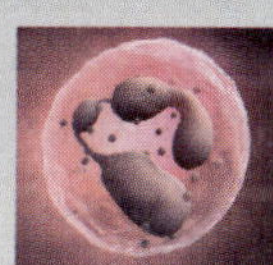	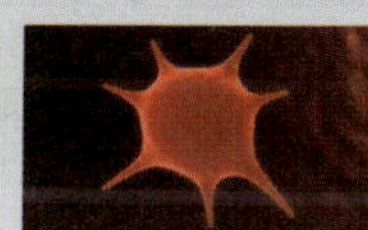

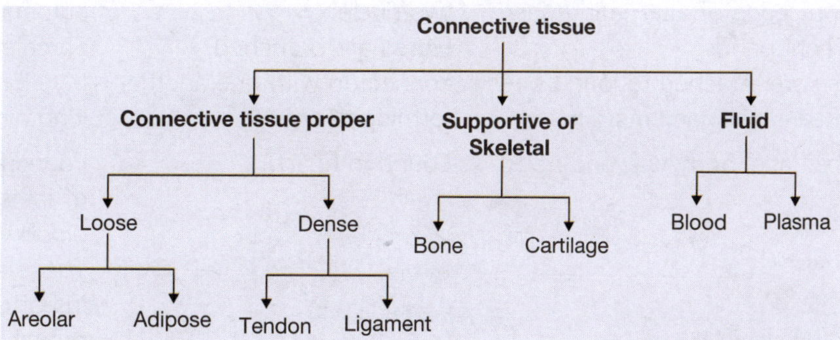

Figure 2.30 Classification of connective tissue

Muscular Tissue

The muscle tissue is composed of cells called myocytes (also known as a muscle cell) and forms muscles in the body. Myocytes are long and tubular. The muscle cells are formed from the cells called myoblasts. The cytoplasm of the cells of the muscular tissue contains elongated fibrils called myofibrils. The cytoplasm of the cells is called sarcoplasm. The muscle fibre, mostly the skeletal muscle fiber, is externally covered by a membrane called sarcolemma. The muscle cells contain special proteins called contractile proteins. These proteins are responsible for the ability of this tissue to contract and relax. Contractility is the special feature of this tissue. Hence, this tissue is also called contractile tissue. The muscle tissues are held together by connective tissues. Based on their structure, location and function, muscles are of three types. They are listed as follows.

1. Striated Muscles
2. Non-striated muscles
3. Cardiac muscles

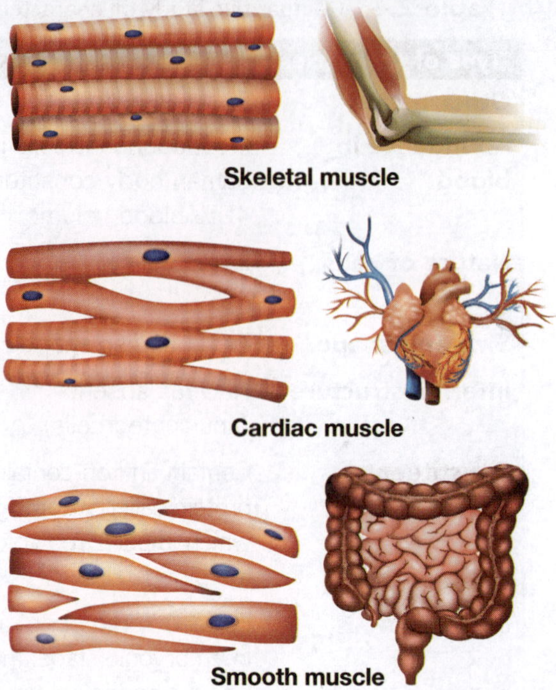

Figure 2.31 Types of muscle tissues

Info Bytes!

On an average, 40% of an animal's weight is constituted by muscle tissue.

Info Bytes!

The gluteus maximus is the largest muscle in the body.

Table 2.5 Comparative study of characteristic features of different types of muscles

Type of muscles	Striated muscles	Cardiac muscles	Non-striated muscles
Structure	Each muscle fibre consists of long, cylindrical and unbranched multi-nucleated cells. Sarcolemma is present. Myofibrils are tightly packed. Muscle fibres are characterized by the presence of alternating dark and light bands. These are attached to long bones by means of ligaments.	Involuntary muscles Cells are cylindrical, branched and uni-nucleated. They are striated with light and dark bands. Centrally located, one or two nuclei Fibres are branched, connected with one another forming network.	Smooth or involuntary muscle Spindle shaped, unbranched, uni-nucleated cells. Contraction and relaxation are slow, steady and automatic. Sarcolemma is absent Myofibrils, running lengthwise, are present.
Location	Limbs, face, body wall and neck.	Found in heart.	Found attached to the walls of intestine, stomach and blood vessels. These are also present in the iris of eye, ureters and in the bronchi of lungs. They are also found in the urogenital ducts.

(Continued)

Table 2.5 *(Continued)*

Type of muscles	Striated muscles	Cardiac muscles	Non-striated muscles
Function	Bring about voluntary movements, i.e., their contractions are under our will and control.	Perform rhythmic contraction and relaxation of the heart.	They are concerned with involuntary movement, i.e., the movement which is not under the control of our will. In the intestines, they help to push the food along the alimentary canal.

Nervous Tissue

Nervous tissue is a special kind of tissue and is the main tissue component of the nervous system which includes brain, spinal cord and nerves. The tissue comprises neurons and neuroglia or glial cells. Neurons are the functional units of nervous system, as they receive and transmit nerve impulses. These cells are sensitive to stimuli. Neuroglia or glial cells help in the propagation of the nerve impulses and provide nutrients for the neurons. Depending on the function associated with the neurons, they are categorized into three types.

1. **Motor neurons:** They are involved in movement and locomotion.
2. **Sensory neurons:** They are involved in perception of sensations.
3. **Interneurons:** They form connections between neurons and help in the transmission of messages and conduction of nerve impulses.

Though there is a slight variation in the structure of these different types of neurons, the basic structure of a typical neuron is almost same. The junction where the dendrite terminal of one neuron is connected to axon terminal of the other neuron is known as synapse. Some nerve fibres are covered by a myelin sheath and are called myelinated nerve fibres. These are generally present in the brain and spinal cord. The bundles of nerve fibres are called nerves.

Structure of Neuron

The neutron is composed of three parts as mentioned:

- The main body is called the cyton. It contains a nucleus.
- Short hair-like processes called dendrons arise from the cell body. These dendrons further branch into many thin cytoplasmic processes called dendrites.
- A long, cylindrical process arising from the cyton is called axon. It forms branches at the other end.
- Neurons are joined end-to-end to form nerve fibres.
- The junction where the axon terminal of one neuron joins with the dendrite terminal of the adjacent neuron is called synapse.

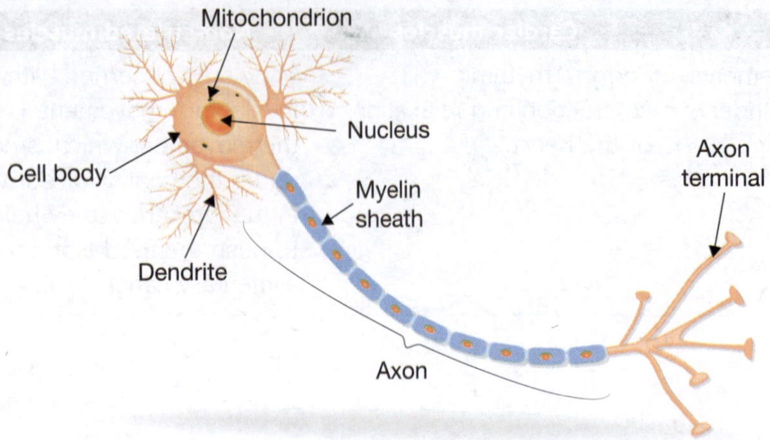

Figure 2.32 Illustration of a neuron

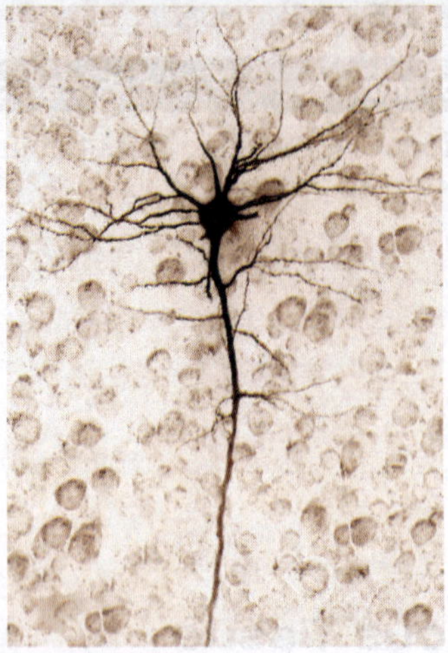

Figure 2.33 Microscopic view of a single brain cell (neuron)

Functions of Neuron

The nerve fibres transmit messages received from brain or spinal cord from one part of the body to the other. They receive stimulus from the outside environment and send messages to the brain and spinal cord which in turn send impulses to various organs. Neurons work in coordination with muscular system to cause various body movements and locomotion. They help the brain to carry out the important functions of memory and coordination.

Quick Recap

✔ **Considering that muscles can only pull and not push, how do our limbs achieve a complete range of motion?**

For every movement in one direction, there is an opposing muscle group responsible for the opposite motion. When one muscle contracts, the opposing muscle relaxes and vice versa. This coordinated action of antagonist and agonist muscles provides a complete range of motion. For instance, the biceps contract to flex the arm, while the triceps relax. To extend the arm, the triceps contract and the biceps relax.

✔ **Explain the role of platelets in the clotting of blood.**

Platelets are a type of blood cells which produce an enzyme called thromboplastin. This thromboplastin combines with a plasma protein, called prothrombin to form thrombin. Thrombin combines with fibrinogen to form fibrin fibres which form a network on RBC and WBC and is known as blood clot.

Prothrombin — thrombokinase → Thrombin
Fibrinogen — thrombin → Fibrin
Fibrin — network on RBC and WBC → Blood clot.

✔ **If neurons are the structural and functional unit of the nervous system, how do they ensure that they transmit the correct information without getting 'overwhelmed' or 'confused'?**

Neurons transmit information using electrical and chemical signals. The specificity and precision in the transmission are ensured through synapses, which are specialized junctions between neurons. At the synapse, neurotransmitters help in the transfer of impulses. The unique pathways and connections, along with the specificity of neurotransmitter receptors, ensure accurate and distinct transmission of signals. Additionally, the refractory period of neurons ensures that signals are not continuously fired, allowing the neuron to reset and avoid 'overwhelm.'

POINTS TO REMEMBER

- Tissues are groups of similar cells that perform specific tasks.
- Several tissues performing a specific function together form an organ.
- Plants and animals show large variation in the type of tissues and hence, in the body organization.
- Plant tissues are of two types: meristematic and permanent tissues.
- Meristematic tissues have cells which divide actively throughout the life of the plant.
- Cells of permanent tissue take up a specific role and lose their ability to divide.
- Based on the structures and functions, all the various types of tissues in the internal structure of plant are categorized into dermal, ground and vascular tissue systems.
- Depending on the location and functions of the tissues in the human body, the tissues are categorized into four types: epithelial, connective, muscular and nervous tissue.
- Epithelial tissue is a thin and protective sheet of cells which is continuous.
- Connective tissue is specialized for connecting various tissues and organs.
- Muscular tissue forms muscles in the body.
- Nervous tissue is a special kind of tissue and is the main tissue component of the nervous system which includes brain, spinal cord and nerves.

DW

CLASSROOM WING

Practice Questions

Very Short Answer Type Questions

Direction for question from 1 to 18.
Fill in the blanks.

1. ______ are groups of cells that have a similar structure and act together to perform a specific function.
2. In plants, the tissues that actively divide throughout the life are known as __________ tissues.
3. The type of tissue that specializes in connecting different tissues and organs in the human body is called ______ tissue.
4. ______ tissue is the primary tissue component of the nervous system, which comprises the brain, spinal cord, and nerves.
5. In plants, based on structures and functions, tissues are categorized into dermal, ground, and _______ tissue systems.
6. In plants, ________ is a dead mechanical tissue.
7. Single-layered cells present in the outer layer as surface tissue in plants is ________.
8. Minute openings present on undersurface of leaves are known as ________.
9. ________ tissue is present in aquatic plants that gives ________ and helps them to float in water.
10. The tissue that provides strength and rigidity to the plant is ________.
11. The epithelial tissue present in the intestine that increases surface area is ________.
12. Alveoli of lungs are lined by ________.
13. The tissue that fixes the skin with the muscle is ________.
14. Type of cartilage present in epiglottis is ________.
15. Presence of ________ discs is the characteristic feature of cardiac muscle.
16. The muscles showing slow and prolonged contractions are ________.
17. ________ are the sites of functional contact between neurons.
18. Neuron has branched processes called ________ and single long process called ________.

Direction for Questions from 19 to 29:
For each of the following questions four choices have been provided. Select the correct alternatives.

19. Which tissue is specialized for connecting various tissues and organs?
    (a) Epithelial tissue
    (b) Connective tissue
    (c) Muscular tissue
    (d) Nervous tissue
20. What characterizes meristematic tissues in plants?
    (a) They lose their ability to divide.
    (b) They are thin and protective sheets of cells.
    (c) They form muscles in the body.
    (d) They have cells which divide actively throughout the life of the plant.
21. Which type of tissue system in plants is responsible for the transport of nutrients and water?
    (a) Dermal tissue system
    (b) Ground tissue system
    (c) Vascular tissue system
    (d) Epidermal tissue system
22. Which of the following is NOT a type of plant tissue?
    (a) Epithelial (b) Meristematic
    (c) Permanent (d) Vascular

23. What role does the epithelial tissue play in the human body?
(a) Connecting various tissues
(b) Forming muscles
(c) Acting as a protective sheet of cells
(d) Transmitting nerve impulses

24. Which tissue type is responsible for movement in the human body?
(a) Connective
(b) Epithelial
(c) Muscular
(d) Nervous

25. Permanent tissues in plants:
(a) Divide actively throughout life
(b) Are always external
(c) Are specialized in one function and lose the ability to divide
(d) Are only found in roots

26. The tissues present in tendons are________.
(a) striated voluntary muscle
(b) smooth and striated muscle
(c) cardiac and smooth muscle
(d) smooth and involuntary muscle

27. Skeletal muscles show which of the following characteristics.
(i) Richly vascular (ii) Striped
(iii) Coluntary (iv) Spindle shaped
(a) (i), (iii) (b) (ii), (iii)
(c) (i), (iv) (d) (i), (ii) and (iii)

28. Glial cells in nervous tissue help in
(i) Support (ii) Conducting impulses
(iii) Nourishment (iv) Multiplication
(a) (i), (ii) (b) (ii), (iii)
(c) (i), (iii) (d) (ii), (iv)

29. Identify the functions of blood from the following.
(i) Transportation of nutrients
(ii) Regulation of body temperature
(iii) Exchange of gases
(iv) Protection against infections
(a) (i), (iv) (b) (ii), (iii)
(c) (iii), (iv) (d) (i), (ii), (iii), (iv)

Direction for Questions 30 and 31:
Match the entries of Column 1 with those of Column 2.

30.

Column 1	Column 2
A. Root tips	(i) Sclerenchyma
B. Lotus leaves	(ii) Collenchyma
C. *Opuntia*	. (iii) Meristematic tissue
D. Bark of trees	(iv) Aerenchyma
E. Petiole	(v) Storage parenchyma

31.

Column 1	Column 2
A. Adipose tissue	(i) Connects bone to bone
B. Glandular epithelium	(ii) Acts as cable wires
C. Tendon	(iii) Secretory
D. Striped muscle	(iv) Connects bone to muscle
E. Axon	(v) Acts as insulator
F. Ligament	(vi) Voluntary
	(vi) Involuntary

Direction for Questions from 32 to 37:
For each of the following questions four choices have been provided. Select the correct alternatives.

32. Meristamatic tissue is absent at the tips of
(a) roots (b) stem
(c) leaves (d) branches

33. The tissue having high water holding capacity is:
(a) chlorenchyma (b) collenchyma
(c) fibres (d) tracheids

34. Identify the vascular tissue mostly made up of dead cells.
(a) Chlorenchyma (b) Xylem
(c) Parenchyma (d) Phloem parenchyma

35. Areolar connective tissue connects:
(a) bone with bone
(b) bone with muscle
(c) fat with muscle
(d) integument with muscle

36. Trachea is made up of ______ tissue.
(a) bone (b) muscle
(c) cartilage (d) adipose

37. **Match the entries of Column 1 with those of Column 2.**

Column 1	Column 2
A. Fluid connective tissue	(i) Skeletal muscle
B. Filling of space inside organs	(ii) Cartilage
C. Striated muscle	(iii) Blood
D. Adipose tissue	(iv) Areolar tissue
E. Surface of joints	(v) Sub-cutaneous tissue

Direction for Questions from 38 to 51:
Correct the following statements.

38. Meristematic tissues are formed from permanent tissues.
39. Meristematic cells are present in bark region.
40. Apical meristems help in increasing the girth of the plant.
41. Old and matured cells are known as meristematic cells.
42. In tender plants, the turgid sclerenchyma gives mechanical support.
43. The tissue having large air cavities and helps in buoyancy is chlorenchyma.
44. Xylem parenchyma helps in storage of organic food materials such as resins and latex.
45. Vascular tissue contains parenchyma and collenchyma.
46. Sclerenchyma consists of actively dividing cells which help in growth.
47. Epithelial cells are supplied with blood vessels.
48. Xylem helps in the conduction of food material from roots to leaves.
49. Minute openings present in the epidermis of leaves are called cork cells.
50. Nails, horns, claws and hoofs are developed from bone.
51. Red blood cells help in clotting of blood.

Direction for Questions from 52 to 55:
Write True or False for the following statements.

52. Ducts of sweat glands are lined by stratified epithelium.
53. The interstitial fluid that passes through the lymphatic vessels is lymph.
54. During secondary growth, periderm is produced by the activity of phellogen.
55. Neurons cannot undergo mitotic divisions.

Short Answer Type Questions

56. Name the tissue associated with the following plant products or parts.
    (a) Jute (b) Rose wood
    (c) Hard shells of fruits (d) Cork
57. What is the utility of tissues in multicellular organisms?
58. Give differences between meristematic tissue and permanent tissue.
59. Identify the figure given below and mention how these parts are useful to the plants.

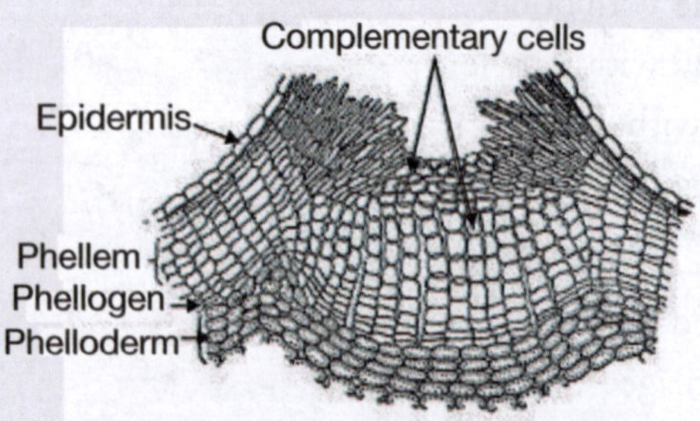

60. What differentiates meristematic tissues from permanent tissues in plants?
61. Explain the primary function of connective tissue in the human body.
62. Write short note on
    (a) tendons (b) ligaments
63. Name the tissue corresponding to the following features.
    (a) Helps in translocation of food in plants.
    (b) Aids in transportation of hormones
64. Observe the following figure and answer the questions.

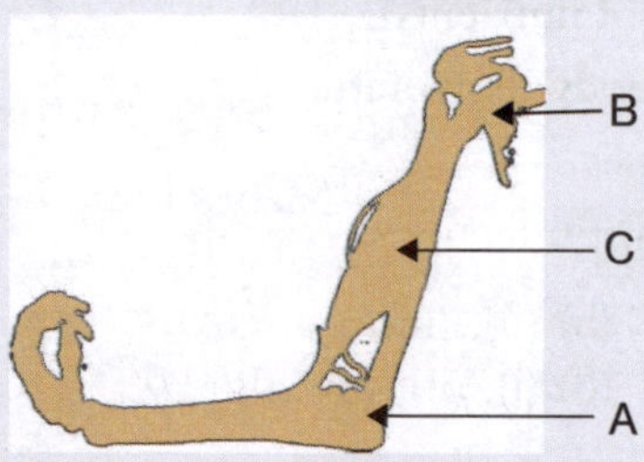

(a) Identify and label the parts A, B and C.

(b) Give the functions of A.

(c) Write a note on functions of B.

65. Mention any four parts in human body which are made up of cartilage.

66. What is the role of areolar and adipose tissues in human beings?

67. Mention differences between cartilage and bone.

68. How do cardiac muscles differ from striated muscles in structure and function?

69. Few cells of plant tissue are known as collocytes. Give their characteristic features.

70. Mention the type of adipose tissue found in infants. How does it differ from adipose tissue of adults?

Essay Type Questions

71. Explain the cells responsible for conduction of food to various parts of the plant.

72. Write a note on the tissue system which forms the main bulk of the plant body.

73. Explain the significance of tissue differentiation in multicellular organisms and how it contributes to the complexity and efficiency of these organisms.

74. Differentiate between simple tissue and complex tissue in animals. Write a note on the types of epithelial tissue and mention their location and function.

COMPETITION WING

Practice Questions

Level 1: Apply your Concepts

Direction for Questions from 1 to 5:
Fill in the blanks.

1. While _______ tissue in plants divides actively, the _______ tissue loses its ability to divide after reaching maturity.
2. Tissues in animals that provide protection by forming continuous sheets are called _______, while those responsible for connecting various organs and tissues are termed _______.
3. Large pores present on the bark which help in aeration of plants are _________.
4. Epidermis of plant body is made up of ________ tissue.
5. The tissue that helps in the transportation of substances through semi-permeable membrane is ________.

Direction for Questions from 6 to 11:
For each of the following questions four choices have been provided. Select the correct alternatives.

6. Which tissue system in plants primarily deals with the transport of water and nutrients?
   (a) Dermal (b) Ground
   (c) Vascular (d) Epithelial
7. Which tissue type in animals is primarily responsible for the reception and transmission of stimuli?
   (a) Epithelial
   (b) Connective
   (c) Muscular
   (d) Nervous
8. What characterizes meristematic tissue in plants?
   (a) It is found only in mature plants.
   (b) Cells of this tissue have lost their ability to divide.
   (c) It consists of cells that actively divide throughout the life of the plant.
   (d) It is responsible for the photosynthesis process in plants.
9. Which of the following best describes the function of connective tissue in animals?
   (a) It acts as a protective sheet.
   (b) It is responsible for movement.
   (c) It connects various tissues and organs.
   (d) It transmits signals throughout the body.
10. If a plant's growth is primarily vertical, with an increase in height rather than width, which type of meristematic tissue is predominantly active?
    (a) Intercalary meristem
    (b) Lateral meristem
    (c) Apical meristem
    (d) Basal meristem
11. Identify the correct combination from the following table.

Type of cartilage	Nature of matrix	Location
(i) Fibrous cartilage	Contain more collagen fibres	Inter-vertebral discs
(ii) Hyaline cartilage	Contain elastic fibres	Tip of nose
(iii) Elastic cartilage	Contain both collagen and elastin fibres	Epiglottis
(iv) Calcified cartilage	Contain megakaryocytes	Pinna of the ear

(a) (i) and (iii) (b) (ii) and (iv) (c) (iii) and (iv) (d) (i) and (iv)

Direction for Questions from 12 to 29: Choose the correct option.

(a) Both A and R are true and R is the correct explanation for A.
(b) Both A and R are true, but R is not the correct explanation for A.
(c) A is true and R is false.
(d) A is false and R is true.

12. Assertion (A): Lateral meristems help in secondary growth of the plant body.
Reason (R): Lateral meristems divide mostly anticlinally and increase the thickness of plant organs.

13. Assertion (A): Parenchyma is responsible for wound healing regeneration and grafting in plants.
Reason (R): Parenchyma can become a meristem by differentiation and produce new cells.

14. Assertion (A): Aerenchyma is the chief anatomical adaptation of hydrophytes.
Reason (R): Aerenchyma helps the plant in the exchange of gases and gives buoyancy.

15. Assertion (A): Young stems and petioles of dicots bend but do not break.
Reason (R): Parenchymatous tissue containing chlorophyll and undergo photosynthesis is chlorenchyma.

16. Assertion (A): Young stems and petioles of dicots bend but do not break.
Reason (R): Sclerenchymatous tissue gives mechanical strength and rigidity to the plant.

17. Assertion (A): Guttation occurs throughout the day in plants.
Reason (R): Stomata have guard cells which open and close and help in transpiration.

18. Assertion (A): Complex tissues are made up of more than one type of cells.
Reason (R): Vascular tissues in plants are a type of complex tissues.

19. Assertion (A): Outgrowths of parenchymatous cells on xylem vessels are known as tyloses.
Reason (R): Tyloses are selectively permeable to water and nutrients.

20. Assertion (A): Tyloses are considered as vascular plugs of plants.
Reason (R): They block the lumen of old and injured vessels.

21. Assertion (A): Seive tubes are made up of sieve plates that help in conduction.
Reason (R): Phloem parenchyma gives mechanical support.

22. Assertion (A): Lymph acts as a middle man between blood and tissue fluid.
Reason (R): Lymph is a colourless fluid.

23. Assertion (A): Areolar tissue supports internal organs and helps in tissue repair.
Reason (R): Areolar tissue is the most widely distributed tissue in the body of adults.

24. Assertion (A): External ear lobe shows high degree of flexibility.
Reason (R): Ear is made up of fibrous cartilage.

25. Assertion (A): Hyaline cartilage is the weakest of all types of cartilages.
Reason (R): Very thin collagen fibres are present in matrix of hyaline cartilage.

26. Assertion (A): Skeletal muscles show rhythmic contractions and relaxations.
Reason (R): Cardiac muscles are skeletal muscles which are voluntary in function.

27. Assertion (A): The main body of neuron is called dendron.
Reason (R): Cell body of a neuron does not contain nucleus.

28. Assertion (A): Epithelial tissue lining the urinary bladder is transitional epithelium.
Reason (R): Transitional epithelium helps in changing the size of the bladder accordingly.

29. Assertion (A): Blood is known as fluid connective tissue.
Reason (R): Blood cells are formed in bone marrow.

Direction for Questions from 30 to 39: Write the missing correlated terms.

30. Muscular tissue: Muscles:: Nervous tissue: ________.

31. Meristematic: Plants:: __________ : Humans

32. Undifferentiated cells : ______ : : differentiated cells : permanent

33. Photosynthesis : chlorenchyma : : ______ : aerenchyma

34. Stomata : transpiration : : Sieve tubes : ______

35. Adipose : insulator : : Areolar : ______

36. Cartilage : trachea : : ______ : tongue

37. Bone : skeletal tissue : : Lymph : ______

38. Flesh : ______ : : Trachea : cartilage

39. Muscular tissue : ______ : : Nervous tissue : sensory

Direction for Questions from 40 to 46: Indicate the odd one from the following.

40. Cellulose, lignin, pectin, collagen

41. Parenchyma, chlorenchyma, collenchyma, cork

42. Carrot, beetroot, *Opuntia*, radish.

43. Sieve tubes, tracheids, vessels, xylem fibres

44. Trachea, pinna of ear, tip of nose, skull

45. Brain, spinal cord, neurons, tendons

46. Cyton, tendon, axon, dendrites

Level 2: Review your Concepts

47. What change do you notice in plant if the stem tip is cut?

48. Plants require less amount of energy. Give reason.

49. What happens to the bone material if the bones are heated at high temperature?

50. A bone is crushed to fine powder and put in concentrated hydrochloric acid. How does this affect the composition of bone?

51. What happens when the tree gets injured? Name the structures responsible for that.

52. Cuticle is absent on epidermis of roots. Give reason.

53. Vascular tissue is responsible for survival of plants in terrestrial conditions. Give reason(s).

54. Comment on the following statement.

    One of the characteristic features of plant cell is the presence of vacuoles. But vacuoles are absent in meristematic cells.

55. Why is spleen known as haemopoietic and haemolytic tissue?

56. Can a person survive if blood is completely drained out from the body? Discuss.

57. Why does our skin shiver during winter?

58. There are 270 bones in the human body at the time of birth. Does this remain same in adult stage? Justify that.

59. Why is the regulation of stomatal opening and closing crucial for a plant's survival?

60. Clusters of egg cells are not considered as tissue. Give reason.

61. Epithelial tissue in animals is non-vascular but permeable. Give reason.

62. Thin people feel colder than fat ones. Give reason.

63. Blood is known as fluid connective tissue. Give reason.

64. Cardiac muscles show rhythmic contractions. Why?

65. Mitochondria are abundant in neurons. Give reason.

66. Bones become more and more fragile in old age. Justify.

67. Camels can remain alive without food for many days. Give reason.

68. When we fall sick for a long period of time, we become thin. Give reason.

69. When we do strenuous and unusual physical activity, we are likely to get inflammation in some body parts. Comment.

70. The bones are harder and stronger than cartilage. Give reason.

71. The body of a baby is soft and becomes harder as the baby grows. Justify.

72. Plants have larger proportion of dead tissue than animals. Justify this statement.

Level 3: Assess Your Concepts

73. Why thickness of the stem increases as age advances in dicot plants?
74. Why heartwood is considered more durable than the sapwood?
75. Sieve tubes do not have nuclei, why are they considered as living cells?
76. Epidermal cells secrete thick and waxy layer in cactus. Why?
77. Why are the surfaces of woody plants impermeable to water and gases?
78. Young stems (twigs) bend but do not break. Why?
79. Why are intervertebral discs considered to be the strongest form of cartilages?
80. Why do wrinkles appear on the skin with growing age?
81. In old people knees make a bit crunching sound when they change their posture from sitting position to standing position. Why does this happen?
82. How do the diversity and specialization of tissues contribute to the complexity and adaptability of higher organisms, ensuring their survival and efficient functioning in diverse environments?

AT

NEET SPECIAL WING

Practice Questions

Multiple-Answer Type Questions

Questions number 1 to 5 are multiple-choice questions. Each question has FOUR options (a), (b), (c), and (d). ONE OR MORE THAN ONE of these four option(s) is/are the correct answer(s).

1. Apical meristems are present in which locations of the plant body?
(a) Radical
(b) Adventitious root tips
(c) Tap root tips
(d) Shoot endings

2. Select the incorrectly matched pair from the following:
(a) Chondrocytes - Bones
(b) Osteocytes - Tendons
(c) Adipocytes - Adipose tissue
(d) Sclerenchyma - dead tissue

3. Areolar connective tissue consists of:
(a) semi solid matrix
(b) Fibroblasts present
(c) Elastic fibres
(d) Collagen fibres

4. Which among the following are types of dense connective tissue?
(a) Areolar (b) Tendons
(c) Adipose (d) Ligaments

5. Identify the functions of the lymphatic system.
(a) Transports nutrients that may have got filtered out of the blood capillaries back into the lungs
(b) Brings back the carbon dioxide and nitrogenous wastes from tissue fluid to the blood
(c) Forms the immune system of the body
(d) Maintains the body temperatures

Comprehension-Based Questions

A. Read the paragraph given below and answer the questions number 6 to 11:

Nervous tissue is the basic constituent of the nervous system. It is also commonly called as neural tissue. It is the nervous tissue that regulates and controls all the processes taking place within the body. Nervous tissue consists of two parts- Central nervous system (CNS) [brain and spinal cord] and the peripheral nervous system (PNS) [peripheral nerves]. The nervous tissue consists of neurons whose main function is to receive and transmit electrical impulses, and neuroglia which help the nerve impulses to propagate and to provide nutrients to the neurons. A nerve cell consists of an axon which is a long strand and send impulses to the next neuron. It has a large nucleus contained in the cyton or soma. It also has many granules called as Nissl's granules (site of protein synthesis). The short strands or processes arising from the soma are called dendrites and they receive nerve impulses from the previous neuron. The axons are insulated by myelin sheath and are made up of a cell called as Schwann cells. There are places on the axon which are not insulated called as Nodes of Ranvier. There is an empty space between two neurons and is known as a synapse or a synaptic junction. Based on the function of neurons, the neurons are classified into three main types- Motor neurons (involved in locomotion), Sensory neuron (involved in perceiving sensations) and Interneurons (form connection between neurons). Entire control and coordination of the body is done with the help of two major systems- endocrine system and nervous system.

6. The direction of passage of electrical impulse is from the _____ to the ______ of a neuron.
(a) Axon, Axon (b) Axon, Dendrite
(c) Dendrite, Dendrite (d) Dendrite, Axon

7. Nerve impulse travels in what form across a synapse?
(a) Physical (b) Kinetic
(c) Electrical (d) Chemical

8. Nissl's granules consists of which organelles?
(a) RER, SER
(b) RER, Free ribosomes
(c) Golgi body, mitochondria
(d) Mitochondria, chloroplast

9. What type of tissue is present in myelin sheath?
(a) Cartilage
(b) Bone
(c) Blood
(d) Fatty tissue

10. What are the substances present in the synapse that help in propagation of impulse?
(a) Neuronal hormones
(b) Neuronal Enzymes
(c) Neurotransmitters
(d) Androgens

11. Match the following:

Column – A	Column – B
(i) Neurons activated by sensations	(a) Motor neuron
(ii) Brain and Spinal cord	(b) Peripheral nervous system
(iii) Neurons that control muscular movement	(c) Sensory neuron
(iv) Neurons that form connections	(d) Central nervous system
(v) Network of nerves	(e) Interneuron

B. Read the paragraph given below and answer the questions number 12 to 17:

Plant tissues consist of two main types- Meristematic tissue and permanent tissue. Meristematic tissue has the ability to divide and give rise to new cells whereas permanent tissue has lost the ability to divide further. Depending on the location meristematic tissue is of three types- apical, lateral and intercalary meristems. Permanent tissue take up specific functions in the plant body and loose the ability to divide further. Permanent tissue is of two main types that is simple permanent tissue and complex permanent tissue. Simple permanent tissue are made up of only one type of cells. Based on their functions are again divided into different types such as parenchyma, collenchyma and sclerenchyma. Complex permanent tissue are made up of more than one type of cells and includes conducting tissues like xylem and phloem. Xylem helps with the conduction of water from the roots to all the parts of the plant body whereas phloem helps with the conduction of food prepared by the green leaves to all the other parts of the plant body. Besides this plant body is made up of different types of tissue systems like dermal tissue system, ground tissue system and vascular tissue system.

12. Which of the following cells are living but have no nucleus in phloem tissue?
(a) Sieve tubes
(b) Companion cells
(c) Phloem parenchyma
(d) Sieve cells

13. Which tissue provides mechanical strength as well as buoyant support to the plant?
(a) Meristematic tissue
(b) Sclerenchyma
(c) Collenchyma
(d) Aerenchyma

14. Sclereids are also called as
(a) Grit cells (b) Coir
(c) Stone cells (d) Both a and c

15. Epidermal cells on stems which are modified into specialized cells in xerophytes are called
(a) Cuticle
(b) Trichomes
(c) Stomata
(d) Cork

16. Breaks in which tissue leads to formation of lenticels?
(a) Periderm
(b) Cambium
(c) Cork
(d) Companion cells

17. Using the data given in the previous paragraph, match the following.

Column – A	Column – B
(i) Secondary growth of lateral meristem	(a) Non-living tapering cells
(ii) Collenchyma	(b) Present at nodal base of twigs
(iii) Tracheids	(c) Cambium
(iv) Lateral meristem	(d) Sideways conduction of water
(v) Phloem parenchyma	(e) Deposition of pectin

Answer Keys

Crossword

Across

4. Trichomes 6. Tendon 7. Apical Meristems 12. Lignin 14. Interneurons
16. Parenchyma 18. Dermal 19. Ciliated 20. Sclereids

Down

1. Areolar 2. Perichondrium 3. Pectin 5. Xylem Parenchyma 8. Haversian
9. Aerenchyma 10. Sieve tube 11. Hydrophytes 13. Meristematic 15. Permanent
17. Smooth

Classroom Wing

Very Short Answer Type Questions

1. Tissues 2. Meristematic 3. Connective 4. Nervous 5. Vascular
6. Sclerenchyma 7. Epidermis 8. Stomata 9. Aerenchyma/buoyancy
10. Sclerenchyma 11. Microvilli 12. Squamous epithelium
13. Areolar connective tissue 14. Elastic cartilage 15. Intercalated
16. Smooth muscles 17. Synapses 18. Dendrites/Axon 19. (b)
20. (d) 21. (c) 22. (a) 23. (c) 24. (c)
25. (c) 26. (a) 27. (d) 28. (c) 29. (d)
30. A → (iii), B → (iv), C → (v), D → (i), E → (ii)
31. A → (v), B → (iii), C → (iv), D → (vi), E → (ii), F → (i)
32. (c) 33. (b) 34. (b) 35. (d) 36. (c)
37. 1 → c, 2 → d, 3 → a, 4 → e, 5 → b. 38. False 39. False 40. False
41. False 42. False 43. False 44. False 45. False
46. False 47. False 48. False 49. False 50. False
51. False 52. True 53. True 54. True 55. True

Competition Wing

Level 1: Apply your Concepts

1. Meristematic, Permanent 2. Epithelial, Connective 3. Lenticels
4. Parenchyma 5. Simple squamous epithelium 6. (c) 7. (d)
8. (c) 9. (c) 10. (c) 11. (a) 12. (c)
13. (a) 14. (a) 15. (b) 16. (b) 17. (d)
18. (a) 19. (b) 20. (a) 21. (c) 22. (b)
23. (b) 24. (c) 25. (a) 26. (d) 27. (d)
28. (a) 29. (b) 30. Nervous system 31. Epithelial 32. Meristems

33. Buoyancy
34. Sieve tubes
35. Packing tissue
36. Muscle
37. Fluid connective tissue
38. Striated muscle
39. Contractile
40. Collagen
41. Cork
42. Opuntia
43. Sieve tubes
44. Skull
45. Tendons
46. Tendon

NEET Special Wing

Multiple-Answer Type Questions

1. (a, b, c, d)
2. (a, b)
3. (a, b, c, d)
4. (b, d)
5. (b, c)

Comprehension-Based Questions

6. (d)
7. (d)
8. (b)
9. (d)
10. (c)
11. (i) → (c); (ii) → (d); (iii) → (a); (iv) → (e); (v) → (b)
12. (a)
13. (d)
14. (d)
15. (b)
16. (c)
17. (i) → (c); (ii) → (e); (iii) → (a); (iv) → (b); (v) → (d)

Hints and Explanations

CLASSROOM WING

Very Short Answer Type Questions

19. The connective tissue is specialized for connecting various tissues and organs.

20. Meristematic tissues are known for their active cell division throughout the plant's life.

21. The vascular tissue system in plants is responsible for the transport of nutrients and water.

22. Epithelial is a type of tissue in animals, specifically humans, and is not found in plants.

23. The epithelial tissue acts as a thin and continuous protective sheet of cells in the human body.

24. The muscular tissue forms muscles in the body which are responsible for movement.

25. Cells of permanent tissue in plants take up a specific role and lose their division capability.

34. The vascular tissue mostly made up of dead cells is xylem. Choice (b)

35. Areolar connective tissue connects integument with muscle. Choice (d)

36. Trachea is made up of tissue cartilage. Choice (c)

37. **1.** Fluid connective tissue – blood

2. Filling space inside organs – Aerolar tissue

3. Striated muscle – skeletal muscle

4. Adipose tissue – sub-cutaneous tissue

5. Surface of joints – cartilage

1 → c, **2** → d, **3** → a, **4** → e, **5** → b.

38. False; Permanent tissue is formed from mersitematic tissue.

39. False; Meristematic cells are present in root tips, stem tips.

40. False; Lateral meristems helps in increasing the girth of the plant.

41. False

42. False – In tender plants collenchyma is the tissue that gives mechanical support.

43. False – The tissue having large air cavities and help in buoyancy is aerenchyma.

44. False – The main function of xylem parenchyma is to store starch and fatty acids.

45. False; Vascular tissue contains xylem and phloem.

46. False; Sclerenchyma consists of dead cells.

47. False; Epithelial cells are not supplied with blood vessels.

48. False; Xylem helps in conduction of water and mineral salts from roots to leaves.

49. False; Minute openings present in the epidermis of leaves are called stomata.

50. False; Nails, horns, claws and hoofs are developed from epidermis.

51. False; Platelets help in clotting of blood.

Short Answer Type Questions

56. Jute—phloem fibres.

Rose wood—secondary xylem.

Hard shells of fruits—sclereids of phloem.

Cork—parenchymatous cells in cortex.

57. **Utility of tissue in multicellular organisms**

In unicellular organisms all the life activities are performed by single cell. Multicellular organisms attain large size and complex body organization. To perform integrated activities efficiently, tissues are necessary.

58. Differences between meristematic tissue and permanent tissue

Meristematic	Permanent
The tissues have the capacity to divide	The tissues have lost the capacity to divide
They have thin cellulose cell wall with no intercellular spaces	They have thick cellulose cell wall with intercellular spaces
Small vacuoles with prominent nucleus	Large vacuoles with normal nucleus
They produce permanent tissue	They are produced from meristematic tissue
Present in root tips and stem tips	Present in the ground tissue of the plant

59. The figure is identified as structure of lenticel. Lenticels are porous tissue which consists of cell with large intercellular space in the periderm (cork) layer of stems and roots of woody plants. They help in the exchange of gases in the woody trees.

60. Meristematic tissues have cells that divide actively throughout the life of the plant, whereas cells of permanent tissue take up a specific role and lose their ability to divide.

61. Connective tissue is specialized for connecting various tissues and organs, providing support, and facilitating the integration of bodily functions.

62. (a) Tendons are made up of white collagen fibres which connect muscle to bone.
(b) Ligaments are made up of elastic fibres which connect bone to bone.

63. (a) The tissue that helps in translocation of food in plants—phloem
(b) Tissue which aids in transportation of hormones—blood

64. (a) 'A' is identified as tendon
'B' is identified as ligament
'C' is the muscle
(b) Functions of tendon: The connectives tissue made up of white fibres which are tough and non-elastic.
Tendon connects muscles to bones.
(c) Functions of ligaments: The connective tissue made up of yellow fibres which are strong and elastic which connect one bone to another bone.

65. The four parts made of cartilage are as follows:
(a) pinna of ear (b) trachea
(c) larynx (d) tip of nose

66. Areolar tissue is the filler tissue which binds skin to the underlying muscles, supports internal organs and keeps them in position.

Adipose tissue contains fat globules, which is present beneath the skin and acts as insulator keeping the body warm. It also acts as a food reserve.

67. Cartilage and bone are skeletal tissue.

Cartilage	Bone
Cartilage is made up of cells called chondroblasts, embedded in matrix.	Bone is made up of cells called osteoblasts, embedded in matrix.
It is flexible and elastic	It is hard, porous, rigid with strong framework.
Cartilage matrix is made of proteins and sugars	Matrix is made up of calcium and phosphorous.

68.

Parameter	Cardiac muscles	Striated muscles
Structure	Cells are cylindrical, branched and uni-nucleated. They are striated with light and dark bands. Centrally located one or two nuclei. Fibres are branched connected with one another forming network.	Spindle shaped, unbranched, uni-nucleated cells. Contraction and relaxation are slow, steady and automatic. Sarcolemma is absent. Myofibrils, running lengthwise, are present.

Parameter	Cardiac muscles	Striated muscles
Function	They perform rhythmic contraction and relaxation of the heart.	They are concerned with involuntary movement, i.e., movement that is not under the control of our will. In the intestines, they help to push the food along the alimentary canal.

69. The cells of collenchymas are called collocytes. These cells are elongated living cells with vacuolated cytoplasm.

These cells are unevenly thickened due to excessive deposition of cellulose and pectin containing high percentage of water.

70. The type of adipose tissue found in infants is brown adipose tissue which contains many liquid droplets in adipocytes. Blood supply and mitochondria are more in this tissue. It produces heat and maintains body temperature. In adults, white adipose tissue is

present which contains a single large liquid droplet in adipocyte. Cytoplasm and nucleus are pushed to one side.

Essay Type Questions

71. The cells responsible for conduction of food is phloem. It conducts food material from leaves to various parts of the plant through different cells.

(a) Seive tubes—elongated cells with perforated ends help in transportation of substances from one cell to the adjacent cell.

(b) Companion cells—living cells help the sieve cells in maintaining the control of transportation through sieve tubes.

(c) Phloem parenchyma—living cells which help in storage

(d) Phloem fibres–elongated tapering dead cells which give mechanical support.

72. The tissue system which forms the main bulk of the plant body is ground tissue. Ground tissue system includes all tissues except epidermis and vascular tissue. This system is made up of different kinds of tissues such as parenchyma, collenchyma and sclerenchyma.

73. In multicellular organisms, tissue differentiation is crucial for specialized functions. As organisms evolved, there was a need for more complex systems to ensure survival. With tissue differentiation, specific cells undertake unique roles, enabling efficient task delegation. For example, while epithelial tissue provides protection, muscular tissue enables movement. This specialization means each cell type can become highly efficient at its designated role. As a result, multicellular organisms can carry out more complex tasks than if every cell had to perform every function. This diversification and specialization of tissues contribute significantly to the enhanced capabilities and survival strategies of complex organisms.

74.

Animal tissue
- Complex tissue (made up of more than one type of cells which work together)
- Simple tissue (made up of one type of cells)
  - **Squamous**
    - Made up of flat cells
    - Lining of alveoli, lungs and blood vessel, etc.
    - Helps in filtration transportation, osmosis and diffusion
  - **Cuboidal**
    - Cube-like cells
    - Lining of kidney, salivary glands, etc.
    - Helps in absorption of useful substances from glomerular filtrate
  - **Ciliated**
    - Columnar cells having cilia
    - Lining of trachea
    - Helps in cleaning respiratory tract

COMPETITION WING

Level 1: Apply your Concepts

6. The vascular tissue system in plants is responsible for the transport of water, nutrients, and food. It includes xylem and phloem tissues.

   Hence, the correct option is (c).

7. Nervous tissue is a specialized tissue that deals with the reception and transmission of stimuli. It includes the brain, spinal cord, and nerves.

   Hence, the correct option is (d).

8. Meristematic tissues have cells that divide actively and continuously throughout the plant's life, leading to growth.

   Hence, the correct option is (c).

9. As the name suggests, connective tissue specializes in connecting different parts of the body, providing support, and anchoring various organs and tissues in place.

   Hence, the correct option is (c).

10. Apical meristem is located at the tips of roots and shoots and contributes to the vertical growth of the plant. Thus, it is responsible for increasing the plant's height.

    Hence, the correct option is (c).

12. Lateral meristems are present on lateral side of the stem which helps in increasing the girth of the plant. Periclinal cell divisions are the cell divisions that occur parallel to the tissue surface which results in increasing the rows of the cells stacked one over the over. In anticlinal division of lateral meristems girth of the plant increases.

    Hence, the correct option is (c).

13. Parenchyma is a simple tissue present in plants, which helps in regeneration wound healing and grafting. This tissue can also undergo differentiation to produce meristematic tissue and helps in production of new cells. Both A and R are true and R is the correct explanation of A.

    Hence, the correct option is (a).

14. Aerenchyma is a plant tissue. It is a type of parenchyma tous tissue which contains air spaces. Most of the hydrophytes bear this tissue. This tissue contains air space and helps in giving buoyancy to the leaves or plants and help in free floating.

    Hence, the correct option is (a).

15. Young stems and petioles in dicots bend but do not break due to the presence of collenchyma tissue. Collenchyma gives flexibility and tensile strength to the plant. Parenchyma tissue containing chlorophyll and helping in photosynthesis is chlorenchyma. Both A and R are true and R is not the correct explanation of A.

    Hence, the correct option is (b).

16. Young stems and petioles of dicots bend but do not break due to the presence of collenchyma tissue. Sclerenchyma tissue gives rigidity and mechanical strength to the plant and help it in standing erect. Both A and R are true but R is not the correct explanation of A.

    Hence, the correct option is (b).

17. Guttation mainly occurs during night time, but at times in areas with high humidity, guttation occurs during day time. Stomata have guard cells which open and close and help in regulating transpiration. A is false and R is true.

    Hence, the correct option is (d).

18. Complex tissue in plants is made up of more than one type of cells. E.g., vascular tissue in plants.

    Xylem and phloem are vascular tissues in plants which are made up of different types of cells and help in conduction. Both A and R are true and R is the correct explanation of A.

    Hence, the correct option is (a).

19. Tyloses are outgrowths on parenchymatous cells of xylem. These helps in preventing the spread of fungal pathogens. These are selectively permeable to water and nutrients. Both A and R are ture R is not the correct explanation of A.

    Hence, the correct option is (b).

20. Tyloses are outgrowths on parenchymatous cells of xylem. These help in preventing the spread of fungal pathogens. These are selectively permeable to water and nutrients. When the plant gets injured, they block the lumen and obstruct the conduction. Hence, the tyloses are called vascular plugs. Both A and R are true and R is the correct explanation of A.

    Hence, the correct option is (a).

21. Phloem tissue is made up of sieve tubes and sieve cells which help in conduction of food by the process of translocation. Phloem parenchyma helps in transporta-

tion of food but it does not give mechanical support. A is true and R is false.

Hence, the correct option is (c).

22. Lymph is a colourless fluid that acts as a middle man between tissue fluid and blood. It is the plasma that has oozed out of the blood vessels.
Hence, the correct option is (b).

23. Areolar connective tissue is the most widely distributed connective tissue type in the body of vertebrates.
Hence, the correct option is (b).

24. External ear is made of elastic cartilage.
Hence, the correct option is (c).

25. Hyaline cartilage is the weakest type amongst the all three types of cartilage due to its highly fine collagen fibres.
Hence, the correct option is (a).

26. Cardiac muscles show rhythmic contraction and relaxation and are not a type of skeletal muscles.
Hence, the correct option is (d).

27. Main body of a neuron is called cyton (cell body) and it contains a nucleus.
Hence, the correct option is (d).

28. Transitional epithelium is involved in facilitating the shape of the surface cells that undergo changes (or transitions) upon stretching.
Hence, the correct option is (a).

29. Blood is a bright-red fluid connective tissue. Bone marrow is responsible for the production of blood corpuscles.
Hence, the correct option is (b).

30. Nervous system. (Explanation: Just as muscular tissue forms muscles in the body, nervous tissue constitutes the nervous system.)

31. Epithelial. (Explanation: Just as meristematic tissues are specific to plants, epithelial tissues are specific to humans, especially in terms of their protective nature.)

Level 2: Review your Concepts

47. If the stem tip of the plant is cut, apical growth of the plant stops growing. Lateral buds start growing due to which branches are formed.

48. Plants have less complex body when compared to animals. Plants are autotrophic as they utilize solar energy for preparing their own food, whereas animals have to move in search of food to different places. Animals are more physically active than plants. As animals have complex body structure to undergo various activities, animals require more energy.

49. Bone tissue contains both organic material and inorganic material.
The organic material comprises fibres made of collagen protein and the inorganic material contains salts of calcium and magnesium (mainly phosphates)
The collagen present in the bone gets denatured on prolonged or strong heating.
The inorganic material is left behind mostly in the form of ash.

50. Bone tissue contains both organic material and inorganic material.
The organic material comprises fibres made of collagen protein and the inorganic material contains salts of calcium and magnesium (mainly phosphates)
As hydrochloric acid is a strong acid, the minerals like calcium phosphate dissolve in the concentrated acid.
The organic material that is collagen is left behind.

51. In xylem tissue, certain structures called teloses are formed which obstruct the flow of water when the plant or tree gets injured. As a result of deficiency of water for a long time, the shoot system of the plant gets dried up and the plant may die if the situation persists for long period.

52. Cuticle is a waxy layer which is formed above epidermis of stem and leaves. This layer checks the loss of water from the plants.
If waxy cuticle is present on roots, it prevents absorption of water and salts from soil, hence cuticle is absent in roots.

53. Xylem and phloem are specialized vascular tissues which help in conduction of water and mineral salts to the plant.
Water is absorbed by roots and transported to different parts of the plants to maintain water balance.
Starch is prepared in leaves by the process called photosynthesis and transported to all parts of the plant.
This tissue provides structural support by forming skeletal structure and helps the plant to grow upright and taller.

54. Vacuoles are cell organelles used to store waste materials, nutrients and excess salts, etc. They are usually

larger in size and more in number in matured cells. Meristematic cells are undifferentiated and constantly diving immature cells. As they do not have any waste material to store, vacuoles are absent.

55. Spleen helps in the formation of blood cells hence known as haemopoietic tissue. It also helps in destruction of blood cells hence known as haemolytic tissue.

56. Blood is a connective tissue that carries oxygen and nutrients to cells.

It contains respiratory pigment, haemoglobin which provides oxygen and nutrients to cells.

Oxygen is provided for the oxidation of glucose and supply of energy to do work.

If blood is drained out, respiration does not occur. Cells do not get oxygen and they decompose and die.

Human body is made up of cells and hence a person cannot survive.

57. During shivering, muscles contract and relax producing large amount of heat. This heat produced keeps our body warm, hence we shiver during winter.

58. A child has 270 separate bones at the time of birth.

During the process of growth and development, many small bones fuse together to form a single bone.

Ossification of bones also takes place during the process of growth.

As a result of these two phenomena, the number of bones decreases to 206.

59. Regulation of stomatal opening and closing is vital for the plant as it controls gas exchange (intake of carbon dioxide for photosynthesis and release of oxygen) and transpiration (loss of water vapour). By regulating these processes, the plant can manage its water balance, optimize photosynthesis, and respond to environmental stresses.

60. A tissue can be defined as a group of similar cells having same structure, performing same specific function in aggregate, and coordinating with each other in the body of multicellular organism.

Eggs in clusters inside or outside the body, are cells just positioned near each other. They do not perform function in and coordination with one other, hence they are not considered as tissues.

61. In epithelial tissue the cells are closely packed without intercellular spaces.

Cells rest on basement membrane which is made up of a network of white, non-elastic collagen fibres.

This tissue has no blood supply. Some epithelial cells are involved in physiological processes such as respiratory gases exchange, absorption, secretion, etc., hence permeable.

62. Sub-cutaneous layer in thin persons does not contain adipose tissue; whereas sub-cutaneous layer in fat persons contains adipose tissue made of fat which acts as an insulator and keeps the body warm. Hence thin persons feel colder than fat persons.

63. Blood contains components known as plasma and corpuscles.

Plasma is the fluid component of blood in which corpuscles float.

This tissue is in fluid form connecting various regions of the body performing various functions, hence known as fluid connective tissue.

64. Cardiac muscles show rhythmic contractions.

Cardiac muscles are the muscles of the heart.

These muscles contract at a time creating an efficient pumping action in the heart.

Due to this the blood is pumped with great pressure, hence cardiac muscles show rhythmic contractions.

65. The main function of neurons is transmission of nerve impulses which is called neurotransmission.

The process of neurotransmission takes place at the expense of large amount of energy.

This energy is in the form of ATP and is used as fuel for most of the biochemical reactions in neurons.

This energy is produced by mitochondria on the oxidation of glucose.

As brain (bundle of neurons) needs more amount of energy for undergoing neuronal activity, large number of mitochondria are present in neurons.

66. As the age advances, calcium and phosporous are reabsorbed in the body from the bones.

This makes the bone weaker and fragile resulting in a condition called osteoporosis.

67. The hump of camel is made up of adipose tissue which stores fat.

During scarcity of water, this fat in the tissue is used up to release energy required for the metabolic activity.

68. Weight loss when we fall sick is due to following reasons.

- Body metabolism raises to fight infections.

- Sweating and increased body temperature leads to dehydration.
- Lack of hunger and insufficient intake of food lead to the breakdown of fats stored in the adipose tissues in muscles. This makes the person lose weight and look thin and lean.

69. When we undergo intense strenuous exercise, more amount of oxygen is required by that particular muscle present in the concerned region of the body.

    When there is deficiency of oxygen, then anaerobic respiration takes place in the respective muscle cells which leads to the formation of lactic acid leading to inflammations.

70. Cartilage is a type of soft connective tissue, made up of cells called chondrocytes which contain collagen and elastin fibres in the matrix.

    Ossification of cartilage forms bone which is formed due to deposition of minerals of calcium and phosphorus. Hence the bone is stronger than cartilage.

71. The body of a baby is mainly composed of cartilage at birth.

    As the baby grows, deposition of calcium and magnesium salts takes place which results in hardening. This results in the conversion of cartilage into bone and is known as ossification.

72. Plants do not show locomotion that is moving from one place to other, but animals move from one place to the other. The dead cells present in the plants can provide mechanical strength just like living cells without spending more energy on maintenance. Thus plants possess more dead tissue than animals.

Level 3: Assess Your Concepts

73. As the dicot trees grow older, formation of secondary vascular tissue takes place due to secondary growth. Due to secondary growth, secondary xylem and phloem take place hence thickness of the stem increases.

74. Heartwood contains organic compounds like aromatic oils, gums, resins, tannins phenols and essential oils. These organic compounds attack microorganisms and insects hence heartwood is considered more durable than sapwood.

75. Sieve tubes are considered as living cells without nucleus because, the nucleus of companion cells control their functional activities.

76. In xerophytic plants (cactus), epidermal layer secrets a thick and waxy layer called cuticle which is made up of chitin.

    This layer closes the stomata and prevents water loss by transpiration process (water-resistant layer). As cactus plant lives in water-deficit area such thick and waxy cutile is seen.

77. Surfaces of woody plants are impermeable to water and gases due to the presence of cork cells. These cells have a layer of suberin on their walls due to which surfaces are impermeable.

78. In young stems (twigs), the tissue that gives flexibility and tensile strength to the plant is collenchyma. It is a living tissue with thickened corners made up of cellulose which provide mechanical support to young plant, hence the stems bend but do not break.

79. The cartilage of intervertebral discs contains matrix of dense network of collagen fibres. It gives strength and rigidity to the vertebral column, hence considered as the strongest form of cartilage.

80. Dermis loses both collagen and elastin, hence skin gets thinner and has trouble in getting enough moisture to the epidermis.

    The fat in the sub-cutaneous layer that gives skin a plumpy appearance, also begins to degenerate, then the epidermis starts to sag and form wrinkles.

81. As we age the tissue that covers the bones and cartilage can develop uneven areas. When we squat or stand sounds come from knees or ankles as their rougher surfaces glide across each other. It could also be due to the tightening of tissue that connects bones to other bones called ligaments, during movement.

82. The diversity and specialization of tissues in higher organisms allow for a range of functions, from support, protection, and movement to communication and coordination. This diversity means that different parts of the organism can be optimized for specific functions, making the organism as a whole more efficient. For instance, nervous tissues facilitate rapid communication, while muscular tissues enable movement. This specialization ensures that the organism can adapt and respond to various environmental stimuli, thereby ensuring its survival. Moreover, the presence of different tissue types also allows organisms to inhabit a range of environments, from aquatic to terrestrial, cold to hot, demonstrating the adaptability conferred by tissue diversity and specialization.

NEET SPECIAL WING

Multiple-Answer Type Questions

1. Apical meristems are found in the growing tips of roots and shoots and help in increasing the length of the plant.
2. Chondrocytes are the cells present in cartilage, Osteocytes are the cells of bones, Adipocyte is the fat containing cell of adipose tissue whereas Sclerenchyma is the dead tissue of the plant made up of cell walls.
3. The areolar tissue mainly consists of transparent, sticky and jellylike matrix. All the three types of fibres are present in the matrix of areolar connective tissue. The cells and fibres are irregularly scattered in the matrix crossing each other in all directions.
4. Dense connective tissue is a tough band of fibrous connective tissue. It has large amounts of fibres in the matrix with relatively less proportion of ground substance. The fibres form the major part of the tissue. The fibres are mainly composed of collagen. The fibre forming cells, called fibroblasts are present in rows in between the collagen fibres. These fibroblasts generate the fibres. These tissues are also of two types, they are: Tendon and Ligament
5. Lymph transports nutrients that may have got filtered out of the blood capillaries back into the heart. It brings back the carbon dioxide and nitrogenous wastes from tissue fluid to the blood. Since, it is loaded with WBCs (lymphocytes), it protects the body against infections. It forms the immune system of the body.

Comprehension-Based Questions

A.

6. Nerve impulses are first received by the dendrites which are the short processes and then the soma followed by the long process that is the Axon.
7. In the synaptic junction the nerve impulses are converted into chemical energy in the from of neurotransmitters and then again into electrical impulse in the next neuron.
8. Nissl's granules consists of rough endoplasmic reticulum as well as free ribosomes which are a major site for protein synthesis in the soma of the neuron.
9. The myelin sheath act as insulators and are basically filled with fatty tissue to provide insulation.
10. In the synapse chemical substance called as neurotransmitters are present which help in the passage of the impulse from one neuron to another.
11. Match the following:

    Sensory neurons receive the sensations from the sensory organs and transmit it to the CNS.
    (i) (c)

    Central nervous system consists of the brain and the spinal cord.
    (ii) (d)

    Motor neurons transmit the impulses from the brain to the motor regions and help in movement and locomotion.
    (iii) (a)

    Interneurons form connections between neurons and help in the transmission of messages and conduction of nerve impulses.
    (iv) (e)

    The peripheral nervous system consists of peripheral nerves which form a network in the peripheral parts of the body.
    (v) (b)

B.

12. Sieve Tubes are elongated, cylindrical, thin-walled cells with perforated ends. Matured sieve tubes lose nuclei and other cell organelles except vacuoles. They are considered living cells without nuclei as the nuclei of companion cells control the functional activities.
13. In aquatic plants, large air spaces are present in the parenchyma tissue to give buoyancy to the plant and help them to float. They also provide mechanical strength to the plant to withstand water currents. This type of parenchyma is called aerenchyma.
14. Sclereids are very thick walled, hard and strongly lignified cells called stone cells or grit cells.
15. Some epidermal cells on the stems are sometimes modified into specialized cells which form fine outgrowths from the surface. These are called trichomes. These are usually present in desert plants or xerophytes.
16. Some breaks appear in the cork tissue which looks like raised openings. These are called lenticels. Lenticels in cork help in the exchange of gases during photosynthesis and respiration and also with transpiration in big trees.

17. Match the following:

Secondary growth of lateral meristem helps with the formation of cambium.
(i) (c)

Collenchyma cells are elongated which are thickened at the corners due to the deposition of cellulose and pectin.
(ii) (e)

Tracheids are non-living elongated cells with tapering ends. Their cell wall is highly thickened with lignin.
(iii) (a)

Lateral meristems are present at the lateral axis parallel to the periphery of the stem or root (below the outer layers of stems and roots).
(iv) (b)

Phloem Parenchyma contains living cells having thin cell walls made up of cellulose. It forms packing tissue in connecting different cells and also helps in the side-ways conduction of water.
(v) (d)

CHAPTER

3

Diversity in Living World—Plants

Key Ideas

After completing this chapter, you should be able to:

- Infer the need for classification and various methods of classification
- Explain the scientific method of naming and identification of plants
- Explain important aspects of the dominant classes of plants

Remember

Before beginning this chapter, you should be able to:

- Interpret the need of classifying living organisms
- Describe the rules of writing scientific names
- Describe the Aristotle system of classification
- Discuss major life processes in plants like photosynthesis, transport, respiration, etc.

Scientific Crypt

A Tribute to Carolus Linnaeus (1707-1778)

The venerable Swedish scientist, deserves a special mention in this chapter on Plant Diversity. Linnaeus, a botanist, physician, and zoologist, is widely regarded as the '*Father of Modern Taxonomy*.' He painstakingly crafted the Linnaean classification system, a hierarchical structure for categorising living organisms based on shared characteristics, thereby expanding our understanding of biological diversity.

Linnaeus' work, '*Systema Naturae*,' introduced the world to binomial nomenclature, a method for assigning a two-part Latin name to each organism that includes the genus and species, a practice that has stood the test of time. This novel approach allowed for more precise communication about various species as well as more accurate scientific discourse.

Linnaeus classified and described thousands of plant species in his quest to understand plant diversity, using his systematic approach to unravel the enthralling variety within the plant kingdom. He diligently studied plant morphology, attributes, and utility, resulting in a more coherent understanding of plant life and its important roles in ecological systems.

Crossword

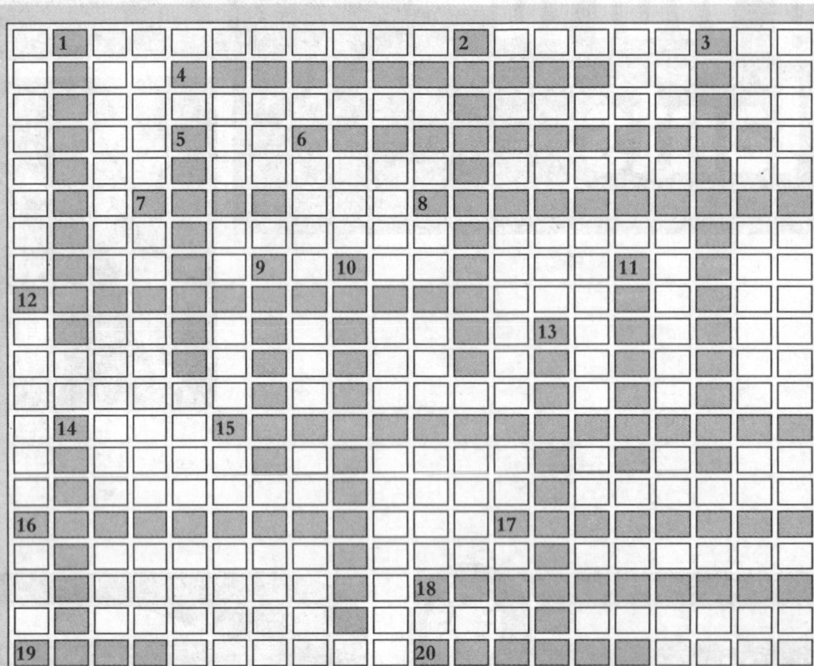

Across

4. Plant body which is not differentiated into root, stem and leaves
6. Root system in maize
7. Condensed disc-shaped modified stem with a terminal bud found in onion
8. Non-flowering primitive plants which have hidden reproductive organs
12. First plants to show vascular tissues
15. Father of taxonomy
16. Amphibians of the plant kingdom
17. Method of reproduction where diploid cells of the sporophytes can directly give rise to the diploid gametophyte
18. Male flower part's essential whorl
19. Roots which grow vertically downwards and give extra support
20. Subaerial stem modification seen in water hyacinth

Down

1. Leaf venation shown by Dicots
2. Plants with visible reproductive organs
3. Minute pores on breathing roots
5. Modified roots seen in Turnips
9. Roots bearing swellings in which bacteria grow and help with nitrogen fixation
10. Aerial stem modification which helps with photosynthesis in Xerophytes
11. Composite organisms which arise from algae living in close association with fungi.
13. Word formed by Greek words meaning vessel containing sperma or seed
14. Substance obtained from red algae which is used for making culture media

INTRODUCTION

The earth is inhabited by millions of wide varieties of living organisms. All living organisms are characterized by certain unique phenomena, such as growth, reproduction, responsiveness, etc., in contrast to the non-living things which do not show these characteristic features. However, different living organisms show wide range of variations in their form, functioning and behaviour. This is known as biological diversity or biodiversity. This broad spectrum of variations in external and internal features along with their behaviour and functioning makes the tasks of identifying these organisms practically difficult or rather impossible without a systematic approach. A systematic approach for the study of living organisms involves identification, naming and categorization of the living organisms. The systematic study of these organisms becomes easier only when the organisms are identified and grouped together on the basis of certain similarities and differences. This practice of identifying, naming and grouping of living organisms is known as classification.

The study of principles and procedures of classification of living organisms is called **taxonomy.**

Systems of Classification

Objectives of Classification

The need for classifying living organisms can be understood by following points:

- Convenience of study and identification
- Understanding the order in which the various groups of organisms evolved
- Understanding of the relationship among the various groups of organisms
- Understanding the interdependence of organisms
- Systematic naming of organisms

Info Bytes!

Around 85% of plant life is found in the ocean.

Scientists have devised the different systems of classification of living organisms from time to time. **Aristotle** was the first person who attempted to classify and name the living organisms. He is hence remembered as the '**Father of Biology**'. His work was mainly focused on animals. Aristotle classified animals according to their habitat, as terrestrial, aquatic or aerial. **Theophrastus** also did some considerable work in the field of taxonomy. Most of his work was in the classification of plants. He attempted to classify plants into herbs, shrubs and trees. He is therefore regarded as the '**Father of Botany**'. These earlier works of Aristotle and Theophrastus were based on some arbitrarily chosen criteria like size, colour or nature of organisms. Hence, these are considered as artificial systems of classification. In the later period, scientists devised various systems of classification based on natural affinities between living organisms and related similarities and differences among the organisms. These are known as the natural systems of classification. Hippocrates and Aristotle categorized living organisms into the plants and animals. This is called two-kingdom classification and was considered to be the first systematic classification of those times.

Two-Kingdom Classification

This classification was mainly based on the distinction between the two groups with respect to certain remarkable differences. According to the two-kingdom classification, all the plants were grouped under the kingdom Plantae and all the animals were grouped under the kingdom Animalia.

Organisms

Kingdom Plantae

- Lack of ability of locomotion
- Indefinite growth throughout life time
- Prepare their own food using solar energy (autotrophic mode of nutrition)
- Presence of cell wall and chloroplasts in the cells

Kingdom Animalia

- Ability of locomotion
- Definite growth up to a specific age
- Lack of ability to prepare their own food by using solar energy (heterotrophic mode of nutrition)
- Absence of cell wall and chloroplasts in the cells

Info Bytes!

Plant species are going extinct about 5000-times faster than they should.

Limitations of Two-Kingdom Classification

The primitive organisms which originated on earth were neither plants nor animals. Another group of organisms called viruses were discovered. They lacked some of the basic characteristic features of living organisms. This two-kingdom classification was convenient for the study of higher organisms. This is because the distinction between the characteristics of plants and animals is very clear and specific. In case of unicellular organisms and lower multicellular organisms, the distinctions are not very clear. Some lower organisms were found to possess few characteristics of animals and few characteristics of plants. They were included either in plants or animals. This inclusion was not justifiable.

For example, position of bacteria, fungi, slime moulds and *Euglena*.

Table 3.1 Characteristic features of lower organisms grouped in Plantae or Animalia

Organism	Cellular organization	Characteristics of plants	Characteristics of animals	Kingdom
Euglena	Unicellular	Presence of chlorophyll Ability of photosynthesis (autotrophic mode of nutrition)	Lack of cell wall with cellulose Dependence on other animals for food (heterotrophic mode of nutrition)	Animalia
Fungi	Multicellular	Presence of cell wall made of chitin	Absence of chlorophyll Nutrition from dead organic matter (saprozoic mode of nutrition)	Plantae
Slime moulds	Unicellular	Presence of cell wall with cellulose in reproductive stage	Dependence on other animals for food (heterotrophic mode of nutrition)	Plantae
Bacteria	Unicellular	Possess cell wall with cellulose	Dependence on other animals for food and shelter (parasitic mode of nutrition)	Plantae

To overcome these drawbacks, a more logical classification, called five-kingdom classification was proposed by Robert Harding Whittaker.

Five-Kingdom Classification

Whittaker proposed the five-kingdom classification for the living organisms based on three basic distinguishing features,

1. Structure of cell
2. Cellular organization
3. Mode of nutrition and reproduction

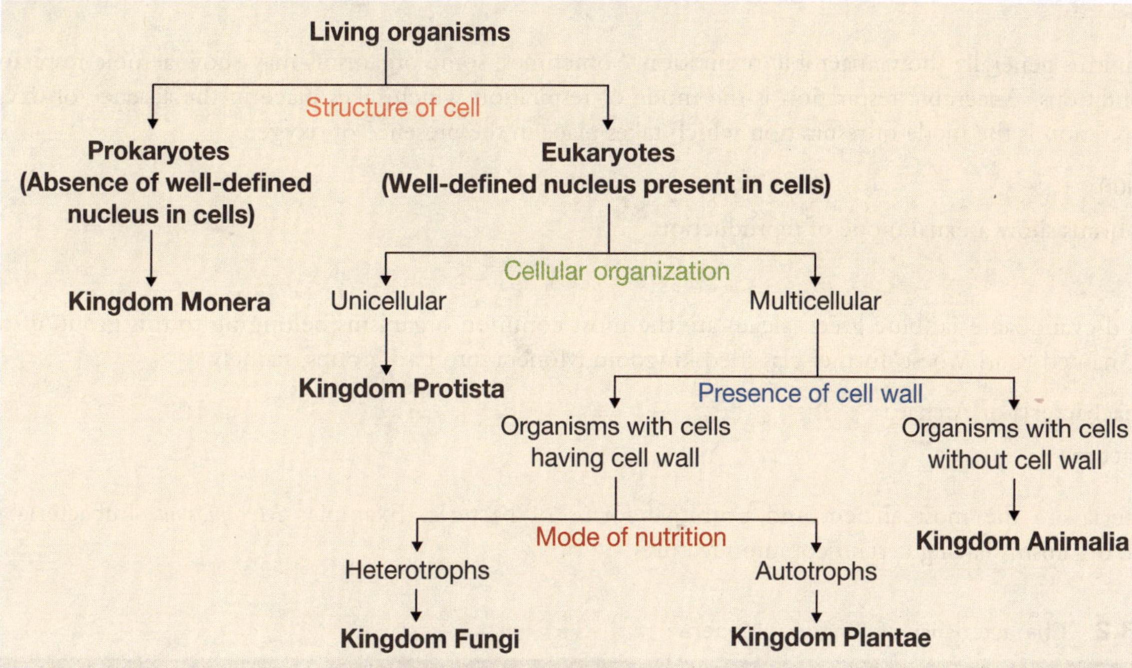

Figure 3.1 Five-kingdom classification

Characteristic Features of Different Kingdoms

Kingdom Monera

Monerans are structurally the simplest of all the living organisms. The word 'monera' is derived from the Greek '*monḗrēs*' meaning 'single'.

Structural Features

All the organisms belonging to kingdom Monera are unicellular organisms with prokaryotic cell organization. They can survive in extreme climatic conditions like hot springs, acidic soils, etc. Some of them may possess cell wall and resemble plants whereas some others do not possess cell wall. Few examples are depicted below:

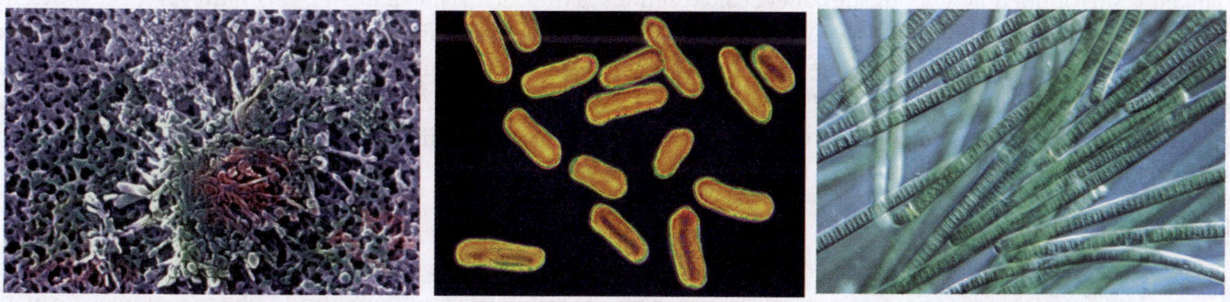

Mycoplasma *Salmonella* *Oscillatoria*

Figure 3.2 Some monerans

Nutrition

Some of them may possess chlorophyll and show autotrophic mode of nutrition. Others show heterotrophic mode of nutrition, predominantly, either symbiotic or parasitic nutrition. Symbiosis is a close association or living together of two living organisms in which both the organisms derive benefit from each other. Parasitism is a relationship in which an organism lives in close association with the other organism and depends on it for food and shelter and in that process, harms the other organism.

Respiration

These organisms generally show anaerobic respiration. Sometimes, some organisms may show aerobic respiration under suitable conditions. Anaerobic respiration is the mode of respiration which takes place in the absence of oxygen while aerobic respiration is the mode of respiration which takes place in the presence of oxygen.

Reproduction

These organisms show asexual mode of reproduction.

Diversity

Bacteria and cyanobacteria (blue green algae) are the most common organisms belonging to this group of organisms. A scientist, named 'Carl Woese' further classified kingdom Monera into two groups, namely

1. Archaebacteria or Archaea
2. Eubacteria

Archaebacteria are the most ancient and primitive forms of bacteria. Example: *Mycoplasma.* Eubacteria comprises prokaryotic organisms having certain common features.

Table 3.2 Characteristics of Kingdom Monera

Kingdom Monera	Organism	Characteristics	
		Cell structure	Mode of nutrition
Archaebacteria	*Mycoplasma*	Absence of cell wall	Heterotrophic
Eubacteria	Bacteria Cyanobacteria	Presence of cell wall	Heterotrophic Autotrophic

Bacteria

Structural Features

Bacteria were first discovered by Antonie van Leeuwenhoek. These are microscopic, unicellular, prokaryotic organisms. Bacterial cell is surrounded by viscous substance, called slime. As the bacterial cell grows, this slimy layer becomes swollen and hard to form capsule which helps in protection. Cell membrane forms invaginations into cytoplasm in the form of vesicles, called mesosomes. They lack a true nucleus, that is, nucleus with a nuclear membrane is absent. Genetic material is present in the region called nucleoid. They lack many cell organelles, such as chloroplasts, mitochondria which are normally present in the cells of eukaryotes. Cytoplasm in the cell contains a single bacterial chromosome in the nucleoid, consisting of single-ring DNA molecule, which is the genetic material.

Life Processes

Cyanobacteria are autotrophs as they carry out photosynthesis. All other bacteria show either symbiotic or parasitic mode of nutrition. Respiration in bacteria can take place either by anaerobic or aerobic method. The mesosomes formed from the cell membrane help in aerobic respiration in bacteria. Reproduction takes place by an asexual mode, called binary fission.

In binary fission, the bacterial cell undergoes mitotic division producing two identical daughter cells which grow in size and cytoplasmic contents being produced in new bacteria. On the basis of the shape of cell, bacteria are further classified into three types:

1. Coccus: The cocci (singular: coccus) are spherical or oval bacteria.
2. Rod or bacillus: Bacilli (singular: bacillus) are rod-shaped bacteria.

3. Spiral: Bacteria in any one of the following spiral shapes,

a. *Vibrio:* Comma-shaped bacteria

b. *Spirillum:* Bacteria with thick and rigid spiral

c. *Spirochete:* Bacteria with thin and flexible spiral

Bacteria

Bacillus	*Coccus*	*Spirillum*
Rod shaped	Spherical shaped	Spiral shaped
Examples: *E.coli*, *Rhizobium*, *Nitrosomonas*	Examples: *Streptomyces*, *Actinomyces*	Examples: *Campylobacter*, *Nitrobacter*

Economic Importance of Bacteria

Bacteria are believed to be the first living organisms originated on earth. They are the most studied primitive organisms because they play an indispensible role in human life, as listed in fig 3.3.

Useful Activities

Medicine
- Production of antibiotics
- Synthesis of vitamins (K, B_2, B_{12})

Food
- Curing of coffee and tea
- Preparation of vinegar
- Conversion of milk into curd

Industry
- Curing of tobacco
- Retting of fibres
- Cleaning of hides of animals
- Conversion of farm refuse to manure and gobar gas

Environment
- Nitrogen fixation
- Decomposition of dead matter
- Sewage disposal

Figure 3.3 Some uses of bacteria

Harmful Activities

While some bacteria are useful for various human activities, there are some which are harmful. Some of the adverse effects of bacteria are:

- Spoilage of food
- Food poisoning
- Deterioration of cotton, leather and wooden articles
- Diseases in humans, animals and plants

Info Bytes!

The study of algae is called phycology.

Kingdom Protista

This kingdom comprises various types of eukaryotic unicellular organisms. The word 'protista' is derived from Greek word 'protos' meaning 'first'.

Structural Features

This kingdom includes all unicellular organisms with eukaryotic cell structure and few multicellular organisms like algae. Algae can be unicellular or multicellular. Diatoms and protozoans are unicellular. Organisms of this kingdom live in aquatic habitat or in moist soil. The cells are advanced with well-defined nucleus and membrane-bound cell organelles.

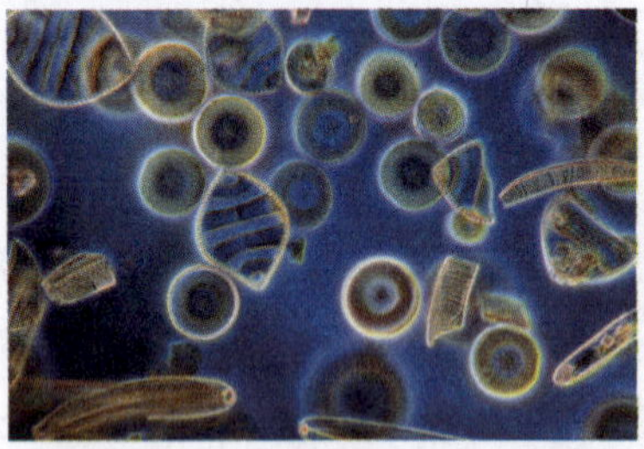

Diatoms

Euglena

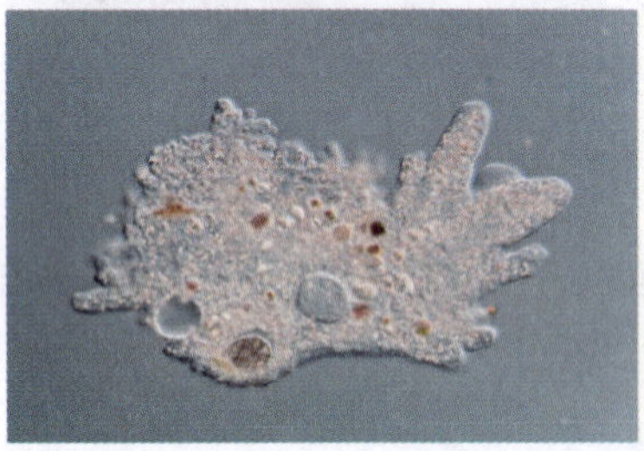

Amoeba

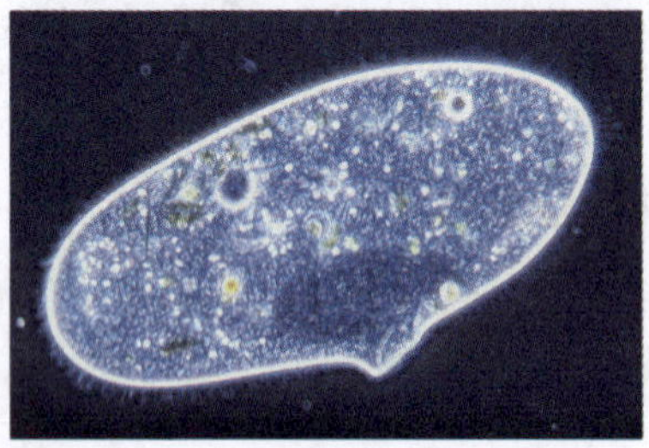

Paramoecium

Figure 3.4 Some protista

Life Processes

Some organisms show both autotrophic and heterotrophic modes of nutrition. For example, *Euglena* (protozoan) contains chloroplasts and can prepare its own food in the presence of sunlight. In the absence of sunlight, it shows heterotrophic mode of nutrition. Most of the protozoans show parasitic nutrition as they live in the systems of animals and feed on their body fluids. Generally, aerobic respiration takes place due to the presence of mitochondria. In parasitic protozoans, anaerobic respiration also takes place. Reproduction takes place by both asexual and sexual modes. Diatoms reproduce by binary fission which is an asexual method. Algae and some protozoans can reproduce by both asexual and sexual modes. The common method of asexual reproduction found in protozoans is binary fission.

Table 3.3 Characteristics of kingdom protista

Characteristics	Protozoans	Diatoms	Algae
Cell structure	Absence of cell wall	Presence of cell wall	Presence of cell wall
Mode of nutrition	Heterotrophic Exception-*Euglena* can be autotrophic also	Autotrophic	Autotrophic
Locomotion	Ability of movement Locomotory organelles *Amoeba*—Pseudopodia *Paramoecium*—Hair-like cilia *Euglena*—Whip-like flagella	Non-motile	Non-motile
Reproduction	Both sexual and asexual	Asexual	Asexual

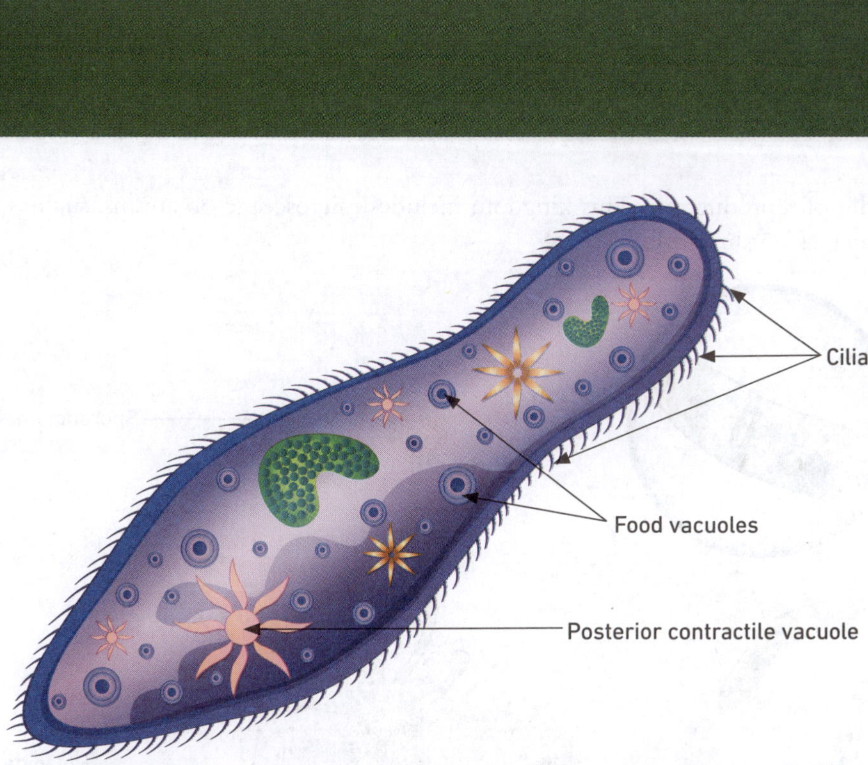

Figure 3.5 Illustration of *Paramoecium* showing cilia

Info Bytes!

Cytoprocts are anal openings in unicellular organisms.

Kingdom Fungi

This kingdom comprises organisms whose body is not differentiated into root, stem and leaves. They are either unicellular or multicellular. They have true nucleus but lack chlorophyll. Examples of some fungi are *Aspergillus*, *Rhizopus*, *Agaricus*, etc.

Structural Features

Kingdom fungi includes multicellular organisms with eukaryotic cells. A single filament of fungus is known as hyphae and the cluster of filaments is called mycelium. The cells are bound by a hard cell wall made up of a complex sugar, known as chitin. This is considered as the characteristic feature of this kingdom.

Info Bytes!

The study of fungi is called mycology.

Figure 3.6 Mycelium of mushroom

Figure 3.7 *Aspergillus*

Life Processes

The cells do not possess chlorophyll at all and hence, these organisms show heterotrophic mode of nutrition. Most of the organisms show saprophytic mode of nutrition. It is a method of heterotrophic nutrition in which the organisms feed on dead organic matter. The food material is reserved in the form of glycogen and oil globules. The respiration is usually aerobic as the cells possess mitochondria where cellular respiration takes place. They do not show movement. The organisms show both asexual and sexual modes of reproduction. This kingdom includes microscopic organisms, such as yeasts and moulds, and also microorganisms such as mushrooms.

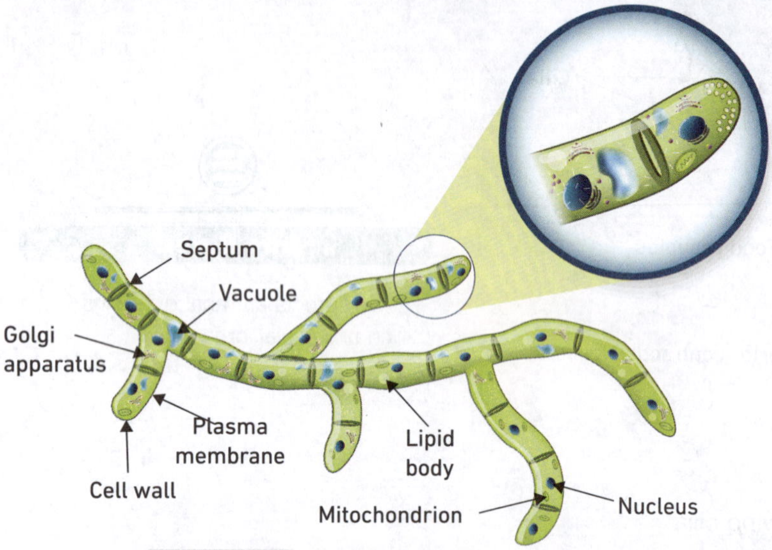

Figure 3.8 Illustration of fungal hyphae

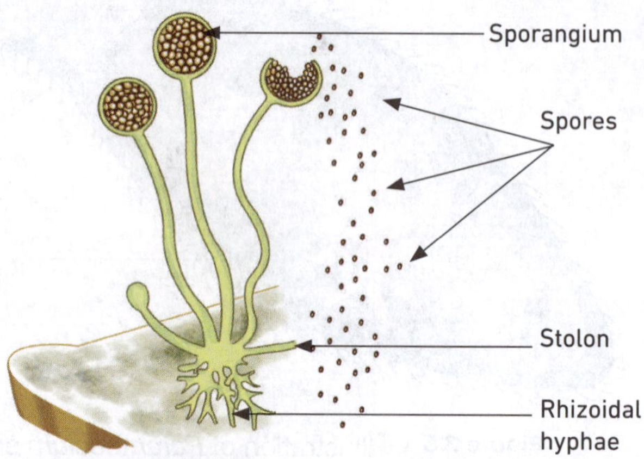

Figure 3.9 Illustration of *Rhizopus*

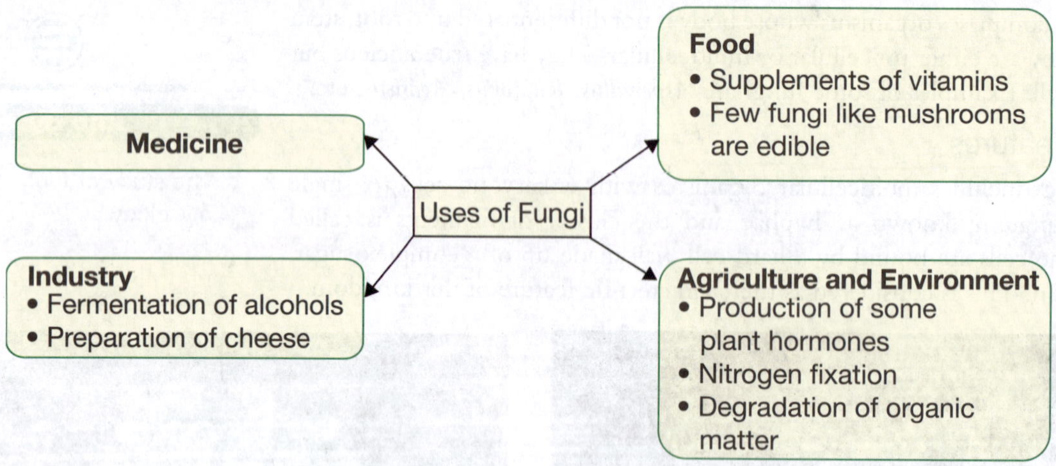

Figure 3.10 Uses of fungi

Kingdom Plantae

This kingdom includes all living organisms which possess the following unique features.

- Multicellular eukaryotes
- Cells bound by cell walls, made up of cellulose
- Cells possess chloroplasts and show autotrophic mode of nutrition

Kingdom Animalia

This kingdom includes all living organisms which possess the following unique features:

- Multicellular eukaryotes
- Cells bound by only cell membrane without any cell wall
- Cells lack chloroplasts and show heterotrophic mode of nutrition

Info Bytes!

The tallest tree ever recorded was a Coast Redwood named 'Hyperion', reaching up to 379.7 feet (115.7 meters).

- Show locomotion
- Sexual mode of reproduction

Modern System of Classification

The five-kingdom classification was widely accepted in the scientific community. However, kingdoms plantae and animalia comprised millions of organisms. So, further classification of plants and animals was needed for a systematic study. Carolus Linnaeus proposed a system of nomenclature and classification of plants and animals into different levels by taking various criteria into consideration. This is known as the modern system of classification. For proposing this, **Linnaeus** is regarded as the '**Father of Taxonomy**'. He introduced a system of nomenclature of plants and animals known as the Binomial System of Nomenclature. This nomenclature helped in the identification of innumerable number of plants and animals and paved the way for devising a system of framework of classification, called taxonomic hierarchy. Therefore, this system of classification by Linnaeus is known as the hierarchical system of classification.

Taxonomic Hierarchy

Taxonomic hierarchy involves the arrangement of organisms into various taxonomic groups in definite order. Each taxonomic group comprises plants or animals having certain similarities. Each category of organisms at a particular level is considered as a unit, called taxon. The different taxonomic units are arranged in the increasing order of specificity of characters of the organisms. The highest level of the hierarchy is kingdom, for both plants and animals. The taxonomic hierarchy of plants starts from the kingdom and ends with the lowest level of taxonomic unit, species. Kingdom is a broad category with least specificity in characters. Species comprises organisms with highly specific features. That means, the organisms belonging to the same species are almost similar in all the characteristics. Between kingdom and species, there are various levels. At each level, plants are grouped based on their similarities. They are further categorized into the lowest level of taxonomic units based on the differences among them. The animal kingdom has also been classified further into various taxonomic units from highest to lowest levels for the same reason.

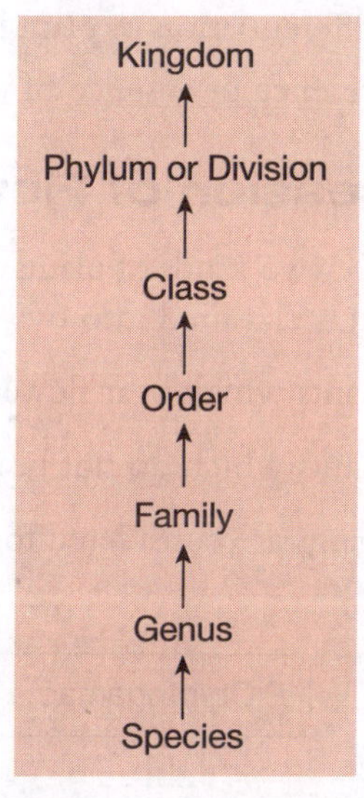

Figure 3.11 Taxonomic hierarchy

Binomial Nomenclature of Plants

The millions of plants in nature are given different names in different parts of the world. But, the scientific study of the plants requires a universal system of nomenclature for all the plants. For this purpose, the system of binomial nomenclature proposed by Carolus Linnaeus is followed all over the world. The names given according to this system are called scientific names. These are derived from Greek or Latin words and are internationally accepted. According to this system, the name of an organism includes two terms. The first term is called genus and the second term is called species. Species includes similar group of organisms which can freely interbreed among themselves and produce fertile offspring. Species forms the basic unit of classification and was proposed by John Ray. Related species are grouped together to form a genus, related genus as family, related family as order, later class and subdivision and so on and so forth. According to the system of binomial nomenclature, certain rules are followed while writing the scientific name of an organism. These rules are as follows:

- The genus name is written with first letter as capital and species name is written with first letter as small.
- The scientific name is printed in italics. In hand written form, the scientific name is underlined.

Table 3.4 Scientific names of some important plants

Common name	Scientific name	Genus	Species
Tulsi	*Ocimum sanctum*	*Ocimum*	*sanctum*
Neem	*Azadirachta indica*	*Azadirachta*	*indica*
Tobacco	*Nicotiana tabacum*	*Nicotiana*	*tabacum*
Potato	*Solanum tuberosum*	*Solanum*	*tuberosum*
Wheat	*Triticum aestivum*	*Triticum*	*aestivum*
Rice	*Oryza sativa*	*Oryza*	*sativa*

Plant Kingdom

The classification of entire plant kingdom into two divisions and then into sub-divisions was done by taking the following features into consideration.

- Possession of flowers
- Formation of seeds and nature of seeds
- Differentiation of plant body into roots, stems and leaves
- Presence or absence of vascular tissue

Info Bytes!

Peaches, pears, apricots are members of the rose family.

Possession of Flowers

Generally, two kinds of plants are seen on the earth. Some bear flowers and some do not bear flowers. On this basis, plant kingdom is classified into two divisions:

1. Plants which bear flowers are grouped as phanerogamae.
2. Plants which do not bear flowers are grouped as cryptogamae.

Cryptogams are considered to be relatively primitive plants and phanerogams are considered to be advanced plants.

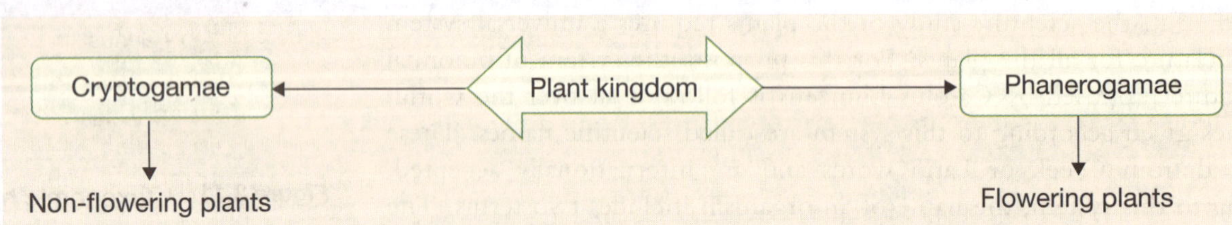

Figure 3.12 Classification of plant kingdom on the basis of flowers

These two subdivisions are discussed in detail in the next section.

Quick Recap

✔ **Identify the 'respective division or kingdom' to which the following descriptions belong and provide a characteristic:**

(a) Organisms that fly, have a three-part body, and possess an exoskeleton.

(b) Stationary marine animals with tentacles that resemble an upside-down jellyfish, often anchored to rocks or other surfaces.

(c) Flowering plants that produce seeds encased within a fruit and possess broad leaves.

(a) Organisms that fly, have a three-part body and possess an exoskeleton are Insects. They belong to the class Insecta in the phylum Arthropoda.

Characteristics:

(i) Have a body divided into head, thorax, and abdomen.

(ii) Typically possess two pairs of wings (though some might be wingless).

(iii) Have a compound eye and paired antennae.

(b) Stationary marine animals with tentacles that resemble an upside-down jellyfish, often anchored to rocks or other surfaces are Sea Anemones and Corals. They belong to the class Anthozoa in the phylum Cnidaria.

Characteristics:

(i) Possess tentacles equipped with cnidocytes (stinging cells).

(ii) Have a simple sac-like gut.

(iii) Can reproduce both sexually and asexually.

(c) Flowering plants that produce seeds encased within a fruit and possess broad leaves are Dicotyledonous plants (Dicots). They belong to the class Dicotyledonae under the phylum Angiosperms in the kingdom Plantae.

Characteristics:

(i) Typically have leaves with net-like veins.

(ii) Seeds have two cotyledons or seed leaves.

(iii) Flower parts usually come in multiples of fours or fives.

✔ **How might the Pomato, as a grafted entity, challenge or change our definitions of individuality in the plant world?**

Traditionally, an individual plant is defined by its unique genetic makeup. But the Pomato, being two distinct genetic entities coexisting as one plant, complicates this definition. It raises philosophical questions about plant identity and what constitutes an 'individual' in the botanical realm.

Cryptogams

The word 'cryptogamae' is derived from Greek words 'cryptos' which means 'hidden' and 'gamae' which means 'to marry'. That means, they have hidden reproductive organs and do not produce flowers, fruits and seeds. They reproduce by means of spores as they do not bear flowers like flowering plants. They are sometimes referred to as plant-like organisms. Cryptogams include non-seed bearing plants. They can further be distinguished on the basis of differentiation of plant body into roots, stems and leaves, and also on the basis of presence of vascular tissue for the conduction of water and nutrients. Cryptogams are classified into three subdivisions based on the above two characteristics. They are listed as follows:

1. Thallophyta
2. Bryophyta
3. Pteridophyta

Cryptogamae

Thallophyta
- No vascular tissue
- No differentiation into roots, stems and leaves
- Aquatic habitat

Bryophyta
- No vascular tissue
- Plant body shows some differentiation into roots, stems and leaves
- Can survive in both aquatic and terrestrial habitats

Pteridophyta
- Presence of vascular tissue
- Plant body shows differentiation into roots, stems and leaves
- Terrestrial habitat

Figure 3.13 Classification of cryptogams

Thallophyta

These are soft thread-like aquatic forms. The plant body is not differentiated into root, stem and leaves. Such plant body is called thallus. Well-organized tissues are absent. These are predominantly multicellular colonial forms. They can be autotrophic or heterotrophic, and have asexual mode of reproduction. In the earlier times, thallophyta was considered to include two classes of organisms namely algae and fungi. But, in recent times, fungi are not considered as the part of plant kingdom because of their heterotrophic mode of nutrition. They are treated as a separate kingdom. Hence, thallophyta is considered to include all multicellular algae. However, the individual members show some variations in features.

Some Important Members of Algae

Spirogyra

- Unicellular, multinucleated, colonial forms
- Presence of ribbon-shaped chloroplast which is turned in spiral manner
- Green in colour and are thus called green algae
- Reserve food material is starch

Figure 3.14 *Spirogyra* species

Gelidium

- Multicellular, filamentous form
- Marine habitat
- Presence of phycoerythrin which imparts red colour and hence, are called red algae
- Reserve food material is glycogen, such as Floridean starch

Figure 3.15 *Sargassum*

Sargassum

- Multicellular, filamentous forms
- Presence of chromatophores with a pigment, called fucoxanthin which is rich in iodine
- Brown in colour and are called brown algae
- Reserve food material is a starch-like substance, called laminarin

Figure 3.16 Orange lichen on bark of a tree

Lichens

- Lichens are composite organisms which arise from algae living in close association with fungi.
- They grow in a wide range of shapes and forms.
- They can live in wide range of habitats.

- The body of lichens is called thallus.
- The thallus is made up of filaments of the fungus, called hyphae.
- The hyphae form a mesh or network which surrounds the algal form. That means, an algal form remains enclosed within complex fungal structure.
- The two organisms live in symbiotic association with each other. This is a mutually beneficial relationship for both the organisms. Algae can prepare carbohydrates by the process of photosynthesis. Fungi depend on the food prepared by algae. In return, Algae get anchorage and protection from fungal filaments. Fungal organism also derives moisture and nutrients from the atmosphere and retains them for algae to grow.
- Green algae are generally found in the form of lichens.
- The lichens generally reproduce by asexual methods.

Info Bytes!

Lichens are very sensitive to sulphur dioxide. If air is badly polluted with sulphur dioxide, lichens will not grow in that environment.

Economic Importance of Algae

Many different kinds of algae in nature are economically important in so many ways. They find various uses in different fields, such as industry, medicine, environment, etc. At the same time, there are many harmful effects of algae.

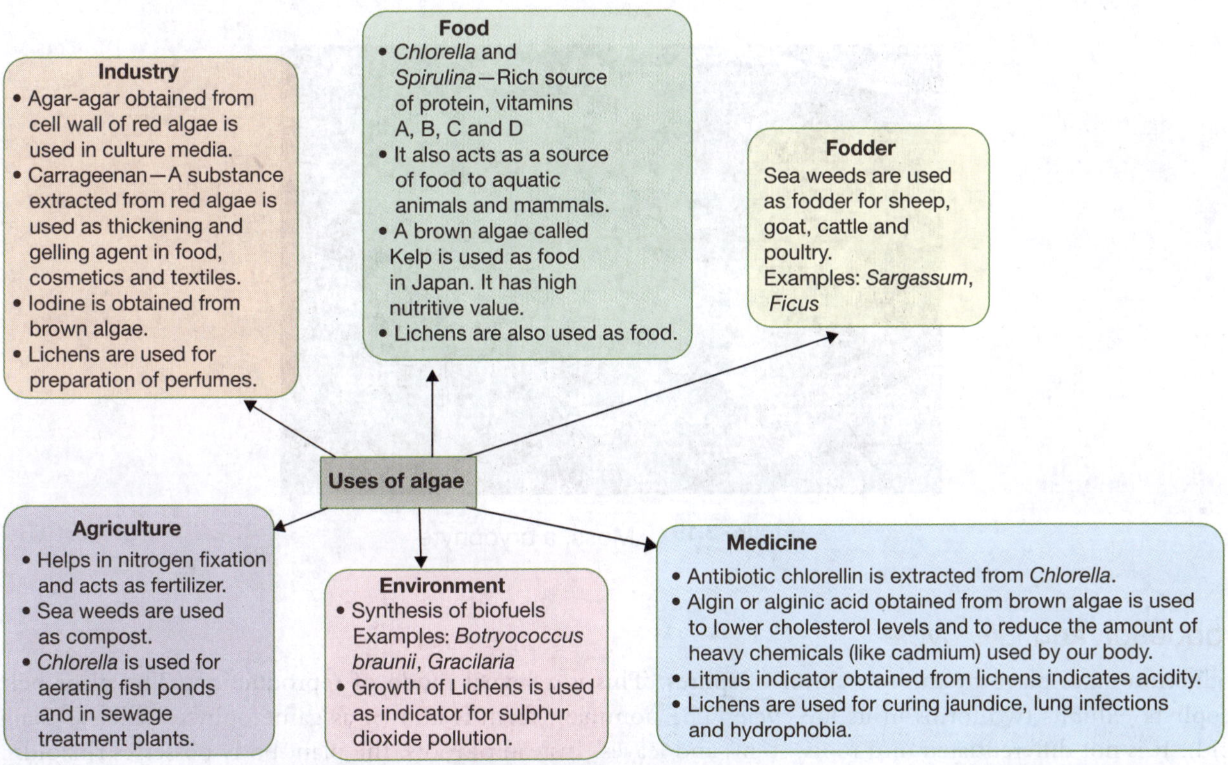

Figure 3.17 Uses of algae

Harmful Effects of Algae

While some algae are useful for various human activities, there are some which are harmful. Some of the adverse effects of algae are mentioned below. These are:

- Algae causes toxicity and death of aquatic organisms by producing toxins.
- Algae when grown on buildings and monuments, damage them and make them slippery.
- Algal bloom grown in lakes and pools changes colour, taste and produces foul smell which decreases the aesthetic value.

Bryophyta

The term 'bryophyta' originated from the Greek words 'bryon' meaning 'moss' and 'phyta' meaning 'plants'. That means, this group comprises moss plants. Bryophyta represents the simplest terrestrial (land) plants. However, they require moist or damp surface particularly during the reproductive stage. These plants can live in both aquatic and terrestrial habitats. Hence, they are called Amphibians of Plant Kingdom. The bryophytes are small plants which generally grow together in dense groups to form green carpets or mats. They are mostly found on damp soils, rocks, walls, tree trunk, etc.

Figure 3.18 Algal bloom in a lake

Structural Features

The plant body is either thallus like or leaf like. Vascular tissues are absent. Hence, the conduction takes place from cell to cell by diffusion. Bryophytes possess enclosed reproductive organs, but they do not produce seeds.

Figure 3.19 Moss, a bryophyte

Reproduction and Life Cycle

Reproduction takes place by the formation of spores. This is a sexual mode of reproduction. The plant belonging to bryophyta exhibits two forms in its life cycle. The dominant form is known as gametophyte which is thallus-like (thalloid). It is not differentiated into roots, stems and leaves. Instead of roots, the plant body possesses rhizoids. These rhizoids fix the plant to the damp soil or rock. They help in the absorption of water and nutrients from the surface or atmosphere. Another form is usually short-lived form which is called sporophyte. It is seen only during reproductive phase. It is more or less leaf-like and can be differentiated into roots, stems and leaves. The sporophyte does not lead an independent life. It is a parasitic form depending on the gametophyte form which is independent. Germination of spores results in the production of a daughter plant in filamentous form which is known as protonema. It later develops into gametophyte. During the life cycle of the plant, gametophyte and sporophyte forms exist alternatively. This phenomenon is called alternation of generations. In addition to the sexual reproduction by means of spores, bryophytes also show vegetative reproduction. Vegetative reproduction is a method of production of new plants from non-reproductive (vegetative) parts of the plant.

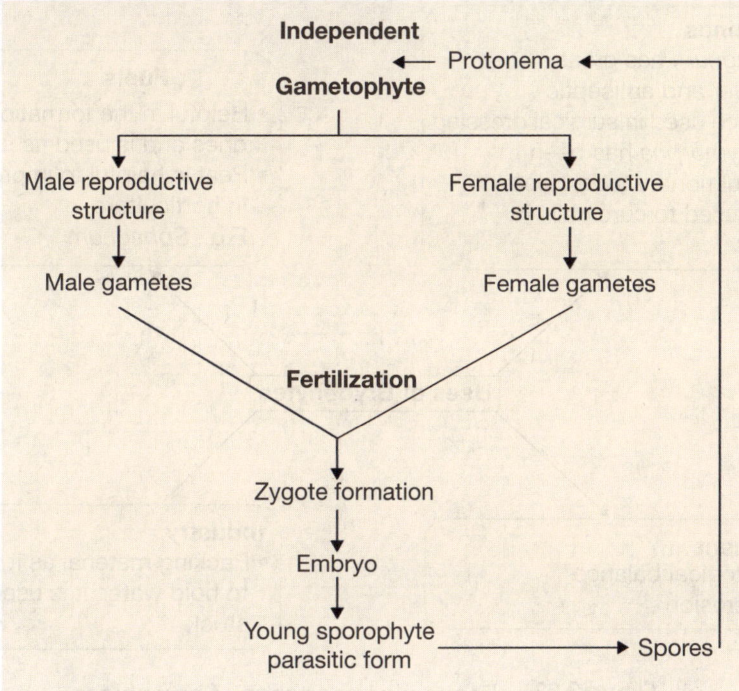

Figure 3.20 Alternation of generation in bryophytes

Diversity

Though there are wide variety of plants under bryophyta, the important classes of bryophytes include liverworts, hornworts and mosses.

1. Liverworts—For example, *Riccia and Marchantia*
2. Hornworts—For example, *Anthoceros*
3. Mosses—For example, *Funaria*

Figure 3.21 Bryophyte plants

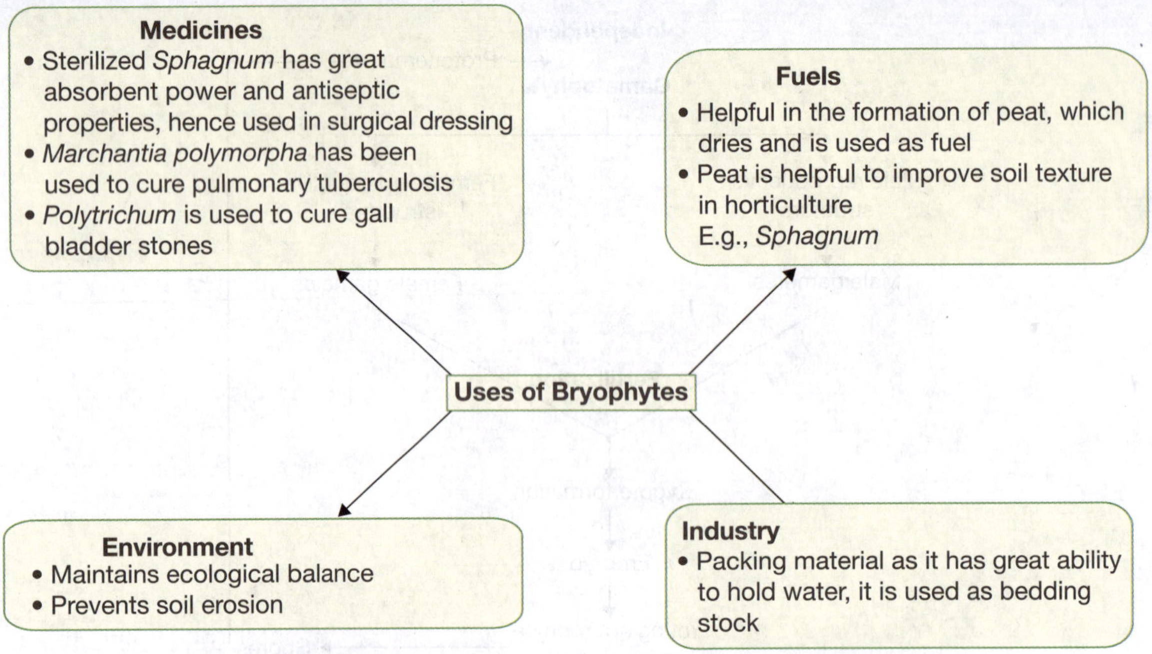

Figure 3.22 Economic importance of bryophytes

Pteridophyta

The term 'pteridophyta' originated from two Greek words, 'pteron' meaning 'feather' and 'phyta' meaning plant. That means, this group comprises feather-like plants, i.e., predominantly ferns. Pteridophyta represents the first totally terrestrial plants.

> **Info Bytes!**
>
> Study of pteridophytes is known as pteridology.

Morphological Features

The plant body is differentiated into true roots, stems and leaves. The plant belonging to pteredophyta exhibits two forms in its life cycle, namely gametophyte and sporophyte forms. The dominant form has plant-like appearance with clear differentiation into roots, stems and leaves. This form is called sporophyte. Another form is called gametophyte. In pteridophytes, the two forms in the life cycle are independent of each other.

Anatomical Features

Presence of vascular tissue for conduction is the main characteristic feature of pteridophyta. In fact, pteridophytes are considered to be the first vascular plants originated on the earth. The vascular tissue includes xylem and phloem. But, these plants possess only primitive forms of xylem and phloem. Xylem tissue has all the elements except vessels. Tracheids carry out the function of vessels. Phloem tissue has all the elements except companion cells. Sieve cells carry out the function of companion cells.

Reproduction and Life Cycle

Pteridophytes reproduce by both asexual and sexual modes. Asexual mode of reproduction can take place either from sporophyte form or gametophyte form. The haploid cells of gametophyte directly develop into haploid sporophyte. This method of reproduction is called apogamy. The diploid cells of the sporophytes can directly give rise to diploid gametophyte. This method of reproduction is called apospory. These two methods do not involve any spore formation or gametic fusion. These are vegetative methods of reproduction. Sexual mode of reproduction in pteredophytes takes place by means of spore formation. Leaves bear the reproductive structures called sporangia. Each sporangium bears spore mother cells which undergo meiotic cell division to form spores. Each spore on germination forms a prothallus. This prothallus develops into a new plant (gametophyte) which possesses male and female reproductive structures. The male and female gametes are produced in these structures. These gametes undergo fertilization (fusion of gametes) resulting in the formation of zygote. The zygote so formed develops into an embryo which develops into young sporophyte. Therefore, life cycle of a pteridophyte shows the phenomenon of alternation of generations as sporophytic generation and gametophytic generation exist alternatively.

Close up of leaf of *Polypodium vulgare* (a pteridophyte)

Athyrium filix plant (a pteridophyte)

Figure 3.23 Pteridophyte plants

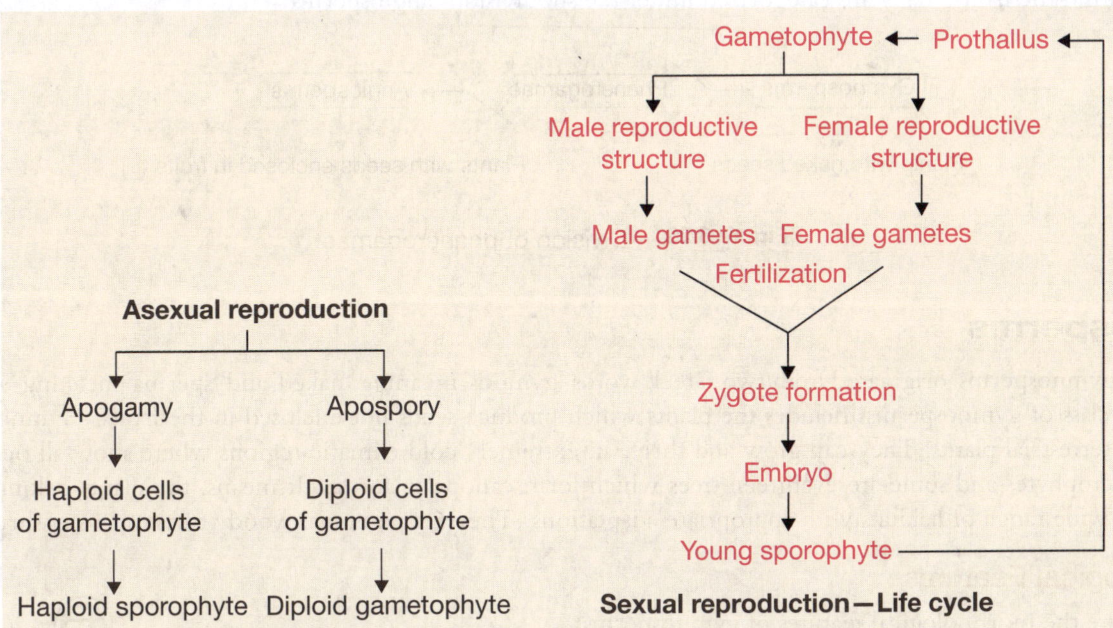

Figure 3.24 Reproduction in pteridophyta

Diversity

There are wide varieties of plants under pteridophyta. Being the oldest and the most primitive vascular plants, some plants have become extinct and they are available as fossils. Pines and ferns are the most widely spread plants of this group.

For example, *Selaginella, Lycopodium, Dryopteris and Salvinia.*

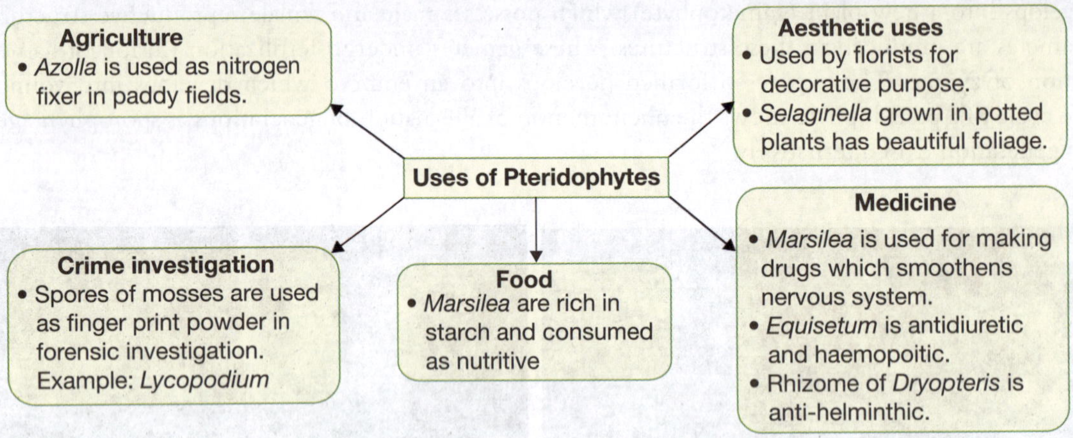

Figure 3.25 Uses of pteridophytes

Phanerogams

The word 'phanerogamae' originated from two Greek words 'phaneros' meaning 'visible' and 'gamae' meaning 'marriage'. That means, phanerogams have visible reproductive organs in contrast to cryptogams which have hidden reproductive organs. Flower is the reproductive organ of these plants and produces seeds by means of sexual reproduction. The division of phanerogams includes all the flower-bearing and seed-producing plants. However, the division phanerogamae is further classified into two subdivisions based on the nature of the seeds they produce. Some plants produce seeds which are not enclosed in the fruits. They are categorized under the subdivision 'gymnosperms'. Some plants produce seeds which are enclosed within the fruits. They are categorized under the subdivision 'angiosperms'.

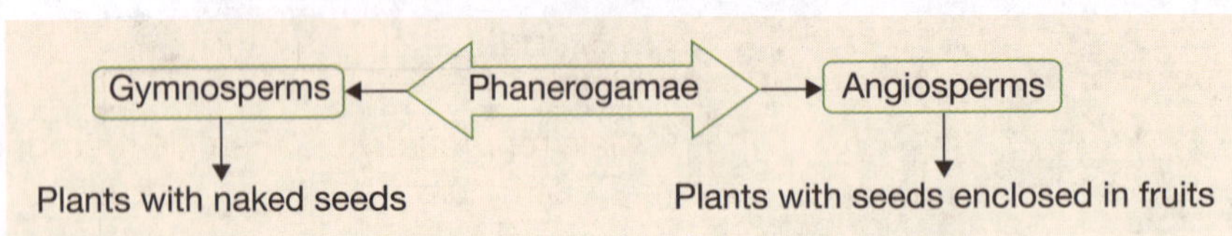

Figure 3.26 Division of phanerogamae

Gymnosperms

The word 'gymnosperms' originated from two Greek words 'gymnos' meaning 'naked' and 'sperma' meaning 'seeds'. That means, the class of gymnosperms includes the plants which produce seeds not enclosed in the fruits. Gymnosperms are exclusively terrestrial plants. They can grow and thrive in extremely cold climatic regions where snowfall occurs. Some plants are xerophytes and some are evergreen trees which form canopy in forests. It means, the plants belonging to this group have wide range of habitats with appropriate adaptations. They are perennial woody trees or bushy shrubs.

Morphological Features

Following are the morphological features of gymnosperms:

- Body of the plant is well-differentiated into root, stem and leaves
- Presence of extensive and well-developed root system
- Erect aerial and branched or unbranched stems
- Presence of leaves bearing resin ducts or latex tubes
- Presence of visible reproductive organs, called cones instead of flowers
- Plants are generally unisexual with separate male and female cones

Info Bytes!

The average tree is made up of 99% dead cells.

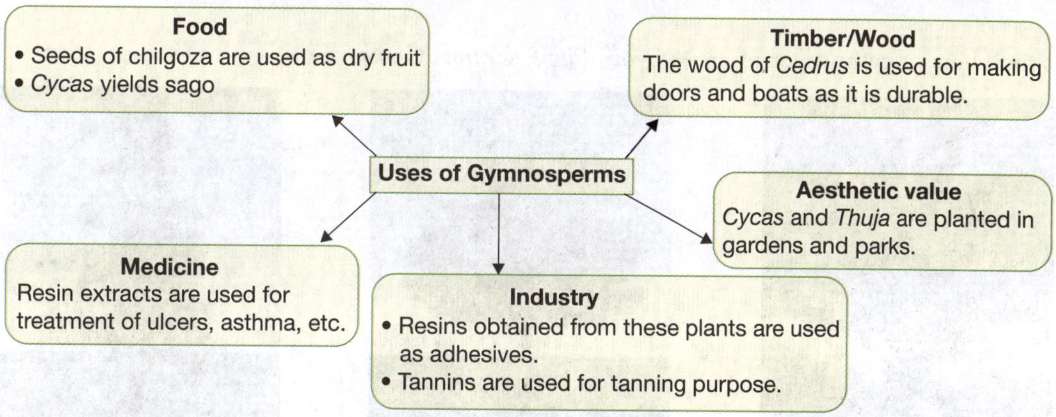

Figure 3.27 Uses of gymnosperms

Anatomical Features

Following are the anatomical features of gymnosperms:

- Formation of well-organized tissue systems with division of labour.
- Presence of well-developed vascular tissues, such as xylem and phloem.
- Gymnosperms show secondary growth and are usually wood-forming trees.

Reproduction and Life Cycle

- Some plants of this group reproduce both by vegetative propagation and sexual reproduction.
- Most of the plants reproduce by means of sexual reproduction, the usual processes as follows.
  - Formation of gametes in the male and female cones by meiotic cell division
  - Transfer of pollen grains to the female cone by pollination
  - Fusion of male and female cones by fertilization
- The male and female cones produce microspores and megaspores, respectively.
- The formation of fruit does not take place as ovary is absent in the female cone.
- Ovules are naked or not enclosed in the ovary and hence, these plants produce naked seeds.

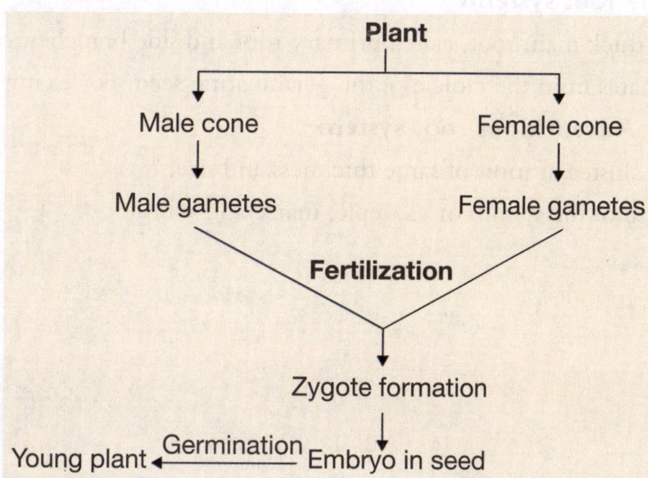

Figure 3.28 Reproduction and life cycle of gymnosperms

Diversity

The important members of gymnosperms are—*Cycas, Pinus, Cedrus, Ginkgo*

Figure 3.29 Cycas plant

Figure 3.30 Pinus

Figure 3.31 Cedrus

Angiosperms

The word 'angiosperms' is derived from two Greek words 'angion' meaning 'vessel' and 'sperma' meaning 'seed'. That means, this group of plants bear flowers and produce seeds enclosed inside fruits. Angiosperms constitute the most important and dominant group of plants in the entire plant kingdom. These plants can survive in almost all kinds of habitats. Angiosperms grow predominantly in terrestrial habitats. These plants are called mesophytes. Among the terrestrial plants, some plants can survive and thrive in desert habitats. Such plants are called xerophytes. Few kinds of vegetation are found in aquatic habitat also. Those plants are called hydrophytes. The plants living in these varied habitats show some distinctive structural features.

The basic morphology of a typical angiospermic plant has a distinct root system and a well-developed shoot system.

Root System

Structure of Root System

Based on the structure and origin, the root system is of two types, namely

1. **Tap root system or True root system**
   - It is characterized by a thick main root, called primary root and side branches, called secondary roots.
   - This root system originates from the radicle of the germinating seed. For example, pea and grams.
2. **Fibrous root system or Adventitious root system**
   - It is characterized by a cluster of roots of same thickness and size.
   - They arise from the base of the stem. For example, maize and wheat.

Figure 3.32 Different types of root system (tap root and fibrous root)

Xerophytic plants possess long and deeply seated root system when compared to a typical mesophytic plant. Hydrophytes possess thin and small roots as they remain in continuous contact with water.

Functions of Root System

The root system carries out two important functions:

1. Anchorage (fixation) of the plant in the soil
2. Absorption of water and minerals from the soil

Root Modifications

In addition to the above mentioned main functions, the root systems in certain plants undergo changes in the structure to perform different kinds of functions. These are known as root modifications. The different kinds of functions supported by the modified roots are as follows:

- Storage of food
- Giving additional support to the plants
- Performing some special functions

Storage of Food

Roots in certain plants become fleshy due to accumulation of stored food. During the process of storage of food, they attain the different shapes in different plants. Both primary roots in tap root system and adventitious roots in fibrous root system can undergo this modification to perform the function of storage of food. On the basis of the shape attained by the respective roots, these can be categorized into various types, as listed below:

Table 3.5 Categories of different types of modified roots

Primary roots		
Spindle like Example: Radish	Conical Example: Carrot	Roundish Example: Turnip

Adventitious roots		
Tuberous Example: Sweet potato	Nodulose Example: Turmeric	Fasciculated Example: *Dahlia*
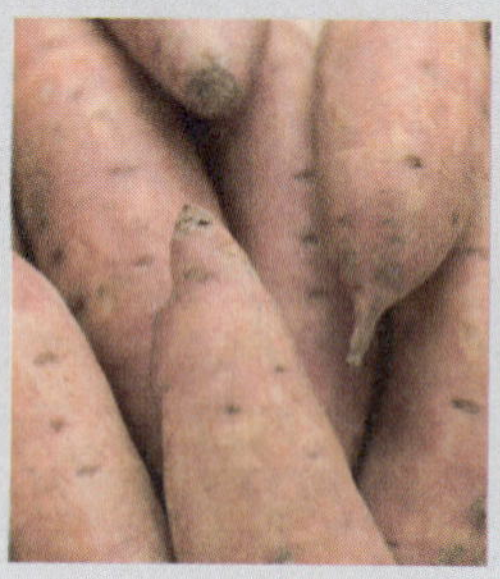		

Additional Support

Generally, roots provide support to the plants. But in case of certain plants, this support is not sufficient. In such cases, some roots get modified into various forms and provide additional support to the plant. There are three different forms of roots which provide additional support,

1. Prop roots
2. Stilt roots
3. Climbing roots

Info Bytes!

Strawberry is the only fruit that bears its seeds on the outside.

Table 3.6 Different forms of roots for additional support

Prop roots	Stilt roots	Climbing roots
Aerial roots growing vertically downward from the horizontal branches. They penetrate into the soil and give support. For example, banyan.	They grow from lower nodes. They grow obliquely downwards into the soil. These roots develop in plants with weak stems. For example, sugarcane.	Cluster of aerial roots develop from nodes or internodes. Cling or twine around the support and help plant climb upwards. For example, money plant.

Special Functions

Roots in some plants are modified to perform some special functions. The type of modification depends on the habitat in which the plants live or the mode of absorption of nutrients from soil or from the atmosphere. The following are four different root modifications which perform special functions:

1. Nodular roots
2. Parasitic roots
3. Epiphytic roots
4. Breathing roots

Info Bytes!

A cluster of bananas is called a hand.

Table 3.7 Different types of root modifications for special functions

Nodular roots	Parasitic roots	Epiphytic roots	Breathing roots
Roots bear small swellings, called **nodules**. Bacteria present in these nodules convert the atmospheric nitrogen into nitrates which help to increase the fertility of the soil. Hence, these roots are also called **nitrogen-fixing roots.** For example, gram, peas, etc.	Adventitious roots are called **haustoria**. They protrude into the host plant for absorption of nutrients. Found in parasitic plants. For example, *Cuscuta*.	They are hanging aerial roots, Growing aerially on the host plant. For example, orchids.	Roots come above the soil like cones Minute pores called **pneumatophores** are present on the roots. Roots absorb atmospheric air for respiration Found in plants which grow in marshy places. For example, white mangrove, *Avicennia*, etc.

Shoot System

The part of the plant which grows above the soil is called shoot system. It bears stem, branches, leaves, flowers and fruits.

Stem

Structure of Stem

The stem is the strongest part of the shoot system. The structure of the stem is such that it supports the entire shoot system. The small and non-woody plants are short and have few branches. These are called herbs. They possess green and tender stems and epidermis as the outer covering. A wax-coated layer called cuticle is present on the epidermis. The slightly taller plants with branching starting from the base of the stem possess thick but not hard stems. These are called shrubs. The younger plants may possess slightly green stems. But the mature plants possess brown stems due to the formation of bark. The big woody trees are very tall with stems having many branches. In these trees, the stems are brown in colour and possess many-layered thick bark. The stem bears nodes, internodes and vegetative buds. The nodes are the regions on the stem where the leaves and branches originate. The part of the stem in between the nodes is called internode. The underdeveloped shoot present at the tip of the stem is called apical bud. The bud present at the axil of the leaf is called axillary bud.

Functions of Stem

Functions of stem are as follows:

- Transport of water and minerals from roots to the aerial parts
- Transport of food from leaves to other parts of the plant
- Acts as support to the plant
- Provides exposure of leaves to sunlight
- Manufacture of food in young plants
- In case of some plants, the stems undergo some structural modifications to perform some other specific functions in addition to the normal functions

Info Bytes!

Onions contain an antibiotic that helps reduce infection and the itch of athlete's foot.

Modifications of Stem for Various Functions

In addition to the main functions, the stems in certain plants undergo changes in the structure to perform different kinds of functions. These are known as stem modifications. The different kinds of functions supported by the modified stems are

- Storage of food
- Giving additional support to the plants
- Performing some special functions

Storage of Food

In certain plants, stems grow under the soil like the roots. These are useful for the storage of food and are called underground stem modifications.

Table 3.8 Different types of underground stem modifications

Tuber	Rhizome	Bulb	Corm
Lower branches of stem grow underground and swell at the tips forming **tubers**. Numerous buds are present which are called **eyes** Eye can produce a new shoot. For example, potato	These are irregular in shape Creep horizontally below the soil Scaly leaves, buds, nodes, internodes. For example, ginger, banana and fern	Condensed disc-shaped stem with a terminal bud Overlapped by scaly leaves Thick and fleshy inner leaves store food. For example, onion, garlic.	Round condensed stem flattened from top to bottom Covered with thin scaly leaves. For example, *Gladiolus*, *Amorphophallus* (zaminkand).

Table 3.8 *(Continued)*

Tuber	Rhizome	Bulb	Corm

Tuber	Rhizome	Bulb	Corm

Sub-aerial Stem Modification

The stems present partly above the ground and partly underground are called sub-aerial stems. These are generally found in weak-stemmed plants and give additional support to the plants. The different types of sub-aerial modification are:

1. Runner
2. Stolon
3. Offset

Table 3.9 Different types of sub-aerial stem modifications

Runner	Stolon	Offset
Stem is soft, thin with slender branch. Creeps on the ground For example, doob grass and wood-sorrel	Stem grows upwards above the ground upto some extent and then bends towards the ground. For example, mint and wild strawberry.	Stem arises from the axil of leaf. Bears thick internodes, These are also called **runners**. For example, water lettuce and water hyacinth.
 runner	 stolon	 offset

Aerial Stem Modifications

The stems which remain above the ground to perform different functions are called aerial stems and such modifications are called aerial stem modifications. The modifications take place to such an extent that these are difficult to be recognized as stems. The four different kinds of aerial stem modifications are:

1. **Thorns:** Axillary buds are modified into thorns. They protect the plants from grazing animals.
2. **Tendrils:** The stem is modified into thin thread-like leafless branches, called tendrils. They coil around a hard object and help the plant in climbing up.
3. **Twiners:** The aerial stems are thin thread-like structures which twine around their own stems. They help the plant to climb up easily.
4. **Phylloclades:** The aerial stems are modified into thick, flat and green leaf-like structure, called phylloclade. They perform the function of photosynthesis.

Table 3.10 Different types of aerial stem modifications

Thorns (Protection)	Tendrils (Support)	Twiners (Climbing)	Phylloclades (Photosynthesis)
Buds modified into hard, pointed small structures, called **thorns.** Help to protect plant from grazing animals. For example, rose, lemon and *Duranta*.	Thin thread-like leafless branches are called **tendrils.** Coil around a hard object. Help the plant in climbing up. For example, grapevine.	Thin thread-like structures Stems twine around their own stems Help the plant to climb up easily. For example, morning glory.	Thick, flat and green stem with nodes and internodes. Help in preparation and storage of food. Xerophytic plants For example, cactus and *Ruscus*
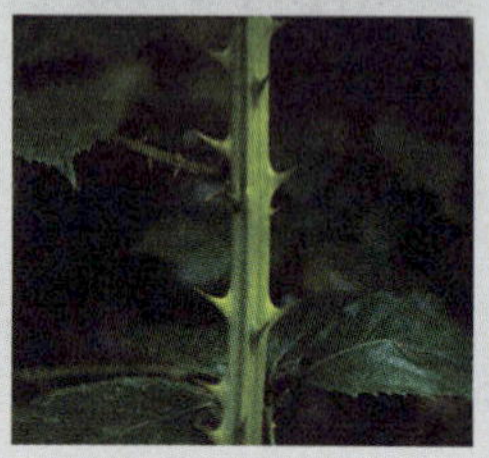			

Leaves

Structure of Leaves

Leaves are the most important parts of the plant as they prepare food by the process of photosynthesis. A leaf has a flat, green, broad part which is attached to the stem at the node of the stem. It is called leaf blade or lamina. The leaf is generally attached to the stem by means of a stalk and the leaf base, called petiole. In some plants, leaves may be directly attached to the stem without a stalk and petiole. Such leaves are called sessile leaves. The petiole extends into the leaf blade as a midrib from where veins and veinlets arise. The small outgrowths born on either side of the petiole are called stipules. Based on the structure of the leaf, leaves are categorized into two types. They are simple leaves and compound leaves.

Functions of Leaves

The most important function of the leaves is preparation of food by the process of photosynthesis. The tissues in the leaf are generally parenchymatous and the cells contain chloroplasts. The grana present in the chloroplasts contain chlorophyll pigment which traps the solar energy. The entire process of photosynthesis takes place in the chloroplasts which results in the formation of glucose. The glucose is converted into starch and is stored in leaves or transported to other parts of the plant. The stomata are generally concentrated on the lower epidermal layer on the leaf. These stomata help the plant for exchange of gases during photosynthesis and transpiration. The cuticle which is present as a waxy layer on the epidermis reduces the rate of transpiration and prevents excess loss of water. In xerophytic plants, a thick waxy coating is present on the aerial parts of the plant which minimizes the transpiration. In hydrophytic plants, cuticle is absent.

Figure 3.33 Parts of a typical leaf

Leaf Modifications

Like in the case of roots and stems, leaves in certain plants undergo changes in the structure to perform additional functions. These are known as leaf modifications. The different kinds of functions supported by leaf modifications are:

- Storage of food
- Giving additional support to the plants
- Defence
- Protection
- Reproduction
- Performing some special functions

Table 3.11 Different kinds of functions by modified leaves

Defence	Support	Reproduction	Protection	Storage of food
Entire leaf or part of the leaf modified into spines.	In weak-stemmed plants, leaves or leaflets get modified into tendrils.	Buds developed on the leaves grow into new plants.	Thin and dry scaly leaves.	Fleshy and thick leaves.
Protection from grazing animals Reduction of loss of water. For example, prickly poppy.	Makes the plant stand erect around support Exposes leaves to sunlight. For example, sweet pea, masur, glory lily.	Example, *Bryophyllum*, *Begonia*.	Protection to buds For example, ginger, onion.	For example, onion, garlic.

Special Functions

Most of the plants are autotrophs and do not depend on other organisms for nutrition. However, there are plants which grow in soils where nitrogen is not sufficient for the plants to prepare their food. Plants which grow in nitrogen-deficient soils, derive their nutrition either partially or totally from the insects which approach them by trapping them. These plants are called insectivorous plants or carnivorous plants. For example, pitcher plant, bladder wort, venus fly trap, etc. In insectivorous plants, the leaf gets modified into a structure which helps the plant in trapping the insects that come in contact with the leaf. In pitcher plant, leaf lamina gets converted into pitcher and apex of leaf is modified into lid. Petiole becomes leaflike.

Figure. 3.34(a) Pitcher plant

Figure. 3.34(b) Venus fly trap

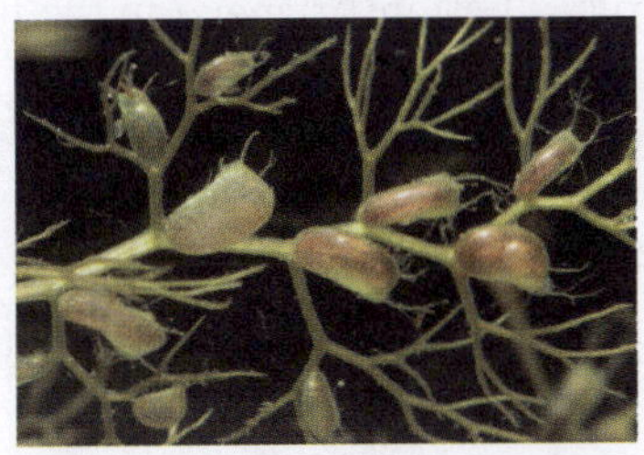

Figure. 3.34(c) Bladderwort

Flower

The most important characteristic organ of the angiosperms is flower which is the reproductive organ. The flower is usually attached to the shoot by means of a stalk called pedicel. Sometimes a flower may be directly attached to the shoot. The flowers with pedicel are called pedicilate flowers while the flowers without pedicel are called sessile flowers. The flattened portion above the pedicel is called thalamus.

Parts of Flower

Parts of the flower are arranged on the thalamus as rings and are known as whorls. The parts of a flower are classified into two types on the basis of their respective roles in the process of reproduction

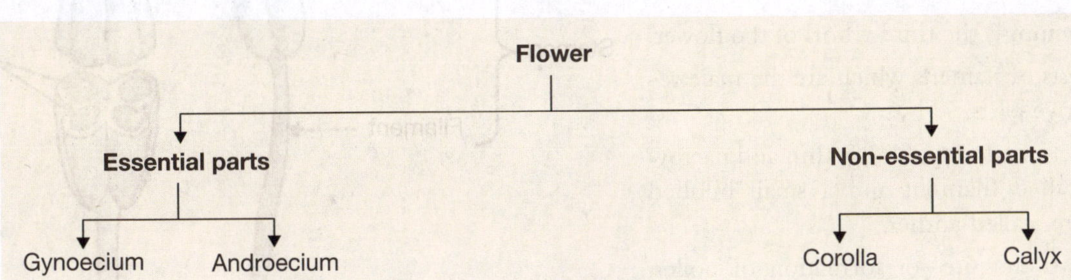

Figure 3.35 Classification of parts of flower

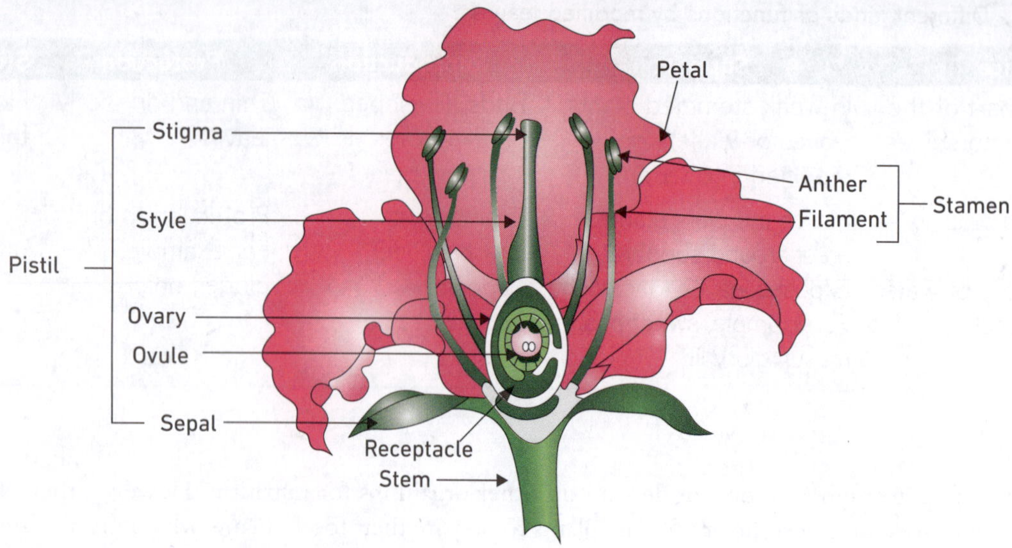

Figure 3.36 Parts of a flower

Non-essential Parts

The non-essential parts of a plant are those which are not directly involved in the process of reproduction. They play only supportive role. They are arranged in the first two whorls. The two non-essential parts of a flower are:

Calyx

- Calyx is the outermost whorl of the flower.
- It consists of green leaf-like structures called sepals.
- The calyx encloses and protects the inner whorls of a flower in bud stage.

Corolla

- Corolla is the second whorl of the flower.
- It consists of brightly coloured and scented structures called petals.
- The corolla serves the function of attracting the insects for pollination.

Essential Parts

The essential parts of a flower are those which are directly involved in the process of reproduction. They are arranged in the inner two whorls of the flower. The two essential parts of a flower are:

1. Androecium
2. Gynoecium

Androecium

- Androecium is the third whorl of the flower.
- It consists of stamens which are the male reproductive parts.
- Stamen is made up of long, thin and narrow stalk, called filament and a small bilobed structure, called anther.
- Anther is the site for formation of pollen grains which possess male gametes and participate in the process of sexual reproduction.

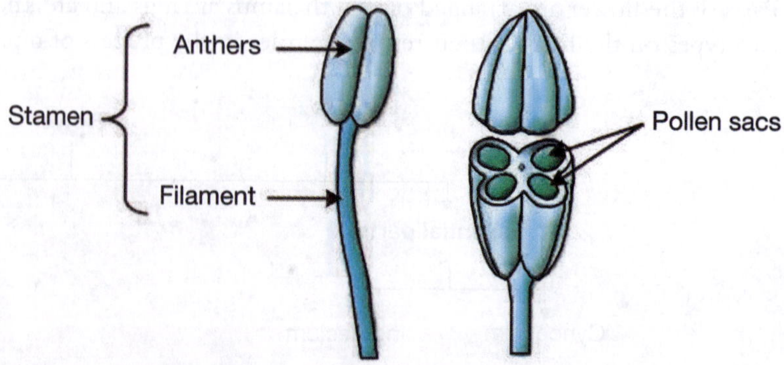

Figure 3.37 Stamen: Male reproductive part

Gynoecium

- Gynoecium is the innermost whorl of the flower.
- It is the female reproductive part.
- Gynoecium is also known as pistil which consists of carpel.
- The carpel bears ovary, style and stigma.
- Ovary is the swollen part at the base of the carpel. Ovary bears ovules which consist of female gamete. They take part in sexual reproduction.
- Style is a long, narrow tabular structure which acts as a passage for entry of male gamete into the ovary.
- Stigma is the disc-like part present at the top of style which helps in pollination.

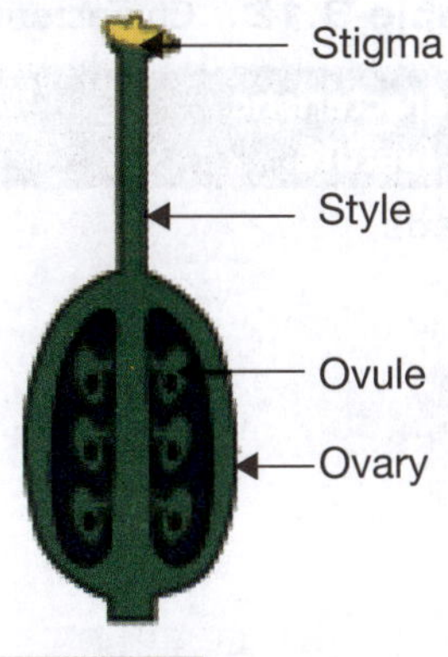

Figure 3.38 Pistil: Female reproductive part

Reproduction, Classification and Importance of Angiosperms

Reproduction and Life Cycle of Angiosperms

The pollen grains produced in the anther contain male gametes. The ovary contains the ovules which are female gametes. The transfer of pollen grains from the anther to the stigma is known as pollination. The fusion of male and the female gametes to give rise to zygote is called fertilization. After fertilization, the petals and sepals of the flower fall off. The ovary increases in size and becomes a fruit. The ovules are converted to seeds. The seed contains embryo (developed from zygote) which develops into a baby plant in future. The food required for the growing embryo is stored in the structures called cotyledons in the seeds.

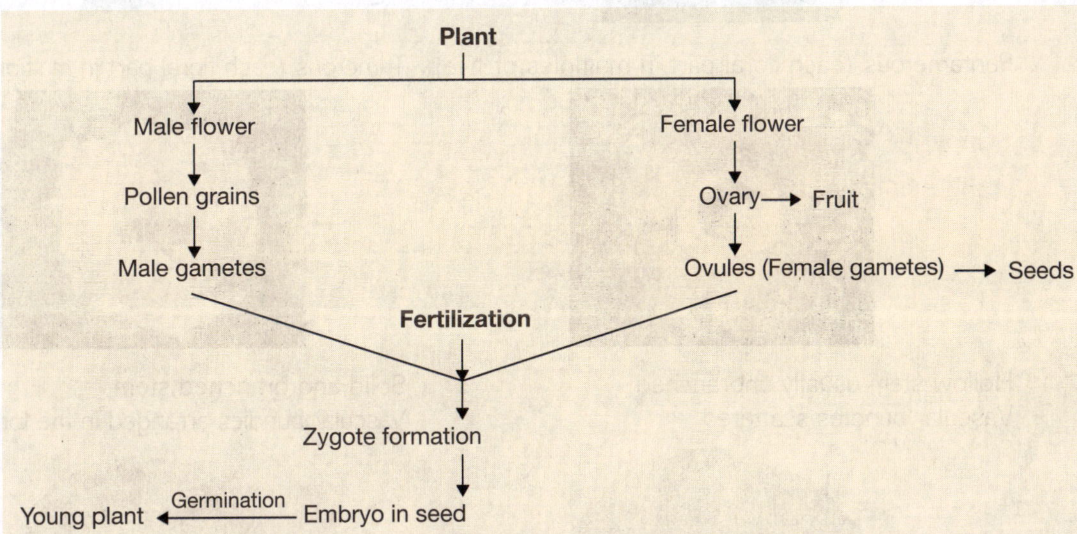

Figure 3.39 Reproduction and life cycle of an angiosperm

Classification of Angiosperms

Depending on the number of cotyledons in the seeds, the seeds of angiosperms are classified into two types. The seeds with one cotyledon are called monocotyledonous seeds. The plants which produce such seeds are called monocotyledons or monocots. The seeds with two cotyledons are called dicotyledonous seeds. The plants which produce such seeds are called dicotyledons or dicot plants. In addition to the difference in the number of cotyledons in the seeds, the monocot plants and dicot plants show large number of variations in the structural features as well as metabolism.

Table 3.12 Characteristics of two important classes angiosperms

Characteristic feature	Monocots	Dicots
Seeds	Single cotyledon 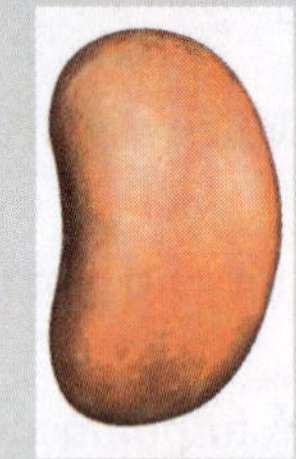	Two cotyledons 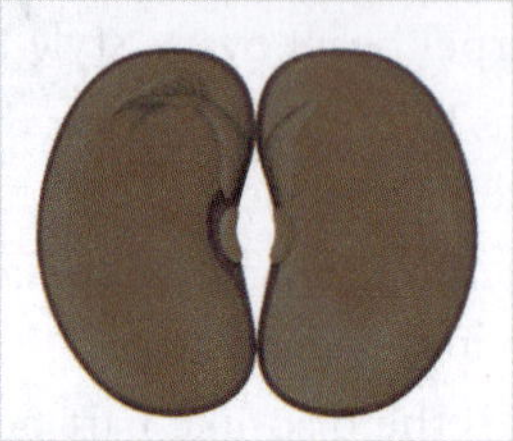
Leaves	Parallel venation Leaves without any distinction between upper and lower surfaces (isobilateral leaves) 	Reticulate venation Leaves show distinction between upper and lower surface (dorsiventral leaves) 
Flower	Pentamerous (each floral part in multiples of five) 	Trimerous (each floral part in multiples of three) 
Stems	Hollow stem usually unbranched Vascular bundles scattered 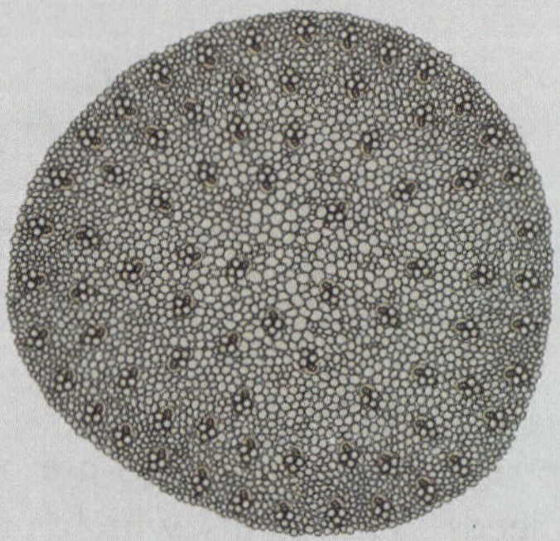	Solid and branched stem Vascular bundles arranged in the form of a ring 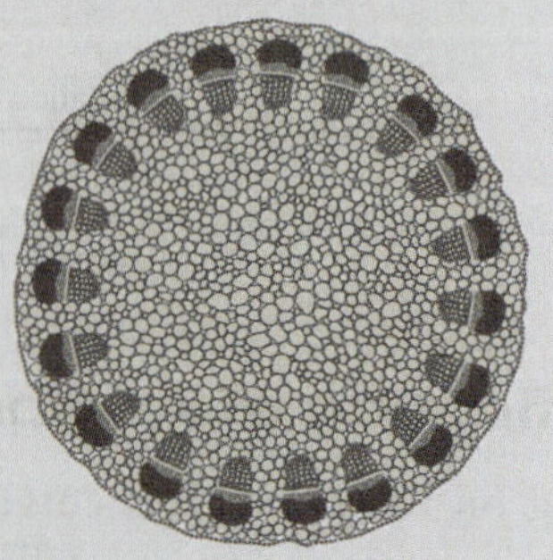
Roots	Adventitious root system	Tap root system
Germination	Hypogeal	Generally epigeal
Examples	Rice, maize and all cereals	Peas, sunflower, beans and all pulses

Table 3.13 Some commercially important angiosperms

Kinds	Common name	Scientific name
Spices	Saffron	*Crocus sativus*
	Turmeric	*Curcuma longa*
	Cloves	*Syzygium aromaticum*
	Sesame	*Sesamum indicum*
	Cardamom	*Elettaria cardamomum*
	Ginger	*Zingiber officinale*
Woods	Teak wood	*Tectona grandis*
	Rose wood	*Dalbergia sissoo*
	Mahogany wood	*Swietenia macrophylla*
	Sandalwood	*Santalum album*
Medicines	Shikakai	*Acacia concinna*
	Neem	*Azadirachta indica*
	Eucalyptus	*Eucalyptus globulus*
	Snake root	*Rauvolfia serpentina*
	Tulsi	*Ocimum sanctum*
Miscellaneous	Cotton	*Gossypium hirsutum*
	Rubber	*Hevea brasiliensis*
	Coconut	*Cocus nucifera*
	Indian gooseberry (amla)	*Phyllanthus emblica*

Info Bytes!

The entire dandelion plant is edible.

Info Bytes!

The oldest known angiosperm or flowering plant is Archaefructus sinensis, which lived over 125 million years ago

Economic Importance of Angiosperms

The trees play the most significant role in providing clean environment by releasing oxygen into the air and by taking in carbon dioxide from the atmosphere. The forests are the home for the wild animals and birds and are important for conserving wild life. Thus, the trees and plants contribute for maintaining ecological balance. The plants provide us the basic necessity of life that is food in the form of cereals, pulses, vegetables, fruits, etc. They also provide shelter in the form of wood, grass, etc., and clothing in the form of cotton, jute, etc. The wide varieties of flora have immense aesthetic value as trees and plants enhance the beauty of the surroundings we live. Apart from these, they provide us many products of commercial importance.

Info Bytes!

Vanilla flavouring comes from the pod of an orchid.

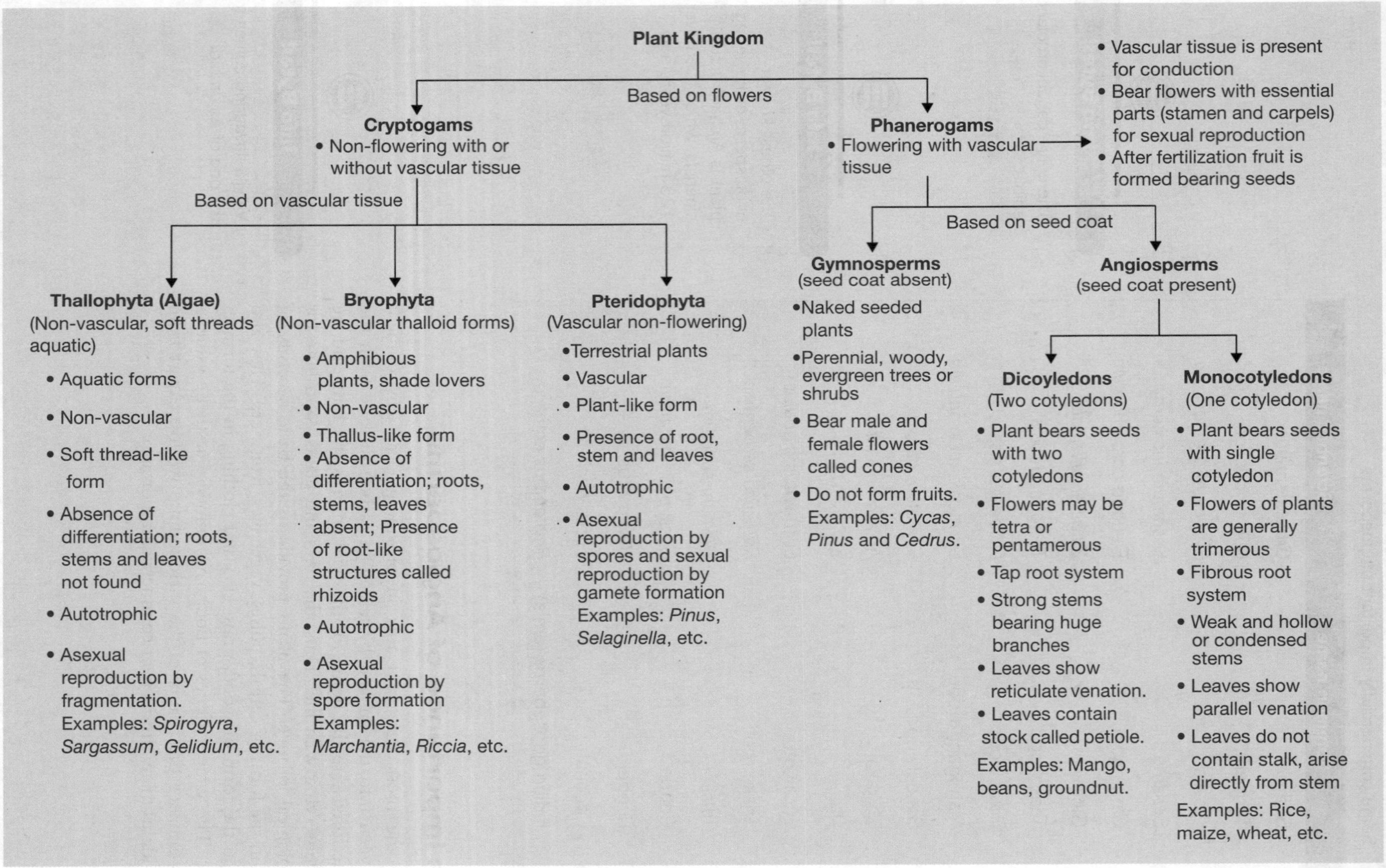

Figure 3.40 Classification of plant kingdom

Quick Recap

✔ **Bryophytes can thrive only in moist places. Give reason.**

Bryophytes do not possess roots. The rhizoids of the thallus fix the plant to the substratum. They absorb water and minerals from the ground or from the atmosphere. Therefore, they require moist surface. Presence of water is essential for swimming the male gametes to the female reproductive structure for fertilization. The sporophyte produces spores which on germination give rise to the filamentous form called protonema. This also requires a moist surface.

✔ **Pteridophytes are the first vascular plants in plant kingdom. Give some reasons for the dominance of vascular plants over non-vascular plants on the earth.**

Possession of strong roots which can penetrate deep into the soil for the absorption of water and minerals. Formation of mechanical tissue which provides support for the trees and facilitates the growth of plants to long heights. Development of vascular tissue for the efficient conduction of water, minerals and food in the plants.

✔ **How does the mutualistic association of mycorrhiza with plant roots benefit both the plant and the fungus?**

Mycorrhizal associations provide a win-win situation. Plants, through their association with mycorrhiza, get enhanced access to essential minerals and nutrients from the soil, which the fungus is adept at absorbing. In return, the fungus receives carbohydrates and sugars produced by the plant through photosynthesis. This partnership not only enhances growth and reproduction for both but also increases their resilience to environmental stresses.

✔ **How do mechanical tissues in vascular plants enable them to attain greater heights compared to non-vascular plants?**

Mechanical tissues in vascular plants, like sclerenchyma, provide structural support. This allows plants to grow taller without collapsing under their own weight. In contrast, non-vascular plants lack these support tissues, which limits their growth primarily to the ground or surfaces they attach to.

POINTS TO REMEMBER

✔ Different living organisms show wide range of variations in form, functioning and behaviour. This is known as biological diversity.

✔ The study of principles and procedures of classification of living organisms is called taxonomy.

✔ Taxonomic hierarchy involves the arrangement of organisms into various taxonomic groups in definite order.

✔ In a scientific name, first term is called genus and the second term is called species.

✔ According to two-kingdom classification, all the plants were grouped under the kingdom plantae and all the animals were grouped under the kingdom animalia.

✔ Whittaker proposed the five-kingdom classification for the living organisms based on three basic distinguishing features: structure of cell, cellular organization and mode of nutrition.

✔ Plants which bear flowers come under phanerogamae and plants which do not bear flowers come under cryptogamae.

✔ Cryptogams are divided into thallophytes, bryophytes and Pteridophytes.

✔ Phanerogams have visible reproductive organs.

✔ Gymnosperms are plants with naked seeds and angiosperms are plants with seeds enclosed in fruits.

CLASSROOM WING

Practice Questions

Very Short Answer Type Questions

Direction for Questions from 1 to 29:
Fill in the blanks.

1. The wide range of differences in the appearance, operation, and behaviour of different living organisms is referred to as ________.
2. The scientific discipline that focuses on defining and naming groups of biological organisms is known as ________.
3. The initial term in a scientific name represents the ________, while the latter term denotes the species.
4. Based on their reproductive parts, conspicuous plants are categorized as ________.
5. Unlike gymnosperms that have exposed seeds, ________ are plants whose seeds are protected within fruits.
6. The sub-division under plant kingdom which includes all ferns is ________.
7. The parasitic green algae which causes red rust in tea is ______.
8. ______ is a marine algae used as food.
9. Algae with rich source of protein is ______.
10. Conducting tissue in mosses is ______.
11. The main plant body of bryophyte plant is ______.
12. In mosses, the spores germinate to give rise to ______.
13. Horsetail is the common name of ______.
14. The leaf that bears spores in fern is known as ______.
15. The phloem of pteridophytes does not possess ______ cells.
16. ______ in ferns form gametophytic generation.
17. _____ are used as indicators of sulpur dioxide pollutants.
18. Spores on germination form ______ in pteridophyta.
19. Red colour in algae is due to the presence of ______.
20. In dicotyledons, the leaves bear ________ type of venation.
21. Resin ducts and latex tubes are seen in ________
22. In xerophytes, the waxy coating on the epidermis prevents ________.
23. Leaves which do not bear distinction between upper and lower surface are called ________leaves.
24. Edible dry fruit formed from gymnosperms is ______.
25. When more than one embryos are developed in a seed, the phenomenon is known as ______.
26. ______ is obtained from the wood of gymnosperms.
27. Plants bearing vascular tissue and seeds without fruit production are ______.
28. ______ leaves with parallel venation are seen in monocotyledons.
29. Resins are obtained from ______.

Direction for Questions from 30 to 72:
For each of the following questions, four choices has been provided. Select the correct alternatives.

30. Which of the following is NOT a distinguishing feature used in Whittaker's five-kingdom classification?
    (a) Structure of cell
    (b) Cellular organization
    (c) Number of chromosomes
    (d) Mode of nutrition
31. Which group of plants is characterized by the absence of flowers?
    (a) Angiosperms (b) Gymnosperms
    (c) Phanerogams (d) Cryptogamae
32. Which of the following falls under the category of cryptogams?
    (a) Mosses (b) Pines
    (c) Roses (d) Apples

33. In the two-kingdom classification system, fungi would be classified under:
(a) Plantae (b) Animalia
(c) Neither (d) Both

34. The study of principles and methods of naming organisms is known as:
(a) Nomenclature (b) Taxonomy
(c) Phylogeny (d) Morphology

35. Identify the group of organisms associated with prokaryotic cells.
(a) Monera (b) Protista
(c) Fungi (d) Algae

36. Name the comma-shaped bacterium.
(a) Spirillum (b) Coccus
(c) Vibrio (d) Bacillus

37. Inter-breeding between two populations can occur if they belong to the same:
(a) order (b) species
(c) class (d) family

38. The edible seaweed used is found in industry for gelling and thickening is:
(a) butter (b) agar-agar
(c) chocolate (d) carrageenans

39. The stored form of reserve food in brown algae is:
(a) laminarin (b) glucose
(c) fructose (d) glycogen

40. The solid fossil fuel coal is formed by burning of:
(a) pteridophytes (b) algae
(c) fungus (d) bacteria

41. The starch stored in red algae is:
(a) laminarin starch (b) glucose
(c) floridean starch (d) cellulose

42. The plant that is responsible for formation of peat is:
(a) *Anthoceros* (b) *Sphagnum*
(c) *Riccia* (d) *Funaria*

43. The plant categorized under living fossil is:
(a) *Marchantia* (b) *Pinus*
(c) *Cycas* (d) *Selaginella*

44. Identify the algae rich in protein.
(a) *Spirulina* (b) *Sargassum*
(c) *Sphagnum* (d) *Polytrichum*

45. Liverworts belong to:
(a) thallophyta (b) bryophyta
(c) pteridophyta (d) gymnosperms

46. Moss plants belong to which category of plants?
(a) Thallophyta (b) Bryophyta
(c) Pteredophyta (d) Gymnosperms

47. Floridean starch is the reserve food material in which of the following orgaisms?
(a) *Gelidium* (b) *Sargassum*
(c) *Spirogyra* (d) All of these

48. The development of haploid cells of gametophyte into a haploid sporophyte is called:
(a) apogamy (b) apospory
(c) budding (d) binary fission

49. Underground stem modification is observed in which plant?
(a) Ginger (b) Onion
(c) Carrot (d) Beetroot

50. The plants that grow in nitrogen-deficient soil is:
(a) *Opuntia* (b) *Vallisneria*
(c) neem (d) venus fly trap

51. Which of the following was taken as a distinguishing feature by Whittaker for proposing five-kingdom classification?
(a) Structure of cell
(b) Cellular organization
(c) Mode of nutrition
(d) All the above

52. Identify unicellular eukaryotic group of organisms.
(a) Monera (b) Protista
(c) Fungi (d) None of these

53. Which of the following bacterium is associated with the roots of legumes?
(a) *Rhizobium* (b) *Nostoc*
(c) *Spirogyra* (d) *Clostridium*

54. Which of the following are eukaryotic multicellular organisms having cells with cell wall and show heterotrophic mode of nutrition?

(a) Plantae (b) Animalia
(c) Protista (d) Fungi

55. Identify the organism which has prokaryotic cell structure and autotrophic mode of nutrition.

(a) *Euglena* (b) *Mycoplasma*
(c) *Cyanobacteria* (d) *Rhizobium*

56. Identify the characteristic features of yeast.

(i) Possession of cell wall made up of chitin
(ii) Prokaryotic cell structure
(iii) Saprophytic mode of nutrition
(iv) Absence of mitochondria in cells

(a) (i), (iii), (iv) (b) (i), (iv)
(c) (ii), (iii) (d) (i), (ii), (iii)

57. In the following line diagram showing taxonomic hierarchy of plants, identify the missing taxonomic unit.

Division ⟶ Class ⟶ Family

(a) Order (b) Family
(c) Species (d) Phylum

58. The taxonomic unit at a level one step higher to Genus is:

(a) Order (b) Family
(c) Species (d) Class

59. Identify the correct statement regarding the taxonomic unit 'species'.

(a) The name of the species is written with first letter in capital
(b) The organisms of the same species can interbreed among themselves
(c) The genus name is written with first letter as capital.
(d) The scientific name is printed in italics.

60. The photosynthetic pigment found in *Sargassum* is:

(a) carotene (b) xanthophyll
(c) phycocyanin (d) fucoxanthin

61. Ground becomes slippery during rainy season because of:

(a) blue algae (b) green algae
(c) blue green algae (d) mosses

62. Gametophytic and sporophytic generations are seen in life history of:

(a) fungi (b) algae
(c) ferns (d) diatoms

63. Pteridophytes differ from bryophytes in possessing:

(a) spores
(b) archegonia
(c) vascular tissue
(d) alternation of generation

64. The diploid cells of gametophyte in *Selaginella* gives rise to diploid sporophyte. Identify the name of the process involved.

(a) Apogamy (b) Apospory
(c) Fragmentation (d) Protonema

65. Which of the following plants possess isobilateral leaves?

(i) Wheat (ii) Banana
(iii) Garden pea (iv) Groundnut

(a) i; ii (b) iii; iv
(c) i only (d) iv only

66. Maize plant possesses which of the following morphological features?

(i) Trimerous flowers
(ii) Leaves with parallel venation
(iii) Solid branched stem
(iv) isobilateral leaves

(a) i; ii (b) ii; iii; iv
(c) i; ii; iv (d) ii; iv

67. Presence of thin and small roots is the characteristic feature of which group of plants?

(a) Mesophytes (b) Xerophyte
(c) Hydrophyte (d) None of these

68. *Cycas* has the embryo with two cotyledons. Yet it is not classified as dicotyledonous plant because:

(a) it looks like palm tree
(b) it bears megasporophylls
(c) its ovules are naked
(d) it bears microsporophylls

69. Coralloid roots help the plant in:
(a) absorption of water
(b) nitrogen fixation
(c) anchorage
(d) climbing

70. Seed-producing plants are called:
(a) spermatophytes (b) pteridophytes
(c) bryophytes (d) embryophytes

71. Leaves are dorsiventral and show reticulate venation in:
(a) onion (b) palm
(c) lily (d) mustard

72. Jiny, microscopic plant classified under angiosperms is:
(a) *Rafflesia* (b) *Wolfia*
(c) *Pistia* (d) *Riccia*

Direction for Questions from 73 to 77:
Match the entries of Column 1 with those of Column 2.

73.

Column 1	Column 2
A. Species	(i) related families
B. Order	(ii) related orders
C. Class	(iii) basic unit of taxonomy
D. Family	(iv) highest taxonomic unit
E. Kingdom	(v) related genera

74.

Column 1	Column 2
A. *Spirogyra*	(i) Fucoxanthin
B. *Gelidium*	(ii) Pigment absent
C. *Sargassum*	(iii) Chlorophyll
D. *Harveyella*	(iv) Phycoerythrin

75.

Column 1	Column 2
A. Antheridia	(i) Pteridophytes
B. Archegonia	(ii) Bryophytes
C. Rhizoids	(iii) Ferns
D. Sporophylls	(iv) Female thallus
E. Rhizome	(v) Male thallus

76.

Column 1	Column 2
A. Chilgoza	(i) Ornamental
B. *Cedrus*	(ii) Dry fruit
C. *Taxus*	(iii) Vegetable
D. *Cycas*	(iv) Medicine
E. *Gnetum*	(v) Timber

77.

Column 1	Column 2
A. Dicots	(i) *Wolffia*
B. Monocots	(ii) *Eucalyptus*
C. Largest flower	(iii) Mango
D. Smallest flower	(iv) Jawar
E. Tallest plant	(v) *Rafflesia*

Short Answer Type Questions

78. What is meant by nucleoid? Which group of organisms are associated with nucleoid? Give examples.

79. Define binary fission. Mention some organisms which show this phenomenon.

80. Define the following.
(a) Taxon
(b) Species
(c) Taxonomic heirarchy

81. Name the kingdom which comprises the first eukaryotic life forms originated on Earth. Give examples.

82. Write the most important characteristic feature of each of the following groups of organisms.
(a) Monera (b) Fungi
(c) Protista

83. Distinguish between parasitic mode of nutrition and symbiotic mode of nutrition.

84. Mention the characteristic features of *Euglena* in support of its inclusion in animal kingdom. Also mention the features which contradict its placement.

85. Mention the taxonomy of bacteria.
Bacteria play both useful and harmful role. Justify.

86. Mention the characteristic features of liverworts.

87. What is the purpose of sporangiophores in fungi?

88. Why are bryophytes called amphibious plants in plant kingdom?

89. Differentiate between angiosperms and gymnosperms based on their seed type.

90. Identify the basic criteria for classifying cryptogams.

91. How can one differentiate algae from fungi?

92. Mention the features taken for the further classification of the following:
(a) Cryptogamae (b) Phanerogamae

93. What are the basic differences between bryophytes and pteridophytes?

94. Explain the nature of vascular tissue in pteridophytes.

95. List out the differences between monocots and dicots.

96. The aerial roots of banyan tree are not considered as true roots. Give reasons.

97. Distinguish between rhizome and stem tuber.

98. The stem is green and fleshy in cactus. Give reason.

99. Distinguish between parasitic roots and epiphytic roots. Give examples.

100. Give one example for each of the following:
(a) Amphibious plant
(b) Symbiotic plant
(c) Colonial coelenterate

Essay Type Questions

101. Define the terms connected to plant kingdom.
(a) Annual (b) Biennial
(c) Perennial (d) Evergreen
(e) Deciduous

102. Observe the figures given below and answer accordingly.

A

B

(a) Identify figure A and B
(b) Which one is a multicellular form commonly known as bread mould.
(c) In which of the above plants, xylem lacks vessels, and phloem is devoid of companion cells.
(d) Identify the form in which spores germinate to form prothallus.

103. Differentiate between the following.
(a) Apogamy and apospory
(b) Homospory and heterospory
(c) Gametophyte and sporophyte
(d) Prothallus and protonema

104. Define the following:
(a) Mesophytes (b) Sporangia
(c) Xerophytes (d) Pentamerous flowers

105. What is the fate of the following organs of a flower after fertilization?
(a) Sepals (b) Petals
(c) Stamens (d) Ovary
(e) Ovule

COMPETITION WING

Practice Questions

Level 1: Apply your Concepts

Direction for Questions from 1 to 8:
Fill in the blanks.

1. While basic naming in biology relies on binomial nomenclature, the broader process of classifying organisms in a systematic manner is termed ________.
2. If one moves from the broadest to the most specific taxonomic rank, ________ comes just before species.
3. The major distinction between the two primary groups in Phanerogams lies in the ________ of their seeds.
4. ________ disrupted the two-kingdom classification by introducing a scheme based on factors like cellular organization.
5. Organisms that fall under cryptogamae and don't differentiate into stems, leaves or roots are called ________.
6. Binomial nomenclature was given by ______.
7. ______ is considered as the basic unit of biological classification.
8. The term species was coined by ______.

Direction for Questions from 9 to 15:
For each of the following questions, four choices have been provided. Select the correct alternatives.

9. Which among the following was NOT a criterion in Whittaker's five-kingdom classification?
   (a) Mode of nutrition
   (b) Type of cell wall
   (c) Number of cellular nuclei
   (d) Cellular organization
10. What is the primary significance of the two-part format in scientific naming?
   (a) To identify the organism's kingdom and phylum.
   (b) To ensure the uniqueness of the name across the globe.
   (c) To provide a name that's easy to pronounce.
   (d) To indicate the organism's predator-prey relationship.
11. Which distinguishing feature primarily categorizes organisms in Whittaker's five-kingdom classification?
   (a) Their ability to reproduce.
   (b) Their habitat.
   (c) Structure of their cell.
   (d) Their lifespan.
12. What characteristic of cryptogams makes them distinct from phanerogams?
   (a) They are vascular plants.
   (b) They have visible reproductive organs.
   (c) They do not produce seeds.
   (d) They are all aquatic.
13. Why was the two-kingdom classification system found to be inadequate as our understanding of biology expanded?
   (a) It did not differentiate between plants and animals.
   (b) It grouped a vast array of diverse organisms under broad categories, overlooking key differences.
   (c) It was based on the reproductive capacity of organisms.
   (d) It primarily considered the habitat of the organisms.
14. Identify the locomotory organelles in *Euglena*.
   (a) Flagella (b) Pseudopodia
   (c) Celia (d) Hyphae
15. Which type of venation is observed in banana?
   (a) Pinnate (b) Palmale
   (c) Reticulate (d) Parallel

Direction for Questions from 16 to 33:
Write True or False.

16. Ferns contain underground stem are called rhizoids.
17. Insectivorous plants grow in soil rich in nitrogen.

18. Lichens act as indicators for sulphur dioxide pollutant.

19. Peat obtained from bryophytes is used as biofuel.

20. Agar-agar is obtained from gelidium.

21. Adventitious root system is seen in dicots.

22. In gymnosperms, sporophylls aggregate to form cones.

23. Anther of the flower bears ovary which form fruit.

24. Turpentine is a solvent resin obtained from gymnosperms.

25. Roots associated with fungi are known as mycorrhizal roots.

26. Liverworts belong to pteridophyta.

27. Algae are classified based on their photosynthetic pigments.

28. Floral whorls in sets of five area seen in monocotyledons.

29. Double fertilization, triple fusion is seen in gymnosperms

30. Pollen grains are considered as male gamates in plants.

31. *Cedrus* (Deodar) is an example of angiosperm.

32. *Pencillium* belongs to algae.

33. *Paramoecium* belongs to protista.

Direction for Question 34:

Write the missing correlated terms.

34. (a) Agar agar : *Gelidium* : : sewage treatment : ______

(b) Lichenology : lichens : : ______ : algae

(c) Bryophyta : ______ : : pteridophyta : prothallus

(d) Cones : gymnosperms : : angiosperms : ______

(e) Dicot : pulses : : ______ : *Smilax*

(f) ______ : flowering plants : : cryptogams : non flowering plants

(g) *Chlorella* : ______ : : *Penicillium* : penicillin

(h) Liverworts : bryophyta : : ______ : *Cycas*

(i) Algae : autotrophic : : fungi : ______

(j) Onion : ______ : : mango : dicot

(k) Polyembryony : gymnosperms : : double fertilization : ______

Direction for Questions from 35 to 58:

Choose the correct option.

(a) Both A and R are true and R is the correct explanation for A.

(b) Both A and R are true but R is not the correct explanation for A.

(c) A is true and R is false.

(d) A is false and R is true.

35. **Assertion (A):** Protozoans and diatoms belong to the kingdom protista

Reason (R): Protozoans and diatoms are parasitic forms.

36. **Assertion (A):** The specificity of characters decreases from family to genus.

Reason (R): The genus is a lower level taxonomic unit than genus.

37. **Assertion (A):** Fungi do not undergo photosynthesis

Reason (R): Fungi usually live in dark places.

38. **Assertion (A):** *Actinomyces* possesses single chromosome

Reason (R): *Actinomyces* is a prokaryote

39. **Assertion (A):** Both bacteria and blue green algae are grouped into one kingdom

Reason (R): The cells of Bacteria and blue green algae possess cell wall made up of cellulose

40. **Assertion (A):** Mushrooms are not considered as plants.

Reason (R): The cells do not possess cell walls

41. **Assertion (A):** Algae are microscopic thallophytes

Reason (R): Green, Red and brown are different types of algae

42. **Assertion (A):** Diatoms do not decay as early as other algae

Reason (R): Diatoms have siliceous cell walls

43. **Assertion (A):** Kelp is a herbal medicine taken from brown algae

Reason (R): Use of kelp causes goitre

44. **Assertion (A):** Sphagnum is used for dressing wounds.

Reason (R): Sphagnum is used as packing material for transportation.

45. **Assertion (A):** Bryophytes are terrestrial plants.

Reason (R): Life cycle of bryophytes occur in two phases gametophyte and sporophyte.

46. **Assertion (A):** All bryophytes are considered as amphibious plants.

Reason (R): Bryophytes complete their life cycle in the presence of water.

47. **Assertion (A):** *Equisetum* is also known as horsetail.

Reason (R): *Equisetum* is used in preparation of medicine

48. **Assertion (A):** Apogamy is a type of vegetative propagation.

Reason (R): Haploid cells of gametophyte without gametic union forms haploid sporophyte.

49. **Assertion (A):** Non-flowering plants are known as cryptogams.

Reason (R): Marchantia belongs to cryptogams.

50. **Assertion (A):** The prothallus of fern is heart shaped.

Reason (R): Prothallus in fern helps in production of gametes.

51. **Assertion (A):** In ferns, the diploid cells of the sporophyte directly give rise to diploid gametophyte

Reason (R): Ferns reproduce by spore formation and gametic fusion

52. **Assertion (A):** A thick waxy coating is found covering the shoot system of cactus

Reason (R): Cactus is generally found in desert areas.

53. **Assertion (A):** Gymnosperms do not produce fruits

Reason (R): Gymnosperms are non flowering plants.

54. **Assertion (A):** Cycas bears reproductive structures on the leaves.

Reason (R): Pteridophytes possess sporangia on leaves

55. **Assertion (A):** Gymnosperms do not produce fruits.

Reason (R): Gymnosperms are non flowering plants.

56. **Assertion (A):** The dominant phase of life cycle in angiosperms is sporophyte.

Reason (R): Sporophyte in angiosperm is developed from diploid zygote.

57. **Assertion (A):** Dicotyledons undergo epigeal type of germination.

Reason (R): Endosperm forms nutritive tissue.

58. **Assertion (A):** Tap root system is seen in monocotyledons.

Reason (R): Fibrous root system anchors the plant firmly into the ground.

Level 2: Review your Concepts

59. Bacteria are considered as plant. Give reason.

60. Explain the role of bacteria in the following.

(a) Curdling of milk

(b) Production of antibiotics

(c) Curing of coffee

(d) Retting of fibre

61. Explain the role of yeast in the preparation of alcohol.

62. Name the algae useful for prolonged space flight. Why?

63. Why are green algae considered as ancestors of land plants?

64. Liverworts and mosses are amphibians of plant kingdom. Give reasons.

65. How does Whittaker's five-kingdom classification address the limitations of the two-kingdom system?

66. Considering cryptogams don't bear flowers, how do they ensure the reproduction and continuation of their species?

67. (a) Which pteridophyte has been proved to be a good biofertilizer for paddy?

(b) Identify the gametophytic stage of pteridophyta.

68. Give an example for the following:

(a) Oviparous mammal

(b) Limbless amphibian

69. Mention some morphological features by which dicotyledonous trees are identified.

70. Give one example for each of the following:

(a) Pseudostem

(b) Bacteria

71. Give the appropriate scientific term for the following:
(a) Fungi used as food.
(b) Leaves which bear sporangia in ferns.
(c) Edible algae rich in protein
(d) Algae used as petro crop.
(e) Fungi from which antibiotic penicillin is extracted
(f) Bryophyte used for surgical dressing.
(g) Gymnosperm which yields Sago
(h) Tallest angiosperm
(i) Haploid stage found in moss plant
(j) An algae with spiral chloroplast
(k) Higher plants which produce seeds

Level 3: Assess Your Concepts

72. Velvety green beds appear on the walls during rainy season. Give reason.

73. Algae are classified based on their photosynthetic pigments Comment.

74. Name the groups of plants which are considered as vascular plants. Why are they so called? Also, mention in what way angiosperms differ from the other groups of vascular plants.

75. Which plant in India is known as Kalpavriksha? Why?

76. Discuss the challenges and limitations of taxonomic systems in accommodating the vast diversity of life, especially with the advent of molecular biology.

AT

NEET SPECIAL WING

Practice Questions

Multiple-Answer Type Questions

Questions number 1 to 5 are multiple-choice questions. Each question has FOUR options (a), (b), (c), and (d). ONE OR MORE THAN ONE of these four option(s) is/are the correct answer(s).

1. Which of the following is/ are example/s of plants that have hidden reproductive organs with developed vascular tissues?
   (a) Riccia
   (b) Selaginella
   (c) Lycopodium
   (d) Marchantia

2. Which among the following is not a harmful effect caused due to excessive growth of a member belonging to Thallophyta?
   (a) Thickening and gelling agent
   (b) Algal bloom
   (c) Synthesis of vitamins
   (d) Antibiotic production

3. Which of the following features belong to the class of plants that are also referred to as 'amphibians of the plant kingdom'?
   (a) Terrestrial land plants
   (b) Require damp surfaces for reproduction
   (c) Used as packing material due to high water holding capacity
   (d) Vascular tissue is absent

4. Which among the following are vegetative forms of reproduction in Pteridophytes?
   (a) Apogamy (b) Spore formation
   (c) Fragmentation (d) Apospory

5. Which among the following are the characteristics related to the tap root system?
   (a) Has primary and secondary roots
   (b) Has a cluster of roots
   (c) Arise from the radicle
   (d) Arise from the base of a stem

Comprehension-Based Questions

A. Read the paragraph given below and answer the questions number 6 to 11:

Root systems perform two important functions in the plant body namely anchorage and absorption of water and minerals from the soil. In addition to these functions, the root systems in certain plants undergo changes in the structure to perform different kinds of functions. These are known as root modifications. The different kinds of functions supported by the modified roots include- storage of food, giving additional support to the plants and performing some special functions. Modified roots on the basis of the shape they attain whilst storing food are of different types- Spindle, Conical, Roundish, Tuberose, Nodulose and Fasciculated. Roots for additional support include- Prop, stilt and climbing roots. On the other hand, some roots perform special functions such as Nitrogen fixation, being parasitic to absorb nutrition; some are aerial hanging roots whereas some are breathing roots.

6. The specialised root structures in parasitic plants are called:
   (a) Nodules (b) Haustoria
   (c) Epiphytes (d) Pneumatophores

7. Identify the example of a hanging aerial root.
   (a) Orchid (b) Avicennia
   (c) Cuscuta (d) Sugarcane

8. What type of root system is seen in pea and grams?
   (a) Fibrous (b) Tap roots
   (c) Adventitious (d) Prop roots

9. The type of modification seen in tubers where the eye gives rise to new shoot.

(a) Root (b) Stem
(c) Leaf (d) Flower

10. Aerial roots which grow vertically downwards and penetrate the soil are called:
(a) Prop (b) Stilt
(c) Parasitic (d) Breathing

11. Match the following:

Column – A	Column – B
(i) Spindle	(a) Radish
(ii) Conical	(b) Dahlia
(iii) Nodulose	(c) Carrot
(iv) Fasciculated	(d) Sweet potato
(v) Tuberous	(e) Turmeric

B. Read the paragraph given below and answer the questions number 12 to 17:

Cryptogams are plants which have hidden reproductive organs and they do not produce fruits, flowers and seeds. They reproduce by spore formation. They can further be distinguished on the basis of differentiation of plant body into roots, stems and leaves, and also on the basis of presence of vascular tissue for the conduction of water and nutrients. They are further subdivided into three subdivisions that is Thallophyta, Bryophyta and Pteridophyta. Thallophytes have flattened bodies and do not have vascular tissues. Bryophytes do not have vascular tissues and need water for reproduction. Pteridophytes have vascular tissues and they need terrestrial habitat.

12. Sargassum which is an important member of algae has a starch like reserve food material called:
(a) Laminarin
(b) Phycoerythrin
(c) Lichens
(d) Kelp

13. One of the important uses of bryophyte is that:
(a) It is used as nitrogen fixer in paddy fields
(b) resin extracts are used for treatment of ulcers and asthma
(c) It helps in the formation of peat which can either be used as fuel or to improve soil texture.
(d) The wood from these plants is used to make durable boats

14. Which of the following Pteridophyte is used as antidiuretic and haemopoietic?
(a) Marsilea
(b) Lycopodium
(c) Selaginella
(d) Equisetum

15. Which part of the plant body is responsible for absorbing water and nutrients from the soil or air in Bryophytes?
(a) Rhizoids
(b) Rhizome
(c) Riccia
(d) Rhizobium

16. Which of the following is not a harmful effect caused by Algae?
(a) Algae causes toxicity and death of aquatic organisms by producing toxins.
(b) Growth of Lichens is used as indicator for sulphur dioxide pollution.
(c) Algae when grown on buildings and monuments, damage them and make them slippery.
(d) Algal bloom grown in lakes and pools changes colour, taste and produces foul smell which decreases the aesthetic value.

17. Match the following:

Column – A	Column – B
(i) Spirogyra	(a) Rich in iodine
(ii) Gelidium	(b) Reserve food material is starch
(iii) Sargassum	(c) Symbiotic association
(iv) Chlorella	(d) Aerating fish ponds
(v) Lichens	(e) Red algae

Answer Keys

Crossword

Across

4. Thallophyta 6. Adventitious 7. Bulb 8. Cryptogams 12. Pteridophyta
15. Carolus Linnaeus 16. Bryophyta 17. Apospory 18. Androecium 19. Prop
20. Offset

Down

1. Reticulate 2. Phanerogams 3. Pneumatophores 5. Roundish 9. Nodular
10. Phylloclades 11. Lichens 13. Angiosperms 14. Agar agar

Classroom Wing

Very Short Answer Type Questions

1. Biological diversity 2. Taxonomy 3. Genus 4. Phanerogamae 5. Angiosperms
6. Pteridophytes 7. Cephaleuros 8. Sargassum 9. Spirulina 10. Parenchyma
11. Gametophyte 12. Protonema 13. Equisetum 14. Sporophyll 15. Companion
16. Prothallus 17. Lichens 18. Prothallus 19. Phycoerythrin or phycocyanin
20. Reticulate 21. Gymnosperms 22. Transpiration 23. Isobilateral 24. Chilgoza
25. Polyembryony 26. Turpentine oil 27. Gymnosperms 28. Isobilateral 29. Gymnosperms
30. (c) 31. (d) 32. (a) 33. (a) 34. (a)
35. (a) 36. (c) 37. (b) 38. (d) 39. (a)
40. (a) 41. (c) 42. (b) 43. (c) 44. (a)
45. (b) 46. (b) 47. (a) 48. (a) 49. (a)
50. (d) 51. (d) 52. (b) 53. (a) 54. (d)
55. (c) 56. (c) 57. (a) 58. (b) 59. (a)
60. (d) 61. (c) 62. (c) 63. (c) 64. (c)
65. (a) 66. (c) 67. (c) 68. (c) 69. (b)
70. (a) 71. (d) 72. (b) 73. A–(iii), B–(i), C–(ii), D–(iii), E–(iv)
74. A–(iii), B–(iv), C–(i), D–(ii) 75. A–(v), B–(iv) C–(ii), D–(i), E–(iii)
76. A–(ii) B–(iii), C–(iv), D–(i), E–(iii) 77. A–(iii), B–(ii), C–(v), D–(i), E–(iii)

Competition Wing

Level 1: Apply your Concepts

1. Taxonomy 2. Genus 3. Enclosure 4. Whittaker 5. Thallophytes
6. Carolus Linnaeus 7. Species 8. John Ray 9. (c) 10. (b)
11. (c) 12. (c) 13. (b) 14. (a) 15. (d)
16. False 17. False 18. True 19. True 20. True

21. False	22. True	23. False	24. True	25. True
26. False	27. True	28. False	29. False	30. True
31. False	32. False	33. True		
34. (a) Chlorella	(b) Phycology	(c) Protonema	(d) Flowers	(e) Monocot
(f) Phanerogams	(g) Chlorellin	(h) Gymnosperms	(i) Saprozoic	(j) Monocot
(k) Angiosperms				
35. (c)	36. (d)	37. (b)	38. (a)	39. (c)
40. (c)	41. (c)	42. (a)	43. (c)	44. (c)
45. (b)	46. (a)	47. (b)	48. (a)	49. (b)
50. (b)	51. (b)	52. (b)	53. (a)	54. (d)
55. (c)	56. (b)	57. (b)	58. (d)	

NEET Special Wing

Multiple-Answer Type Questions

1. (a, b, c, d)	2. (a, c, d)	3. (a, b, c, d)	4. (a, d)	5. (a, c)

Comprehension-Based Questions

6. (b)	7. (a)	8. (b)	9. (b)	10. (a)

11. (i) → (a); (ii) → (c); (iii) → (e); (iv) → (b); (v) → (d)

12. (a)	13. (c)	14. (d)	15. (a)	16. (b)

17. (i) → (b); (ii) → (e); (iii) → (a); (iv) → (d); (v) → (c)

Hints and Explanations

CLASSROOM WING

Very Short Answer Type Questions

30. Whittaker's classification is based on cell structure, cellular organization, and nutrition mode, not the chromosome count.

31. Cryptogams do not produce flowers, whereas phanerogams can be either gymnosperms or angiosperms, both of which are seed-producing.

32. Mosses are bryophytes, which are a type of cryptogam. The others are seed-producing plants.

33. In the old two-kingdom system, fungi, despite their unique characteristics, were placed in the plant kingdom.

34. Nomenclature deals with the rules and conventions for naming organisms.

Short Answer Type Questions

78. The prokaryotic cells do not possess a membrane-bound, distinct nucleus. A single chromosome with DNA is present in the cytoplasm. This is called nucleoid. The organisms belonging to kingdom monera possess this kind of cell structure. For example, bacteria.

79. Binary fission is the asexual mode of reproduction in which a single organism becomes two independent organisms. Organisms like bacteria, bacillus, cocci show this phenomenon.

80. (a) Taxon: Each category of organisms at a level is considered as a unit, called taxon.

(b) Species: An individual belonging to a group of organisms (or the entire group itself) having common characteristics and usually capable of mating with one another to produce fertile offspring.

(c) Taxonomic hierarchy: Systematic framework of classification in which taxonomic groups are arranged in a definite order from higher to lower categories.

81. Kingdom protista is associated with eukaryotic life forms originated on earth.

82. Monera—Prokaryotic cell structure

Fungi—Cell wall made up of chitin; Saprophytic mode of nutrition

Protista—Unicellular with eukaryotic cells

83. In parasitic mode of nutrition, the organisms depend on other organisms for their food and shelter. Generally, they feed on the body fluids of other animals.

In symbiotic mode of nutrition, two organisms depend on each other for either food or shelter requirement. But, in this association, the other organism also derives benefit out of this association.

84. *Euglena* is placed in protozoans under kingdom Protista. It does not possess cell wall. It has locomotory organelles called flagella. Hence, its placement in animal kingdom is justified.

Euglena shows autotrophic mode of nutrition. This is the characteristic feature of plant. Hence, this feature contradicts its placement in animal kingdom.

85. Bacterial cell is a prokaryotic cell.

Bacteria belong to kingdom Monera where the organisms are free living or parasitic.

Bacteria play a very important useful role in our life.

(i) Bacteria present in soil help in the degradation of organic matter. That means they clean the environment.

(ii) Certain bacteria help in nitrogen fixation and provide nutrients to the soil.

(iii) Bacteria also provide food. For example, the bacteria called *Lactobacillus* help in the conversion of milk to curd.

Free living from—*Lactobacillus* (useful)

Parasitic form—*Mycobacterium tuberculosis* (harmful as it causes tuberculosis)

86.
- Thalloid forms with less foliage and dichotomous branching.
- These are bryophytes bearing dichotomous branching.
- The flat leaves with rounded lobes resemble human liver hence known as liverworts.
- They are non-vascular flowerless plants.
- Reproduce by means of spores.

87. Fungal hyphae produces very long stalks known as sporangiophores. These sporangiophores bear the sporangia above the main mycelium. On the repture of sporangia, sporangiospores are released. These long sporangiospores help the sporangiophores in dispersal through air currents.

88. Plants can live in soil but need water for undergoing sexual reproduction, hence known as amphibious plants.

89. Angiosperms have seeds that are enclosed within fruits, which are developed from the ovary of the flower. Gymnosperms, on the other hand, have seeds that are exposed and are not enclosed within a fruit.

90. The basic criterion for classification of cryptogams (non-flowering plants) is the seed coat. If seeds are enclosed in fruit, they are grouped under angiosperm. If seeds are not enclosed in fruits (i.e., naked seeded) they are grouped under gymnosperms.

91.

Algae	Fungi
Prokaryotic or eukaryotic	Eukaryotic
Mostly aquatic forms	Aquatic and terrestrial forms
Chlorophyll is present, hence autotrophic nutrition	Chlorophyll is absent, hence heterotrophic nutrition
Cell wall is made up of cellulose	Cell wall is made up of chitin
Reserve food material is starch	Reserve food is glycogen and oil globules
Reproduces asexually and sexually	Reproduces asexually, very rarely sexually

92. (a) Cryptogamae: They can be further distinguished on the basis of differentiation of plant body into roots, stems and leaves and also on the basis of presence of vascular tissue for the conduction of water and nutrients.

(b) Phanerogamae: This division is further classified into two subdivisions based on the nature of seed.

93. Bryophytes do not possess vascular tissue. That means, they are non-vascular plants. Pteridophytes possess vascular tissue for the conduction of materials. They are the first vascular plants.

94. Presence of vascular tissue for conduction is the main characteristic feature of pteridophyta. In fact, pteridophytes are considered to be the first vascular plants originated on the earth. The vascular tissue includes xylem and phloem. But, these plants possess only primitive forms of xylem and phloem. Xylem tissue has all the elements except vessels. Tracheids carry out the function of vessels. Phloem tissue has all the elements except companion cells. Sieve cells carry out the function of companion cells.

95. Differences between monocots and dicots

Monocots	Dicots
Fibrous root system	Tap root system
Hollow stem, usually unbranched	Solid and branched stem
Isobilateral leaves with parallel venation	Dorsiventral leaves with reticulate venation
Trimerous flowers	Pentamerous flowers
Examples: Rice, Maize and all cereals	Examples: All pulses, sunflower

96. Aerial roots of banyan tree grow downwards from the main stem and branches. These roots are called prop roots. They act as pillars giving support to huge horizontal branches of banyan tree. Supporting roots or prop roots are one of the root modifications.

97. Underground main stem that creeps horizontally below the surface of soil is rhizome. This is fleshy and helps in storage. For example, ginger.

Underground part of root or structure derived from tip of underground branches is tuber. This helps in storage of starch. For example, potato, beetroot.

98. Cactus is a xerophytic plant. The stem of the plant is modified into flat, green, fleshy structure, which helps in storage of water and also performs photosynthesis. The leaves are modified to spines and help in reducing transpiration.

99.

Epiphyte	Parasite
Plants that grow on other plant for support	Plants that grow on other plant for absorbing nutrients
They do not cause damage to the plant which they grow on	They cause damage to the plant on which they grow

100. (a) Amphibious plants—Bryophyta

(b) Symbiotic plants—Lichens

(c) Colonial coelenterate—Coral

Essay Type Questions

101. Annual: Plant that completes its life cycle within one year. It germinates, grows, produces flowers fruits and seeds in the same year and then dies. For example, Maize.

Biennial: Plant that completes its biological life cycle in two years. In the first year, vegetative parts grow and in the second year they start flowering and fruiting. For example, Cabbage, Onions.

Perennials: Plants that live for more than two years. Shrubs and trees are perennials.

Evergreen: Plants that have leaves throughout the year and are always green.

Deciduous: Shrubs are trees that shed their leaves seasonally.

102. (a) Figure A is identified as Rhizopus and B is identified as fern.

(b) Rhizopus is the multicellular form commonly known as bread mould.

(c) In fern, xylem lacks vessels and phloem is devoid of companion cell.

(d) In ferns, spores germinate to form prothallus.

103. (a) Apogamy: Formation of haploid sporophytes from haploid cells of gametophytes without fusion of gametes.

It is a type of asexual reproduction discovered by Farlow in Pteris.

Apospory: Formation of diploid gametophyte from diploid cells of sporophyte (which do not undergo meiotic cell division)

This was discovered by Druery in fern Athyrium.

(b) When all the spores are of same type, i.e., same size, shape, etc., then the condition is considered as homosporous.

When spores produced are of different types i.e., macro- and microspores which germinate to produce female and male gametophytes, respectively. Such condition is known as heterospory.

(c) Gametophyte: The dominant phase of life cycle in bryophytes which produces haploid gamates. These gamates unite to form zygote from which sporophytes arises.

Sporophyte: The diploid multicellular stage in the life cycle of plant which produces haploid spores that develop into gametophyte.

(d) Prothallus: The gametophyte produced by the germination of spores is thalloid and bears both male and female sex organs, and is called prothallus.

Protonema: The haploid spore of a moss plant germinates to produce a branched photosynthetic filamentous juvenile stage called protonema. This is seen in bryophytes.

104. (a) Mesophytes: Angiosperms which grow predominantly in terrestrial habitats are called mesophytes.

(b) Sporangia: The leaves of pteridophyta which bear the reproductive structures are called sporangia.

(c) Xerophytes: The terrestrial plants of angiosperms which can survive and thrive in desert habitats are called xerophytes.

(d) Pentamerous flowers: These flowers are seen in dicot plants. These are flowers with all five floral parts in number.

105. The sepals, petals and stamens fall off after the fertilization. The ovary is converted into fruit. The ovules are converted into seeds.

COMPETITION WING

Level 1: Apply your Concepts

9. Whittaker's classification was based on cell structure, mode of nutrition, and cellular organization, but not on the number of nuclei.

10. The binomial nomenclature, which includes the genus and species, ensures that each species has a unique name worldwide. This system avoids confusion that might arise due to common names.

11. Whittaker's classification fundamentally categorizes organisms based on the structure of cells, cellular organization, and mode of nutrition.

12. Cryptogams are non-seed producing plants, whereas phanerogams produce seeds. This is the primary distinction between them.

13. The two-kingdom classification was too simplistic, lumping together vastly different organisms without considering fundamental differences like cellular organization, mode of nutrition, and cell structure.

35. Protozoans and diatoms are unicellular organisms and hence are placed in one Kingdom that is Protista. But, protozoans show heterotrophic nutrition mostly parasitic. Diatoms show autotrophic nutrition.

    Hence, the correct option is (c).

36. The different taxonomic units are arranged in the increasing order of specificity of characters of the organisms. Species is the lowest taxonomic unit in the hierarchy. Therefore, it is the level with greatest specificity. Genus which is the next higher taxonomic unit has lesser specificity than species.

    Hence, the correct option is (d).

37. Fungal cells do not possess chlorophyll at all and hence, these organisms show heterotrophic mode of nutrition. They live in moist and dark places to grow.

    Hence, the correct option is (b).

38. Actinomyces is a type of bacteria and is a prokaryote. Prokaryotic cell possesses a single chromosome floating in the cytoplasm.

    Hence, the correct option is (a).

39. Both bacteria and blue green algae are grouped into kingdom monera. The cells of both possess cell wall made up of cellulose

    Hence, the correct option is (c).

40. Mushrooms belong to Kingdom Fungi. They possess a hard cell wall made up of a complex sugar known as chitin.

    But, they show heterotrophic mode of nutrition while autotrophic mode of nutrition is the characteristic feature of plants.
    Hence, they are not considered as plants.

    Hence, the correct option is (c).

41. Gymnosperms do not produce fruits as they produce only naked seeds. But they are flowering plants just like angiosperms.

    Hence, the correct option is (c).

42. Siliceous skeleton of diatoms do not readily decay.

    Hence, the correct option is (a).

43. Kelp is used to treat goitre as it contains high concentration of iodine.

    Hence, the correct option is (c).

44. Sterilized Sphagnum has great absorbent power and antiseptic properties, hence used in surgical dressing.

    Hence, the correct option is (c).

45. Bryophyta represents the simplest terrestrial (land) plants. The dominant form of their life is known as gametophyte which is thallus-like (thalloid). Another form is usually short-lived form which is called sporophyte.

    Hence, the correct option is (b).

46. Bryophyta represents the simplest terrestrial (land) plants. However, they require moist or damp surface particularly during the reproductive stage. These plants can live in both aquatic and terrestrial habitats. Hence, they are called Amphibians of Plant Kingdom.

    Hence, the correct option is (a).

47. Horsetail is the common name of Equisetum. It is antidiuretic and haemopoitic.

    Hence, the correct option is (b).

48. The haploid cells of gametophyte directly develop into haploid sporophyte. This method of reproduction is called apogamy and does not involve gametic fusion.

    Hence, the correct option is (a).

49. The word 'cryptogamae' is derived from Greek words 'cryptos' which means 'hidden' and 'gamae' which means 'to marry'. That means, they have hidden reproductive organs and do not produce flowers, fruits and

seeds. They are classified into: thallophyta, bryophyta and pteridophyta.

Hence, the correct option is (b).

50. Leaves bear the reproductive structures called sporangia. Each sporangium bears spore mother cells which undergo meiosis cell division to form spores. Each spore on germination forms a prothallus. This prothallus develops into a new plant (gametophyte) which possesses male and female reproductive structures. The male and female gametes are produced in these structures. Prothallus is heart shaped.

Hence, the correct option is (b).

51. In ferns, the haploid cells of gametophyte directly develop into haploid sporophyte. This method of reproduction is called apogamy. They have both asexual and sexual modes of reproduction.

Hence, the correct option is (b).

52. A thick waxy coating is found covering the shoot system of cactus plant because this coating helps in sealing the moisture. As the moisture in desert areas is less.

Hence, the correct option is (b).

53. The word 'gymnosperms' originated from two Greek words 'gymnos' meaning 'naked' and 'sperma' meaning 'seeds'. That means, the class of gymnosperms includes the plants which produce seeds not enclosed in the fruits.

Hence, the correct option is (a).

54. Cycas is a flowering plant and is a gymnosperm. It bears cones as reproductive structures. Pteridophytes are non-flowering plants. They do not bear separate reproductive structures as in case of flowering plants. They bear small nodule-like structures called sporangia on the surface of leaves.

Hence, the correct option is (d).

55. Gymnosperms are flowering plants. But they are naked seeded plants. The seeds are not enclosed in fruits. They do not possess ovary and hence fruit formation does not take place.

Hence, the correct option is (c).

56. Sporophyte phase is the main phase of an angiosperm's life cycle.

Hence, the correct option is (b).

57. Dicots like peas and beans undergo epigeal type of germination. Endosperm is a nutritive tissue as it supplies nutrients to the developing embryo.

Hence, the correct option is (b).

58. Tap root system is seen in dicots. Fibrous root system does not anchor the plant firmly to the ground. They facilitate absorption of water and minerals over a large surface area.

Hence, the correct option is (d).

Level 2: Review your Concepts

59. Bacteria are considered as plants. In the traditional system of classification, they were kept under plant kingdom. This is because of presence of cell wall made up of cellulose in them.

60. (a) A small amount of curd (starter) is added to milk. Curd contains a bacterium known as Lactobacillus. This induces the chemical reaction of conversion of lactose sugar in milk into lactic acid. This lactic acid imparts sour taste to curd. Increased acidity causes the conversion of milk proteins (casein) into a solid mass. This changes the texture of curd.

The Lactobacillus bacteria when consumed through curd are beneficial to us. They help in preventing diarrhoea and other similar infections. They help in the digestion process and also enhance the efficiency of absorption of nutrients.

(b) The antibiotics can be produced by the process of fermentation in which microorganisms such as fungi or soil bacteria are grown in a liquid growth medium under controlled conditions of temperature, oxygen, pH, etc. Before the cells die, the useful product is extracted.

Antibiotics from fungi—Pencillin; Cephalosporin

Antibiotics from bacteria—Streptomycin; Tetracycline

(c) Yeast helps in the fermentation process. Bacteria produce acids which help in the prevention of sprouting during the process and prevent the growth of moulds. The acids also impart the required flavour to the coffee.

(d) Retting of jute involves the hydrolysis and fermentation of pectins which bind the fibres together. This process separates the fibres and is carried out by means of a genus of bacteria namely Clostridium.

61. The enzymes produced by yeast carry out the conversion of sugar into alcohol and carbon dioxide. This enzymatic hydrolysis of sugar is called fermentation. This is useful not only in the manufacture of alcohol, but also in the baking for making bread or cake.

The carbon dioxide and alcohol make the dough rise as the complex carbohydrates in the dough undergo fermentation. The alcohol also imparts the characteristic taste and flavour to the baked product.

62. The algae used for prolonged space flight is Chlorella.
   (i) Liberation of oxygen (aeration)
   (ii) Consumption of carbon dioxide
   (iii) Disposal of wastes (sewage treatment)
   (iv) Food purpose (good source of protein)

63. The similarities between green algae and land plants are:
   (i) Both have photosynthetic pigment, chlorophyll.
   (ii) Cellulose cell wall is present in both.
   (iii) Starch is the common carbohydrate stored in both. Therefore, green algae is the ancestor group from which land plants have evolved.

64. Liverworts and mosses are partially adapted to life on land (terrestrial environment) in their mode of spore dispersal. They are still dependent on availability of water for sexual reproduction. They also absorb mineral salts through the wet soil surface, as they do not have well-developed root system. Hence the amphibians of plant kingdom.

65. Whittaker's five-kingdom classification provides a more detailed and comprehensive categorization by considering the cell structure, cellular organization, and mode of nutrition. Unlike the simplistic two-kingdom system that lumped vastly different organisms together, the five-kingdom system offers separate classifications for fungi, and protists, and distinguishes between unicellular and multicellular organisms, among other distinctions.

66. Cryptogams reproduce through non-seed mechanisms. Thallophytes primarily reproduce through spores or binary fission, bryophytes reproduce using spores produced in capsules, and pteridophytes reproduce through spores generated on the underside of their fronds. These methods ensure the propagation and continuation of species without the need for flowers or seeds.

67. (a) Azolla is the pteridophyte which has been proved to be a good fertilizer for paddy fields.

   (b). Prothallus develops into a new plant (gametophyte) which possesses male and female reproductive structures. The male and female gametes are produced in these structures. The gametes undergo fertilization (fusion of gametes) resulting in the formation of zygote.

68. (i) Oviparous mammal – Platypus
   (ii) Limbless amphibian – Ichthyophis

69. Reasons for identification are:
   (a) Leaves are dorsiventral
   (b) Reticulate venation
   (c) Hard woody stem
   (d) Tetra or pentamerous flowers
   (e) Seeds bearing two cotyledons

   If root system is observed, tap root system is seen.

70. (i) Pseudostem – Banana
   (ii) Bacteria – *E. Coli*

71. (a) Mushrooms
   (b) Sporophylls
   (c) Spirulina
   (d) Botryococcus brauni
   (e) Pencillium notatum
   (f) Sphagnum
   (g) Cycas
   (h) Eucalyptus
   (i) Protonema
   (j) Spirogyra
   (k) Spermatophyta

Level 3: Assess Your Concepts

72. Velvety green beds which appear on the walls during rainy season belong to bryophyta division. They grow in moist and shady region.

73. Algae are mainly classified on the basis of their pigments. Flagellation, storage products and chemistry of cell wall are also considered.

   The three classes of algae are Chlorophyceae (green algae), Phaeophyceae (brown algae) and Rhodophyceae (red algae).

   Chlorophyceae: The members of Chlorophyceae are commonly called green algae. The pigments, chlorophyll-a, chlorophyll-b, carotene and xanthophyll are present in them. They are usually grass green in colour due to the dominance of pigments i.e.chlorophyll a and b.

   Phaeophyceae: The members of Phaeophyceae are commonly called brown algae. Brown algae are found primarily in marine habitats. They possess the pigments chlorophyll a and c, carotenoids and xanthophylls.

Rhodophyceae: The members of Rhodophyceae are commonly called Red Algae. The pigments present in them are r-phycoerythrin, r-phycocyanin, chlorophyll-a and chlorophyll-d. The characteristic red colour is due to the predominance of the red pigment r-phycoerythrin.

74. Pteridophytes, gymnosperms and angiosperms are considered as vascular plants. That means they possess special tissue, that is, vascular tissue for the conduction of water, minerals and food material in the plant.

Pteridophytes do not possess xylem vessels and companion cells in phloem. Gymnosperms and angiosperms possess fully developed xylem and phloem.

Angiosperms are the most advanced group of vascular plants and differ from the other groups in some basic features.

75. Coconut plant is known as Kalpavriksha.

(i) Coconut plant parts such as leaves and fruits are considered to be sacred for Hindus.

(ii) Almost all the parts of coconut plant are useful in some way or the other for various purposes. They provide the basic needs of life such as food, fuel, shelter, etc.

76. Taxonomic systems aim to categorize the vast diversity of life into manageable groups based on shared characteristics. However, as scientific understanding evolves, these systems face challenges. The two-kingdom system was simplistic and overlooked many nuances. Whittaker's five-kingdom classification addressed some of these issues, but with advances in molecular biology, even this faced limitations. DNA sequencing revealed evolutionary relationships not evident from morphology alone. The discovery of horizontal gene transfer, especially among bacteria, further complicated matters. Molecular data sometimes contradicted traditional classifications, necessitating revisions. Additionally, as new organisms get discovered and our understanding of known organisms deepens, taxonomic systems need continuous updating. It's a balance of accommodating new data while maintaining a usable system for classification.

NEET SPECIAL WING

Multiple-Answer Type Questions

1. Hidden reproductive organs are seen in Cryptogams. Cryptogams which possess developed vascular tissues are Pteridophytes. Among the given options Selaginella and Lycopodium are Pteridophytes.

2. Algae is an example of Thallophyta. Due to their excessive growth in lakes or ponds, it forms Algal bloom which reduces oxygen and light supply to other aquatic organisms. This harmful effect cause Eutrophication and results in death of aquatic organisms.

3. Bryophyta represents the simplest terrestrial (land) plants. However, they require moist or damp surface particularly during the reproductive stage. These plants can live in both aquatic and terrestrial habitats. Hence, they are called Amphibians of Plant Kingdom. The bryophytes are small plants which generally grow together in dense groups to form green carpets or mats. They are mostly found on damp soils, rocks, walls, tree trunk, etc. The plant body is either thallus like or leaf like. Vascular tissues are absent. It is used as packing material as it has great ability to hold water, it is used as bedding stock.

4. Pteridophytes reproduce by both asexual and sexual modes. Asexual mode of reproduction can take place either from sporophyte form or gametophyte form. The haploid cells of gametophyte directly develop into haploid sporophyte. This method of reproduction is called apogamy. The diploid cells of the sporophytes can directly give rise to diploid gametophyte. This method of reproduction is called apospory. These two methods do not involve any spore formation or gametic fusion. These are vegetative methods of reproduction.

5. Tap root system is characterized by a thick main root, called primary root and side branches, called secondary roots. This root system originates from the radicle of the germinating seed. For example, pea and grams.

Comprehension-Based Questions

6. Adventitious roots are called haustoria. They protrude into the host plant for absorption of nutrients. Found in parasitic plants. For example, Cuscuta.

7. Epiphytic roots are hanging aerial roots, Growing aerially on the host plant. For example, orchids.

8. Tap root system is characterized by a thick main root, called primary root and side branches, called secondary roots. This root system originates from the radicle of the germinating seed. For example, pea and grams.

9. Lower branches of stem grow underground and swell at the tips forming tubers. Numerous buds are present which are called eyes. Eye can produce a new shoot. For example, potato

10. Prop roots are aerial roots growing vertically downward from the horizontal branches. They penetrate into the soil and give support. For example, banyan.

11. Roots in certain plants become fleshy due to accumulation of stored food. During the process of storage of food, they attain the different shapes in different plants. Both primary roots in tap root system and adventitious roots in fibrous root system can undergo this modification to perform the function of storage of food.

Spindle - Radish
(i) (a)

Conical - Carrot
(ii) (c)

Nodulose - turmeric
(iii) (e)

Fasciculated - Dahlia
(iv) (b)

Tuberous - Sweet potato
(v) (d)

B.

12. Sargassum is brown in colour and are called brown algae. It contains reserve food material which is a starch-like substance, called laminarin

13. Bryophytes helps in the formation of peat which can either be used as fuel or to improve soil texture. They are also used to make medicines, maintaining ecological balance and packing material.

14. A lot of medicines are produced from Pteridophytes. For example. Equisetum is used as an antidiuretic and haemopoietic.

15. The plant belonging to Bryophyta exhibits two forms in its life cycle. The dominant form is known as gametophyte which is thallus-like (thalloid). It is not differentiated into roots, stems and leaves. Instead of roots, the plant body possesses rhizoids. These rhizoids fix the plant to the damp soil or rock. They help in the

absorption of water and nutrients from the surface or atmosphere.

16. Lichens are composite organisms which arise from algae living in close association with fungi. Growth of Lichens is used as indicator for sulphur dioxide pollution and thus help with control pollution.

17. Match the following:

Spirogyra are unicellular, multinucleated, colonial forms which show the presence of ribbon-shaped chloroplast which is turned in spiral manner. They are green in colour and are thus called green algae. Their reserve food material is starch.
(i) (b)

Gelidium is a multicellular, filamentous form. It shows the presence of phycoerythrin which imparts red colour and hence, are called red algae
(ii) (e)

Sargassum are multicellular, filamentous forms. They show presence of chromatophores with a pigment, called fucoxanthin which is rich in iodine
(iii) (a)

Chlorella is used for aerating fish ponds and in sewage treatment plants.
(iv) (d)

Lichens are composite organisms which arise from algae living in close association with fungi. The two organisms live in symbiotic association with each other. This is a mutually beneficial relationship for both the organisms. Algae can prepare carbohydrates by the process of photosynthesis. Fungi depend on the food prepared by algae. In return, Algae get anchorage and protection from fungal filaments. Fungal organism also derives moisture and nutrients from the atmosphere and retains them for algae to grow.
(v) (c)

CHAPTER

4

Diversity in Living World—Animals

Key Ideas

After completing this chapter, you should be able to:

- Infer taxonomic hierarchy of animals
- Describe the characteristic features of ten phyla grouped under animal kingdom
- Explain in detail the complexity and diversity in mammals

Remember

Before beginning this chapter, you should be able to:

- Explain the need of classifying living organisms
- Define the rules of writing scientific names
- Relate basics of five-kingdom classification
- Interpret salient features of human digestive, locomotory, respiratory and circulatory systems.

Scientific Crypt

A Tribute to Maria Sibylla Merian (1647–1717), Mark Catesby (1683–1749), and Jane Colden (1724–1766)

Maria Sibylla Merian (1647-1717), Mark Catesby (1683-1749), and Jane Colden (1724-1766) were pioneers in biological diversity research. Merian, a German-born naturalist, changed our understanding of insect metamorphosis by providing detailed illustrations of butterfly and moth life cycles.

Catesby, an English naturalist, made significant contributions to ornithology and was among the first to illustrate American flora and fauna, laying the groundwork for future ecological studies. His seminal work, *'The Natural History of Carolina, Florida, and the Bahama Islands,'* demonstrates his commitment to biodiversity.

Jane Colden, America's first female botanist, meticulously catalogued New York's plant life using her own system of plant classification and illustrations. Her unconventional path enlightened the world to the previously unknown realms of plant science, making her a posthumous botany icon. Despite their diverse backgrounds and specialities, these trailblazers all shared an unwavering commitment to unravelling the myriad mysteries of the living world, each leaving an indelible mark on the study of biological diversity.

Crossword

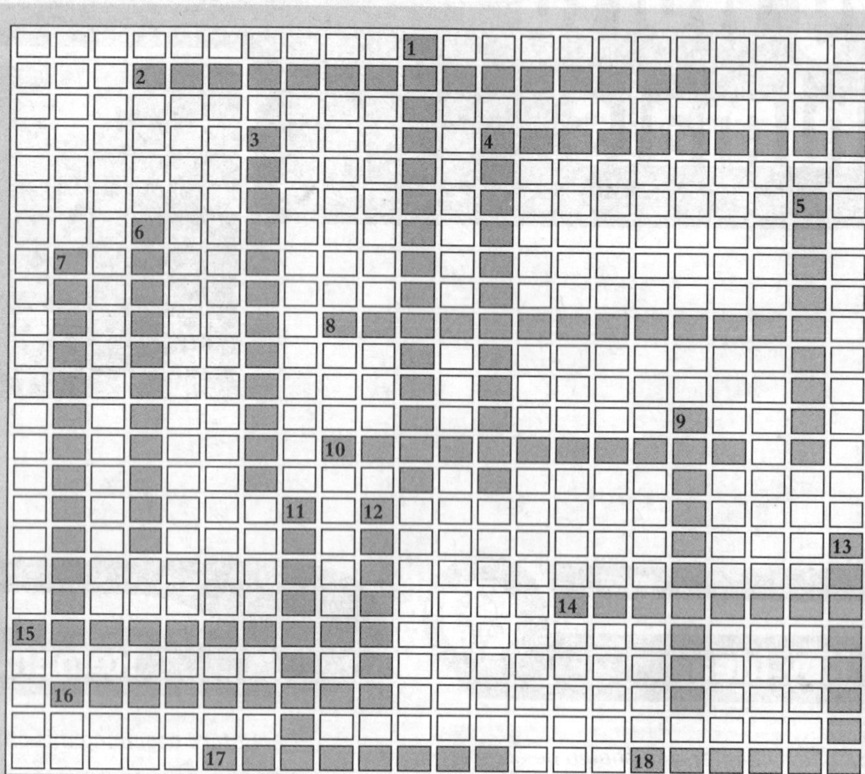

Across

2. Phylum which has an open circulatory system
4. Phylum which includes animals with jointed feet or legs.
8. Embryos which possess three germinal layers
10. Pigment present in the blood of Molluscs
14. Phylum under which organisms possess radial symmetry
15. Mammals whose young ones are protected in a special pouch on the mother's abdomen
16. Organisms which lay eggs
17. In mammals, foetus is nourished by the mother through a special structure called
18. Sexual forms of animals like *Hydra* are called

Down

1. Phylum which has flatworms
3. Jawless fishes belong to which subclass of Pisces
4. Absorption of the digested food into the cells
5. Cartilaginous rod like structure which separates the digestive tract from the nervous tissue
6. Summer sleep adopted by organisms to tide over weather conditions is called
7. Phylum which contains first Chordates
9. The dentition in mammals which is characterized by two sets of teeth
11. Centipedes and Millipedes belong to the class
12. Periodical shedding of exoskeleton
13. Another name for phylum Vertebrata wherein the brain of the animal is enclosed within the bony skull

INTRODUCTION

Animals are the most diverse group of living organisms. They inhabit various kinds of habitats with different food habits. All animals are eukaryotic, multicellular organisms, and almost all animals have a complex tissue structure with differentiated and specialized tissues. Therefore, just like plant kingdom, the animal kingdom has also been classified further into the various taxonomic units from higher to lower levels.

Classification of Animal Kingdom

The various methods used for the classification of animal kingdom are discussed as follows:

Binomial Nomenclature and Classification of Animals

The system of binomial nomenclature, proposed by Carolus Linnaeus, is followed for naming the animals, just like plants. The scientific names are derived from Greek or Latin and are internationally accepted. According to this system, the name of an animal includes two terms. The first term is called genus and the second term is called species. Same rules are followed for writing the scientific names of the animals as for plants.

Table 4.1 Scientific names of some animals

Common name	Scientific name	Genus	Species
Lion	*Panthera leo*	*Panthera*	*leo*
Cat	*Felis domesticus*	*Felis*	*domesticus*
Horse	*Equus caballus*	*Equus*	*caballus*
Human being	*Homo sapiens*	*Homo*	*sapiens*
House fly	*Musca domestica*	*Musca*	*domestica*
Honey bee	*Apis cerana*	*Apis*	*cerana*

Taxonomic Hierarchy of Animals

Just like plants, the taxonomic hierarchy of animals also starts from the highest taxonomic unit called kingdom and ends with the lowest level unit, i.e., species. Between kingdom and species, there are various levels. At each level, animals are grouped based on their similarities. As in plants, in animals also, species includes similar group of organisms which can freely interbreed among themselves and produce fertile offspring. This forms the basic unit of classification. Related species are grouped together to form a genus, related genus as family, related family as order and later class and related classes as phylum.

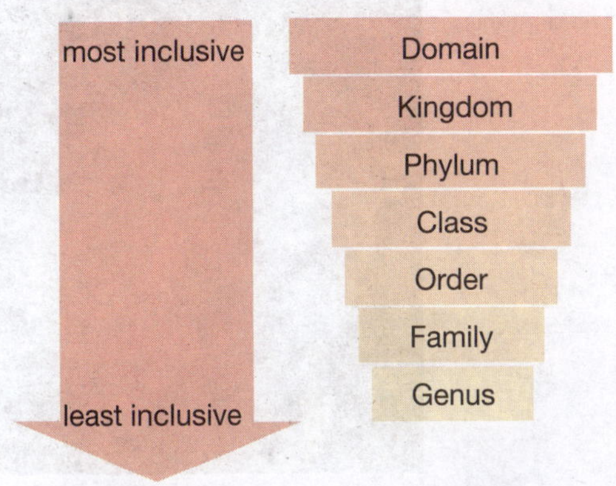

Figure 4.1 Hierarchy of animal kingdom

Though all the animals possess the common basic characteristics which distinguish them from plants, they also show a wide range of deviations in terms of complexity in structure and functioning. The innumerable numbers of animals are broadly categorized into two major groups based on the presence or absence of vertebral column or back bone. The vertebral column is a long rod-like structure made up of bones. It is a part of skeletal system which separates the nervous tissue from the digestive tract and runs along the back of the animal. The animals which possess the **vertebral** column are called vertebrates and the animals which do not possess the vertebral column are called **invertebrates**.

Invertebrates are the organisms at the lower level of evolutionary hierarchy. Whereas, vertebrates are the advanced group of organisms and show greater complexity in structure and functioning than invertebrates. Hence, they are grouped together as a separate phylum. On the whole, the entire animal kingdom is classified into ten phyla, as listed below. Among these, nine phyla are the invertebrates and the tenth phylum is the vertebrata. The ten phyla are listed as follows. These are:

1. Porifera
2. Cnidaria (Coelenterata)
3. Platyhelminthes
4. Aschelminthes (Nematoda/Nemathelminthes)
5. Annelida
6. Arthropoda
7. Mollusca
8. Echinodermata
9. Protochordata
10. Vertebrata

Info Bytes!

Carl Linnaeus classified over 12,000 species during his lifetime, laying the foundation for modern taxonomy.

The classification of entire animal kingdom into various phyla was based on certain distinguishing features. These features represent the increasing complexity of structure and functioning. Therefore, they form the basis of classification at various levels.

Distinguishing Features as Basis of Classification

In this section, we shall discuss the broad characteristics/parameters that are used to classify the animals into ten different phyla.

Cellular Organization

Animal kingdom basically comprises multicellular organisms with eukaryotic cell structure. However, the primitive organisms possess cellular level of organization and do not have tissues. These are closer to unicellular organisms as they lack tissue-level organization. All the organisms which possess this kind of primitive cellular level organization are grouped together in one phylum, i.e., Porifera. The animals belonging to all other phyla possess tissue-level organization and are classified on the basis of other characteristics.

Figure 4.2 Bath sponge, a poriferon with cellular level organization

Figure 4.3 Hydra, a cnidarian with tissue-level organization

Body Shape and Symmetry

All the animals having tissue-level organization are characterized by definite shape of the body. Generally, the various parts of an animal are arranged in a particular fashion. The body of the animal can be cut into two similar halves by one or more planes. Thus, these are said to be symmetrical. In few animals, the body cannot be cut into two equal halves from any plane. Such animals are said to be asymmetrical. For example, few organisms belonging to phylum Mollusca, such as snail. Depending on the number of planes of symmetry, the animals are categorized into Radiata and Bilateria.

1. **Radiata:** These organisms possess radial symmetry. That means, any plane passing through the middle from top to bottom can cut the body into two equal halves. The phylum Cnidaria shows this kind of symmetry. For example, *hydra.*
2. **Bilateria:** These organisms possess bilateral symmetry. That means, the body of an animal can be cut into two equal haves by only one plane which passes through the centre. All the rest of the phyla generally show this symmetry. Hence, they are grouped together as bilateria. Bilateral symmetry is considered to be a more advanced feature when compared to radial symmetry.

Figure 4.4 Different symmetry in animals

Number of Germ Layers

The embryo of an animal possesses primary layers of cells. These cells undergo cell differentiation to give rise to different kinds of tissues, which in turn form the various body organs during the course of development. These are called germ layers. In some animals, there are two germ layers, called ectoderm and endoderm. Such animals possessing two germ layers in their embryos are called diploblastic animals. For example, animals under phylum Porifera and phylum Cnidaria.

The other group of animals possess three germ layers in their embryos. The extra layer, called mesoderm is present between ectoderm and endoderm. Such animals are called triploblastic animals. This is a more advanced feature. For example, all the rest of the phyla from Platyhelminthes. The transition from diploblastic structure to triploblastic structure of the embryo represents the evolutionary hierarchy of animals.

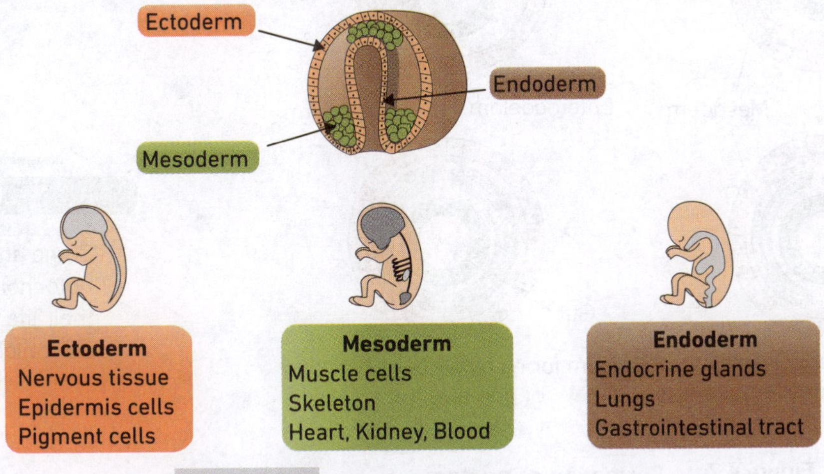

Figure 4.5 Germ layers in animal cells

Presence of Body Cavity or Coelom

Coelom or body cavity is a closed cavity in the body of an animal. This encloses the various body organs. Depending on the nature of a coelom, animals are categorized into following three groups:

1. **Acoelomate animals:** These animals do not possess a coelom. All the diploblastic animals come under acoelomates. For example, phylum Porifera and phylum Cnidaria. The triploblastic animals belonging to phylum Platyhelminthes are also acoelomate animals. For example, tapeworm.
2. **Pseudocoelomate animals:** These animals possess a false or pseudocoelom. A false coelom is the body cavity which is not completely lined by layers of epithelial cells (peritoneum) on the inner and outer sides. The animals belonging to phylum Aschelminthes are pseudocoelomates. For example, roundworm (*Ascaris*).
3. **Coelomate animals:** These animals possess a true coelom. A true coelom is the body cavity completely lined by the layers of epithelial cells (peritoneum) on inner and outer sides. The phyla starting from Annelida include coelomate animals.

   Depending on the origin of coelom, the coelomates are further categorized into two groups. The coelom can be originated from the mesodermal cells of the embryo. For example, the phyla Annelida, Mollusca and Arthropoda. The coelom can be originated from the pouches pinched off from the endoderm of the embryo. For example, the phylum Echinodermata and Protochordata of invertebrates and all the vertebrate animals.

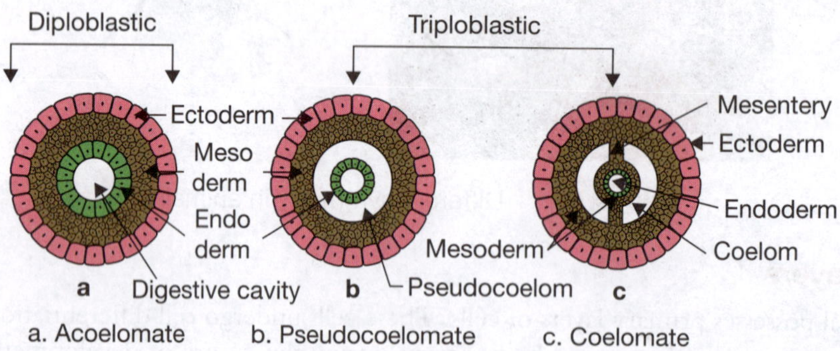

Figure 4.6 Categories of animals according to nature of coelom—Acoelomate, Pseudocoelomate and Coelomate

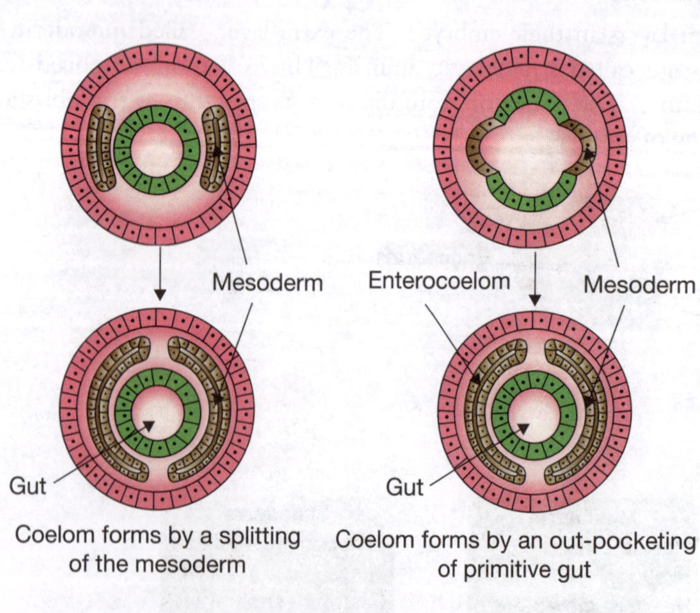

Figure 4.7 Formation of coelom

Info Bytes!

Some animals possess notochord at some stage in their life cycle. Such animals are called chordates.

Presence of Notochord

Notochord is a long rod-like structure mostly made up of cartilage. It separates the digestive tract from the nervous tissue. It runs along the back of an animal. In most of the chordates, this notochord is present only in their embryonic stage and is replaced by vertebral column in the adult stage. The chordates in which notochord in embryonic stage is replaced by vertebral column in the adult stage are grouped together in phylum Vertebrata. In few chordates, notochord is present only up to tail. It is not replaced by the vertebral column even in the adult stage. They are grouped together in phylum Protochordata. The protochordates are included as the ninth phylum along with the non-chordates and are studied under invertebrates. Since vertebral column is an obvious and significant distinguishing feature, the entire animal kingdom is divided into two broad categories as invertebrates and vertebrates for the sake of convenience of study.

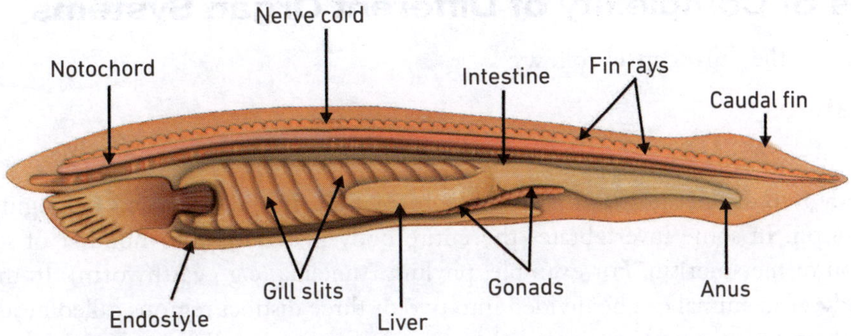

Figure 4.8 Illustration of an invertebrate with a notochord

Classification of Animals into Various Phyla Based on Distinguishing Features

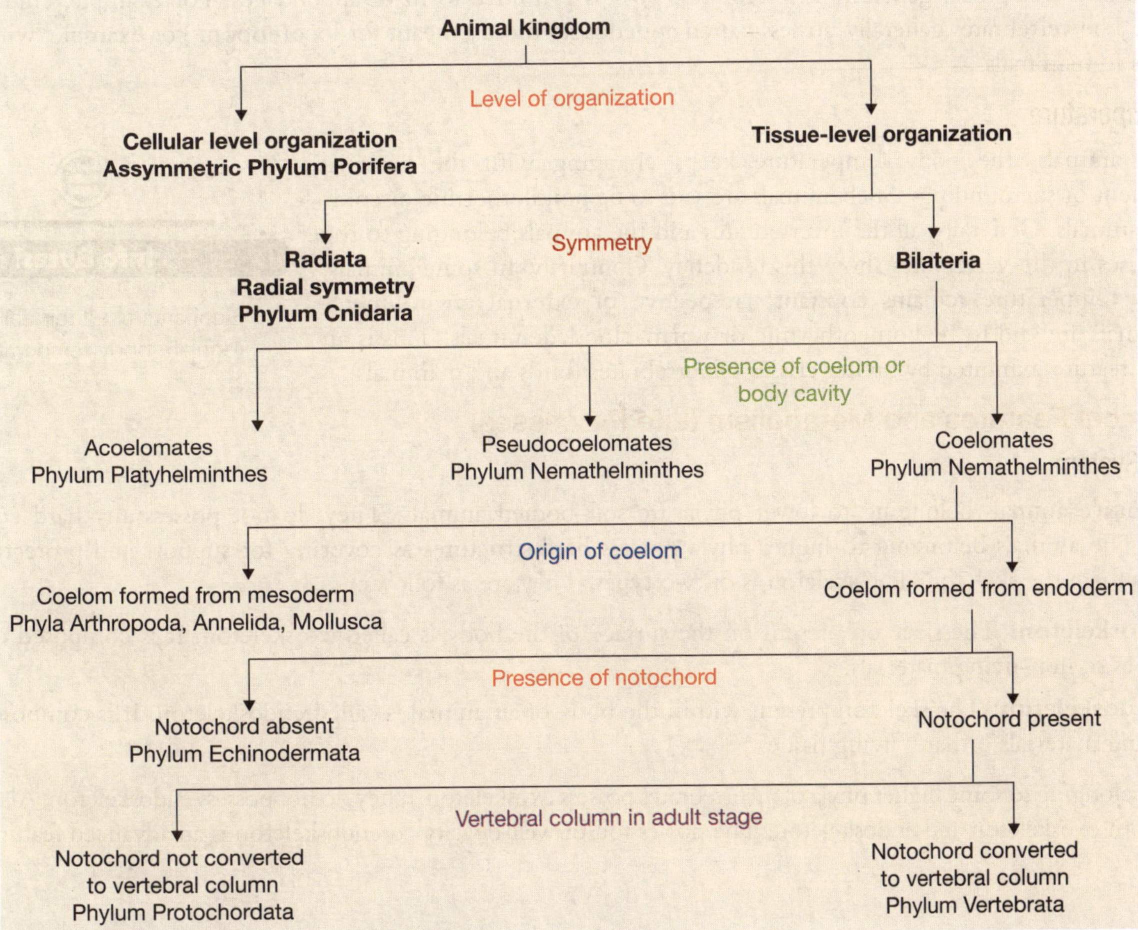

Figure 4.9 Classification of animals

The entire animal kingdom is classified into ten phyla. The phyla are arranged in the increasing order of complexity of body organization. The complexity of body organization involves various morphological and anatomical features and hence, they have different types of metabolism and life cycle. Phylum Porifera has only cellular level of organization. It has no organ systems. Phylum Cnidaria has tissue-level organization. But it is not associated with distinct organ systems. The other phyla of Invertebrates and phylum Vertebrata show gradual increase in complexity of the organ systems from primitive to complex.

Konnect

The animals which do not possess notochord at any stage in their life cycle are called nonchordates.

Various Levels of Complexity of Different Organ Systems

The levels of complexity of the organs are as follows:

Morphological Features

Body Segmentation

The division of the body into distinct portions is called segmentation. In the organisms belonging to lower phyla, there is no such kind of division. In some invertebrates the entire body is divided into number of segments. This is called metameric segmentation or metamerism. For example, phylum Annelida (e.g., earthworm). In the organisms belonging to higher phyla, the body of an animal can be divided into two or three distinct regions called head, thorax and abdomen. Sometimes, head and thorax may not be distinct and hence, the region is called cephalothorax. For example, phylum Arthropoda (e.g., cockroach). All the vertebrates possess this distinct division of the body.

Appendages

The structures which project from the body of an animal used for locomotion and feeding are called appendages. The organisms of lower phyla, generally invertebrates, possess primitive form of appendages. For example, cnidarians have tentacles. The vertebrates generally possess paired appendages mostly meant for locomotion. For example, wings in birds and limbs in mammals.

Body Temperature

In some animals, the body temperature keeps changing with the external environment or surroundings. Such animals are said to be poikilothermic or cold-blooded animals. Generally, all the invertebrates and the animals belonging to the lower classes in the vertebrates show this tendency. Contrarily, In some animals, the body temperature remains constant irrespective of external environment. Such animals are said to be homeothermic or warm-blooded animals. This is an advanced feature exhibited by higher classes of vertebrates (birds and mammals).

Info Bytes!

Elephants use their ears to regulate body temperature.

Anatomical Features and Metabolism (Life Processes)

Skeletal System

The primitive animals belonging to lower phyla are soft-bodied animals. They do not possess any hard covering for support. The animals belonging to higher phyla possess hard structures as covering for support and protection. These structures form the skeleton. The skeleton is of two types. They are as follows:

1. **Exoskeleton:** The skeleton present on the surface of the body is called exoskeleton. It is composed of different types of non-living materials.
2. **Endoskeleton:** The skeleton present within the body of an animal is called endoskeleton. It is composed of non-living materials or hard, living tissues.

Animals belonging to some higher phyla of invertebrates possess exoskeleton. They do not possess endoskeleton. All vertebrates possess both exoskeleton and endoskeleton. The possession of well-developed endoskeleton is an advanced feature.

Digestive System and Process of Digestion

The digestive system comprises the various organs associated with different stages of digestion. Following are the steps involved in the process of digestion:

- Intake of food (ingestion)
- Breaking down of the food into simpler substances (digestion)
- The absorption of the digested food into the cells (assimilation)
- The elimination of wastes from the system (egestion)

All the organs associated with these stages of digestive system constitute digestive tract.

There can be basically two kinds of digestive tracts:

1. **Incomplete digestive tract:** It possesses a single opening for intake of food and elimination of wastes. For example, animals upto phylum Platyhelminthes.
2. **Complete digestive tract:** It possesses a mouth for ingestion and anus for egestion. For example, invertebrates from Nemathelminthes and all vertebrates.

The possession of complete digestive tract is an advanced feature found in the higher phyla of invertebrates and vertebrates.

The mode of digestion is basically of two types, namely:

1. **Intracellular digestion:** The process of digestion which takes place in the vacuoles inside the cell is the intracellular digestion. The digestive juices are poured into the vacuoles and the products of digestion are poured into the cytoplasm. This is a primitive method of digestion which takes place in the lower phyla of invertebrates. For example, upto phylum Platyhelminthes.
2. **Extracellular digestion:** The process of digestion which takes place outside the cell in a cavity is called extracellular digestion. The digestive juices are poured into the cavity and the products of digestion diffuse into the walls of the intestine. For example, invertebrates from Nemathelminthes and all vertebrates.

Circulatory System

Circulatory system involves the organs associated with the transport of materials in the body. In the phyla at lower levels in the hierarchy, the circulatory system is absent as the transportation takes place by the process of diffusion. The animals belonging to the higher phyla in the hierarchy possess specific circulatory system, consisting of a fluid, called blood which is circulated in the body to carry the materials to various parts. Depending on the mode of circulation of blood, there are two types of circulatory systems. These are:

1. **Open circulatory system**
   - Blood flows in open spaces called sinuses.
   - Body cavity remains filled with blood.
   - For example, upto phylum Nemathelminthes.
2. **Closed circulatory system**
   - Blood flows in blood vessels.
   - For example, invertebrates from phylum Annelida and all vertebrates.
   - The colour of the blood depends on the pigments present in the blood.

Konnect

Four main types of pigments found in the blood of animals are: haemoglobin, haemocyanin, chlorocruorin and haemerythrin.

Respiratory System and Process of Respiration

The animals generally show aerobic respiration. Only few parasitic organisms living in the systems of other animals show anaerobic respiration. The aerobic respiration involves the following stages:

- Taking in oxygen (Inhalation)
- Exchange of gases through a medium
- Releasing out carbon dioxide (Exhalation)

The animals belonging to different phyla possess different organs for various stages. The type of respiratory organs in various animals mainly depends on their habitat. For example, fish possess gills as respiratory organs for their aquatic habitat. Mammals, on the other hand, possess lungs as respiratory organs as they mostly found on terrestrial habitat.

Excretory System and Process of Excretion

Excretion is the process of removal of nitrogenous waste materials formed during the metabolic processes in the body. The animals belonging to lower phyla have no specific excretory organs. They excrete wastes by the process of diffusion. However, the animals belonging to different phyla possess different excretory organs. These excretory organs also help in maintaining the water level in the body. This phenomenon is called osmoregulation. The different animals excrete the nitrogenous wastes in different forms. The animals are grouped into three categories based on the excretory products—Ammonotelic, ureotelic and uricotelic.

Info Bytes!

Urea is a product of the degradation of amino acids.

Table 4.2 Categories of animals based on excretory products

Excretory product	Category of animals	Example of phylum
Ammonia	Ammonotelic	Fish
Urea	Ureotelic	Mammals
Uric acid	Uricotelic	Birds

Reproductive System and Life Cycle

The animals belonging to lower phyla of invertebrates usually show both asexual and sexual modes of reproduction. Asexual reproduction takes place by various methods. Regeneration is the most common mode of asexual reproduction found in lower invertebrate phyla. In all the animals in higher phyla, the reproduction takes place by sexual mode. The sexual mode of reproduction involves following three stages:

1. Formation of gametes (Gametogenesis)
2. Fusion of male and female gametes to form zygote (Fertilization)
3. Development of zygote into a fully formed young one (Development)

Formation of gametes: The animals possess reproductive organs called gonads for the formation of gametes. Depending on the possession of gonads, the animals can be categorized into two types:

1. **Hermaphrodite** or **bisexual**
    - Both male and female gonads are present in the same individual.
    - This is a primitive feature found in most of the invertebrates.
    - For example, upto phylum Platyhelminthes.
2. **Unisexual**
    - Male and female sex organs are present in separate individuals.
    - This is an advanced feature found in some invertebrate phyla and most of the vertebrates.
    - For example, Phylum Nemathelminthes and all vertebrates.
    - In most of the vertebrates and few invertebrates which show unisexuality, the male and female organisms can be distinguished by external appearance.
    - Male and female animals possess some distinctive morphological features and hence, can be distinguished from their physical appearance is known as sexual dimorphism. For example, phylum Annelida among invertebrates and most of the vertebrates.

Figure 4.10 Female and male Nyala.

Fertilization: The fusion of male and female gametes is called fertilization. The process of fertilization is also different for animals in lower phyla and higher phyla. It can be of two types mentioned as below:

1. **External Fertilization:**
   - Male and female gametes are released into water.
   - Fertilization takes place outside the body of the female organism.
   - This is a primitive feature found in most of the invertebrates. For example, upto phylum Platyhelminthes in invertebrates and lower vertebrates.
2. **Internal Fertilization:**
   - Sperms are released into the reproductive tract of female during copulation or mating.
   - Fertilization takes place in the genital tract of female. For example, from phylum Nemathelminthes in invertebrates to higher vertebrates.

Development: The process of formation of an adult organism (young one) from the zygote is called development. In the case of external fertilization, further development of the young one from zygote invariably takes place in the external environment only.

In the case of internal fertilization, the zygote can undergo the process of development either in the external environment or in the reproductive tract of the female animal. The egg can be laid by the female and can be hatched in the outside environment. Such animals are called oviparous animals. The phenomenon is called oviparity. For example, most of the invertebrates with few exceptions and most of the vertebrates except mammals.

The development of the young one from the zygote may involve a larval stage. This transformation of zygote into an adult involving such larval stage is said to be indirect development. In such cases, the larval form shows a lot of structural variation and differs in functioning, habitat and food requirement from its adult form. The phenomenon in which the larval and the adult forms show wide variation in structure, form and functioning is called metamorphosis. For example, phylum Arthropoda in invertebrates and lower vertebrates.

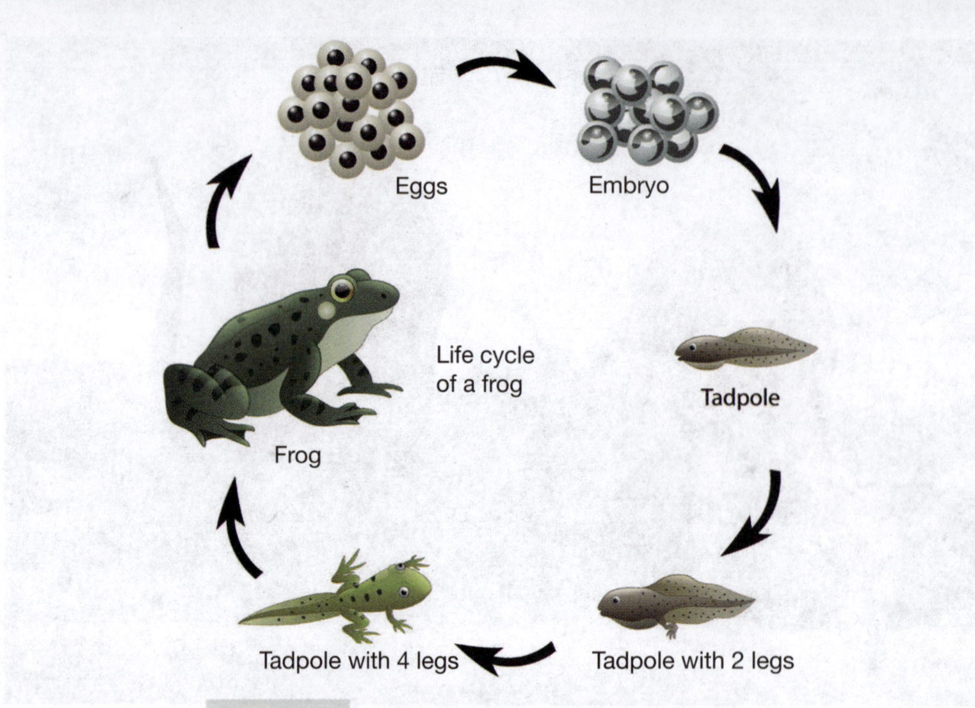

Figure 4.11 Reproduction and life cycle of frog

The zygote can be transformed into the young one directly without involving any larval stage. This is known as direct development. For example, birds in vertebrates. In the case of some animals belonging to higher phyla, the zygote undergoes the process of development in the reproductive system of the female itself. That means, the female animal gives birth to the almost fully formed young one. Such animals are called viviparous animals. The phenomenon is said to be viviparity. For example, few arthropods, few annelids and most of the mammals.

The animals belonging to invertebrate phyla show oviparity and indirect development. Few animals belonging to invertebrata may show another phenomenon in which the zygote may undergo development within the eggs while the eggs remain in the body of the female animal. The eggs are hatched in the womb of the female animal where the young ones come out of the egg by breaking the shell. These young ones are then released out by the female animal. Such animals are said to be ovoviviparous animals and the phenomenon is known as ovoviviparity. For example, phylum Nemathelminthes among invertebrates and few arthropods like scorpion.

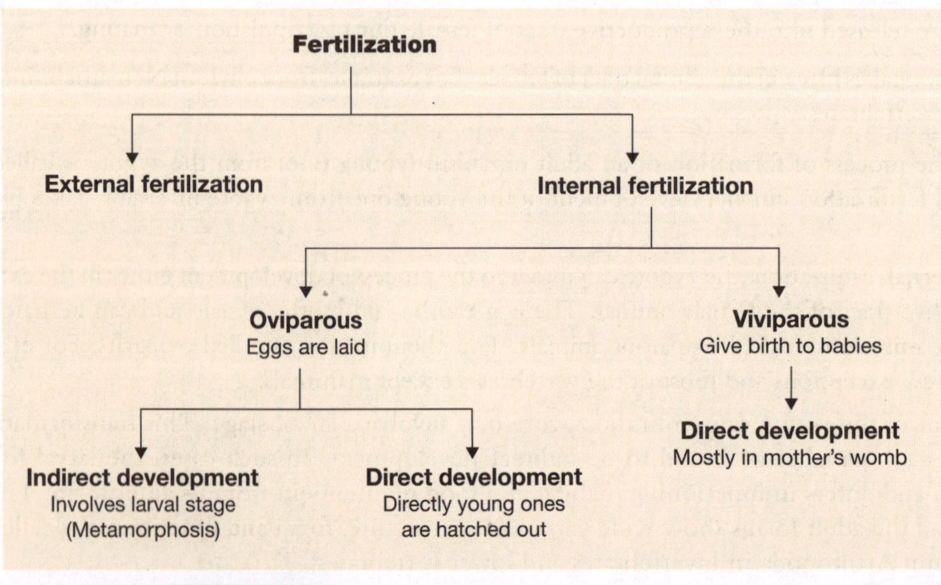

Figure 4.12 Different types of fertilization methods

Quick Recap

✔ **How does triploblastic nature aid in the complexity of advanced vertebrate organisms?**

Triploblastic organisms possess three germ layers: ectoderm, mesoderm, and endoderm. This division of labour, so to speak, facilitates the formation of diverse and specialized organ systems, thus leading to the evolution of more complex organisms. The distinct germ layers contribute to the formation of specific organ systems, allowing advanced vertebrates to perform a multitude of functions.

✔ **Identify the following parasites and the phylum to which they belong.**

(a) It lives in the intestine of humans and causes vomiting.

(b) It invades the skin of humans and causes elephantiasis.

(c) It resides in the stomach of humans and causes itching anus and stomach ache.

(a) Pinworm (*Enterobius vermicularis*) causes Enterobiasis characterized by vomiting.

(b) Filarial worm (*Wuchereria bancrofti*) causes elephantiasis or filariasis.

(c) Hookworm (*Necator americanus*) causes stomach ache and itching anus.

These organisms belong to the phylum Nemethelminthes or Nematoda.

Features:

- Mostly parasitic with separate sexes.
- Triploblastic and bilaterally symmetrical with a cylindrical body shape.
- A primitive body cavity is present. This is known as pseudocoelom as it is not lined by mesoderm.

✔ **How do hermaphroditic organisms increase their chances of reproductive success?**

Hermaphroditic organisms possess both male and female reproductive organs. This dual capability can enhance their reproductive success, especially in environments where finding a mate is challenging. They can potentially reproduce with any individual they encounter, leading to a higher likelihood of producing offspring.

Animal Kingdom—Invertebrata

Let us understand the characteristic features of all phyla and some notable examples of each phylum.

Phylum Porifera

The name 'porifera' originated from the words 'pori' meaning pores and 'pherein' meaning 'bearing'. That means, these organisms bear pores on their body. This phylum includes the most primitive animals and are associated with the simplest form of body organization. The cells are loosely held together and there is no tissue or organ formation. These organisms show certain similarities with plants and hence, these are also called sponges.

Figure 4.13 A yellow tubular sponge Clathrina clathrus from the Mediterranean Sea

Figure 4.14 Members of the phylum Porifera showing ostia

Table 4.3 Characteristic features of Porifera

Characteristics	Description
Habitat	Aquatic and mostly marine Generally attached to rocks For example, *Leucosolenia, Sycon, Spongia, Euspongia* (bath sponge) Few are fresh water forms For example, *Spongilla*, etc.
Morphological features	Body shape is cylindrical, vaselike, rounded, sac-like or branched Asymmetrical or radially symmetrical Porous body with pores, called **ostia** Single large opening, called **osculum** at the top
Movement and locomotion	Mostly sessile and stationary Plant-like appearance
Anatomical features	Skeleton made up of **siliceous spicules** (needle-like structures made up of silicon dioxide) or **calcareous spicules** (made up of calcium carbonate) or proteinaceous **spongin fibres** Interconnected network of channels called canal system is present for circulation No mouth and alimentary canal No respiratory organs No excretory organs No nervous system
Metabolism	Intake of water and food through ostia Intracellular digestion Food and oxygen are carried along with water entering through ostia Carbon dioxide and nitrogenous wastes are thrown out through osculum by diffusion Excretory matter is ammonia Nutrition, respiration and excretion through canal system
Reproduction	Both asexual mode and sexual modes Asexual mode–Budding; gemmules (internal buds) Internal fertilization

Phylum Cnidaria

The name 'cnidaria' originated from the word 'knide' meaning 'nettle or stinge cells'. That means, this name denotes the stinging nature of cells. This is a new name which replaced the old name 'coelenterata'. The name coelenterata originated from the word 'koilos' meaning 'hollow' and 'enteron' meaning 'intestine' or 'gut'. That means, the body of these animals possesses a hollow sac-like body cavity with a single opening to the outside for ingestion and egestion, which means they possess incomplete digestive tract. This phylum includes animals with simplest tissue-level organization and show clear division of labour. They have tissues but do not possess organ systems. They also lack body cavity as they are diploblastic. Example, *Hydra*

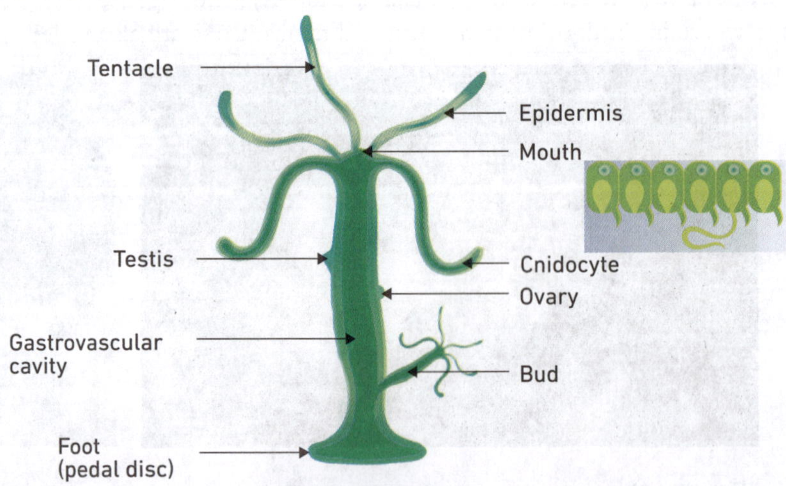

Figure 4.15 *Hydra*

Table 4.4 Characteristic features of Cnidaria

Characteristics	Description
Habitat	Aquatic and exclusively marine Generally attached to rocks. For example, jelly fish and sea anemone. Only one fresh water animal For example, *Hydra*.
Morphological features	Body shape—cylindrical, vaselike, sac-like Radially symmetrical A number of slender, flexible, finger-like processes called **tentacles** are present around the mouth Tentacles help in capturing food and are also used for defence Some animals secrete calcium compounds around them which later form hard **corals**.
Movement and locomotion	Sedentary or free swimming Animal exists in two forms **(polymorphism)**. These forms are called **zooids.** Asexual form (phase) is called **polyp.** Polyp leads sedentary colonial life. Sexual form is called **medusa.** Medusa is a free-living form.
Anatomical features	Some organisms possess hard, calcareous exoskeleton. For example, Corals. Incomplete digestive tract No respiratory organs No excretory organs Primitive nervous system with nerve cells and their processes Sensory cells are present Special stinging cells called **cnidoblasts** on the body and abundant in tentacles. They help in paralyzing the prey. Gonads (testes and ovary) are present without any ducts.
Metabolism	Intake of water and food through mouth Partly extracellular digestion in the coelenteron and partly intracellular digestion Distribution of food through coelenteron Respiration and excretion through body surface Food and oxygen are carried along with water entering through ostia Carbon dioxide and nitrogenous wastes are thrown out through osculum by diffusion Excretory matter is ammonia
Reproduction	Both asexual mode and sexual modes Asexual mode–budding in polyp form Sexual reproduction in medusa form External or internal fertilization Zygote develops into larva called **planula** Alternation of generations with polyp form and medusa form is found

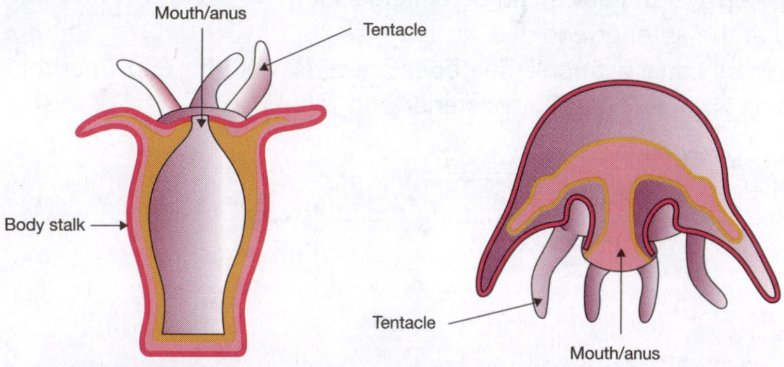

Figure 4.16 Medusa and polyp forms of Phylum Cnidaria

Phylum Platyhelminthes

The name 'platyhelminthes' originated from the words 'platys' meaning 'flat' and 'helminth' meaning 'worm'. Hence, these are also called 'flatworms'. This phylum includes animals with bilateral symmetry. They are the simplest triploblastic animals. But these are acoelomate animals. They have tissues and possess primitive organ systems. Example, Tapeworm

Figure 4.17 Tapeworm

Table 4.5 Characteristic features of Platyhelminthes

Characteristics	Description
Habitat	Mostly parasitic animals For example, liver fluke, tapeworm, blood fluke, etc. Some are free-living, may be terrestrial or marine or fresh water For example, *Planaria* (living in both marine and freshwater), etc.
Morphological features	Body shape—Narrow, elongated and cylindrical Flat or ribbon-like appearance Bilaterally symmetrical Unsegmented body with anterior and posterior ends Dorsal and ventral sides can be distinguished Head at the anterior end Alimentary canal with only one opening at the anterior end (mouth) There is no opening at the posterior end (anus)
Movement and locomotion	Ciliated body surface Cilia help in locomotion

(*Continued*)

Table 4.5 *(Continued)*

Characteristics	Description
Anatomical features	No skeleton The space between body wall and body organs filled with special connective tissue The tissue consists of a network of large irregular cells with fluid filled spaces Branched digestive cavity Digestive system absent or incomplete digestive tract No respiratory organs No excretory organs Ladder-like nervous system with brain and two longitudinal nerve cords joined at intervals Primitive sense organs in the form of a pair of eye spots on dorsal side, only in free-living forms Gonads with ducts leading to copulatory organs are present
Metabolism	Intake of water and food through mouth Respiration through body surface Excretory system with **flame cells** Flame cells absorb excretory matter from the body and discharge through excretory ducts Excretory matter is ammonia Osmoregulation
Reproduction	Generally sexual mode Hermaphrodite or bisexual Cross-fertilization Life cycle includes more than one larval stage Parasitic forms involve more than one host for the completion of life cycle Asexual reproduction is less common. Takes place by transverse fission Power of regeneration

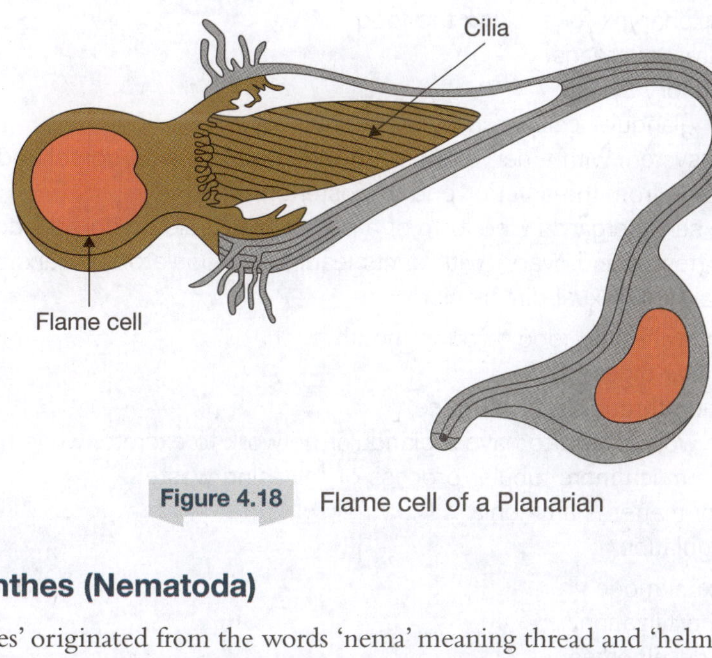

Figure 4.18 Flame cell of a Planarian

Phylum Nemathelminthes (Nematoda)

The name 'nemathelminthes' originated from the words 'nema' meaning thread and 'helminth' meaning 'worm'. Hence, these are also called threadworms or roundworms or nematodes. This phylum includes animals with bilateral symmetry. They are triploblastic and pseudocoelomate animals. They possess some organ systems. Example, *Ascaris*

Figure 4.19 *Ascaris*

Table 4.6 Characteristic features of Nemathelminthes

Characteristics	Description
Habitat	Mostly free-living animals. May be terrestrial or marine or fresh water Some are parasitic For example, *Ascaris* (roundworm), *Wuchereria* (Filarial worm), etc.
Morphological features	Body shape—Cylindrical body with tapering ends Thin thread-like appearance Bilaterally symmetrical Unsegmented body with anterior and posterior ends Dorsal and ventral sides can be distinguished Head at the anterior end and anus at the posterior end
Movement and locomotion	Ciliated body surface Cilia help in locomotion
Anatomical features	No skeleton The fluid in pseudocoelom maintains body shape. This is called **hydroskeleton**. Complete digestive tract with mouth bordered with lips having sensory papillae Muscular pharynx for sucking the food No respiratory organs No circulatory system A pair of glandular cells or intracellular canals for excretion Nervous system with a nerve ring round the pharynx with dorsal and ventral longitudinal nerve cords from the anterior end to posterior end Primitive sense organs in the form of a pair of eye spots on dorsal side, only in free-living forms Gonads (testes and ovary) with ducts leading to copulatory organs are present Unisexual with sexual dimorphism
Metabolism	Intake of water and food through mouth Extracellular digestion Respiration through body surface Parasitic worms tend to have a glandular network to excrete, while non-parasitic worms tend to have a much more tubular process of releasing waste Excretory matter is ammonia Osmoregulation
Reproduction	Only sexual mode Internal fertilization Indirect development Parasitic forms involve more than one host for the completion of life cycle

Phylum Annelida

The name 'annelida' originated from the word 'annulus' meaning 'ring'. Hence, these are also called 'ringworms'. That means, the body is composed of rings or segments. This phylum includes the animals with bilateral symmetry. They are triploblastic and coelomate animals. They possess almost all the organ systems. Some of the organs systems are primitive. Example, earthworm, leech, etc.

Figure 4.20 Lumbricina (Earthworm)

Figure 4.21 Hirudinaria (Leech)

Table 4.7 Characteristic features of Annelida

Characteristics	Description
Habitat	Mostly free-living animals. May be terrestrial (moist soil) For example, Earthworm Marine or fresh water Few are parasitic For example, Leech
Morphological features	Body shape—Cylindrical body with tapering ends Bilaterally symmetrical Body made up of rings or segments, called metamers Segmented body with anterior and posterior ends Dorsal and ventral sides can be distinguished Head at the anterior end and anus at the posterior end
Movement and locomotion	Locomotory organs are called **setae** or parapodia which are made up of chitin
Anatomical features	No skeleton The fluid in coelom maintains body shape. This is called **hydroskeleton**. Complete digestive tract with mouth bordered with lips having sensory papillae Muscular pharynx for sucking the food Gills as respiratory organs in some animals Closed circulatory system Coiled tubular structures called **nephredia** for excretion Nervous system with a nerve ring and a solid ventral nerve cord with **ganglia** (A ganglion is an aggregation of nerve cells) Primitive sense organs in the form of a pair of eye spots on dorsal side, only in free-living forms Gonads with ducts leading to copulatory organs are present Bisexual or unisexual with sexual dimorphism

(Continued)

Table 4.7 *(Continued)*

Characteristics	Description
Metabolism	Intake of water and food through mouth Extracellular digestion Respiration through body surface or gills Blood contains hemoglobin in plasma Nephridia absorb excretory matter from the body and discharge through excretory ducts Excretory matter is ammonia
Reproduction	Generally sexual mode Internal fertilization Oviparity is seen Indirect development Asexual reproduction by regeneration in some, for example, earthworm

Phylum Arthropoda

The name 'arthropoda' originated from the word 'arthron' meaning 'joint' and 'podos' meaning 'foot'. That means, this phylum includes animals with jointed feet or legs. The arthropods are the most successful group of animals. They contribute more than 80 per cent of the animal species. Presence of three or more jointed legs is the characteristic feature of these organisms. They show bilateral symmetry and are triploblastic. The body is divided into head, thorax and abdomen. Example, Ants, Bees, Dragonflies, Crabs, Lobsters, Scorpions, Centipedes, Shrimps, Spiders

Figure 4.22 Cockroach, scorpion, prawn and spider

Table 4.8 Characteristic features of Arthropoda

Characteristics	Description
Habitat	Present everywhere on earth For example, ant, mosquito, etc. Few are parasitic For example, lice, etc.
Morphological features	Body shape is variable Body segmented into head, thorax and abdomen Head and thorax—Cephalothorax Dorsal and ventral sides can be distinguished Body covered by hard exoskeleton made up of **chitin** Exoskeleton has joints **Compound** eyes with many lenses
Movement and locomotion	Locomotory organs–paired legs Number of pairs variable
Anatomical features	Hard chitinous exoskeleton The exoskeleton is shed periodically during the life cycle. This is called **ecdysis** or **moulting** Reduced body cavity filled with blood **(haemocoel)** Distinct digestive system with movable mouth parts Respiratory organs—Gills, trachea and book lungs Open circulatory system **Green glands** or **Malpighian tubules** as excretory organs Green glands open directly to the exterior and Malpighian tubules open into the gut Nervous system with a nerve ring and a solid ventral nerve cord with ganglia A pair of simple or compound eyes Compound eyes have many lenses unlike simple eyes which have one lens each A pair of antennae First animals to have endocrine system (glands which release hormones) Gonads with ducts leading to copulatory organs are present Usually unisexual with sexual dimorphism in some animals
Metabolism	Intake of water and food through mouth Extracellular digestion Respiration through body surface or gills or tracheae or book lungs Blood contains hemoglobin in plasma Excretory matter is ammonia Nervous system similar to annelids Characterized by mosaic vision
Reproduction	Only sexual mode Internal fertilization Some are oviparous In oviparous animals, development is indirect and involves metamorphosis For example, insects, etc. Some animals are viviparous For example, aphids, etc. Scorpion is ovoviviparous

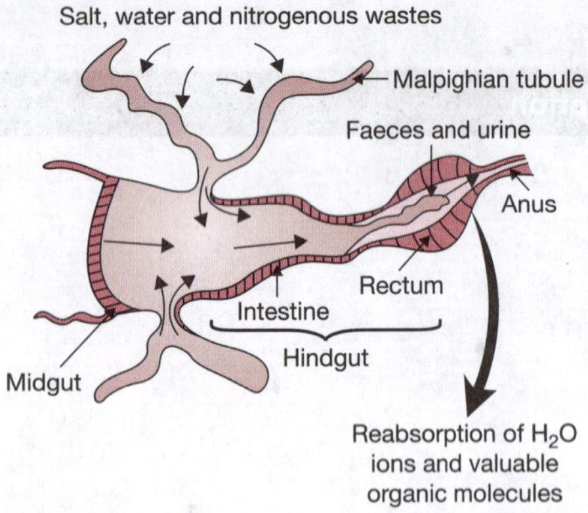

Figure 4.23 Illustration of Malpighian tubules

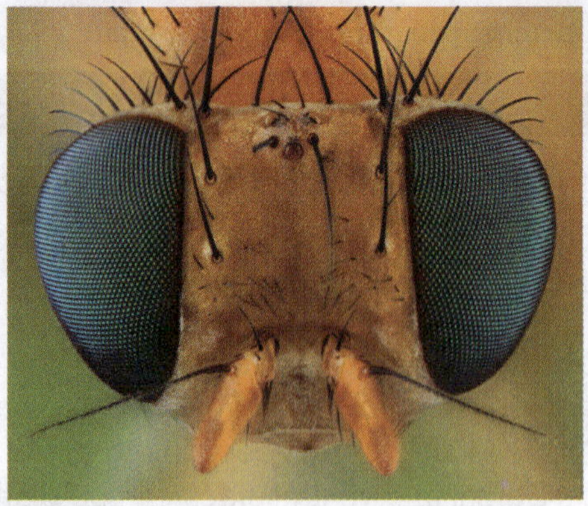

Figure 4.24 Close up of head of an arthropod showing compound eyes

Classification of Arthropoda

This phylum comprises huge number of animals and shows a wide range of variations in form and functioning among them. This phylum is further classified into four important classes:

1. Crustacea (For example, crabs, lobsters, shrimps, etc.)
2. Myriapoda (For example, centipedes, millipedes, etc.)
3. Insecta (For example, houseflies, ants, butterflies, grasshoppers, mosquitoes, cockroaches, etc.)
4. Arachnida (For example, spiders, scorpions, mites, ticks, etc.)

Among all these, the class insecta comprises the largest class of animals and the most successful land invertebrates. Hence, it is the most studied group of arthropods.

Info Bytes!

- A cockroach can survive decapitation.
- Butterflies use their feet to taste food.

Characteristic features of class insecta:

- Live on land and in air
- Body divisible into head, thorax and abdomen
- Head bears one pairs of antennae
- Distinct type of mouth parts
- Respiration by trachea
- Excretion through Malpighian tubules
- Development includes metamorphosis

Phylum Mollusca

The name 'mollusca' originated from the word 'molluscus' meaning 'soft'. That means, this phylum includes soft-bodied animals. The molluscs are a very diverse and successful group of animals. They constitute the second largest group of animal species after arthropods. Presence of shells in which the soft bodies are enclosed is the characteristic feature of these organisms. They show bilateral symmetry and are triploblastic. The body is divided into head, thorax and abdomen.

Figure 4.25 Life cycle of a butterfly

Figure 4.26 Snail and cuttle fish

Table 4.9 Characteristic features of Mollusca

Characteristics	Description
Habitat	Mostly aquatic and marine habitat For example, octopus, etc. Few live in fresh water For example, snail, etc.
Morphological features	Soft and unsegmented body Body divided into anterior head, ventral muscular foot and a dorsal visceral mass or hump Dorsal and ventral sides can be distinguished
Movement and locomotion	Soft, muscular foot on ventral side as locomotory organ
Anatomical features	Hard exoskeleton made up of calcium carbonate in the form of shell **Visceral hump** on the dorsal side of the foot It is covered by a thin fleshy fold called **mantle** or **pallium**. It scretes the shell It encloses space between itself and body, called mantle Mantle secretes a calcareous shell in most of the molluscs Reduced body cavity filled with blood (haemocoel) Complete digestive tract with **radula** as rasping organ and **chitinous teeth**; anus opens into mantle cavity Respiratory organs—Gills, ctenidia located in mantle cavity Terrestrial forms—lungs or air sacs Open circulatory system with dorsal heart and few arteries which open into sinuses One or two pairs of kidneys **(organs of Bojanus)** which open into mantle cavity as excretory organs Nervous system with a few pairs of ganglia joined by nerve connections Sense organs include eyes, tentacles and **statocyst** A pair of antennae Gonads with ducts leading to copulatory organs are present Usually unisexual with sexual dimorphism in some animals
Metabolism	Intake of water and food through mouth Extracellular digestion Respiration through gills or ctenidia Excretory matter is ammonia Blood contains **haemocyanin** in plasma

(Continued)

Table 4.9 (*Continued*)

Characteristics	Description
Reproduction	Only sexual mode Internal fertilization or external fertilization Generally oviparous Fertilized eggs develop into larvae In some animals, development may be direct while in some it is indirect

Phylum Echinodermata

The name 'echinodermata' originated from the words 'echinos' meaning spines and 'derma' meaning skin. That means, the animals of this phylum include spiny skinned animals. They show radial symmetry and are triploblastic. Example, Starfish

Figure 4.27 Starfish

Table 4.10 Characteristic features of Echinodermata

Characteristics	Description
Habitat	Exclusively marine habitat They live at the bottom of the sea
Morphological features	Star- or disc- or flower-like body (pentamerous symmetry) Unsegmented body Does not possess head or tail No left and right distinction Mouth on lower surface Anus on upper surface
Movement and locomotion	Soft and retractable tube feet as locomotory organs

(*Continued*)

Table 4.10 *(Continued)*

Characteristics	Description
Anatomical features	Hard exoskeleton with spines or projections Complete and simple digestive system Body cavity modified into water **vascular system with tube** feet Tube feet help in food collection Respiratory organs—Gills Terrestrial forms—Lungs or air sacs Reduced circulatory system without heart No excretory organs Primitive nervous system with a nerve ring and radial nerve cords Brain is absent Unisexual without sexual dimorphism
Metabolism	Food intake by tube feet Extracellular digestion Respiration through gills or ctenidia Excretory matter is ammonia
Reproduction	Asexual mode by regeneration External fertilization Oviparous Development indirect Fertilized eggs develop into larvae

Phylum Protochordata

The term 'protochordata' originated from the words 'protos' meaning first and 'chordata' meaning notochord. That means, these animals are the first group of animals evolved with notochord. Protochordates are considered as invertebrate chordates. Protochordata is otherwise called acraniata due to the absence of cranium. The animals are bilaterally symmetric. There is of a notochord at some stages of life. Respiration by means of gill slits, located in dorsal position. Open type of blood vascular system with colourless blood. For example, *Balanoglossus, Herdmania, Amphioxus, etc.*

Figure 4.28 Amphioxus

Quick Recap

✔ **Why do some organisms, like the hydra, rely on specialized cells for capturing their prey?**

Many aquatic organisms, like the hydra, rely on specialized cells to capture their prey due to the dynamics of the underwater environment. In the case of the hydra, these specialized cells are cnidoblasts, which contain toxins to paralyze small organisms. This method ensures an efficient way to capture and consume prey without expending unnecessary energy in the process.

✔ **What are the advantages of being an endoparasite like the tapeworm?**

Being an endoparasite, like the tapeworm, provides several advantages:

Protection: Living inside a host offers protection from external predators and environmental fluctuations.

Nutrient Supply: Since they absorb some of the host's semi-digested food, there is a consistent source of nutrients.

Stable Environment: Living inside a host provides a stable environment, reducing the need for constant adaptation to external conditions.

✔ **Considering tapeworms lack a specific digestive system, how does it affect their evolution and adaptation?**

Since tapeworms don't have a digestive system, they've evolved as endoparasites, adapting mechanisms to absorb nutrients from their host's semi-digested food. This adaptation allows them to reduce body complexity and focus more on attachment mechanisms (like suckers) and reproduction. Their lack of a digestive system means they are heavily dependent on their host for survival.

✔ **Explain the different stages of metamorphosis in insects (Butterfly).**

The phenomenon in which the larval and the adult forms show wide variation in structure, form and functioning is called metamorphosis. The various stages in the life cycle include egg, larva, pupa and adult. Usually insects such as butterflies and houseflies show this phenomenon during their life cycle. This phenomenon is generally controlled by hormones secreted by the animal during the reproductive phase.

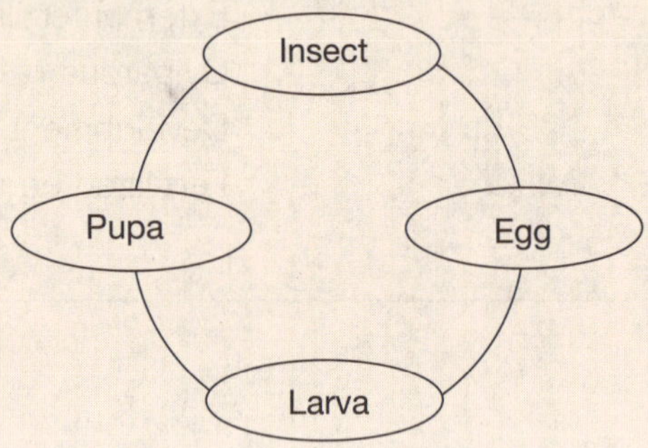

Animal Kingdom—Phylum Vertebrata

The phylum Vertebrata comprises majority of chordates. Except protochordates, all the rest of the chordates are vertebrates. Therefore, the features of vertebrata and chordata are almost same. The animals belonging to phylum Vertebrata possess cranium which encloses the brain. Therefore, this phylum is also known as craniata.

Characteristic Features

In vertebrates, notochord is present in the embryonic stage. It is replaced by vertebral column in the later stages. These organisms generally show distinct division into head, thorax and trunk. Head is well differentiated. They generally have two pairs of limbs and hence, are called tertrapods. They have well-developed organ systems for carrying out different functions. Blood vascular system is closed type with heart located on ventral side. The blood vascular system of vertebrates also includes lymphatic system. The blood possesses red blood corpuscles containing haemoglobin, a red coloured pigment. The animals possess different respiratory organs depending on their habitats. Most of the animals possess a pair of kidneys as excretory organs. They show sexual mode of reproduction. Just like the invertebrates, the various animals in vertebrata also show different levels of complexity in their structure and functioning. Based on the distinctive features, the phylum vertebrata is further classified into various classes.

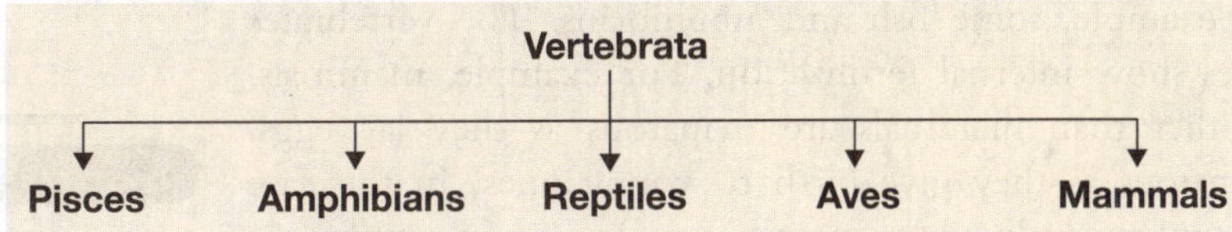

Figure 4.29 Classification of vertebrata

Different Levels of Complexity of Body Organization

Habitat

Among vertebrates, we can find a regular transition from aquatic habitat to terrestrial habitat. They are generally free-living animals. Some of them may lead a solitary life while others live in groups.

Body Form

Vertebrate animals invariably possess organ system level of organization with bilateral symmetry. They are all triploblastic. The body shapes are variable depending on their habitats.

Appendages

Vertebrates are characterized by the presence of paired appendages. The type of appendages depends on the living habitats and feeding habits of the animals.

Skeletal System

All vertebrates possess both exoskeleton and endoskeleton. Exoskeleton depends upon the type of habitat. Endoskeleton lies entirely within the body of the animal. It is generally made up of hard living tissues, known as cartilage and bones. Endoskeleton basically comprises skull and vertebral column.

Digestive System and Process of Digestion

All the classes of vertebrates possess a well-developed digestive system with a complete digestive tract. However, the animals show some variations in the structure of digestive system according to their habitat and feeding habits. All animals show extracellular digestion only.

Respiratory System

Vertebrates possess special respiratory organs. All the land vertebrates respire with the help of lungs. This respiration which takes place by means of lungs is called pulmonary respiration. In aquatic vertebrates, respiration may take place with the help of gills or skin. However, all the mammals show pulmonary respiration irrespective of their habitat.

Circulatory System

All animals of phylum Vertebra possess closed circulatory system. Most of the animals also possess lymphatic system. Blood circulatory system and lymphatic system are together known as blood vascular system. The blood in these animals consists of red blood cells, which contain haemoglobin pigment.

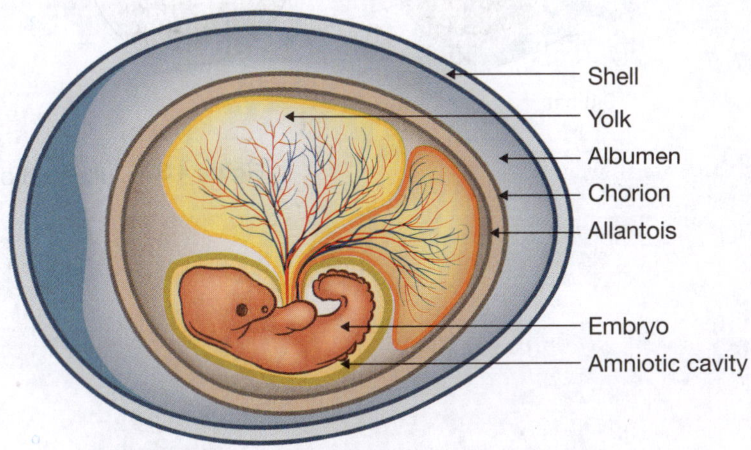

Figure 4.30 Illustration of embryonic membranes

Excretory system

Vertebrates possess a specific system for the elimination of waste materials. Usually, they possess a pair of kidneys as excretory organs.

Reproductive System

Vertebrates are unisexual and most of them show sexual dimorphism. They show sexual reproduction. The vertebrates belonging to lower classes show external fertilization. For example, some fish and amphibians. The vertebrates belonging to higher classes show internal fertilization. For example, mammals. Majority of vertebrates other than mammals are oviparous as they lay eggs. Mammals are mostly viviparous as they give birth to young ones. In the case of higher vertebrates, the embryo is lined by membranes, known as embryonic membranes. These are amnion, chorion, yolk sac and allantois.

Info Bytes!

Goldfish can see infrared radiation.

Body Temperature

Vertebrates other than aves and the mammals are cold-blooded animals. Aves and mammals are warm-blooded animals. Vertebrata is divided into five main classes as follows:

1. Pisces **2.** Amphibia **3.** Reptilia **4.** Aves **5.** Mammalia

Class Pisces

This class of vertebrates includes all fish. They are exclusively aquatic, either fresh water or marine. All fish possess a streamlined body without limbs. The exoskeleton is generally made up of scales. They possess fins and muscular tail for locomotion. Respiration is by means of gills. They possess a two-chambered heart. Brain possesses olfactory lobes and cerebellum along with ten cranial nerves. A pair of eyes and nostrils are present. Only internal ears are present. Presence of lateral line sense organ is the characteristic feature of this class. They are unisexual and show sexual dimorphism. This class is further classified into three subclasses on the basis of certain distinctive features.

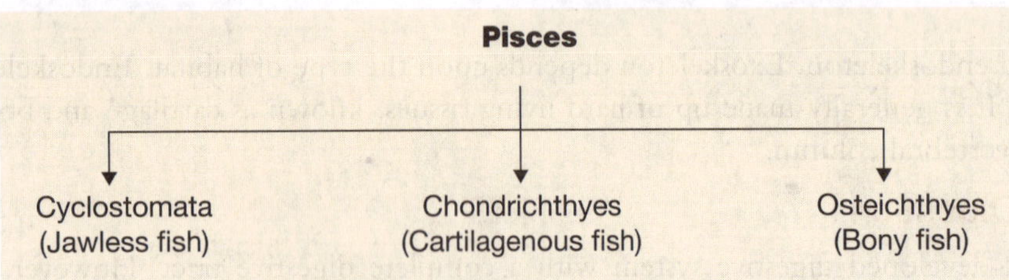

Figure 4.31 Classification of pisces

Info Bytes!

An electric eel can discharge a current of 600 V.

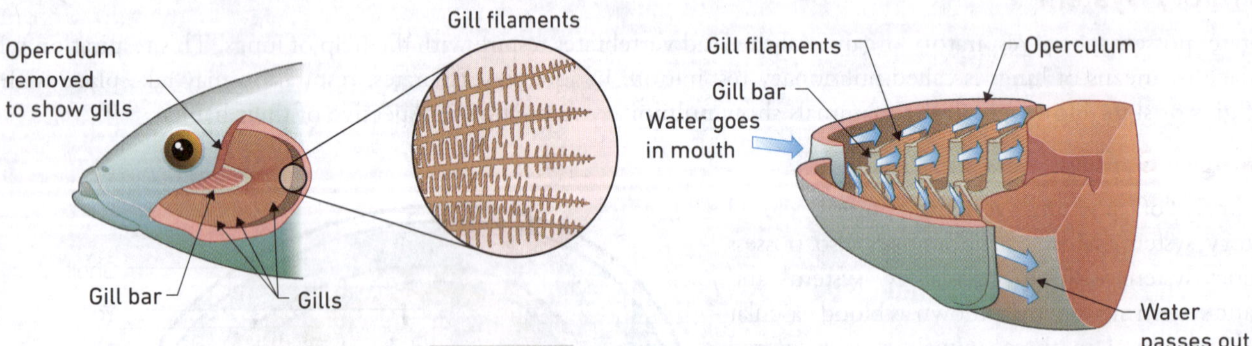

Figure 4.32 Illustration of fish gills

Table 4.11 Comparison of distinguishing features of three subclasses of Pisces

Characteristics	Cyclostomata (Jawless fish)	Chondrichthyes (Cartilagenous fish)	Osteichthyes (Bony fish)
Origin of name	Cyklos—circular ; stome—mouth	Chondron—cartilage ; ichthyes—fish	Ostein—bone; ichthyes—fish
Habitat	Hagfishes—Marine Lamprays—Freshwater	Mostly marine Few sharks and rays are fresh water	Both fresh water and marine
Feeding habit	Ectoparasites on fish	Swimming predators or scavengers	Swimming predators
Body shape	Long eel-like body with compressed tail	Laterally compressed Spindle shaped or flattened disc shaped	Generally spindle shaped
Morphological features	Soft, smooth and slimy skin without scales Cartilagenous exoskeleton Jawless circular mouth (suctorial mouth)	Exoskeleton with placoid scales Paired fins Tail fin with two unequal lobes External nares on the ventral side of head A pair of eyes without eye lids on the head Mouth on ventral side of head Well-developed movable jaws	Exoskeleton with cycloid scales Clear demarcation into head, trunk and tail Paired fins Tail fin with equal lobes A pair of eyes and nostrils Mouth on ventral side of head Well-developed movable jaws
Anatomical features	Notochord as a cylindrical rod Endoskeleton made up of cartilage Gills enclosed in gill pouches Poorly developed head and brain Gonads without gonoduct	Endoskeleton made up of cartilage with calcium carbonate coating Gills generally not enclosed in gill pouches or not covered by any covers Brain with large cerebellum and 10 pairs of cranial nerves Paired gonads with gonoducts	Endoskeleton partly or wholly made up of bones Presence of gas-filled swim bladder or air sac above alimentary canal Gill slits covered by gill covers called operculum Brain with large cerebellum and 10 pairs of cranial nerves Paired gonads with gonoducts
Metabolism	Attaches to host fish with mouth Ureotelic	Well-developed circulatory system Ammonotelic	Well-developed circulatory system Ammonotelic
Reproduction	External fertilization Development is indirect	Internal fertilization Development is direct Mostly oviparous; Ovoviviparous (rays) Viviparous (sharks)	External fertilization Development is direct Generally oviparous Sometimes ovoviviparous or viviparous Primitive form of parental care seen
Diversity	*Petromyzon*, *Myxine* (hag fish), etc.	Sharks, rays, etc.	*Labeo* (Rohu), catfish, etc.

Class Amphibia

These are the first land vertebrates. The term of 'amphibia' originated from two terms 'amphi' meaning both and 'bios' meaning life. That means, these animals can live both in water and on land. They are generally present in fresh water or moist places. They are usually nocturnal animals as they are active during night and inactive during day time. They exhibit hibernation (winter sleep) and aestivation (summer sleep). The structural features of these animals are such that they adapt to both the habitats.

Info Bytes!

The largest amphibian is the Chinese Giant Salamander.

Table 4.12 Structural and functional features of Amphibia

Characteristics	Description
Morphological features	Smooth or rough moist skin Skin possesses mucous glands and pigment cells (chromatophores) Body without scales Distinct head and trunk (some may have tail) Eyes with movable eyelids Eardrum on skin Lateral line sense organ may be present Four limbs with 5 fingers each (tetrapodus and pentadactyl) Toes without claws and nails, but may possess webs **(webbed feet)**
Anatomical features	Endoskeleton is mostly bony Respiration by lungs or skin in adult stage and gills in larval stage 3-chambered heart (two auricles and one ventricle) Blood with biconvex, oval and nucleated RBC A pair of kidneys and urinary bladder Brain not well-developed Males without copulatory organ
Reproduction	External fertilization Indirect development Metamorphosis is seen (characteristic feature of this class) Life cycle includes fish-like aquatic larva **(tadpole)** Oviparous Primitive form of parental care seen in some animals
Diversity	Frogs, toads, salamanders, etc.

Class Reptilia

The name 'reptilia' originated from the word 'reptare' meaning to creep. That means, this class includes creeping vertebrates. The reptiles are the first completely terrestrial vertebrates originated on the earth. However, some reptiles live in aquatic habitat. They are generally adapted to live in warm climates. Reptiles were believed to be the dominant group of organisms during the Jurassic period of Mesozoic era. This was hence, called age of reptiles. Some of the reptiles of that period are called dinosaurs. Pythons are the present day largest living reptiles. Most of the reptiles show carnivorous mode of nutrition, very few are herbivorous. Terrestrial reptiles are uricotelic while aquatic reptiles are ureotelic.

Info Bytes!

Most venomous snake is sea snake and longest poisonous snake is King cobra

Table 4.13 Structural and functional features of reptiles

Characteristics	Description
Morphological features	Usually elongated and low-statured body. Few are short and broad. The body is differentiated into head, neck, trunk and tail. A pair of eyes, a pair of nostrils and a pair of ear openings are present on the head. Four limbs with five fingers; (tetrapodus and pentadactyl) each digit has a claw. However, some reptiles are limbless. For example, snakes Dry and non-glandular skin Exoskeleton with bony epidermal scales Some reptiles shed their scales periodically. This is called **moulting** For example, snakes and lizards Large mouth with movable jaws Tongue may or may not be protrusible
Anatomical features	Endoskeleton consists of bony skull and ribs Respiration by lungs 3-chambered heart (two auricles and one incompletely divided ventricle) Crocodiles have a 4-chambered heart. Blood with biconvex, oval and nucleated RBC A pair of kidneys and urinary bladder Brain with 12 pairs of cranial nerves Males generally possess copulatory organ.
Reproduction	Internal fertilization Oviparous. Some are ovoviviparous Presence of shell and embryonic membrane for egg Embryo lies in fluid filled sac (amnion) Direct development Primitive form of parental care is seen in some
Diversity	Terrestrial forms: Snakes and lizards Aquatic forms: Crocodiles, tortoises and alligators Largest living reptile—Python

Class Aves

The aves (birds) possess some unique morphological features and hence, are most easily recognizable animals. Most familiar unique features include wide variety of body colours and presence of feathers. They show some behavioral features which are not found in other groups of animals. The most interesting habits such as singing, nest building, parental care and tendency of migration make them the most studied group of animals. The study of birds is known as ornithology. The birds can survive in variety of habitats and hence, are omnipresent. Birds are homeothermic or warm-blooded animals.

Table 4.14 Structural and functional features of Aves

Characteristics	Description
Morphological features	Streamlined body divisible into head, neck, trunk and short tail A pair of eyes, a pair of nostrils and a pair of ears openings are present on the head Two pairs of limbs. Forelimbs modified into wings. Hind limbs covered with horny epidermal scales. Their digits end in claws Exoskeleton made up of feathers Skin thin and dry with preen gland at the tail Jaws modified into beak Large and powerful eyes

(Continued)

Table 4.14 *(Continued)*

Characteristics	Description
Anatomical features	Endoskeleton made up of fused and hollow bones. It also includes bony skull Alimentary canal ends in 3-chambered **cloaca** Spongy, inelastic lungs connected to air sacs Breast muscles attached to large breast bone Pharynx without vocal cords Special organ, syrinx present at the base of trachea which produces sound A pair of kidneys. Urinary bladder is absent 4-chambered heart with two auricles and two ventricles Blood with biconvex, oval and nucleated RBC Large brain with optic lobes and cerebellum 12 pairs of cranial nerves Female bird has only one ovary and oviduct (left side)
Reproduction	Internal fertilization Oviparous. Some are ovoviviparous Eggs contain yolk and are enclosed in calcareous shells Embryonic membranes are present (amnion, chorion, yolk sac, allantois) Development is direct Hatching of eggs at constant temperature by female bird in the nest Large extent of parental care seen even after hatching
Diversity	Peacock and crow; Flightless birds: Ostrich, Penguin, Kiwi and Duck

Class Mammalia

The name 'mammalia' originated from the word 'mamma' meaning breast. That means, the animals belonging to this class are characterized by the feature where the females are involved in breast feeding their young ones. Mammals are the most dominant group of living organisms. These are primarily terrestrial animals. Most of the animals lead arboreal life. That means, they live on the trees. However, few of them are adapted to aquatic mode of life. For example, whales. Few mammals also show aerial mode of life. For example, bats. Mammals are exclusively warm-blooded animals.

Table 4.15 Structural and functional features of mammalia

Characteristics	Description
Morphological features	Body with variety of shapes and sizes The body is differentiated into head, neck, trunk and tail. Trunk is further divisible into thorax and abdomen Skin is covered by exoskeleton of hair A pair of eyes with movable lids, a pair of nostrils and a pair of external ears (pinnae) are present on the head Mouth bounded by movable lips Movable jaws possess teeth embedded in sockets. This is called **thecodont dentition**. **Dentition** is the characteristic feature of mammals Mammals are characterized by the development of two sets of teeth in the life time (milk teeth; permanent teeth) This is called **diphyodont dentition**. Different types of teeth are developed to suit their varying feeding habits. This is called **heterodont dentition**. Two pairs of pentadactyl limbs are present. The digits may be provided with horny claws, nails and hoofs

(Continued)

Table 4.15 (*Continued*)

Characteristics	Description
Anatomical features	Skin is glandular. The skin glands include sebaceous (oil) glands, wax glands, sweat glands and milk glands Endoskeleton made up of bones. It includes bony skull, vertebral column, ribs and girdles. Alimentary canal ends in anus Spongy and elastic lungs for respiration. A muscular diaphragm separates chest cavity from abdomen Larynx is the sound-producing organ A pair of bean-shaped kidneys. Ureters open into urinary bladder 4-chambered heart with two atria and two ventricles Well-developed blood vascular system which includes lymphatic system Blood with biconcave, circular and anucleated RBC Large and well-developed brain with cerebrum and cerebellum Sensory centres in cerebrum 12 pairs of cranial nerves Unisexual with sexual dimorphism Paired gonads in males and females Testes descent into scrotal sacs. Males possess copulatory organ called penis Females possess well-developed mammary glands
Reproduction	Internal fertilization Eggs are small and microscopic without any shells The eggs retain in the uterus of female for development Embryonic membranes are present Most of the mammals are viviparous Young ones are fed by mother's milk Greatest extent of parental care by means of feeding, protection from enemies and training to lead the life independently
Diversity	Monkeys, Chimpanzees Humans, elephants, cattle Arboreal animals Largest mammal—Blue whale

Due to the large population of mammals and their varied habitats, they show wide range of structural and behavioral features. Mainly on the basis of the mode of child birth and child care, mammals are categorized into three groups as discussed below.

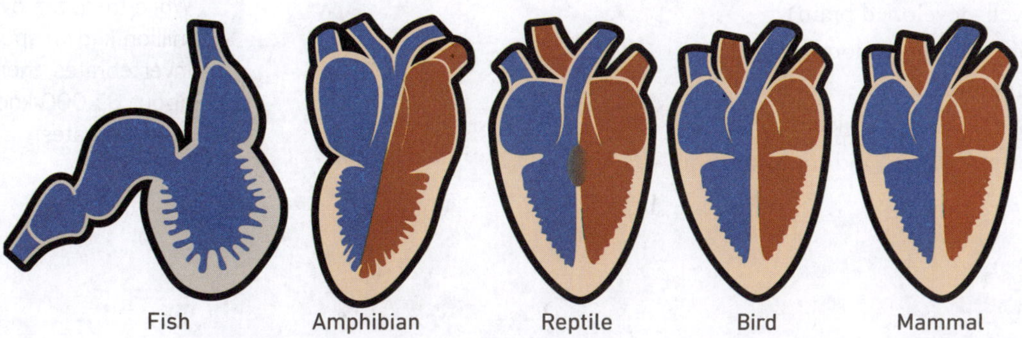

Figure 4.33 Heart's anatomy in different vertebrates

Diversity in Placental Mammals

The placental mammals are the most successful group of mammals. They can live in wide range of climatic conditions. They are further categorized on the basis of many morphological characteristics and modes of feeding. Among the various groups, **primates** include the most evolved mammals. The name primates means foremost in rank. This group includes lemurs, monkeys, apes, etc., along with humans. Humans are the most intelligent mammals evolved so far. In evolutionary hierarchy, humans are at the peak.

Info Bytes!

A blue whale's tongue weighs as much as an elephant.

Mammals

Egg-laying mammals

- **Characters** of reptiles are seen
- **These** are oviparous
- **Lay** eggs enclosed in hard shells
- **After** hatching, young ones are fed on mother's milk
- **For** example, spiny ant eater, (*Echidna*), Duck-billed platypus

Marsupial mammals

- **These** are viviparous
- **Young** ones are small and tiny when born
- **They** are protected in a special pouch on mother's abdomen **(marsupium)**
- **They** are fed on mother's milk in the pouch
- **For** example, kangaroo, koala bear, etc.

Placental mammals

- **These** are viviparous
- **Foetus** remains in uterus (womb) till an advanced stage
- **While** in womb, foetus is nourished by mother through a special structure called **placenta**
- **This** group of animals are only considered as true mammals as they possess all the characteristic features of this class
- **For** example, cat, lion, monkey, human, etc.

Figure 4.34 Classification of mammalia

Characteristic Features of Humans

Following are the characteristic features of humans.

- Totally erect posture
- Bipedal locomotion
- Sparse hair on the body
- Highly well-developed brain
- Ability of communication by speech
- Unique memory
- Ability of thinking and decision making
- Ability of innovation and sophistication

Info Bytes!

While there are over a million known species of invertebrates, there are only about 62,000 known species of vertebrates.

Quick Recap

✔ **Distinguish between ectoparasites and endoparasites. Give examples for both.**

Ectoparasites	Endoparasites
They live on the host	They live in the systems of the host
They feed on the body fluids like blood	They feed on the semidigested food of the host
They show aerobic respiration	They show anaerobic respiration
They possess digestive system	They do not possess a digestive tract
The life cycle may be simple with one host	The life cycle may involve more than one host during its life cycle
For example, leech, lamprey, hagfish, etc.	For example, tapeworm, roundworm, filarial worm, etc.

✔ **Why do endoparasites generally lack a digestive system?**

Endoparasites live inside their hosts and feed on semi-digested food or nutrients that are already broken down by their host's digestive system. Since the food is already in a readily assimilable form, endoparasites don't need a complex digestive system of their own. Their structure has evolved to absorb these nutrients directly, rather than having to digest them first.

✔ **How can gills in amphibian larvae be seen as evidence for evolution from fish-like ancestors?**

Gills are specialized organs for extracting oxygen from water. The presence of gills in amphibian larvae indicates their adaptation to an aquatic environment, similar to fish. As amphibians grow and undergo metamorphosis, most lose their gills and develop lungs for extracting oxygen from the air, suggesting an evolutionary transition from aquatic to terrestrial environments. This dual-respiratory mechanism (gills in larvae and lungs in adults) can be seen as evidence of their evolutionary link from fish-like ancestors and their adaptation to a terrestrial lifestyle.

✔ **Why is external fertilization common in aquatic animals like fish and amphibians, while internal fertilization is more common in terrestrial animals?**

External fertilization involves the release of gametes (sperm and eggs) into the external environment, usually water. In aquatic habitats, the water medium facilitates the meeting and fusion of gametes. On the other hand, terrestrial habitats lack this supportive medium. Internal fertilization, where sperm is introduced into the female's body to meet the egg, ensures a more protected environment for gamete fusion in terrestrial settings, increasing the chances of successful reproduction.

POINTS TO REMEMBER

- The taxonomic hierarchy of animals starts from the highest taxonomic unit, kingdom and ends with the lowest level unit, species.
- Phylum porifera includes the most primitive animals.
- Cnidarians possess a hollow sac-like body cavity with a single opening to the outside for ingestion and egestion.
- Platyhelminthes are the simplest triploblastic animals.
- Nematodes includes the animals with bilateral symmetry.
- The body of annelids is composed of rings or segments.
- Arthropods are animals with jointed feet or legs.
- Presence of shells in which the soft bodies are enclosed is the characteristic feature of molluscs.
- Echinoderms denote spiny skinned animals.
- Protochordates are acraniates due to the absence of cranium.
- The animals belonging to phylum Vertebrata possess cranium which encloses the brain.

DW

CLASSROOM WING

Practice Questions

Very Short Answer Type Questions

Direction for question from 1 to 37.
Fill in the blanks.

1. The taxonomic hierarchy moves from a broad category like _______ to a specific one like _______.
2. Phylum Porifera is considered as the most _______ animals.
3. Annelids are recognized by their body which is composed of _______.
4. Arthropods are distinguished by their _______.
5. Molluscs have a unique _______ that encloses their soft bodies.
6. In animals belonging to phylum Platyhelminthes, locomotory organelles are _______.
7. The excretory organs in round worm are _______.
8. The periodical shedding of exoskeleton in arthropods is called _______.
9. Soft-bodied animals belong to phylum _______.
10. A _______ is present on the dorsal side of the foot in snail.
11. _______ are considered as invertebrate chordates.
12. Food intake in starfish takes place with the help of _______.
13. *Amphioxus* belongs to the phylum _______.
14. The sponge which is generally gifted in marriages by Japanese is _______.
15. The pathway of entering and coming out of water in sponges is known as _______.
16. Coral animals secrete an exoskeleton, it is composed of _______.
17. Type of respiration seen in parasitic helminthes is _______.
18. In tapeworm, body is made up of segments called _______.
19. Metameric segmentation is seen in _______.
20. Water vascular system is present in _______.
21. Spiders and scorpions belong to class _______ under phylum Arthropoda.
22. The worm which is known as filarial worm is _______.
23. The class of vertebrates which has exclusively aquatic habitat is _______.
24. The pigment cells present on the skin of amphibians are called _______.
25. In birds, the alimentary canal ends in three-chambered _______.
26. The development of two sets of teeth during the life time found in mammals is called _______ dentition.
27. The endoskeleton in vertebrates is made up of hard, living tissues such as _______ and _______.
28. All the land vertebrates show _______ respiration.
29. Swim bladder in fish is an organ for _______.
30. Cartilaginous fish are grouped under _______.
31. The exoskeleton of birds is made up of _______.
32. When teeth are embedded in sockets, such condition is known as _______.
33. The muscular layer separating thoracic and abdominal cavity in mammals is called _______.
34. The pouch in which new born kangaroo is taken care is called _______.
35. The respiratory pigment present in chordates is _______.

36. In snakes, poison fangs are modified ________.

37. Bones in birds are hollow and are said to be ________.

Direction for Questions from 38 to 72.

For each of the following questions four choices have been provided. Select the correct alternatives.

38. Jointed legs is the characteristic feature of which of the following phylum?

(a) Arthropoda (b) Annelida

(c) Nematoda (d) Echinodermata

39. The common bath sponge is ___________.

(a) *Sycon* (b) *Euplectella*

(c) *Spongilla* (d) *Euspongia*

40. Tentacles of hydra help in ___________.

(a) locomotion

(b) food capturing

(c) locomotion and food capturing

(d) reproduction

41. *Physalia* is commonly known as:

(a) sea fan

(b) sea pen

(c) jelly fish

(d) Portuguese man o' war

42. Round worms differ from flatworms in having ________.

(a) flame cells

(b) pseudocoel

(c) segmented body

(d) flagella

43. Identify the locomotary organs in Annelida.

(a) Tube feet (b) Setae

(c) Pseudopodia (d) Flagella

44. Blue-coloured pigment present in the blood of molluscs is known as:

(a) hemocyanin (b) hemerythrin

(c) hemoglobin (d) phytochromes

45. The body cavity of arthropods is called:

(a) haemocoel (b) pseudocoel

(c) coelom (d) exterior

46. Identify the phylum in which symmetry is radial in adults but bilateral in larvae.

(a) Chordata (b) Craniata

(c) Protochordata (d) Echinodermata

47. Identify the phylum/phyla in which some animals show parasitism.

(a) Nematoda (b) Platyhelminths

(c) Annelida (d) All of these

48. Identify the wrongly matched pair among the following.

(a) Excretory matter ammonia released directly into water—Echinodermata

(b) Book lungs as respiratory organs—Arthropoda

(c) Alternation of generations—Cnidaria

(d) Skeleton made up of siliceous or calcareous spicules—Mollusca

49. Identify the phylum in which endocrine system appeared for the first time.

(a) Arthropoda (b) Annelida

(c) Mollusca (d) Protochordata

50. Which of the following animals possesses blood with haemoglobin in plasma?

(i) Earthworm (ii) *Balanoglossus*

(iii) Snail (iv) Butterfly

(a) (i) and (iv) (b) (ii) and (iii)

(c) (i), (ii), (iv) (d) (ii) and (iv)

51. Which class of animals possess two chambered heart?

(a) Pisces (b) Amphibians

(c) Reptiles (d) Both (a) and (b)

52. The animals belonging to which class of vertebrates generally lead an arboreal life?

(a) Aves (b) Reptiles

(c) Mammals (d) All of these

53. Name the special pouch in which a female koala bear protects its young one after birth.

(a) Womb (b) Uterus
(c) Placenta (d) Marsupium

54. Identify the glands present in birds.

(a) Preen gland (b) Sebaceous gland
(c) Sweat gland (d) Mammary gland

55. Urinary bladder is absent in which of the following animals?

(a) Duck billed platypus (b) Snake
(c) Peacock (d) Kangaroo

56. Identify an organism in which brachial respiration takes place.

(a) Chameleon (b) Peacock
(c) Tortoise (d) Shark

57. An animal which contain three-chambered heart is ________.

(a) man (b) rabbit
(c) fish (d) frog

58. Diaphragm in mammals plays a major role in ________.

(a) digestion (b) excretion
(c) respiration (d) co-ordination

59. Operculum is a bony plate covering gills of ________.

(a) bony fishes (b) cartilaginous fishes
(c) all fishes (d) tadpole

60. Which of the following is not the characteristic feature of pisces?

(a) Presence of streamlined body
(b) Presence of lateral line sense organ
(c) Presence of fins
(d) Pentadactyl

61. Identify the fish which is ureotelic.

(a) Shark (b) Catfish
(c) Ray (d) *Petromyzon*

62. Which of the following animals can survive both in land and water habitats?

(a) Salamenders (b) Alligators
(c) Crocodiles (d) Penguins

63. Which of the following mammals possess few characteristics of reptiles?

(a) Kangaroo (b) Spiny ant eater
(c) Koala bear (d) Whale

64. Identify the sound producing organ in mammals.

(a) Pharynx (b) Syrinx
(c) Larynx (d) Adam's apple

65. Presence of biconcave, circular and anucleated RBC is the characteristic feature of which animal?

(a) Ostrich (b) Whale
(c) Crocodile (d) All of these

66. Which oviparous animal feeds its young one with mother's milk after hatching?

(a) Kangaroo (b) Bat
(c) Penguin (d) Duck billed platypus

67. Mammary glands in mammals are modified into:

(a) sweat glands (b) sebaceous glands
(c) lacrimal glands (d) preen glands

68. Mammal which contains nucleated red blood cell is:

(a) man (b) monkey
(c) camel (d) rabbit

69. Ventricle of frog contains:

(a) oxygenated blood
(b) deoxygenated blood
(c) no blood
(d) mixed blood

70. Jaws are absent in:

(i) *Balanoglossus* (ii) *Myxine*
(iii) vertebrates (iv) *Petromyzon*

(a) (i), (iv) (b) (ii), (iv)
(c) (i), (ii) (d) (iii), (iv)

71. Identify poikilotherms.

(i) Elephants (ii) Frogs

(iii) Sharks (iv) Whales

(a) (i), (ii) (b) (ii), (iv)

(c) (ii), (iii) (d) (iii), (iv)

72. Exoskeleton is absent in:

(i) fishes (ii) frog

(iii) rabbit (iv) toad

(a) (i), (ii) (b) (ii), (iii)

(c) (i), (iii) (d) (ii), (iv)

Direction for Questions from 73 to 80:
Match the entries of Column 1 with those of Column 2.

73.

Column 1	Column 2
A. Radial	(i) Pila
B. Bilateral	(ii) *Nereis*
C. Asymetrical	(iii) Helminthes
D. True coelomates	(iv) Annelida
E. Parapodia	(v) Coelenterata

74.

Column 1	Column 2
A. Jointed appendages	(i) Pigeon
B. Pneumatic bones	(ii) Tapeworm
C. Circular mouth	(iii) *Balanoglossus*
D. Flame cells	(iv) Grasshopper
E. Proboscis	(v) *Myxine*

75.

Column 1	Column 2
A. Aminotelic	(i) Frog
B. Ureotelic	(ii) *Ascaris*
C. Uricotetic	(iii) Fishes
D. Acoelomata	(iv) Birds
E. Pseudocoelomata	(v) Tapeworm

76.

Column 1	Column 2
A. Hemichordata	(i) Asymmetric
B. Pila	(ii) Pentaradial Symmetry
C. Sea anemone	(iii) Spherical Symmetry
D. Starfish	(iv) Bilateral Symmetry
E. Sea urchin	(v) Radial Symmetry

77.

Column 1	Column 2
A. Ostia	(i) Star fish
B. shell	(ii) Leech
C. Suckers	(iii) Sycon
D. Jointed appendages	(iv) Oysters
E. Tube feet	(v) Spiders

78.

Column 1	Column 2
A. Archaeopteryx	(i) Electric organ
B. Cyclostoma	(ii) Fossil birds
C. Mammals	(iii) Dual habitat
D. Torpedo	(iv) Jawless vertebrates
E. Amphibia	(v) Mammary gland

79.

Column 1	Column 2
A. Toad	(i) Aves
B. Rohu	(ii) Reptiles
C. Ostrich	(iii) Amphibian
D. Rodents	(iv) Pisces
E. Tortoise	(v) Mammal

80.

Column 1	Column 2
A. Prototheria	(i) Rays and Skates
B. Metatheria	(ii) Turtles
C. Chelonia	(iii) *Balanoglossus*
D. Hemichordata	(iv) Marsupials
E. Chondrichthyes	(v) *Echidna*

Short Answer Type Questions

81. Define the following.
(a) Bilateral symmetry
(b) Germ layers
(c) Notochord

82. Distinguish between vertebrates and invertebrates.

83. How is complete digestive tract different from incomplete digestive tract?

84. In what way does the body plan of annelids differ from arthropods, even though both may have segmented appearances?

85. What is the primary distinguishing characteristic of animals in the phylum Mollusca?

86. Why is Phylum Porifera considered to have the most primitive animals in the animal kingdom?

87. Give the difference between open and closed circulation.

88. Distinguish between diploblastic animals and triploblastic animals.

89. What is meant by a true coelom? On what basis coelomates are further categorized?

90. Define sexual dimorphism. Give an example of an invertebrate phylum which shows this feature.

91. What is meant by osmoregulation?

92. List out the characteristic features of protochordates.

93. Distinguish between Polyp and Medusa

94. Sponges are considered as pore bearers. Discuss.

95. Mention the differences between cartilaginous and bony fishes.

96. Give classification for the following.
(a) Parrot (b) Cockroach

97. What is meant by a streamlined body? Which classes of vertebrates possess such body morphology? Justify that.

98. Which structural features help the amphibians to get adapted to both terrestrial and aquatic habitats?

99. How would you identify a fish as cartilaginous or bony on observing its head region?

100. Mention few flight adaptations in birds.

101. How is pectin useful in birds?

Essay Type Questions

102. Define the following terms of giving examples.
(a) Oviparous
(b) Viviparous
(c) Radial symmetry
(d) Bilateral symmetry
(e) Homeotherms
(f) Poikilotherms
(g) Diploblastic

103. What evolutionary significance does the presence of a cranium in vertebrates and the absence of it in protochordates suggest about the progression and adaptation of animals over time?

104. Give the difference between
(a) Oviparous and Viviparous animals
(b) External and Internal fertilization
(c) Direct and Indirect development

105. How do the following terms originate?
(a) Nematoda (b) Echinodermata
(c) Porifera

106. Write short notes on the following.
(a) Ecdysis (b) Polymorphism

107. Explain the following terms.
(a) Tetrapodus (b) Pentadactyl
(c) Nocturnal (d) Arboreal habitat

108. What is meant by dentition? Explain the following terms with respect to dentition.
(a) Thecodont (b) Heterodont
(c) Diphyodont

109. How did the following terms originate?
(a) Amphibia (b) Reptilia
(c) Mammalia

COMPETITION WING

Practice Questions

Level 1: Apply your Concepts

Direction for question from 1 to 5.

Fill in the blanks.

1. While phylum Porifera showcases the basic foundations of multicellular life, ______ signifies the pinnacle of evolutionary complexity in the animal kingdom.
2. The absence of a cranium in protochordates suggests a more ______ position in the evolutionary ladder compared to vertebrates.
3. While annelids exhibit segmentation externally, ______ exhibit segmentation at an internal organ level.
4. While ______ are the most primitive animals, ______ are characterized by the presence of jointed legs.
5. The taxonomic hierarchy starts at the broad category of ______ and culminates in the specific category of ______.

Direction for Questions from 6 to 20:

Write True or False.

6. The liver of shark is a rich source of vitamin A.
7. Snakes have four-chambered heart.
8. Ostrich is considered to be the smallest bird.
9. *Ichthyophis* is a blind limbless mammal.
10. The largest venomous snake is *Ophiophagus hannah* (King Cobra)
11. Preen gland or uropygial gland is helpful in lubricating feathers in birds.
12. When two sets of teeth are formed during lifetime then the organism is considered as diphyodant.
13. Nematodes lack lateral appendages.
14. Spicules are present in coelenterata.
15. Earthworm is an sanguivorous animal.
16. Larvae are called caterpillar in silk moth which produces silk.
17. Water vascular system is present in sponges.
18. *Pinctada vulgaris* belonging to mollusca produces pearls.
19. Hirudin in an anticoagulant extracted from earthworm.
20. Sea Urichins are used by Japanese as food.

Direction for Questions from 21 to 22:

Write the missing correlated terms.

21. (a) Pulmonary : lungs : : ______ : Skin.
    (b) Draco : Flying lizard : : ______ : flying fish.
    (c) Frog : tetrapod : : Birds : ______
    (d) ______ : birds : : Larynx : Mammals.
    (e) Platypus : Prototheria : : ______ : metatheria.
    (f) Vanadium : ______ : : Iron : Hemoglobin.
22. (a) Fishes : ______: : Birds : feathers
    (b) Dicots : reticulate venation : : Monocots : ______.
    (c) Bivalve : mollusca : : Sea urchins : ______.
    (d) *Physalia* : ______ : : Sycon : porifera.
    (e) *Struthio camelus* : ______: : *Ichthyophis* : amphibian.
    (f) Hydra : solitary form : : Corals : ______

Direction for Question 23:

Find the odd one out with reasons.

23. (a) Tortise; Turtle; Crocodile; Frog.
    (b) Shark; Whale; Dog fish; Rohu.

Direction for Questions from 24 to 49:
Choose the correct option.

(a) Both A and R are true and R is the correct explanation for A.
(b) Both A and R are true but R is not the correct explanation for A.
(c) A is true and R is false.
(d) A is false and R is true.

24. **Assertion (A):** Organisms belonging to cnidaria do not possess coelom.
Reason (R): Cnidarians are diploblastic animals.

25. **Assertion (A):** In vertebrates, coelom is lined by peritoneum.
Reason (R): In vertebrates, coelom originates from endoderm.

26. **Assertion (A):** All viviparous animals show indirect development.
Reason (R): In all oviparous animals, development involves larval stage.

27. **Assertion (A):** The endoskeleton of animals is totally composed of living tissues.
Reason (R): Bone and cartilage are living tissues.

28. **Assertion (A):** Animals belonging to phylum Porifera are often called sponges
Reason (R): The animals have porous bodies

29. **Assertion (A):** Coelenterates may form corals
Reason (R): Coelenterates possess hard calcareous exoskeleton

30. **Assertion (A):** Tapeworm does not possess a digestive tract
Reason (R): Tapeworm is an ectoparasite

31. **Assertion (A):** The blood of annelids is red in colour
Reason (R): The blood of annelids possess haemoglobin in red blood cells.

32. **Assertion (A):** All chordates possess open circulatory system.
Reason (R): *Balanoglossus* possesses open blood vascular system.

33. **Assertion (A):** Mixed blood circulates in the body of a fish.
Reason (R): Fishes are characterised by the presence of two chambered heart.

34. **Assertion (A):** The excretory product of lizards is uric acid.
Reason (R): Lizards show terrestrial habitat.

35. **Assertion (A):** Placental mammals are considered as true mammals.
Reason (R): Only placental mammals feed their young ones with mother's milk.

36. **Assertion (A):** In Kangaroo, the development is partially direct.
Reason (R): Kangaroo is ovoviviparous animal.

37. **Assertion (A):** Animals belongimg to phylum Porifera are often called sponges.
Reason(R): The animals have porous bodies.

38. **Assertion (A):** Crocodile has a four chambered heart.
Reason (R): Crocodile is a reptile.

39. **Assertion (A):** Bat nourishes its young one in mother's womb by means of placenta.
Reason (R): Bat is a bird with few features of mammals.

40. **Assertion (A):** Shark belongs to cartilaginous fishes.
Reason (R): Gill slits are not covered by opericulum.

41. **Assertion (A):** Single circulation is seen in fishes.
Reason (R): Only deoxygenated blood passes through it.

42. **Assertion (A):** Fish are not considered as tetrapods.
Reason (R): They have paired fins.

43. **Assertion (A):** Hibernation during winter and aestivation during summer is seen in frogs.
Reason (R): Frogs are poikilotherms.

44. **Assertion (A):** *Ichthyophis* lives in borrows.
Reason (R): It is known as blind snake.

45. **Assertion (A):** Lizards can regenerate their lost tail.
Reason (R): Lizards have limbs.

46. **Assertion:** Protochordates lack a protective casing around their brain.
Reason: Protochordates are acraniates due to the absence of cranium.

47. **Assertion:** Evolutionary advancements in animal phyla are reflected in the complexity of their body plans and systems.
Reason: Protochordates lack cranium, but vertebrates possess one, signifying a more advanced protective mechanism for the nervous system.

48. **Assertion:** The presence of shells in molluscs serves as a defining characteristic for the entire phylum.
Reason: The shell not only provides protection against potential predators but also supports certain internal structures of these soft-bodied animals.

49. **Assertion:** Arthropods have an evolutionary advantage in varied terrains due to their jointed legs.
Reason: Jointed legs or feet allow arthropods greater mobility and adaptability in diverse environments.

Level 2: Review your Concepts

50. How does the presence or absence of certain germ layers correlate with the complexity of an organism's organ systems?

51. How is ovoviviparity different from oviparity and viviparity?

52. How does mosaic vision benefit arthropods in their environment?

53. Explain the feeding process in Hydra.

54. The animals belonging to lower phyla of invertebrates like tapeworm, earthworm etc., are hermaphrodite or bisexual.
Does this result in self fertilization? Justify.

55. Arthropods have mosaic vision. Give reason.

56. Locusts can survive in extreme climatic conditions. Give reason.

57. Blood is usually blue in colour in molluscs. Give reason.

58. Arthropods constitute the largest group of the animal kingdom. Give reasons.

59. *Balanoglossus* can be considered to be a link between nonchordates and chordates. Comment on this statement.

60. Justify the position of *Echidna* in mammals though it lays eggs.

61. Mammals show heterodont dentition. Give reason.

62. Write any two points of difference between flatworms and roundworms.

63. Complete the following table.

Common name	Scientific name
	Mangifera indica
Rose	
Tiger	
Tulsi	
Lion	
	Triticum aestivum
Peacock	
National flower	

64. Distinguish between oviparous animals and viviparous animals.

65. Give one example for each of the following.
(a) Fish that breathes by lungs.
(b) Aquatic mammals.
(c) Connecting link between reptiles and birds.
(d) Animals which live underground or in burrows.
(e) Reptile having four chambered heart.
(f) Vertebrates bearing pneumatic bones.
(g) Egg-laying mammals.
(h) Voice box in birds.
(i) Fishes in which opericulum is seen.
(j) Egg laying blind amphibian.
(k) Subclass of Pisces which includes jawless fish.
(l) Animals that bear four limbs.

Level 3: Assess Your Concepts

66. The viviparous animals can produce lesser number of young ones per litter when compared to the oviparous young ones. Give reason.

67. Amphibians are considered to show a transition from fishes to reptiles. Justify on the basis of their characteristic features.

68. Yolk sac in the embryo of human female is non functional. Give reason.

69. Cartilaginous fishes swim continuously without any interval. Give reason.

70. Some vertebrates show hibernation in winter. Birds and mammals do not show this feature. Give reason.

71. Higher animals like mammals do not have a specific mating season like birds. Give reason.

72. Identify the odd one and justify.

    (a) *Psittacula*, Ostrich, Kiwi, *Tinamus*.

    (b) Sweat gland, Subaceous gland, preen gland, Mammary gland.

    (c) Glucose, Urea, Uric acid, Ammonia.

73. How might the presence of shells in molluscs or the external segmentation in annelids be linked to evolutionary pressures and environmental adaptations? How do these structures compare to the internal advancements seen in higher phyla like Vertebrata?

74. Why are whales not considered to be fishes?

75. Blood does not clot while leach is sucking blood. Explain.

76. Give reason why oviparous animals lay more eggs.

77. Whale, shark and crocodile are all aquatic organisms. But, they have wide differences in their characteristic features. Draw a comparison of some features and justify.

78. Which classes of phylum chordata are associated with organisms with streamlined bodies? What purpose does such body structure serve?

79. Why do frogs croak during rainy reason?

AT

NEET SPECIAL WING

Practice Questions

Multiple-Answer Type Questions

Questions number 1 to 5 are multiple-choice questions. Each question has FOUR options (a), (b), (c), and (d). ONE OR MORE THAN ONE of these four option(s) is/are the correct answer(s).

1. Which among the following is/are characteristic feature of Molluscans?
(a) Visceral hump on ventral side
(b) Have radula as rasping organ
(c) Have tentacles and statocyst
(d) Green glands as excretory organs

2. Which of the following features are shown by Cyclostomata?
(a) Spindle shaped
(b) Eel like body
(c) Suctorial mouth
(d) Ectoparasites

3. Consider the following sets A, B, C and D. The sets that consists of all animals belonging to the same phylum are:
(a) A- Cockroach, prawn, butterfly, spider
(b) B- Earthworm, Hirudinaria, Planaria, Petromyzon
(c) C- Balanoglossus, Herdmania, Amphioxus
(d) D- Tapeworm, Hydra, Planaria, Ascaris

4. Animals that are warm blooded:
(a) Aves
(b) Pisces
(c) Mammals
(d) Amphibia

5. Which among the following is not a character seen in Echinodermata?
(a) Disc or flower like body
(b) Shows a visceral hump
(c) Hard exoskeleton with spines
(d) Has sense organs like statocyst

Comprehension-Based Questions

A. Read the paragraph given below and answer the questions number 6 to 11:

Vertebrates and invertebrates have evolved from a common ancestor which lived 550 million years ago. Vertebrates diverged from the invertebrates around 525 million years ago. A true vertebrate is an animal which shows a tough rod through the length of the animal which maybe a vertebral column and / or notochord. All vertebrates possess a notochord as an embryo which develops into a vertebral column in later stages. Spinal cord runs above the vertebral column and they possess alimentary canal below it. This alimentary canal ends in anus which opens to the exterior whereas the mouth is present at the anterior side. On the basis of the differences in the anatomical features vertebrates are classified into 5 classes- Pisces, Amphibians, Reptilia, Aves and mammals. Class Pisces includes fishes and is further subdivided into three subclasses- Cyclostomata (jawless fish), Chondrichthyes (cartilaginous fishes) and Osteichthyes (Bony fish). Class Amphibia include ectothermic organisms which live both in land and water. Class Reptilia are ectotherms that crawl on the ground. Class Aves includes egg laying birds which are endothermic. Class Mammals are endotherms and based on their morphological features and feeding habits they are further classified as egg laying mammals, marsupial mammals and placental mammals.

6. Why are bats classified as mammals?
(a) They have mammary glands
(b) They are egg laying
(c) They have ear pinna
(d) They have excretory organs

7. Presence of milk glands is a characteristic feature of:
   (a) All vertebrates
   (b) All mammals
   (c) All placental mammals
   (d) All reptiles

8. Which of the following class of animals does not have cloaca?
   (a) Amphibians
   (b) Reptiles
   (c) Aves
   (d) Mammals

9. Which of the following group of animals show separation of oxygenated and deoxygenated blood?
   (a) Amphibians and Reptiles
   (b) Pisces and Reptiles
   (c) Amphibians and Aves
   (d) Aves and Mammals

10. The mammal which lays eggs:
   (a) Kangaroo
   (b) Platypus
   (c) Echidna
   (d) Koala bear

11. Match the following:

Column – A	Column – B
(i) Young one in pouch	(a) Whale
(ii) Hatched young ones fed on mothers milk	(b) Marsupials
(iii) Foetus nourished by special structure	(c) Egg laying mammals
(iv) Largest mammal	(d) Koala bear
(v) Viviparous animal protected on mother's abdomen as a young one	(e) Placental mammal

B. Read the paragraph given below and answer the questions number 12 to 17:

Non-chordates are animals which do not possess a notochord. They are invertebrates and are divided into various phyla like Porifera, Coelenterata, Ctenophora, Platyhelminthes, Nemathelminthes, Annelida, Arthropoda, Mollusca, Echinodermata and Protochordata. Their bodies are usually cylindrical, some are diploblastic while most are triploblastic. Respiration in these lower order animals can take place through gills, trachea or even body surface. Sexes are not distinguished in the members most of the time. Both asexual as well as sexual modes of reproduction is seen among these animals. Fertilization is mostly external and open type of circulation occurs in their bodies. Phylum protochordata consists of animals which were the first to have a notochord.

12. Asexual forms of Phylum Cnidaria is called:
   (a) Zooids
   (b) Polyp
   (c) Medusa
   (d) Both b and c

13. Excretion in Phylum Platyhelminthes occurs via:
   (a) Flame cells
   (b) Malphigian body
   (c) Osculum
   (d) Anus

14. Hydroskeleton is the:
   (a) Digestive tract with sensory papillae
   (b) Coiled tubular structures called nephridia
   (c) Ventral nerve cord with ganglia
   (d) Fluid filled pseudocoelom which maintains body shape

15. Excretory organs in Phylum Mollusca consists of:
   (a) Green glands
   (b) Organs of Bojanus
   (c) Malphigian tubules
   (d) Nephridia

16. In Cnidarians, zygote develops into:
   (a) Blastoderm
   (b) Larva called planula
   (c) Parasitic form
   (d) Animals with locomotory organs

17. Match the following:

Column – A	Column – B
(i) Tube feet	(a) Nematoda
(ii) Pseudocoelomates	(b) Mollusca
(iii) Acraniata	(c) Millipedes
(iv) Haemocyanin in blood	(d) Star fish
(v) Myriapoda	(e) Protochordata

Answer Keys

Crossword

Across

2. Nemathelminthes 4. Arthropoda 8. Triploblastic 10. Haemocyanin 14. Cnidaria
15. Marsupials 16. Oviparous 17. Placenta 18. Medusa

Down

1. Platyhelminthes 3. Cyclostomata 4. Assimilation 5. Notochord 6. Aestivation
7. Protochordata 9. Diphyodont 11. Myriapoda 12. Ecdysis 13. Craniata

Classroom Wing

Very Short Answer Type Questions

1. Kingdom, species 2. Primitive 3. Rings or segments 4. Jointed feet or legs 5. Shell
6. Cilia 7. Flame cells 8. Ecdysis or moulting 9. Mollusca
10. Protochordates 11. Visceral hump 12. Tube feet 13. Protochordata 14. *Euplectella*
15. Canal system 16. Calcium carbonate 17. Anaerobic 18. Proglottids
19. Annelida 20. Echinodermata 21. Arachnida 22. *Wuchereria* 23. Pisces
24. Chromatophores 25. Cloacae 26. Diphyodont 27. Bone/cartilage 28. Pulmonary
29. Buoyancy 30. Chondrichthyes 31. Feathers 32. Thecodont 33. Diaphragm
34. Marsupium 35. Haemoglobin 36. Teeth 37. Pneumatic 38. (a)
39. (d) 40. (c) 41. (d) 42. (b) 43. (b)
44. (a) 45. (a) 46. (d) 47. (d) 48. (d)
49. (a) 50. (a) 51. (a) 52. (c) 53. (d)
54. (a) 55. (c) 56. (d) 57. (d) 58. (c)
59. (a) 60. (d) 61. (d) 62. (a) 63. (b)
64. (c) 65. (b) 66. (d) 67. (a) 68. (c)
69. (d) 70. (b) 71. (c) 72. (d)
73. A → (v); B → (iii); C → (i); D → (iv); E → (ii) 74. A → (iv); B → (i); C → (v); D → (ii); E → (iii)
75. A → (iii); B → (i); C → (iv); D → (v); E → (ii) 76. A → (iv); B → (i); C → (v); D → (ii); E → (iii)
77. A → (iii); B → (iv); C → (ii); D → (v); E → (i) 78. A → (ii); B → (iv); C → (v); D → (i); E → (iii)
79. A → (iii); B → (iv); C → (i); D → (v); E → (ii) 80. A → (v); B → (iv), C → (ii); D → (iii); E → (i)

Competition Wing

Level 1: Apply your Concepts

1. Vertebrata 2. Primitive 3. Arthropods 4. Porifera; Arthropods
5. Kingdom; Species 6. True 7. False 8. False 9. False
10. True 11. True 12. True 13. True 14. False

15. False **16.** True **17.** False **18.** True **19.** False
20. True
21. (a) Cutaneous (b) Exocoetus (c) Bipedal (d) Syrinx (e) Marsupials
(f) Vanadocytes
22. (a) Scales (b) Parallel venation (c) Echinodermata (d) Coelenterata (e) Aves
(f) Colonial
23. (a) Frog (b) Whale **24.** (a) **25.** (d) **26.** (d)
27. (d) **28.** (a) **29.** (a) **30.** (c) **31.** (c)
32. (d) **33.** (b) **34.** (a) **35.** (c) **36.** (c)
37. (b) **38.** (d) **39.** (d) **40.** (a) **41.** (b)
42. (b) **43.** (a) **44.** (a) **45.** (b) **46.** (a)
47. (a) **48.** (a) **49.** (a)

NEET Special Wing

Multiple-Answer Type Questions

1. (b, c) **2.** (b, c, d) **3.** (a, c) **4.** (a, c) **5.** (b, d)

Comprehension-Based Questions

6. (a) **7.** (b) **8.** (d) **9.** (d) **10.** (b)
11. (i) → (b); (ii) → (c); (iii) → (e); (iv) → (a); (v) → (d)
12. (b) **13.** (a) **14.** (d) **15.** (b) **16.** (b)
17. (i) → (d); (ii) → (a); (iii) → (e); (iv) → (b); (v) → (c)

Hints and Explanations

CLASSROOM WING

Short Answer Type Questions

81. (a) Bilateral symmetry: It means that the body of an animal can be cut into two equal halves by only one plane which passes through the centre.

(b) Germ layers: The embryo of an animal possesses primary layers of cells. These cells undergo cell differentiation to give rise to different kinds of tissues which in turn form the various body organs during development. These are called germ layers.

(c) Notochord: It is a long rod-like structure mostly made up of cartilage. It separates the digestive tract from the nervous tissue. It runs along the back of an animal.

82.

Vertebrates	Invertebrates
The animals which possess the vertebral column are called vertebrates.	The animals which do not possess the vertebral column are called invertebrates.
These are the advanced group of organisms and show greater complexity in structure and functioning than invertebrates.	These are the organisms at the lower level of evolutionary hierarchy.

83. Incomplete digestive tract possesses a single opening for intake of food and elimination of wastes whereas complete digestive tract possesses mouth for ingestion and anus for egestion. The possession of complete digestive tract is an advanced feature found in the higher phyla of invertebrates and vertebrates.

84. Annelids possess a body that is composed of rings or segments, giving them a segmented appearance. Arthropods, while also appearing segmented, are mainly characterized by their jointed legs or feet. Additionally, arthropods have an exoskeleton, whereas annelids do not. The segmented appearance of annelids comes from the body rings, while the defining feature of arthropods is their jointed appendages.

85. The primary distinguishing feature of animals in the phylum Mollusca is the presence of shells that enclose their soft bodies. Molluscs are notably characterized by their shells which offer protection and structural integrity.

86. Phylum Porifera is considered to house the most primitive animals because these organisms exhibit a simple cellular-level organization without true tissues or organs, and they lack distinct features seen in more advanced animals. Poriferans or sponges represent the basic, foundational level of animal complexity.

87. Incomplete digestive tract possesses a single opening for intake of food and elimination of wastes whereas complete digestive tract possesses mouth for ingestion and anus for egestion. The possession of complete digestive tract is an advanced feature found in the higher phyla of invertebrates and vertebrates.

88.

Diploblastic animals	Triploblastic animals
Animals in which there are two germ layers, called ectoderm and endoderm in their embryos are called diploblastic animals.	Animals which possess three germ layers in their embryos are called triploblastic animals. In these animals there is an extra layer called mesoderm between ectoderm and endoderm.
Example: Phyla Porifera and Cnidaria	Example: All the phyla above Platyhelminthes.

89. A true coelom is the body cavity completely lined by the layers of epithelial cells (peritoneum) on inner and outer sides.

Depending upon the origin of coelom, coelomates are classified into two groups:

(a) The coelom can be originated from the mesodermal cells of the embryo. Example: phyla Annelida, Mollusca and Arthropoda

(b) The coelom can be originated from the pouches pinched off from the endoderm of the embryo. Example: Phylum Echinodermata and Protochordata of invertebrates, all the vertebrate animals.

90. Sexual dimorphism: In this feature, the male and female animals possess some distinctive morphological features and can be distinguished from their physical appearance. This feature is observed in Phylum Annelida among invertebrates.

91. Osmoregulation: Maintenance of constant osmotic pressure in the fluids of organism by the control of water and salt concentrations.

92. Characteristic features of Protochordates are:

(a) Protochordates are considered as invertebrate chordates.
(b) They are called acraniata otherwise due to absence of cranium.
(c) The animals are bilaterally symmetrical.
(d) Presence of notochord at some stage of life is seen.
(e) Respiration is by means of gill slits (located in dorsal position).
(f) Open type of blood vascular system with colourless blood.

93. Differences between polyp and medusa

Polyps	Medusa
Fixed forms	Free living swimming forms
Cylindrical with long stalk	Saucer shaped with reduced stalk
Sense organs absent	Sense organs present
Gonads absent	Gonads present
Reproduces asexually	Reproduces sexually

94. Sponges are multicellular organisms with division of labour. Tissue grade of organization is not seen in these animals. These animals bear minute pores on surface of the body known as ostia. water enters through these pores and expelled through large pore known as osculum. This system is known as canal system. As these animals bear minute pores on the body, hence known as pore bearers.

95. Differences between cartilaginous and bony fish.

Cartilagenous fish	Bony fish
They are grouped under elasmobranchs or chondrichthyes.	They are grouped under osteichthyes.
Live in marine water.	Live in fresh, marine or brackish water.
Endoskeleton made of cartilage.	Endoskeleton made of bone.
Gill slits are 5–7 pairs.	Gill slits are 4 pairs.
Opericulum is absent.	Opericulum is present.
Air bladder is absent.	Air bladder is present
Ureotelic.	Amminotelic.
Caudal fin is heterocercal. E.g., Sharks.	Caudal fin it homocercal or diphycarcal. E.g., Catla, rohu.

96. Classification:

Taxonomical unit	Parrot	Cockroach
Kingdom	Animalia	Animalia
Phylum	Vertebrata	Insecta
Class	Aves	Arthropda

97. A streamlined body is a shape that lowers down the frictional drag (which slows down the motion) between a fluid, like air and water.

98. Following are the structural features which help the amphibians to get adapted to both terrestrial and aquatic habitats:

(a) External set of gills which allow amphibians to take up oxygen from water, into their bodies.
(b) Moist skin (as they breathe through their skin and lungs interchangeably). Oxygen transfer requires a moist membrane. It also facilitates processes like cutaneous respiration and osmosis in these species. Their skin is specifically designed to minimize the amount of water loss. Some amphibians release toxins from their skin which is another defence mechanism in some species of amphibians which keep predators at bay.
(c) Limbs–help them move without having to depend on buoyancy of water.
(d) Lungs–replaced the gills to facilitate respiration.
(e) Hind legs–help them take large leaps and change direction with utmost ease when it comes to movement on the land.
(f) Eye position on the top of the head not only facilitates the wide-angle view but also help them stay in water with their eyes just above the water surface. This proves to be an important adaptation when it comes to hunting as well as defense. Transparent eye lid which helps them see underwater with relative ease.
(g) Typical colour pattern with dark body and light underside plays an important to camouflage in water as well as on the land.

99.

Cartilaginous fish	Bony fish
Opericulum is absent	Opericulum is present.
No. of gills are 4–7 pairs. E.g., Shark.	No. of gills are only 4 pairs. E.g., Murrel.

100. Flight adaptation in birds.

(a) Streamlined body: It offers minimum resistance to wind.

(b) Fore limbs modified into wings for flight.

(c) Bipedal locomotion: Hind limbs balance and support the entire weight of the body.

(d) Pneumatic bones: Bones are hollow filled with air rather than bone marrow.

101. A comb-shaped structure projects from retina into vitreous humour known as pectin. It nourishes retina and removes metabolic wastes from vitreous humour.

Essay Type Questions

102. (a) Oviparous—Organisms that reproduce by laying eggs. E.g., Birds

(b) Viviparous—Organisms that give birth to young ones. E.g., mammals

(c) Radial symmetry—Any plane that passes through the central axis which divides the organism into two identical halves. E.g., Coelenterata.

(d) Bilateral symmetry—A plane passing through the central axis, which divides the organism into two identical left and right halves. E.g., Annelida

(e) Homeotherms or warm blooded organisms—When the body temperature of an organism is maintained constant in any environmental conditions. E.g., Birds.

(f) Poikilotherms or cold blooded organisms—When the body temperature changes according to the environment. E.g., Pisces.

(g) Diploblastic—Zygote divides by mitotic cell division, and later the cells are arranged into two embryonic layers, i.e., ectoderm and endoderm. E.g., Coelenterata.

103. The presence of a cranium in vertebrates represents a significant evolutionary leap. A cranium, or skull, provides a hard protective casing for the brain, indicating an evolutionary pressure to safeguard this vital organ as it grew in complexity. In contrast, protochordates, being acraniates, suggest an earlier stage in evolution where the nervous system was simpler and didn't require such protection. Over time, as animals adapted to varied environments and faced different survival challenges, the development of structures like the cranium became essential. It denotes the progression from simpler to more complex organisms, showcasing nature's way of ensuring the survival of the fittest.

104. (a) Oviparous: If the animals lay eggs and the young ones develop from eggs, then they are known as oviparous. E.g., fish.

Viviparous: If the animal gives birth to young ones, then they are known as viviparous. E.g., mammals.

(b) External fertilization: If fertilization takes place outside the body, then it is known as external fertilization. E.g., frog.

Internal fertilization: If fertilization takes place inside the body, then it is known as internal fertilization.

(c) Direct: The developmental stages do not include larval forms.

Indirect: Larval forms are seen in course of development.

105. (a) 'Nematoda' or 'Nemathelminthes' originated from the words 'nema' meaning thread and helminth meaning 'worm'. Hence, these are also called 'threadworms' or 'roundworms' or 'nematodes'.

(b) The name 'Echinodermata' originated from the words 'echinos' meaning 'spines' and 'derma' meaning 'skin'. That means, this name denotes spiny-skinned animals.

(c) The name 'Porifera' originated from the words 'pori' meaning 'pores' and 'pherein' meaning 'bearing'. That means, these organisms bear pores on the body.

106. (a) When the exoskeleton is shed periodically during the life cycle. This is called ecdysis or moulting.

(b) Polymorphism: The occurrence of more than one kind or form of organisms of the same species that exist together in one locality.

107. (a) Tetrapodus: A four-footed animal, belonging to vertebrates higher than fish.

(b) Pentadactyl: A vertebrate limb having five toes or fingers. It is a characteristic of all tetrapods.

(c) Nocturnal: These animals are the ones who sleep during day and come out at night.

(d) Arboreal habitat: Animals which spend a lot of time on trees are called arboreal animals. Their body is suited to live on trees.

108. Dentition is the arrangement or condition of teeth in different species.

(a) Thecodont: Movable jaws possess teeth embedded in sockets. This is called thecodont dentition.

(b) Heterodont: When different types of teeth are developed to suit their varying feeding habits. This is called heterodont dentition.

(c) Diphyodont: Development of two sets of teeth in the life time of a mammal (milk teeth and permanent teeth). This is called diphyodont dentition.

109. (a) The term 'Amphibia' originated from two terms 'amphi' meaning 'both' and 'bios' meaning 'life'. That means, these animals can live both in water and on land.

(b) The name 'Reptilia' originated from the word 'reptare' meaning to 'creep'. That means, this class includes creeping vertebrates.

(c) The name 'Mammalia' originated from the word 'mamma' meaning 'breast'. That means, the animals belonging to this class are characterized by the feature where the females are involved in breast feeding their young ones.

COMPETITION WING

Level 1: Apply your Concepts

24. Most complex multicellular animals have a coelom. Cnidarians are not considered to have coelom as they are diploblastic, that means they do not have any mesodermal layer.

Hence, the correct option is (a).

25. In vertebrates a false coelom is the body cavity which is not completely lined by layers of epithelial cells (peritoneum) on the inner side and the outer side. And in vertebrates the coelom can be originated from endoderm of the embryo.

Hence, the correct option is (d).

26. All viviparous animals show direct development as they do not involve any larval stage. But in viviparous animals, fertilization takes place in the reproductive system of female animal.

Hence, the correct option is (d).

27. The presence of endoskeleton is one of the characteristic features of vertebrates. It is made up of living tissues such as bone and cartilage and also some nonliving materials such as phosphates of calcium.

Hence, the correct option is (d).

28. Organisms belonging to phylum porifera are the organisms with a low degree of individuality and cellular organization. They appear plant-like and their body bears several pores hence they are called porifera or sponges. These pores form a part of canal system through which water enters the body and several processes like nutrition, respiration, circulation and excretion is done at its simplest level through this system.

Hence, the correct option is (a).

29. The hard calcareous exoskeleton is made up of non-living materials. The soft parts of the animals undergo degradation after their death. But, these nonliving materials form deposits resulting in coral formation.

Hence, the correct option is (a).

30. Tapeworm is an endoparasite as it lives inside the body of the host animal (within cells or tissues or in alimentary canal)

Hence, the correct option is (c).

31. The blood of annelids possesses haemoglobin in plasma.

Hence, the correct option is (c).

32. Chordates have a closed circulatory system. *Balanoglossus* is an invertebrate and shows some primitive features of the nonchordates though it is a chordate.

Hence, the correct option is (d).

33. Mixed blood circulates in the body of fish because blood circulation in fish is incomplete.

Hence, the correct option is (b).

34. Terrestrial adaptation requires the production of less toxic nitrogenous wastes like urea (ureotelic) and uric acid (uricotelic) for the conservation of water. Aquatic lizards excrete ammonia which requires large amount of water to dissolve. The huge quantity of water is easily available to such animals from surroundings. However, for terrestrial animals such a huge quantity of water is not available, hence they modify comparatively less toxic products like urea and uric acid which require less amount of water for their excretion.

Hence, the correct option is (a).

35. Placental mammals are considered as true mammals because they possess all the characteristic features of this class. Placental mammals, egg laying and marsupial mammals, all feed their young ones with mother's milk.

Hence, the correct option is (c).

36. Kangaroo is viviparous animal. But, it gives birth to the young ones in partially developed stage. The young ones of kangaroo are very small and tiny. They cannot lead an independent life after birth. So, till the development is complete, kangaroo protects and feeds the baby by keeping it in the abdominal pouch called marsupium which possesses mammary glands.

Hence, the correct option is (c).

37. Organisms belonging to phylum porifera show certain similarities with plants and hence are called sponges.

Hence, the correct option is (b).

38. Crocodile is a reptile and has three chambered heart (two auricles and one incompletely divided ventricle)

Hence, the correct option is (d).

39. In bats nourishment of the young one is done with milk from their mothers.

Hence, the correct option is (d).

40. Both assertion and reason are correct.

Hence, the correct option is (a).

41. Blood passes through the heart only once. It is known as single circulation, hence reason is incorrect.

Hence, the correct option is (b).

42. Tetrapoda are four limbed vertebrates. Hence fishes are not considered under tetrapods but they possess paired fins. Fins and limbs are different organs.

Hence, the correct option is (b).

43. Both assertion and reason are correct.

Hence, the correct option is (a).

44. *Ichthyophis* lives in burrows which are dark and got adapted to it hence it became blind and known as blind snake.

Hence, the correct option is (a).

45. Lizards exhibit caudal autotomy and have limbs. Reason is not correct to assertion.

Hence, the correct option is (b).

46. Protochordates do lack a cranium; hence they don't have a protective covering for their brain. The term 'acraniate' describes this absence.

Hence, the correct option is (a).

47. The evolutionary journey from protochordates to vertebrates showcases the development of complex systems, with the cranium being a prime example.

Hence, the correct option is (a).

48. Molluscs are characterized by their shells, which provide protection and structural support to these organisms.

Hence, the correct option is (a).

49. Arthropods' jointed legs indeed provide them with mobility that aids in thriving in various environments.

Hence, the correct option is (a).

Level 2: Review your Concepts

50. The number and type of germ layers play a crucial role in determining the complexity of an organism. Diploblastic organisms, with only ectoderm and endoderm, typically have simpler structures like those seen in cnidarians (jellyfish, corals). Triploblastic organisms possess an additional layer, the mesoderm, which facilitates the formation of more advanced organ systems, enhancing the organism's functional capabilities.

51. **Oviparity:** Female lays eggs, hatches outside with yolk sac nourishment.

Ovoviviparity: Eggs develop inside female's body, hatch internally with yolk sac nourishment, and young are released.

Viviparity: Embryo develops inside the female's womb, nourished via placenta. Ovoviviparity is a transitional stage.

52. Mosaic vision, a result of compound eyes, allows arthropods to detect fast movements and slight changes in their surroundings. This multi-faceted vision can be particularly beneficial for:

Predation: To swiftly spot and capture prey.

Avoiding Predators: Detecting slight movements can aid in avoiding threats.

Navigation: Navigating through complex terrains, especially for flying arthropods.

53. *Hydra* generally lives in ponds or any other small water bodies. It hangs upside down from either water plants or from flat surfaces such as rocks and keeps its tentacles trailing in the water. The tentacles carry stinge cells which can paralyze small organisms which touch them. Then, it feeds on the prey. The undigested remains leave through the same opening.

54. In bisexual animals, both the male and female sex organs are present in the same individual. However, self-fertilization is prevented.

This can happen in many ways. In earthworm, the male and female organs are located at the opposite ends. This prevents the sperms fertilizing the eggs of the same individual. When two earth worms moving in opposite directions meet each other, they align themselves in such a way that their opposite sex organs lie side by side.

The earthworms secrete lot of mucus which forms a slime mould into which sperms and eggs are released. After that, the worms are separated, and fertilization and development take place later.

Self-fertilization can also be prevented by the different times of development and maturation of testes and ovary (gonads) and also different times of production or maturation of sperms and ova.

55. Arthropods possess compound eyes in contrast to the other animals which possess simple eyes. Simple eyes have one lens each while the compound eyes have many lenses. Therefore, they have mosaic vision.

56. The exoskeleton of a locust has a waxy waterproof layer which helps to reduce the water loss from the body of the locust. Due to this feature, locusts can survive in hot and dry climate.

57. Molluscs have blood with respiratory proteins called haemocyanins, and their molecule contains copper atoms. It is very similar to haemoglobin which is another type of respiratory protein which gives red colour to the blood of animals. When haemocyanin is not bound to oxygen, it is colourless, but oxygenation turns haemocyanin blue.

58. Arthropods constitute the largest group because of the following reasons:
(a) Presence of Chitinous exoskeleton
(b) Adaptation to different environments

59. *Balanoglossus* is an animal which belongs to phylum Hemichordata. Non-chordates are mainly characterized by the absence of notochord in contrast to chordates which possess the notochord as the characteristic feature.

Notochord is a long rod-like support structure that runs along the back of the animal separating the nervous tissue from the other. This develops into skull and a true vertebral column in the adult stage.

Balanoglossus possesses notochord in the embryonic stage in the proboscis region. But later in the adult stage, it disappears. Therefore, the presence of primitive notochord is an advanced feature and shows a transition from non-chordates to chordates. Hence, this organism can be considered as a link between non-chordates and chordates.

60. *Echidna* belongs to class Mammalia. These are only egg-laying mammals. In addition to mammalian features, they also possess reptilian features, like laying of eggs. They also have cloaca, a single opening to pass out urine, faeces, sperms or eggs which is a reptilian feature.

61. The presence of heterodont dentition in mammals provides an evidence that they have some variety of feeding and or hunting specialization in species. Heterodont condition pertains to animals where teeth are differentiated into different forms such as incisors, premolars and molars.

62.

Flat worms	Round worms
• Belong to phylum platyhlminthes • Acoelomates • Hermaphrodite Flat form like a ribbon Eg: *Planaria*	• Belong to phylum Nematehelminthes • Pseudocoelomates • Unisexual Eg. round worm

63.

Common name	Scientific name
Mango	*Mangifera indica*
Rose	*Rosa gallica*
Tiger	*Panthera tigris*
Tulsi	*Ocimum sanctum*
Lion	*Panthera leo*
Wheat	*Triticum aestivum*
Peacock	*Pavo cristatus*
House cat	*Felis domesticus*
National flower (Lotus)	*Nelumbo nucifera*

64.

Oviparous animals	Viviparous animals
Animals in which the egg can be laid by the female and can be hatched by it in outside environment. Such animals are called oviparous animals.	Animals in which the zygote undergoes the process of development in the reproductive system of the female itself. That means, the female animal gives birth to the almost fully formed young one. Such animals are called viviparous animals.
Eg: Most of the invertebrates with few exceptions, Most of the vertebrates except mammals	Eg: Few arthropods, Few annelids, most of the mammals.

65. (a) Protopterus
(b) Whales and dolphins
(c) *Archaeopteryx*
(d) Fossorial
(e) Crocodile
(f) Aves
(g) Duck billed platypus and echidna
(h) Syrinx
(i) Bony fishes
(j) Ichthyophis
(k) Cyclostoma
(l) Tetrapods

Level 3: Assess Your Concepts

66. Oviparous animals produce their young ones by laying large number of eggs per litter. They reproduce by laying eggs and their egg contains an embryo. Development of embryo to a complete young one takes place inside the egg. The egg is protected by hard cover or shell whereas viviparous animals produce their offspring by giving birth to a young one. At a time, they can produce only one young one at a time or twins as in the case of humans. They do not lay eggs, but they reproduce by giving direct birth to young one baby. The young ones develop inside the body of the mother and get nourishment from mother's body and after it is fully developed, young ones are delivered or expelled out of mother's body as a complete baby unlike oviparous animals.

    The major difference between oviparous and viviparous animals is of producing an egg by oviparous and offspring by viviparous.

67. The adult form of amphibians is quite different from the fish in morphological and anatomical features. But, the larval stage of amphibians shows marked similarities to the fish. Some of the similarities are the possession of tail, gills and lateral line sense organ. The tadpoles of amphibians are purely aquatic in habitat and feeding habits are also similar to fish. All these features indicate that the fish are ancestral forms of amphibians.

    Adult amphibians show some similarities to reptiles also. The similarities include possession of lungs and three-chambered heart. The partially terrestrial habitat of amphibians also shows that they are the ancestral forms for the reptiles.

68. In humans, the yolk sac attaches outside the developing embryo and is connected to the umbical cord by a yolk sac. This yolk sac acts as a preliminary circulatory system and is eventually absorbed into the gut of embryo. The yolk sac is lined by extra-embryonic endoderm.

    Humans are placental mammals. They possess a placenta through which the embryo receives the nutrients directly from the mother. Therefore, they do not possess a yolk sac. In other animals where there is no placenta, the embryos can not receive nourishment from the mother. Yolk sac possesses all the nutrient material required for the growth and development of embryo. Therefore, human females possess eggs devoid of yolk sacs.

69. Cartilaginous fish do not have swim bladders, so a swimming motion must be maintained continuously even when sleeping or they will sink to the bottom. They also need to swim constantly to keep oxygen-rich water flowing over the gills. They also must swim to avoid sinking to the bottom of the water column. The ability to move up and down freely in the water column is in fact one of the extraordinary adaptations of cartilaginous species.

70. Birds and mammals are homeothermic. That means, they maintain a constant body temperature irrespective of the surroundings. Therefore, their physiological systems are not much affected by the external climatic conditions.

    However, the other vertebrates belonging to lower phyla are poikilothermic. That means, their body temperature changes according to the external climatic conditions. As a result, the animals do not have the ability to cope with the extreme climatic conditions. Hence, they minimize their activity and go into a passive state during extreme winter and extreme summer. These are called hibernation and aestivation, respectively.

71. Other than mammals, all other animals are mostly oviparous. So, they lay eggs when the external climatic conditions are suitable for hatching. Due to this reason, they follow a definite mating season. Most of the mammals are viviparous where the embryonic development takes place inside the womb of the female animal and

the embryo gets nourishment from the body fluids of the mother. The fully developed young one comes out from the mother's womb. Therefore, no specific mating season is required for these animals.

72. (a) *Psittacula* is parrot, it is a flying bird, all others are flightless.
(b) Preen gland is present only in birds.
(c) Glucose give energy, all others are excretory products.

73. Shells in molluscs likely evolved as protective mechanisms against predators, and environmental hazards, and to prevent desiccation. Annelids' external segmentation allows for locomotion and flexibility in diverse terrains. These external features represent primary evolutionary responses to external pressures. In contrast, Vertebrata, while having external adaptations, exhibits profound internal complexities like advanced nervous and circulatory systems. These internal advancements suggest a shift from merely surviving external threats to efficiently managing intricate internal processes, signalling an evolutionary trend towards optimization and specialization.

74. Whales belong to class mammalia. Fish and whales are aquatic but differ in basic characteristics mentioned as below.
(a) Fish are cold blooded and whale is warm blooded.
(b) Fish undergo respiration by gills and whales by lungs.
(c) Fish have scales and slimy skin, whales do not have scales.
(d) Two-chambered heart is seen in fish, whales have four-chambered heart.

75. Leech is a sanguivorous parasite (blood-sucking parasite). The saliva of leech contains an enzyme called hirudin which prevents blood from clotting, acting as an anti-coagulant.

76. Oviparous animals lay large number of eggs because many eggs are destroyed due to environmental hazards and lack of parental care only few of them hatch to produce young ones.

77. Whale is an aquatic mammal and comes under the class mammalia. Shark is a type of cartilaginous fish and comes under the class pisces. Crocodile comes under the class reptilia. These organisms basically possess the characteristic features of the respective classes they belong to.

Whale	Shark	Crocodile
Pulmonary respiration through lungs	Respiration by gills	Pulmonary Respiration
Four-chambered heard	Two-chambered heart	Four-chambered heart
Warm blooded (temperature constant)	Cold blooded (temperature varies according to the temperature of the environment)	Cold blooded
Viviparous (gives birth to young ones	Oviparous (lays eggs) with external fertilization	Oviparous with internal fertilization
Possess mammary glands	Do not possess mammary glands	Do not possess mammary glands

78. The organisms belonging to the classes Pisces and Aves are associated with streamlined bodies.

The presence of streamlined body facilitates the swimming of fish in water bodies by pushing the water backwards by which the animal moves forward. Similarly, streamlined body in birds enables them to fly by pushing the air backwards by which the bird moves forward.

79. Rainy season is the season for breeding of frogs.
Male frogs make a croak sound during breeding period to attract females for mating purpose.

NEET SPECIAL WING

Multiple-Answer Type Questions

1. Molluscans show visceral hump on the dorsal side of their foot and not the ventral side. They have complete digestive tract with radula as rasping organ. They also possess sense organs which include eyes, tentacles and statocyst.
2. Cyclostomata are jawless fishes which have an eel like body with compressed tail, have jawless suctorial mouth and are ectoparasites on fishes.
3. The set A consists of all animals belonging to the largest phylum Arthropoda and set C consists of animals belonging to the phylum protochordata.
4. Aves and Mammals are two phyla which consists of warm-blooded animals of endotherms which maintain a fixed body temperature irrespective of the temperature outside unlike the ectotherms or cold-blooded animals which do not maintain a fixed body temperature.
5. Echinodermata have a spiny exoskeleton and also possess a disc or flower shaped body. But visceral hump and sense organs like statocyst is shown by animals belonging to phylum Mollusca.

Comprehension-Based Questions

A.

6. The most characteristic feature shown by all mammals is the presence of a mammary gland through which mothers are able to nurse their young one. Bats also show this feature.
7. Presence of milk glands is seen in all types of mammals even those that are egg laying.
8. The alimentary canal in most vertebrates ends in a three chambered structure called as cloaca. This structure is a common cavity for release of both excretory and genital products. Mammals are an exception, they show complex structures in their body which replaces cloaca.
9. Aves and Mammals are two class of animals which show a complete separation between oxygenated and deoxygenated blood and are able to maintain a constant body temperature and are warm blooded.
10. Platypus is an egg laying oviparous animal.
11. Match the following:

    Young one in pouch is a characteristic feature of Marsupials.
    (i) (b)

    Oviparous mammals are also called as egg laying mammals.
    (ii) (c)

    Special structure called placenta nourishes the foetus within the womb of a mother.
    (iii) (e)

    Whale is the largest mammal because of its sheer size.
    (iv) (a)

    In Koala bears the young one is protected on the mother's abdomen.
    (v) (d)

B.

12. In Phylum Cnidaria, animals exists in two forms also known as polymorphism. Asexual form (phase) is called polyp. Polyp leads sedentary colonial life. On the other hand sexual form is called medusa. Medusa is a free-living form.
13. In flat worms, flame cells absorb excretory matter from the body and discharge through excretory ducts. Excretory matter is in the form of ammonia.
14. The fluid in pseudocoelom maintains body shape. This is called hydroskeleton.
15. Molluscans possess one or two pairs of kidneys or organs of Bojanus which open into mantle cavity and behave as excretory organs.
16. In Cnidarians zygote develops into larva called planula.
17. Match the following:

    In star fish, body cavity modified into water vascular system with tube feet. This tube feet help in food collection
    (i) (d)

In Nematoda, animals possess a false or pseudocoelom. A false coelom is the body cavity which is not completely lined by layers of epithelial cells (peritoneum) on the inner and outer sides.

(ii) (a)

Protochordates are considered as invertebrate chordates. Protochordata is otherwise called Acraniata due to the absence of cranium.

(iii) (e)

Molluscs have blood with respiratory proteins called haemocyanins, and their molecule contains copper atoms. When haemocyanin is not bound to oxygen, it is colourless, but oxygenation turns haemocyanin blue.

(iv) (b)

Phylum Arthropoda is further classified into four classes. One of the class is Myriapoda which consists of animals with many legs, example Centipedes and Millipedes.

(v) (c)

CHAPTER 5

Human Health and Diseases

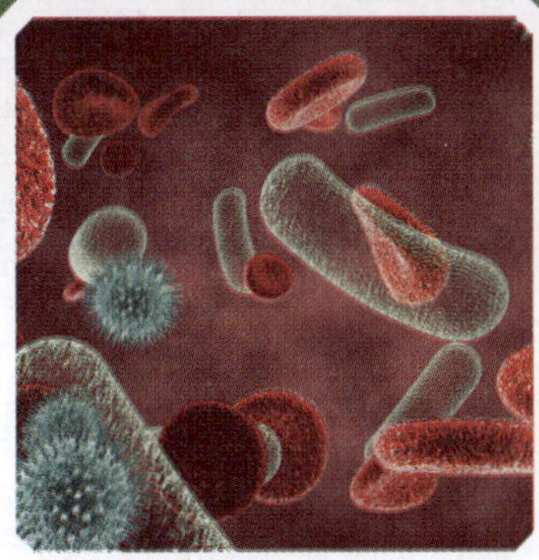

Key Ideas

After completing this chapter, you should be able to:

- Interpret the concept of health and disease
- Infer diseases on the basis of various parameters
- Describe the mechanism of transmission of diseases
- Explain innate and adaptive immunities

Remember

Before beginning this chapter, you should be able to:

- Define the basic concepts related to microorganisms
- Discuss some common human diseases

Scientific Crypt

A Tribute to Marie François Xavier Bichat (1771–1802)

A French anatomist and pathologist, is a medical science luminary. Bichat developed the concept of pathological anatomy, focusing on the intricate structures of tissues, which was a game changer in the study of human health and disease. He classified tissues into 21 distinct types, laying the groundwork for modern histology's development. This was a significant step forward, allowing for a more in-depth understanding of how diseases manifest in specific organs.

Bichat performed approximately 70 autopsies in just three years to elucidate the characteristics and behaviours of tissues in various disease states. His work emphasized the critical relationship between tissue morphology and function, allowing for a more comprehensive understanding of organ pathology. Links between organ function and pathological states, resulting in a conceptual breakthrough in the field. His research and discoveries were captured in several publications, the most notable of which was '*Traité des membranes*' in 1800, which provided unprecedented insights into tissue pathology.

Despite the fact that Bichat's life was cut short at the age of 31, his legacy lives on in the halls of medical science. He was posthumously honoured, and his name is immortalized in anatomical terms such as 'Bichat's fat pad'.

Crossword

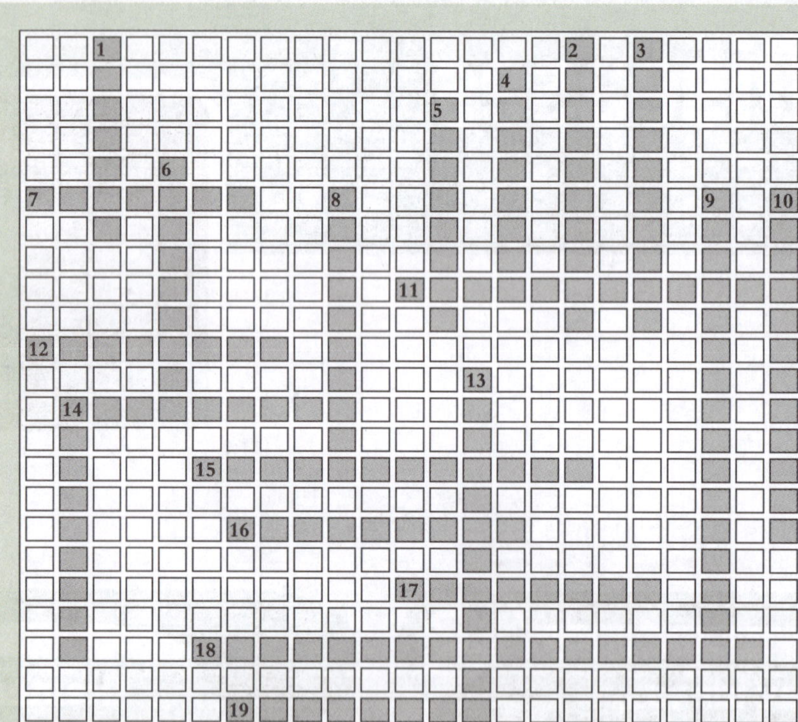

Across

7. Type of disease which is confined to a specific area, only affecting few people
11. Type of non- communicable diseases which includes normal wear and tear of the tissues due to unhealthy lifestyle
12. Type of disease which occurs infrequently and irregularly
14. Hypersensitivity of the body to certain substances
15. ________proved that microbes are present in the environment
16. Pathogenic disease caused by tapeworm
17. Vector for diseases like cholera, typhoid, amoebiasis, etc.
18. Causative protozoan of sleeping sickness
19. Protein which fights against the antigen

Down

1. Inactive toxic substances extracted from bacteria and are useful for the development of antibodies
2. Cells which ingest pathogens that invade our body
3. Diseases which are inherited by an individual at the time of birth
4. Tear glands secrete an enzyme called
5. Immunity developed after the birth and throughout the life due to the generation of antibodies
6. First cause identified for a disease
8. Another name for the disease Elephantiasis
9. Type of immunity introduced to our body through vaccination
10. Degenerative disease of the bones
13. Non-disease-causing secondary factors.
14. Type of mosquito which spreads Malaria

INTRODUCTION

We have discussed in previous chapters that cell is the structural and fundamental unit of life. There are subcellular entities (organelles) that are involved in the functioning of the cells as they are assigned specific functions. Also, Tissues and organs perform specialized activities to sustain life. For example, heart beats continuously to pump blood, lungs are involved in breathing to supply oxygen to cells of the body, intestinal lining absorb nutrients to provide adequate supply of raw materials to the cells, kidneys function to filter out harmful toxic wastes out of our body, etc. All these activities are interconnected and their proper execution is crucial for maintenance of life. Anything that hampers the proper functioning of cells, tissues, organs and organ systems will lead to inefficient working of our body.

Health

World Health Organization (WHO) defines health as '*a state of complete physical, mental and social well-being and not merely the absence of disease or infirmity*'. By this definition, we can address three fundamental elements of health as follows:

1. **Physical element:** This element pertains to proper functioning and maintenance of constituents of our body, that is, efficient functioning of cells, tissues, organs and organ systems.
2. **Mental element:** This element is concerned with an individual's balance in relation to its environment. WHO defines mental health as '*a state of well-being in which every individual realizes his or her own potential, can cope with the normal stresses of life, can work productively and fruitfully, and is able to make a contribution to her or his community.*'
3. **Social element:** This element implies that all individuals living in a society have basic requirements of life, i.e., hygiene, sufficient earning, collective interactions, etc.

> **Info Bytes!**
>
> World Health Day is celebrated on 7 April to mark the anniversary of the founding of WHO in 1948.

Conditions Necessary for Good Health

The conditions required to maintain good health are listed as follows:

- Proper sanitation, that is, provision of clean drinking water and efficient sewage disposal.
- Nutritious food
- Social equality

Table 5.1 Difference between healthy and disease-free states

Parameter	Healthy	Disease-free
State	State of physical, social and mental well-being	State of absence of discomfort in body
Inclusion	Refers to an individual and its society and environment	Refers to an individual only
Conditions	Good sanitation, adequate economic conditions and social harmony	Hygienic surroundings and defence against common diseases

Disease

A disease is a deviation from the normal functionality of the body and mind of a person. Diseases can be defined as the malfunctioning of one or more organs of the body. Many of such deviations/abnormal conditions can be cured, but sometimes they become serious and can be fatal. Diseases are diagnosed with the help of specific set of signs associated with them. Symptoms are the manifestations of a disease. For instance, headache could be a symptom of malaria, dengue, jaundice, problem in eyesight, blood pressure, etc. Hence, symptoms do not provide an exact cause of the disease. Whereas, signs are definite evidences of a disease. A physician tries to look for signs of a disease on the basis of the symptoms.

Causes of a Disease

Physical health of a human body could be affected by a number of factors. These factors may be of the following two types,

1. Immediate causes
2. Contributory causes

> **Info Bytes!**
>
> A disease-free person may or may not be healthy.

Immediate Causes

Immediate cause is the first cause identified when a person is suffering from a disease. For example, if an individual is suffering from cold, we can say that the cause of the cold is an infection with a virus. So, the immediate cause of the disease is virus. Immediate causes are subdivided into two types:

1. **External factors:** These are the external or extrinsic factors which affect the normal functioning of a disease. They can be pathogens, inadequate diet, pollutants and drugs.
2. **Internal factors:** These factors exist within the human body. They can be genetic disorders, improper functioning of the immune system, malfunctioning of any organ, etc.

Contributory Causes

Contributory causes, by themselves, do not lead to a disease, they are the second-level causes. For example, a baby has some genetic condition which makes it more prone to suffer from cold when exposed to virus. Without the pathogen (virus), the genetic condition alone would not be able to cause any disease. However, it does become a contributory factor to causing the disease.

Classification of Diseases

Diseases can be classified in a number of ways. Five important parameters of their classification are listed below.

1. Extent
2. Occurrence
3. Communicability
4. Pathogens
5. Transmitting agents

On the Basis of Extent

Diseases can be classified into following four types on the basis of their extent of occurrence,

1. **Endemic:** This type of disease is confined to a specific area only affecting few people. For example, Rift valley fever is endemic in eastern Africa, goitre is endemic in India (sub-Himalayan region), etc.
2. **Sporadic:** This type of disease occurs infrequently and irregularly. They occur randomly in scattered instances without no known cause. For example, Chikungunya, diphtheria, etc.
3. **Pandemic:** This type of disease refers to an epidemic that has spread over several countries or continents, usually affecting a large number of people. For example, Covid-19 coronavirus is pandemic.
4. **Epidemic:** This type of disease refers to a sudden increase in the number of cases of a disease above what is normally expected in that population in that area. Many people get affected by the disease in a short span of time in a localized area (a district or a state or a country). For example, plague became epidemic in India in 1994.

On the Basis of Occurrence

Diseases can be broadly classified into two categories based on the occurrence,

1. Congenital diseases
2. Acquired diseases

Congenital Diseases

The diseases which are inherited by an individual at the time of birth are called congenital disease. No external agents are involved in the development of these diseases. Genetic or chromosomal disorder is one of the major reasons for congenital diseases. Congenital heart diseases, congenital cataract are few examples.

Info Bytes!

In the years 1918 and 1919, a world epidemic of simple Influenza killed 20 million people in the USA and Europe.

Acquired Diseases

The diseases which are acquired during the lifetime of an individual at any age after the birth and not inherited at the time of birth are called acquired diseases. Acquired diseases can be of different types based on the way, they are acquired. It can be broadly categorized into two types on the basis of communicability,

1. Communicable diseases
2. Non-communicable diseases

Communicable Diseases

The diseases which are transmitted from one person to another through different media like air, water, food, physical contacts and insects are called communicable diseases. These diseases are also called infectious diseases. Different microorganisms which are responsible for communicable diseases are called pathogens and they are transmitted through different media, mentioned above. Different types of pathogens are as follows:

Info Bytes!

The investigation for identifying the reasons for the diseases is called etiology.

- Bacteria
- Virus
- Fungi
- Protozoa
- Parasitic worms

Louis Pasteur and Robert Koch showed for the first time that microorganisms are responsible for the diseases to occur and spread. Pasteur proved through a series of experiments, that microorganisms are present in the environment around us. Koch proved that a rod-shaped bacterium causes a disease called anthrax. Generally, animals suffer from anthrax.

Non-communicable Diseases

Non-communicable diseases do not get transmitted from one person to another. These diseases can be classified into the following categories depending on the factors responsible for them.

Table 5.2 Classification of non-communicable diseases

Non-communicable diseases	Factors responsible	Examples
Degenerative diseases	Normal wear and tear of the tissues, unhealthy lifestyle	Arteriosclerosis Osteoporosis
Deficiency diseases	Lack of intake of one or more nutrients	Rickets Scurvy
Allergies	Hypersensitivity of the body to certain substances	Asthma Hay fever
Social diseases	Addiction	Alcoholism Drug addiction

Transmission of Communicable Diseases

Communicable diseases are transmitted from one person to another. The transmission can take place in two ways,

1. Direct transmission
2. Indirect transmission

Direct Transmission

This kind of transmission of disease takes place by direct contact with the infected person. No agents or media are required for the transmission of these diseases.

The following table represents the modes of direct transmission of communicable diseases and examples.

Table 5.3 Modes of direct transmission of communicable diseases

Modes of transmission	Examples of diseases
Direct contact with infected person	Chicken pox Small pox
Droplet infection by: • Sneezing • Coughing • Spitting	Common cold Diphtheria Influenza Tuberculosis
From the pregnant mother (through placenta)	German measles
Body fluids like blood, semen, etc.	AIDS Hepatitis B

Konnect

Vector is an organism that carries pathogens from infected person to another person, but itself remains unaffected

The disease which are transmitted by direct transmission are contagious. Some contagious disease are serious and fatal. In such cases, generally patients are given treatment by keeping them isolated to avoid the spread of disease. Such condition is called quarantine. For example, swine flu.

Indirect Transmission

This kind of transmission of diseases requires some media to carry the pathogens from the infected person.

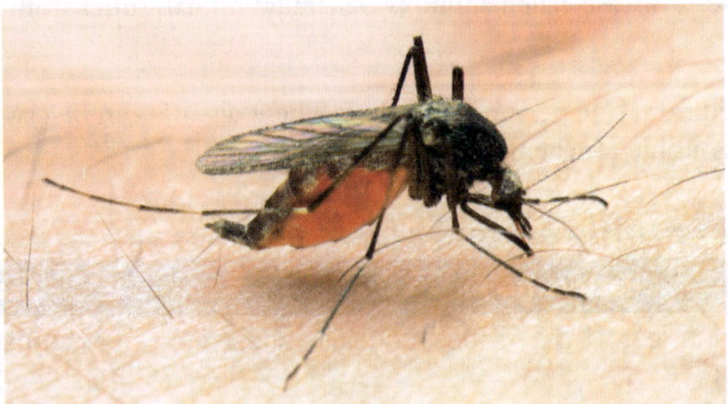

Figure 5.1 Female *Anopheles* mosquito feeding on blood of an infected individual

Info Bytes!

Only female mosquitoes bite. Both male and female feed on fruit nectar but the female also feeds on blood as it needs the protein in blood for development of the eggs.

The following table represents the modes of indirect transmission of communicable diseases and examples.

Table 5.4 Modes of indirect transmission of communicable diseases

Modes of transmission	Examples of diseases
Vector	Malaria—By female *Anopheles* (mosquito) Cholera, dysentery and typhoid—By housefly
Air	Epidemic typhus
Unclean hands and fingers	Ascariasis
Articles like garments and utensils used by infected person	Diphtheria Hepatitis A Eye and skin infections
Animal bite transmission from the animals, especially dogs to human beings	Rabies

The given table represents the transmission and control of the diseases caused due to the transmission by vectors.

Table 5.5 Transmission and control of communicable diseases

Vectors	Diseases	Transmission	Control
Housefly	Cholera Typhoid Amoebiasis	Houseflies carry pathogens from the infected person's stool, vomit discharge to the food and drinks consumed by healthy person	Eatables must be covered Maintenance of proper sanitation Use of insecticide Safe disposal of garbage
Rats	Plague Typhus fever	Rat flea, a parasite of rats carries the pathogen from the dead rat to human being	Eatables must be covered Rat-proof bins must be used for the storage of cereal grains Killing of rats by using zinc phosphide
Mosquito *Anopheles* *Culex* *Aedes*	Malaria Filaria Yellow fever	The mosquito sucks the blood of an infected person and carries the pathogen When it bites the healthy person, the pathogen gets transmitted into the blood	Using insecticides to kill mosquitoes Prevention of breeding of mosquitoes by eliminating the stagnant water Spraying kerosene over the surface of water to prevent the dissolution of oxygen Introduction of certain fish (that eat mosquito larvae) in the stagnant water bodies
Cockroachesa	Several diseases like cholera, gastroenteritis, etc.	Transmission takes place indirectly due to consumption of food items contaminated by cockroaches	Spraying insecticides like DDT Maintenance of sewerage system

Comparative Study of Diseases Caused by Pathogens

The pathogens cause diseases, as they release toxins or kill the living cells in our tissues. The capacity of the microorganisms to produce toxins is called pathogenicity. The treatment involves the production of anti-toxins to neutralize the effect of toxins.

The given table represents the diseases caused by different pathogens and symptoms, transmission, prevention and control of those diseases.

Info Bytes!

Zinc phosphide is used as rodenticide bait. When an animal eats the bait, the acid in the animal's stomach turns the zinc phosphide into phosphine which is very toxic.

Table 5.6 Diseases caused by different pathogens

Diseases and the pathogens	Symptoms	Transmission	Control/Treatment	Prevention
		Pathogen (Bacteria)		
Cholera Causative bacterium is ***Vibrio cholerae***	Watery diarrhoea, Frequent vomiting, Sunken eyes, muscular cramp, etc., due to dehydration.	Consumption of food and water contaminated by flies.	Administration of oral rehydration syrup (ORS)*	Consumption of boiled water and properly cooked food Proper disposal of waste Immunization by cholera vaccine
Tuberculosis Causative bacterium is ***Mycobacterium***	Cough Fever Sweating in the night Pain in the chest Blood in sputum Loss of weight Breathlessness on exertion	Inhalation of droplets released by an infected person during sneezing, coughing or spitting.	Patient must be quarantined. Anti-Tubercular Therapy (ATT) can be used.	Immunization by BCG (Bacillus Calmette Guerin) vaccine.
Typhoid Causative bacterium is ***Salmonella typhi***	Continuous fever which is higher in the afternoon than in the morning Headache during fever	Ingestion of contaminated food, water and unwashed raw vegetables. The bacteria present in the excretory substances of the infected person can be transmitted by flies.	Patient must be isolated. Patient excretory matter must be disinfected before disposal.	Prevention of breed of flies with the help of insecticide. Administration of TAB vaccine or live oral vaccine
		Pathogen (Virus)		
AIDS Causative virus is **Human Immuno-deficiency virus**	Victim becomes susceptible to other infections like flu, diarrhoea, etc. Swollen lymph nodes Reduction in platelets count	Sexual contact Contact of blood between infected and disease-free person.	HIV screening of blood before transfusion No treatment is available	Safe sex Avoiding transfusion of blood of the infected person. Usage of sterile needles and disposable syringes.

(*Continued*)

Table 5.6 *(Continued)*

Diseases and the pathogens	Symptoms	Transmission	Control/Treatment	Prevention
Hepatitis A Causative virus is **hepatitis A virus (HAV)** **Hepatitis B** Causative virus is **hepatitis B virus (HBV)**	Symptoms are like those of jaundice Nausea, vomiting, weakness, loss of appetite, dark urine	**Hepatitis A** is transmitted by contaminated food and water **Hepatitis B** is transmitted through body fluids, such as blood, semen, etc.	Washing of hands before and after using toilets Avoiding contamination of water, milk and food	**Hepatitis A** Immunization by vaccines and interferons High-calorie diet Limited consumption of protein and fat **Hepatitis B** People of all age groups should be vaccinated
Chicken pox Causative virus is **varicella zoster virus (VZV)**	Crusts are formed all over the body Fever Headache and discomfort	Direct contact with infected person Using articles of infected person	Isolation of the patient Avoidance of the use of articles of infected person	An attack of chicken pox imparts ever lasting immunity
Pathogen (Protozoan)				
Malaria Causative protozoan is ***Plasmodium***	High fever accompanied with violent shivering and chills Headache Enlargement of liver	By the bite of *Anopheles* mosquito carrying the protozoan.	Administration of chloroquine drug	Prevention of the breeding of mosquito as well as killing mosquitoes Avoiding stagnation of water
Amoebic dysentery Causative protozoan is ***Entamoeba histolytica***	Acute abdominal pain Diarrhoea Mucus and blood with stool	Flies carrying the protozoan contaminate the food	Administration of the drug, metronidazole	Maintaining hygienic condition Covering the food and water properly
Sleeping sickness or African trypanosomiasis Causative protozoan is ***Trypanosoma brucei***	Anxiety Headache Fatigue Insomnia Swelling of lymph nodes	Bite of tsetse fly carrying the protozoan Blood transfusion	Administration of drugs, such as pentamidine, suramin	Prevention of the growth of tsetse flies Avoiding insect bite by covering the body and using insecticide
Pathogen (Helminths)				
Ascariasis Causative helminth is a roundworm, ***Ascaris lumbricoides***	Abdominal discomfort Loss of appetite Vomiting and diarrhoea	Transmitted through unwashed raw vegetables Lack of personal hygiene	Use of the drugs, such as albendazole, mebendazole	Effective sewage system Maintaining proper personal hygiene
Taeniasis Causative helminth is ***Taenia solium***, commonly called **tapeworm**	Abdominal pain, indigestion, vomiting and diarrhoea Anaemia Weight loss	Transmitted through contaminated food and water The parasite is mainly found in pork, which is called measly pork.	Use of the drug, praziquantel or albendazole	Intake of properly cooked food Maintenance of sanitation

(Continued)

Table 5.6 (*Continued*)

Diseases and the pathogens	Symptoms	Transmission	Control/Treatment	Prevention
Filariasis, commonly called elephantiasis Causative helminth is ***Wuchereria bancrofti***	Obstruction in the flow of lymph Swelling (lymphoedema) of legs	Bite of an infected *Culex* mosquito	Use of the drug, diethylcarbamazine	Use of mosquito repellant Eradication of the vector, *Culex*

*ORS contains the given substances: potable water, sucrose, glucose, potassium chloride, sodium chloride and sodium bicarbonate.

**Tetanus is a disease caused by bacteria *Clostridium tetani,* which is commonly found in soil, saliva, dust and manure. This infection generally occurs when the bacteria enters skin through a break such as a cut or a wound. Though this is caused by bacterial infection, it cannot be transmitted from one person to another person. That means, tetanus is a non-communicable pathogenic disease.

The period between exposure to an infection and the appearance of the first symptoms is called incubation period.

Table 5.7 Some common diseases and their incubation periods.

Disease	Incubation period
Chicken pox	Between 9 and 21 days
Smallpox	Between 7 and 17 days
Typhoid	Between 7 and 21 days
Mumps	Between 14 and 18 days
Measles	Between 9 and 12 days
Cholera	Between 2 and 6 days

Immunity

Most of the pathogens are present in our surrounding. Hence, we are susceptible to different diseases. But our body has some in-built defence mechanism, which protects us from the pathogens. This defence mechanism is our immune system.

Immunity is the ability of an organism to recognize the disease-causing germs and provide resistance against them. Immunity can be of two types based on the way it is imparted or developed in our body. The two types of immunity are stated below:

1. Innate immunity
2. Acquired or adapted immunity

Info Bytes!

31 May: World No Tobacco Day
25 April: World Malaria Day
28 July: World Hepatitis Day
1 December: World AIDS Day

Innate Immunity

Immunity inherited by a child at the time of birth is called innate immunity. Since, it is naturally acquired by a person due to its genetic make-up, it is not disease specific. Innate immunity provides self-defence mechanism to our body. There are two orders of self-defence mechanism, namely

1. The first line of defence
2. The second line of defence

Table 5.8 Representation of the first line of defence

Body part or secretion that acts as a first line of defence	Mechanism of defence
Skin	Prevents invasion of pathogens. Oil secreted from the oil glands present in the skin and the sweat kills microbes
Mucous membranes	Act as protective layers of gastrointestinal, respiratory and urinary tracts. Also provide lubrication
Tear glands	Secrets an enzyme, called lysozyme. Destroys the bacteria and thus, protects eyes from infection
Saliva	Contains enzymes which kill microorganisms
Nose	Mucous membrane and hair present in nose trap dust particles and microorganisms and thus, filter the air inhaled
Gastric juice	Secreted by stomach. It contains enzymes, HCl and mucus, which destroys pathogens

If the pathogens overcome all the above physical barriers and enter our body, there is an in-built second line of defence mechanism in our body. The second line of defence mechanism includes the following:

Phagocytes: Phagocytes are the cells which ingest pathogens that invade our body. Neutrophils and macrophages are the types of white blood cells which carry out phagocytosis.

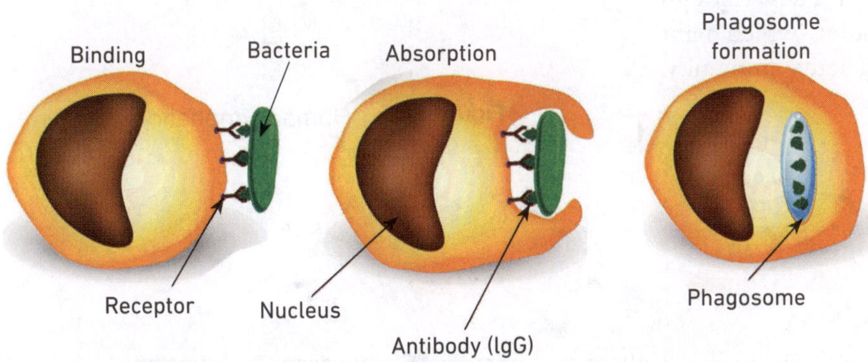

Figure 5.2 Diagram showing phagocytosis in three steps

Info Bytes!

Interferons are proteins made by our cells in response to viral infection that prevent the growth of the virus.

Inflammation: Inflammation is the response of the immune system against foreign objects entering our body.

Fever: Fever is response under inflammation.

Anti-microbial proteins: Anti-microbial substances are different proteins generated in our body which destroy pathogens.

Lymphatic system: It is a network of tissues and organs that help the body get rid off the toxins and waste. The primary function of the lymphatic system is to transport lymph, a fluid containing infection-fighting white blood cells, throughout the body. The lymphatic system primarily consists of lymphatic vessels which are connected to lymph nodes, where the lymph is filtered. Tonsils, spleen and thymus are important parts of the lymphatic system.

Acquired or Adapted Immunity

Every pathogen possesses a type of protein which is unique. This unique protein is called **antigen**. Antigens present in the pathogens are harmful to our body and cause diseases. When an antigen enters our body, another type of proteins get developed spontaneously in our body and fights against the antigen. The protein developed is called **antibody**. These antibodies are mainly produced by lymphocytes, which are the most important white blood corpuscles. The blood serum containing the antibodies against particular antigen is called anti-serum. Immunity developed after the birth and throughout the life due to the generation of antibodies is called acquired immunity. Acquired immunity gets developed in two different ways,

Active Immunity

Active immunity gets developed due to the generation of antibodies in our body in response to the entry of the antigen from outside. The development of this kind of immunity takes some time, but it lasts for long time. Active immunity can be of two types depending on the way the antigen enters our body. These are,

Natural Active Immunity

An antigen can enter our body naturally from the environment, and then the development of antibodies takes place in our body to resist the antigen. This is called natural active immunity. For example, an attack of chicken pox imparts a life-long immunity.

Artificial Active Immunity

An antigen can also be introduced to our body through vaccination for the generation of antibodies, which fight against the antigen. This is called artificial active immunity. For example, vaccines of polio and measles.

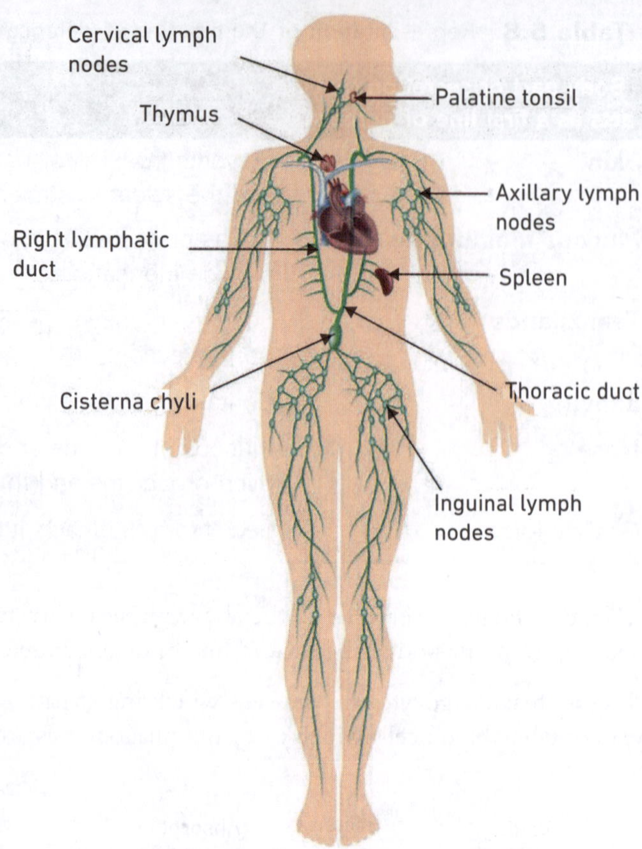

Figure 5.3 Human lymphatic system

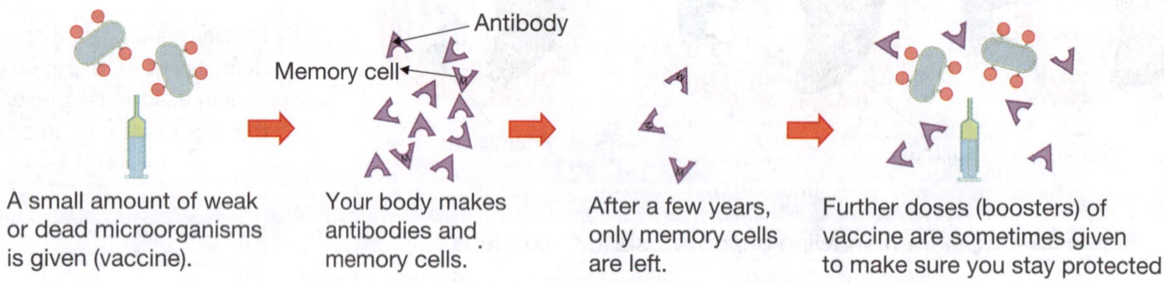

Figure 5.4 Diagram showing how vaccination works

Passive Immunity

Passive immunity is developed by the introduction of antibodies into our body. Passive immunity can provide immediate relief as direct antibodies are introduced into the body, but this immunity does not persist for long time. For example, antibodies for fighting tetanus and diphtheria. Passive immunity can be of two types based on the sources of antibodies. These are:

Natural Passive Immunity

Antibodies from the mother enter the body of the foetus during its developmental stage inside the womb of the mother. The immunity developed in this process, is called natural passive immunity.

Artificial Passive Immunity

When antibodies are developed in other organisms for fighting against a specific disease and they are introduced into the body of a person suffering from that disease, the immunity developed is called artificial passive immunity. Pathogens are introduced into the body of an animal. Antibodies against that pathogen are produced in the blood of that animal. Anti-serum from the animal is prepared by taking its blood. Then, anti-serum injections are introduced into the patient's body. For example, treatment of snake bite is carried out using anti-venom.

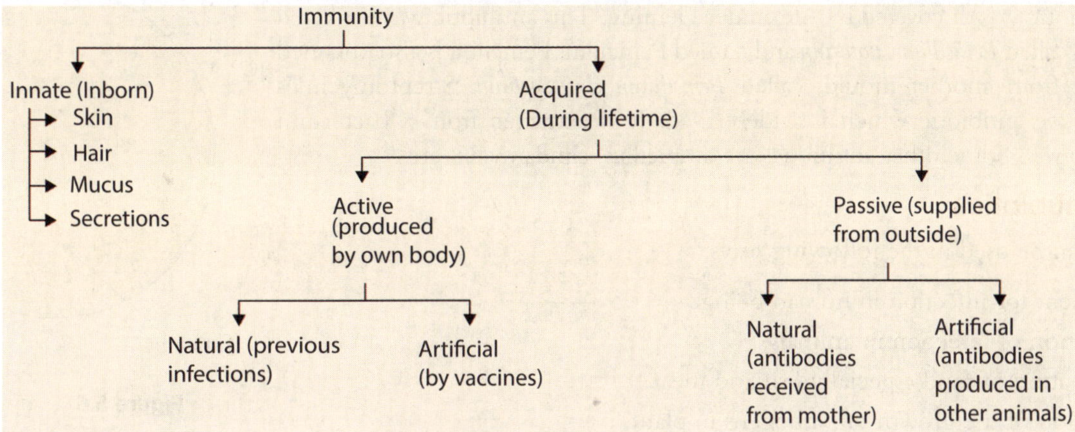

Figure 5.5 Types of Immunity

Immunization

The process of development of immunity in our body to fight against diseases by introducing dead and weakened antigens is called immunization. One of these processes is vaccination. A vaccine is a liquid substance, which contains dead or weakened antigens and the process of administration of vaccines is called vaccination. The first vaccine was developed by Edward Jenner and it was the vaccine for small pox. Vaccines can be administered in two different ways, either by oral administration or by injection. Administration of vaccine by injection is called inoculation. Vaccines can be of different types based on its content. Some of them are listed below:

Info Bytes!

Edward Jenner is known as the Father of Immunology.

Table 5.9 Different types of vaccine

Content of the vaccine	Name of the vaccine	Disease resisted by the vaccine
Dead germs (disease-causing microorganisms)	TAB vaccine	Typhoid
Living, weakened germs	BCG (Bacillus Calmette–Guérin)	Tuberculosis
Living germs	Small pox vaccine contains Cowpox virus	Small pox (totally eradicated now)
Toxoids (they are inactive toxic substances extracted from bacteria, but useful for the development of antibodies)	DPT vaccine	Diphtheria Pertussis (Whooping cough) Tetanus

Some other common vaccines are hepatitis B vaccine, measles vaccine, Salk's vaccine and oral polio vaccine for poliomyelitis. Through the vaccination, a defence mechanism against a specific disease is developed in our body. Our in-built defence mechanisms and vaccines may not always protect us from the attack of microorganisms. During such times, an intake of an external chemical substance is required for killing the microorganisms which cause diseases. An antibiotic is one such kind of chemical substances.

Antibiotics

An antibiotic is a chemical substance which can kill as well as inhibit the growth of bacteria. Antibiotics are generally prepared from bacteria or fungi. In the year 1929, the first antibiotic was discovered by Alexander Fleming. This antibiotic was extracted from a mould called *Penicillium notatum* and named Penicillin. Penicillin is also obtained at large scale from another mould, called *Penicillium chrysogenum*. Streptomycin is another effective antibiotic which is widely used. It is extracted from a bacterium called *Streptomyces*. Some other antibiotics are ampicillin, clindamycin, etc.

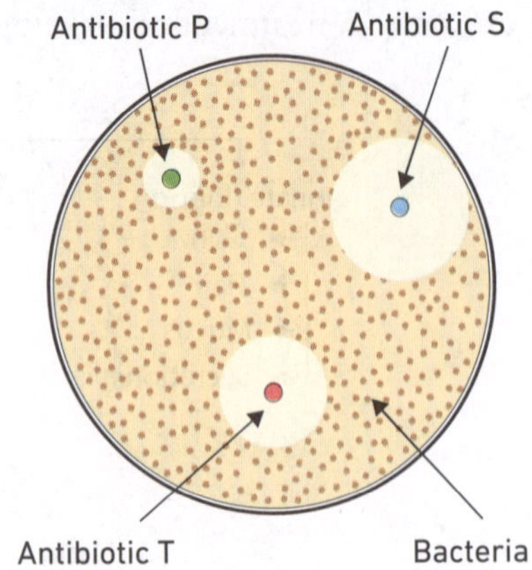

Figure 5.6 Diagram of antibiotics and colonies of bacteria. Observe bacteria do not grow around area where antibiotic is present.

Uses of Antibiotics

Antibiotics can be used in the following ways:

- Treatment for infection in human being
- Prevention of infection in animals
- Preservation of food especially fish and meat
- Inhibition of the growth of pathogens in plants

Sulphonamide

Sulphonamide is another group of drugs which fight against pathogens particularly, fungi and bacteria. This drug is prepared synthetically. Urinary and bowel infections, pneumonia, etc., are treated with this drug. Other than the above categories of drugs, there are several other drugs which can be used for fighting against different pathogens.

Hygiene

It is always better to lead a healthy and disease-free life instead of depending on different drugs for fighting against diseases as prevention is always better than cure. For maintaining a healthy life, we need to adopt some hygienic habits at personal level as well as at community level.

Personal Hygiene

The practices performed by a person for maintaining a good health constitute personal hygiene. Regular bath helps keep our body clean and germ-free. Changing and washing clothes every day prevent breeding of microbes. Deodorant can be used to get rid of the bad odour due to perspiration. Regular brushing of teeth in the morning and before going to bed helps prevent dental diseases. Our eyes, ears and nose also must be cleaned regularly to avoid infections. Trachoma and conjunctivitis are two common eye infections. Other than cleanliness, there are some other healthy habits which are essential to lead a healthy life. Adequate sleep, having balanced diet at appropriate time, regular bowel movement, etc., are some of the healthy habits. A balanced diet provides all sorts of nutrients essential for our growth and prevention of diseases. Deficiency in any of the nutrients in our diet leads to malnutrition. Regular physical exercise is another important practice for maintaining our good health. Physical exercise keeps our muscles toned by improving blood circulation.

Along with personal hygiene, we need to keep our surrounding clean for the prevention of diseases. Community hygiene is another important aspect for maintaining our good health.

Community Hygiene

Health measures that can be undertaken only by the community as a whole form the parts of community hygiene. These include water source protection, proper disposal of solid waste and excreta, controlling animal rearing and market hygiene.

Following measures can be taken to ensure community hygiene,

- Supply of safe drinking water
- Safe disposal of domestic and industrial wastes

- Recycling or reusing the waste generated
- Proper maintenance of sewage system
- Using disinfectant like DDT (dichlorodiphenyltrichloroethane) in the area where garbage is disposed to prevent the growth of bacteria.

Antiseptics and Disinfectants

Antiseptics are mild chemical substances that kill germs when applied on body. Their concentrations are kept low enough so that they do not cause any harm to our body. Examples of some antiseptics are alcohol, boric acid, carbolic acid, hydrogen peroxide and iodine.

Disinfectants are chemical substances that have stronger degree of action. They are applied on the places where germs thrive. Examples of commonly used disinfectants are Lysol, 40% formalin, DDT, etc. They should not come in contact with human skin as they are very strong.

Info Bytes!

Boiling also kills germs, hence, it is called physical disinfectant.

International Health Organizations

Health is the major concern of all the governments across the world. Different health organizations are established in our country as well as all over the world to address the health-related issues and safeguard the health of the people.

World Health Organization and Red Cross are the two major international health organizations.

Info Bytes!

World Health Organization is the directing and coordinating authority on international health, within the United Nations' system.

Red Cross

Red Cross was established in 1864. The main activities of Red Cross are as follows:

- Providing health aids to the victims of natural calamities like flood, famine, etc., as well as the wounded soldiers during war.
- Focusing on disaster-prone areas and crisis management.
- Arranging ambulances for the accident victims, and providing first aid and blood whenever required.
- Training midwives and other people regarding first aid related skills.

World Health Organization (WHO)

WHO was established in 1948, as a specialized agency of UNO (United Nations Organization). The headquarter of WHO is at Geneva, Switzerland. Following are the activities of WHO,

- Spreading awareness among the people regarding the communicable diseases and epidemics.
- Monitoring quarantine measures for preventing spread of contagious diseases.
- Imparting health education to people.
- Formulating health policies.
- Improving pharmaceutical products and maintaining international standards.
- Curbing environmental pollution.

Figure 5.7 Logo of the World Health Organization

Acquired Immunodeficiency Syndrome (AIDS)

AIDS was first recognized in 1981. AIDS is a series of symptoms caused by the human immunodeficiency virus (HIV). A person is said to have AIDS when his/her immune system is too weak to fight off infections and there is development of certain defining symptoms and illnesses. This is the last stage of HIV.

Human Immunodeficiency Virus

HIV is found in semen, blood, breast milk and vaginal fluids.

HIV is a virus that attacks the immune system, which is our body's defence against diseases and infections. The virus destroys a type of white blood cell in the immune system called T-helper cell, and makes copies of itself inside these cells.

As HIV destroys more and makes more copies of itself, it gradually breaks down a person's immune system. This means that if someone is infected with HIV and is not receiving treatment, he/she will find it harder and harder to fight off infections and diseases.

Info Bytes!

HIV cannot be transmitted through body fluids such as sweat, saliva or urine.

If HIV is left untreated, it can take up to 15 years for the immune system to be so severely damaged that it cannot defend itself against infections at all. However, the speed with which HIV progresses will vary depending on age, health and background.

Transmission of AIDS

AIDS can be transmitted by any one of the following ways:

- Sexual intercourse when any one of the partners is infected.
- Blood transfusion of contaminated blood.
- Transmission from infected mother to child.
- Sharing of injection needles by more than one person may transmit the virus from an infected person to a healthy person.

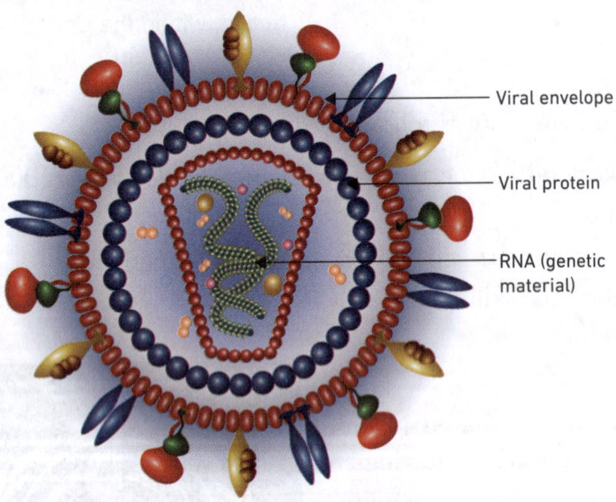

Figure 5.8 Illustration of HIV

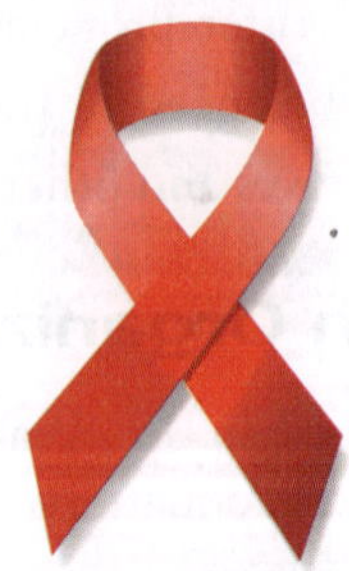

Figure 5.9 AIDS awareness ribbon

Prevention of AIDS

Transmission of HIV can be prevented by taking following measures:

- Using a condom during sexual intercourse.
- Avoiding sharing of syringes.
- For HIV-positive women, giving birth by caesarian section should be considered.

Quick Recap

✔ Tuberculosis **is considered a droplet infection. Give reason.**

When a person suffering from tuberculosis coughs or sneezes, *Mycobacterium tuberculosis* are catapulted in the air along with fine droplets. When these disease-carrying droplets are inhaled by a healthy individual, tuberculosis gets transmitted. Hence, it is called a droplet infection.

✔ **How does early exposure to certain diseases help in building immunity? Use chicken pox as an example.**

Early exposure to certain diseases, like chicken pox, helps the immune system develop antibodies specific to that disease. In the case of chicken pox, the disease is generally milder in children. Once a person recovers, the memory cells in our body remember the antigens of the disease. If the antigens try to attack again in the future, these memory cells quickly recognize them and produce antibodies, granting life-long immunity against the disease.

✔ **What role do vectors play in disease transmission, and how can community hygiene help?**

Vectors are living organisms, such as mosquitoes and houseflies, that carry and transmit diseases from an infected person to a healthy individual. By maintaining community hygiene, which includes proper sanitation, garbage disposal, clean sewage systems, and the use of insecticides, the breeding and proliferation of these vectors can be reduced or eliminated. This, in turn, can reduce the spread of vector-borne diseases.

✔ **Differentiate between innate immunity and adaptive immunity using their specificity as a basis.**

Innate immunity is the body's initial line of defence and is non-specific, meaning it defends the body against all types of pathogens in a general way. Examples include skin barriers and phagocytosis. Adaptive immunity, on the other hand, is tailored to combat specific pathogens. It recognizes specific antigens and develops antibodies against them. While innate immunity offers immediate protection, adaptive immunity takes time to develop but provides long-lasting, disease-specific immunity.

POINTS TO REMEMBER

- ✔ Anything that hampers the proper functioning of cells, tissues, organs and organ systems will lead to inefficient working of our body.
- ✔ World Health Organization (WHO) defines health as '*a state of complete physical, mental and social well-being and not merely the absence of disease or infirmity*'.
- ✔ A disease is a deviation from the normal functionality of the body and mind of a person.
- ✔ Symptoms are the manifestations of a disease.
- ✔ Physical health of a human body could be affected by immediate and contributory factors.
- ✔ The disease which is inherited by an individual at the time of birth is called a congenital disease.
- ✔ The diseases which can be developed at any age after the birth and not inherited at the time of birth are called acquired diseases.
- ✔ Vector is an organism that carries pathogens from an infected person to another person, but itself remains unaffected.
- ✔ Immunity is the ability of an organism to recognize the disease-causing germs and provide resistance against them.
- ✔ The process of development of immunity in our body to fight against diseases by introducing dead and weakened antigens is called immunization.

CLASSROOM WING

Practice Questions

Very Short Answer Type Questions

Direction for Questions from 1 to 10: Fill in the blanks.

1. Diseases that are not present from birth but develop later in life are termed as _______ diseases.
2. A _______ is an intermediary organism that transfers pathogens from one individual to another without being affected.
3. The innate power of an organism to recognize and resist pathogens is termed as _______.
4. _______ involves introducing weakened or dead antigens into the body to stimulate resistance against diseases.
5. Health, as defined by the WHO, transcends the mere absence of disease, emphasizing a holistic approach encompassing physical, mental, and ________ well-being.
6. Pathogens contain a unique type of protein, called _____ which causes diseases in our body.
7. ______ immunity gets developed due to the generation of antibodies in our body in response to the entry of an antigen from outside.
8. Small pox vaccine contains _______ virus.
9. Mouth wash is a type of _______.
10. The antibiotic, penicillin is extracted from a mould called _______.

Direction for Questions from 11 to 31: For each of the following questions four choices have been provided. Select the correct alternatives.

11. How might the social aspect of health, as defined by WHO, be compromised?
    (a) Bone fracture
    (b) Isolation and loneliness
    (c) Bacterial infection
    (d) High blood sugar levels
12. Which of the following best describes the role of a vector in disease transmission?
    (a) It causes the disease.
    (b) It gets affected by the disease.
    (c) It acts as a passive carrier of the pathogen.
    (d) It actively replicates the pathogen.
13. Congenital diseases primarily arise due to:
    (a) Poor lifestyle choices
    (b) Pathogenic infections
    (c) Genetic factors present at birth
    (d) Environmental exposure after birth
14. Which among the following is a direct manifestation of a disease?
    (a) A genetic mutation
    (b) A symptom like a fever
    (c) A weakened antigen
    (d) A preventive vaccine
15. What does immunization primarily introduce to the body?
    (a) Active pathogens
    (b) Vitamins and minerals
    (c) Dead or weakened antigens
    (d) Synthetic drugs
16. _______ is the pathogen which is responsible for Ascariasis.
    (a) *Taenia solium*
    (b) *Ascaris lumbricoides*
    (c) *Wuchereria bancrofti*
    (d) *Mycobacterium*
17. *Anopheles* spreads _______.
    (a) malaria (b) filariasis
    (c) dysentery (d) HIV

18. A parasite named ______ remains in the large intestine of the infected person and is responsible for blood stool sometimes.
(a) *Entamoeba histolytica*
(b) *Trypanosoma brucei*
(c) *Ascaris lumbricoides*
(d) HBV

19. ______ is a fatal disease which reduces the immunity of the body.
(a) TB
(b) Typhoid
(c) Syphilis
(d) Acquired Immuno deficiency Syndrome

20. The disease which is transmitted through placenta is ______.
(a) rabies (b) German measles
(c) tetanus (d) influenza

21. The immunity developed in our body due to the vaccination of polio and measles is an example of:
(a) innate immunity
(b) natural active immunity
(c) artificial active immunity
(d) artificial passive immunity

22. ______ is the vaccine used to cure the disease caused by *Salmonella typhi*.
(a) TAB (b) BCG
(c) OPV (d) DPT

23. *Penicillium chrysogenum* is a mould from which ______ is obtained.
(a) penicillin (b) ampicillin
(c) streptomycin (d) All of these

24. We use ______ to destroy the bacteria on the surface of the non-living objects.
(a) antiseptic (b) disinfectant
(c) antibodies (d) antibiotics

25. Identify the commonly used substance which acts as both antiseptic and disinfectant.
(a) Lysol (b) Odonil
(c) Naphthalene balls (d) Dettol

26. Our body produces ______ to provide immunity against the poisonous substance present in the microorganisms.
(a) toxins (b) pathogens
(c) antibodies (d) antigens

27. Which of the following cannot be used as an antiseptic?
(a) Alcohol
(b) Carbolic acid
(c) Boric acid
(d) Hydrochloric acid

28. Which of the following is not a content of a vaccine?
(a) Dead pathogens
(b) Living, weakened microorganisms
(c) Toxoids
(d) Antibiotics

29. Trachoma is an infection in the________.
(a) eyes (b) stomach
(c) brain (d) intestine

30. The full form of DDT is_______.
(a) dichlorodiphenyltrichloroethane
(b) diphenyldichlorotrichloroetane
(c) dichlorodiphenyltetrachloroethane
(d) dichlorodiphenyltrichloromethane.

31. Identify the disease caused by parasitic infection which is not communicable.
(a) Diphtheria (b) Tetanus
(c) Chicken pox (d) Typhoid

Direction for Questions from 32 to 34:
Match the entries of Column 1 with those of Column 2.

32.

Column 1		Column 2	
A.	Cholera	(i)	Helminthic disease
B.	Malaria	(ii)	Viral disease
C.	Filariasis	(iii)	Bacterial disease
D.	Athlete foot	(iv)	Protozoan disease
E.	Common cold	(v)	Fungal disease

33.

Column 1 Basis for occurrence of diseases	Column 2 Diseases
A. Epidemic	(i) Malaria
B. Pandemic	(ii) Goitre
C. Endemic	(iii) Plague
D. Sporadic	(iv) AIDS

34.

Column 1	Column 2
A. Innate immunity	(i) Rheumatoid arthritis
B. Acquired immunity	(ii) Breast milk
C. Passive immunity	(iii) Natural infection
D. Active immunity	(iv) Interferons
E. Auto immunity	(v) Antibodies

Short Answer Type Questions

35. Write the methods to be adopted for the control of the carrier responsible for yellow fever.

36. A communicable disease can be prevented by BCG vaccine. Identify the disease and write a short note on it.

37. What are the measures to be taken to control the disease spread by *Salmonella typhi*?

38. Write a short note on the communicable disease which leads to the damage of liver.

39. What are interferons?

40. Explain the mode of transmission of the disease caused by *Plasmodium*.

41. Write the symptoms and mode of transmission of sleeping sickness.

42. Differentiate between communicable and non-communicable diseases.

43. Mention one synthetically prepared drug which is generally used to treat fungal infections. Name one disease which can be treated with this drug.

44. How does the process of immunization help in building immunity against diseases?

45. Why is it crucial to understand the symptoms of a disease, and how do they differ from the actual disease?

Direction for Questions from 46 to 49:
Answer the following questions.

46. What are endemic diseases? Give one example.

47. Write briefly about the discovery of Robert Koch.

48. Name the two International Health Organizations.

49. What are the activities of WHO?

Essay Type Questions

50. Name the following:

(a) The disease caused by a bacteria named *Mycobacterium tuberculosis* is cured by

(b) The vaccine used to cure poliomyelitis

(c) The vaccine used to cure pertusis

(d) The vaccine to cure polio

51. Differentiate the following:

(a) Active immunity and passive immunity

(b) Innate immunity and acquired immunity

52. Considering that symptoms are just manifestations of a disease, why is it sometimes more beneficial to treat symptoms rather than the disease itself?

COMPETITION WING

Practice Questions

Level 1: Apply your Concepts

Direction for Questions from 1 to 15:
Fill in the blanks.

1. Microorganisms which are responsible for diseases are called ______.
2. Organisms which carry specific germs are called ______.
3. The insect, female *Anopheles* is the vector of ______.
4. The transmission of diseases to a healthy person without intermediate agents is called ______.
5. Plague is transmitted by ______.
6. The diseases which spread worldwide are considered as____________ diseases.
7. The diseases that are developed at any age after the birth but not inherited are called ________.
8. _________ diseases occur occasionally or irregularly.
9. Acquired diseases are classified as _______ and ______.
10. The investigation for identifying the reasons for the diseases is called ___________.
11. __________ membrane acts as a protective layer of gastrointestinal track.
12. The WHO describes health as a state of complete __________, ___________, and social well-being, emphasizing that it's not just about the absence of physical ailments.
13. While a congenital disease is one that is present from __________, an acquired disease develops __________ and is not inherited.
14. The process of __________ introduces the body to dead or weakened antigens, thereby helping develop __________ against specific pathogens.
15. Vectors play a crucial role in transmitting diseases from one individual to another without getting affected themselves because they are merely __________ and not the __________ hosts.

Direction for Questions from 16 to 20:
For each of the following questions four choices have been provided. Select the correct alternatives.

16. Which among the following is not a communicable disease?
    (a) Arteriosclerosis (b) Baldness
    (c) Scurvy (d) Chicken pox.
17. Identify the diseases where no agent is required for the transmission.
    (a) Small pox (b) Tuberculosis
    (c) Hay fever (d) Both (a) and (b)
18. Identify the vector that is responsible for yellow fever.
    (a) Female *Anopheles* (b) *Culex*
    (c) *Aedes* (d) Rats
19. Which among the following comes under the group of drugs that fights against pathogens.
    (a) Antibiotics (b) Sulphonamide
    (c) BCG (d) TAB
20. Identify the chemical substance that destroys the bacteria.
    (a) Pathogen (b) Antibiotic
    (c) Disinfectant (d) Antiseptic

Direction for Questions from 21 to 25:
Correct the following statements.

21. Typhus fever is caused due to cockroaches.
22. Rabies is a disease that is caused by indirect transmission from dogs to human beings.

23. Streptomycin is the drug that is used to treat urinary and bowel infections.

24. Mouth wash is an antibiotic that is used to prevent the growth of the microbes in our body.

25. DDT when sprayed on the garbage increases the growth of the bacteria as it acts like a disinfectant.

Direction for Questions from 26 to 30:
Write the missing correlated terms.

26. Congenital disease : Cataract ::__________ : Scurvy.

27. ______________ : Antharax :: Non-communicable disease : Alcoholism.

28. Typhoid : __________ :: Tuberculosis : *Mycobacterium*.

29. Alexander Fleming : Penicillin : : ____________ : Small pox vaccine.

30. _______ : Perspiration : : Antiseptic : Microorganisms.

Direction for Questions from 31 to 48:
Choose the correct option.

(a) Both A and R are true and R is the correct explanation for A.

(b) Both A and R are true, but R is not the correct explanation for A.

(c) A is true and R is false.

(d) A is false and R is true.

31. **Assertion (A):** Immunization is a crucial process for maintaining public health.

Reason (R): Immunization involves introducing dead and weakened antigens to stimulate the body's natural defence mechanisms.

32. **Assertion (A):** Immunization is essential for public health.

Reason (R): Immunization involves introducing weakened or dead antigens to build immunity.

33. **Assertion (A):** Vectors play a significant role in the transmission of diseases.

Reason (R): Vectors are organisms that get infected with the diseases they transmit.

34. **Assertion (A):** Congenital diseases are present from the time of birth.

Reason (R): Congenital diseases arise due to lifestyle choices made by an individual post-birth.

35. **Assertion (A):** *Gambusia* is a fish which is being introduced into the ponds to check vector-borne disease.

Reason (R): AIDS is a vector-borne disease.

36. **Assertion (A):** Both AIDS and Hepatitis B are infectious viral diseases.

Reason (R): Both the diseases are transmitted by vectors.

37. **Assertion (A):** *Plasmodium*, a protozoan parasite initially multiplies in liver cells and enters blood cells.

Reason (R): It is responsible for the cause of filariasis.

38. **Assertion (A):** Skin provides innate immunity to the body.

Reason (R): Skin has mucous membrane which does not allow the pathogen to enter our body.

39. **Assertion (A):** Artificial chemicals are injected through vaccination.

Reason (R): Vaccination is a process of immunization.

40. **Assertion (A):** Antibiotics inhibit the growth of disease-causing bacteria.

Reason (R): Antibiotics are obtained from different moulds.

41. **Assertion (A):** Toxoids are used in vaccines.

Reason (R): Toxoids are bacterial toxins which help in the formation of antibodies.

42. **Assertion (A):** Innate immunity is non-specific type of defence present at the time of birth.

Reason (R): Saliva, tears and sweat act as physiological barriers for innate immunity.

43. **Assertion (A):** Fever is a symptom for an infection.

Reason (R): Pathogens cannot tolerate high temperature.

44. **Assertion (A):** Immune system becomes weak in old people.

Reason (R): Haemoglobin is less in the blood of old people.

45. **Assertion (A):** Spleen is considered as one of the lymphoid organs.

Reason (R): Spleen helps in the formation of red blood cells.

46. **Assertion (A):** Consumption of antibiotics makes a person feel weak.

Reason (R): Antibiotics kill all the tissues of the respective organ in host body.

47. **Assertion (A):** Damaged lymphocytes do not produce antibodies against antigens.

    Reason (R): Injection of dead pathogens causes passive immunity.

48. **Assertion (A):** Transplantation of organs to save certain patients often fail.

    Reason (R): Blood vascular system and blood groups are responsible for such failures.

Level 2: Review your Concepts

49. How does passive immunity develop naturally?
50. How does skin provide first line of defence against diseases?
51. How does vaccination help in the development of immunity?
52. Chronic disease shows adverse effects on health. Give reasons.
53. AIDS is considered a syndrome and not a disease. Give reasons.
54. Cholera is considered as an acute disease and arthritis as a chronic disease. Discuss.
55. Why does jaundice cause yellowing of skin, eyes, nails, etc.?
56. Symptoms of disease appear only after a certain period of mosquito bite in case of diseases spread by mosquitoes. Give reason.
57. Developing vaccine for AIDS is very difficult. Give reason.
58. Though malarial parasite invades liver, liver functioning is not considerably affected in malaria. Give reason.
59. Stagnated water increases the chances of malarial attack manifold. Give reason.
60. Common cold spreads much faster than AIDS. Give reason.
61. Breastfed babies are less likely to get infections. Why?
62. Person suffering from AIDS cannot fight small infections. Why?
63. Antibiotics are effective in curing tuberculosis but not effective in curing common cold. Given reason.
64. Vaccine against polio virus is an example of active immunity. Justify.
65. Rheumatoid arthritis is an autoimmune disease. Give reason.
66. A transplanted cornea of eye is rarely rejected. Why?
67. Excessive use of antibiotics leads to deficiency disorders. Why?
68. The first line of defence in the immune system is provided by skin. Discuss.
69. The life of an infant is saved from three diseases. Identify the vaccines and diseases.
70. Give an account on hypersensitivity or allergic reaction.
71. No vaccination is possible for AIDS. Give reason.
72. Chemotherapy for cancer results in temporary reduction in the lymphocyte count. Give reason.
73. What is an auto immune disease?
74. Explain the mechanism of functioning of vaccines.
75. Complete the following table:

Pathogen	Disease	Prevention
	Plague	Using zinc phosphide to kill the pathogens
Varicella zoster virus		Isolation of the patient and the articles used by them.
	African trypanosomiasis	Prevention of growth of tsetse flies.
Wuchereria bancrofti		

Level 3: Assess Your Concepts

76. How does the intake of zinc impact immunity of a person?

77. Vitamin C invariably enhances the immunity in the body. What is the effect of vitamin C? Explain.

78. The disease AIDS results in the drastic decrease in the immunity of the affected person. Explain the mechanism involved.

79. It is highly recommended to breast feed the new born babies as soon as they are born. Justify.

80. Antibiotics destroy the bacterial cells in the host body without causing harm to the host cells. Give reason.

81. Pregnant women are not advised to have certain vaccinations such as MMR, chicken pox, etc., while some vaccinations such as DPT are considered to be harmless. Give reason.

82. Vaccination for small pox lasts for life time whereas vaccination for typhoid lasts for 2-3 years. Give reason.

83. Pregnant women are vaccinated for tetanus. Give reason.

84. Considering the intricate relationship between health, disease, and immunity, how does the broader socio-economic environment influence these factors? Discuss the importance of community awareness and participation in maintaining collective well-being.

AT

NEET SPECIAL WING

Practice Questions

Multiple-Answer Type Questions

Questions number 1 to 5 are multiple-choice questions. Each question has FOUR options (a), (b), (c), and (d). ONE OR MORE THAN ONE of these four option(s) is/are the correct answer(s).

1. Identify diseases that are spread by female mosquito bite:
(a) Chikungunya
(b) Cholera
(c) Dengue
(d) Malaria

2. Which of the following are endemic diseases?
(a) Goitre
(b) Diphtheria
(c) Plague
(d) Rift valley fever

3. The diseases that are caused by protozoa:
(a) Sleeping sickness
(b) Malaria
(c) Ascariasis
(d) Taeniasis

4. Symptoms of Hepatitis A include:
(a) Loss of appetite
(b) Dark urine
(c) Vomiting
(d) Headache and discomfort

5 Identify the functions of antibiotics.
(a) Prevention of further infection
(b) Inhibition of growth of pathogens
(c) Transmission of infection
(d) Preservation of perishable food like fish and meat

Comprehension-Based Questions

A. Read the paragraph given below and answer the questions number 6 to 11:

Immunity provides our body with physiological mechanisms which enables our body to identify foreign substances and eliminate them from the system. It achieves this without causing any harm to the body's own tissues and it thus prevents any further infection caused by the invading pathogen or foreign substance. Body's first line of defence is made up of physical barriers such as skin, mucus, saliva, etc. This is innate immunity. The second line of defence comprises of specialised cells called macrophages which is formed by the innate immunity. Acquired immunity is when the body acquires the immunity during its lifetime. Acquired immunity is of two types-active and passive. Active immunity is developed due to the production of antibodies which are produced by the body itself against foreign antigens. Passive immunity is achieved by developing antibodies that are produced outside and then introduced in the body.

6. Foetus receives antibodies from the mother through:
(a) Blood (b) Lymphatic fluid
(c) Placenta (d) Serum

7. An antigen can be introduced in our body through vaccination which generates antibodies. This is called:
(a) Natural active immunity
(b) Artificial active immunity
(c) Natural passive immunity
(d) Artificial passive immunity

8. Skin, hair, mucus and secretions are examples of:
(a) Innate immunity
(b) Acquired immunity
(c) Antibody dependent immunity
(d) Antigen dependent immunity

9. Which of the following immunity is present since birth?
(a) Active immunity
(b) Passive immunity

(c) Innate immunity
(d) Acquired immunity

10. Physical barriers are part of:
(a) First line of defence
(b) Second line of defence
(c) Third line of defence
(d) All of the above

11. Match the following:

Column – A	Column – B
(i) Antidote against snake venom	(a) Weakened germs
(ii) Antibodies from mother to foetus	(b) Artificial passive immunity
(iii) Immunisation against tetanus contains	(c) Artificial active immunity
(iv) Attack of Chicken pox	(d) Natural active immunity
(v) Vaccines of polio	(e) Natural acquired passive immunity

B. Read the paragraph given below and answer the questions number 12 to 17:

Diseases are classified into different forms like communicable and non-communicable diseases. Non communicable diseases are further classified into degenerative diseases, deficiency diseases, allergies and social diseases. Diseases are also classified on the basis of whether they can be transmitted from a diseased person to a healthy person. These are communicable and non-communicable diseases. Diseases can also be classified on the basis of the extent of occurrence like endemic, sporadic, pandemic and epidemic. Direct and indirect transmission of diseases also causes a host of different diseases.

There are various pathogens like bacteria, virus, etc., which cause diseases by releasing toxins or killing the living cells in our tissues. The amount of toxins produced by the microbes is called pathogenicity. This is treated by injection of anti- toxins which neutralizes the effect of toxins.

12. Disease which is caused due to deficiency of Vitamin A is:
(a) Night blindness
(b) Goitre
(c) Rickets
(d) Scurvy

13. Diseases which happen to people confined in a specific region is called:
(a) Endemic
(b) Sporadic
(c) Pandemic
(d) Epidemic

14. Itching, redness and blisters on the skin when a specific food item is consumed causes:
(a) Degenerative diseases
(b) Deficiency diseases
(c) Allergies
(d) Social diseases

15. Vector for yellow fever is:
(a) Housefly
(b) Anopheles
(c) Aedes
(d) Culex

16. As a control measure for tuberculosis ________ can be used
(a) Consumption of boiled water
(b) TAB vaccine administration
(c) Anti-Tubercular therapy
(d) Administration of ORS

17. Match the following:

Column – A (Diseases)	Column – B (Preventive Measure)
(i) Plague	(a) DDT
(ii) Yellow fever	(b) Rat proof bins
(iii) Amoebiasis	(c) Spraying kerosene over water
(iv) Gastroenteritis	(d) Maintenance of proper sanitation
(v) Hepatitis A	(e) Immunization by interferons

Answer Keys

Crossword

Across

7. Endemic
11. Degenerative
12. Sporadic
14. Allergies
15. Louis Pasteur
16. Taeniasis
17. Housefly
18. *Tripanosoma Brucei*
19. Antibody

Down

1. Toxoids
2. Phagocytosis
3. Congenital
4. Lysozymes
5. Acquired
6. Immediate
8. Filariasis
9. Artificial Active
10. Osteoporosis
13. Contributory
14. Anopheles

Classroom Wing

Very Short Answer Type Questions

1. Acquired
2. Vector
3. Immunity
4. Immunization
5. Social
6. Antigen
7. Active
8. Cowpox
9. Antiseptic
10. *Penicillium notatum*
11. (b)
12. (c)
13. (c)
14. (b)
15. (c)
16. (b)
17. (a)
18. (a)
19. (d)
20. (b)
21. (c)
22. (a)
23. (a)
24. (b)
25. (d)
26. (c)
27. (d)
28. (d)
29. (a)
30. (a)
31. (b)
32. A → (iii); B → (iv); C → (i); D → (v); E → (ii)
33. A → (iii); B → (iv); C → (i); D → (ii)
34. A → (iv); B → (v); C → (ii); D → (iii); E → (i)

Competition Wing

Level 1: Apply your Concepts

1. Pathogens
2. Vectors
3. *Plasmodium*
4. Direct transmission
5. Rat fleas
6. Pandemic
7. Acquired diseases
8. Sporadic
9. Communicable and non communicable
10. Etiology
11. Mucous
12. Physical, mental
13. Birth, after birth
14. Immunization, immunity
15. Carriers, primary
16. (d)
17. (d)
18. (c)
19. (b)
20. (c)
26. Acquired
27. Communicable
28. *Salmonella typhi*
29. Edward Jenner
30. Deodrant
31. (a)
32. (a)
33. (b)
34. (c)
35. (c)
36. (c)
37. (c)
38. (c)
39. (d)
40. (b)
41. (a)
42. (b)
43. (a)
44. (b)
45. (b)
46. (c)
47. (c)
48. (b)

NEET Special Wing

Multiple-Answer Type Questions

1. (a, c, d) **2.** (a, d) **3.** (a, b) **4.** (a, b, c) **5.** (a, b, d)

Comprehension-Based Questions

6. (c) **7.** (b) **8.** (a) **9.** (c) **10.** (a)

11. (i) → (b); (ii) → (e); (iii) → (c); (iv) → (d); (v) → (a)

12. (a) **13.** (a) **14.** (c) **15.** (d) **16.** (c)

17. (i) → (b); (ii) → (e); (iii) → (c); (iv) → (d); (v) → (a)

Hints and Explanations

CLASSROOM WING

Very Short Answer Type Questions

11. The social aspect of health pertains to an individual's relationships and interactions within society. Isolation and loneliness directly impact this dimension.

12. Vectors carry and transfer pathogens without being affected or actively replicating them.

13. Congenital diseases are those present from birth, typically due to genetic factors.

14. Symptoms are direct manifestations or indicators of a disease.

15. Immunization involves introducing dead or weakened antigens to stimulate the immune response.

Short Answer Type Questions

35. Yellow fever in humans is spread by *Aedes*. The precautions to be taken for the control of yellow fever are the following.

- Spraying insecticides to kill mosquitoes during their developmental stages.
- Elimination of small ponds and puddles to prevent breeding of mosquito.
- Spraying kerosene on the surface of water to prevent the dissolution of oxygen and thus the larvae of the mosquitoes can be destroyed.
- Introducing certain fish in the ponds which eat the mosquito.

36. Tuberculosis is the communicable disease which can be prevented by BCG vaccine.

This disease is caused by the bacteria *Mycobacterium tuberculosis*.

Some of the symptoms are as follows:

- Cough
- Fever
- Sweating in the night
- Pain in the chest
- Blood in sputum
- Loss of weight
- Breathlessness on exertion

Prevention and control

- The patient must be completely isolated in a separate room.
- Articles used by the patient like utensils, towels, bed sheets should not be used by other persons.
- Immunization against this disease can be developed by BCG (Bacillus Calmette Guerin) vaccination.
- Anti-tubercular therapy can be used to control the disease.

37. Typhoid is the disease which spreads by a bacterium named *Salmonella typhi*.

Following are the measures to be taken to prevent typhoid:

- The infected person should be isolated.
- The stool and urine of the person should be collected in a closed container and disposed by burning or flushing.
- Their attendants should disinfect their hands, and the clothing and bedding of the patient are required to be disinfected by boiling.
- Insecticides should be sprayed for the prevention of flies.
- Immunization by TAB vaccine lasts for 3 years.
- Oral vaccines are also available to prevent typhoid.

38. Hepatitis is the serious communicable disease which damages liver.

There are different types of Hepatitis—hepatitis A, B, C, D, E and G.

Hepatitis B can be fatal also.

This is a common disease in children and young adults. Each type of hepatitis is caused by its respective hepatitis virus. For example, hepatitis A is caused by hepatitis A virus.

Some of the symptoms are:

- The person suffers from high fever, headache and joint pains.
- Rashes, weakness and loss of appetite are also the symptoms.
- Symptoms of jaundice like nausea, vomiting, dark urine are observed.
- It is transmitted by contaminated food, water, milk. Blood transfusion, dialysis, use of contaminated syringes transmit hepatitis B.

Some of the measures that help in preventing this disease are as follows:

- Washing hands before eating and after going to toilets.

- Taking vaccine and interferon'
- Having nutritious and protein-rich diet.

39. Interferons are the proteins released by the host cells in response to the invasion of pathogens like virus, bacteria, etc.

40. Malaria is the disease which is caused by *Plasmodium*. The disease gets transmitted in the following way,
    - The protozoan is transmitted from an infected person to a healthy person by the bite of a female *Anopheles* mosquito.
    - When a female *Anopheles* mosquito bites the infected person, the protozoa are sucked up in the stomach of the insect, along with the blood.
    - When that mosquito bites a healthy person, the protozoa enter the body of the healthy person and thus the disease is transmitted.

41. Sleeping sickness is caused by *Trypanosoma brucei*.

    It is a vector-borne disease.

    Symptoms:
    - Pain in muscles and joints.
    - Swollen lymph nodes.
    - Weight loss as the illness progresses.
    - Headache, fever and rashes.

    Transmission:
    - By the bite of an infected tsetse fly.
    - Infection could also occur through transfusion of blood.

42.

Communicable diseases	Non-communicable diseases
These diseases spread from one person to another person through direct contact of the healthy person or through different medium like air, water, contaminated food, vector, etc.	The diseases which cannot spread from one person to another or by carriers or by contact.
Different microorganisms like viruses, bacteria, fungi, protozoa and worms are responsible for these diseases.	Degeneration of tissues, deficiency of nutrients, hypersensitivity to certain substances are responsible for these diseases.

43. Sulphonamide is the drug which is synthetically prepared.

    Pneumonia is treated with this drug.

44. Immunization involves introducing dead or weakened antigens, often in the form of vaccines, into the body. The immune system recognizes these antigens as foreign invaders and produces antibodies against them. This process 'trains' the immune system to recognize and combat the disease-causing germs in the future, thus providing resistance against them.

45. Symptoms are the external manifestations or indications of a disease in an organism. Recognizing symptoms is vital because they provide early signs of an underlying health issue, enabling timely intervention and treatment. While the disease refers to the actual pathological condition affecting the body or mind, symptoms are merely the visible or perceivable effects of that condition on the individual.

46. A disease is called endemic if it persists in a geographic region for a long period of time. Goitre is endemic in India in sub Himalayan region.

47. Robert Koch for the first time showed that microorganisms are responsible for the diseases to occur and spread. He proved that a rod shaped bacterium causes a disease called anthrax.

48. WHO – World Health Organisation and Red cross are the two International health organisations.

49. Following are the main activities of WHO:
    - Spreading awareness among the people regarding the communicable diseases and epidemics.
    - Monitoring quarantine measures for preventing spread of contagious diseases.
    - Imparting health education to the people.
    - Formulating health policies.
    - Curbing environmental pollution
    - Improving pharmaceutical products and maintain international standards.

Essay Type Questions

50.

(a) The disease caused by bacteria named *Mycobacterium tuberculosis* is cured by taking BCG vaccine.

(b) The vaccine used to cure poliomyelitis is Salk's vaccine.

(c) The vaccine used to cure Pertussis is DPT.

(d) The vaccine used to cure polio is OPV (oral polio vaccine).

51. (a)

Active immunity	Passive immunity
This immunity is developed in response to the entry of an antigen in our body.	This immunity is developed when antibodies are introduced in our body
It has a long-lasting protection against the disease	It provides immunity for a short period of time

(b)

Innate immunity	Acquired immunity
Immunity inherited by a child at the time of birth is called innate immunity.	Immunity developed after the birth is called acquired immunity
The immunity is developed because of genetic makeup.	This immunity is developed due to the introduction of antigen or antibody to our body
This immunity is not disease specific	This immunity is disease specific.

52. Treating symptoms can provide immediate relief to patients, making them feel better and improving their quality of life, even if the underlying disease is still present. In some cases, directly addressing the disease might take time or might not be immediately possible, so alleviating symptoms becomes essential. For instance, pain management in chronic conditions doesn't cure the disease but provides necessary relief to patients. However, it's crucial to ensure that treating symptoms doesn't overshadow the need to address the root cause.

COMPETITION WING

Level 1: Apply your Concepts

6. The diseases are considered pandemic if it spreads worldwide.
7. The diseases that are developed at any age after the birth but not inherited are called acquired diseases.
8. Sporadic diseases occur occasionally or irregularly.
9. Acquired diseases are classified as communicable and non communicable.
10. The investigation for identifying the reasons for the diseases is called etiology.
11. Mucous membrane acts as a protective layer of gastro-intestinal track.
12. Phagocytes are the cells which ingest pathogens invaded our body.
13. Inflammation is the response of the immune system against foreign objects entered our body.
14. Passive immunity can provide immediate relief by direct introduction of the antibodies into the body.
15. The proteins that are generated in our body and are destroy the pathogens are termed as antimicrobial proteins.
16. Chicken pox is a communicable disease where as others are non communicable diseases.
17. Small pox and tuberculosis are transmitted by direct contact with the person and no mode of transmission is required.
18. The vector that is responsible for yellow fever is Aedes.
19. The group of drugs that fights against pathogens is known as sulphonamide.
20. The chemical substance that destroys the bacteria is called disinfectant.
21. Typhus fever is caused due to rats.
22. Rabies is a diseases that is caused by direct transmission from dogs to human beings.
23. Sulphonamide is the drug that is used to treat urinary and bowel infections.
24. Mouth wash is a antiseptic that is used to prevent the growth of the microbes in our body.
25. DDT when sprayed on the garbage prevents the growth of the bacteria as it acts like a disinfectant.
26. Congenital disease : Cataract ::Acquired : : Scurvy
27. Communicable : Antharax :: Non -communicable disease : Alcoholism.
28. Typhoid : Salmonella typhi :: Tuberculosis : Mycobacteirum.
29. Alexander Fleming : Penicillin : :Edward Jenner : Small pox vaccine.
30. Deodrant : Perspiration : : Antiseptic : Microorganisms.
31. Immunization helps in promoting public health by preventing the spread of diseases, and it does so by introducing dead or weakened antigens.

    Hence, the correct option is (a).
32. Immunization is crucial for public health as it prevents outbreaks of contagious diseases. The process of immunization, which introduces dead or weakened antigens, helps to develop immunity against those diseases.

    Hence, the correct option is (a).
33. Vectors do play a crucial role in disease transmission by carrying pathogens from one host to another. However, vectors do not typically get infected by the diseases they transmit; they merely act as carriers.

    Hence, the correct option is (b).
34. Congenital diseases are indeed present from birth, but they do not arise due to post-birth lifestyle choices. They are typically due to genetic factors or conditions in the womb.

    Hence, the correct option is (c).
35. Certain diseases like malaria, Filaria and plague are considered to be vector-borne diseases. This diseases are transferred from one person to another through agents like mosquitoes, flies, rats, etc., To get rid of such infectious diseases, a fish called *Gambusia* is introduced into the periods to check the growth of vectors.

    AIDS is not a vector-borne disease. It is caused by Human immuno-deficiency virus. HIV cannot survive outside the host and hence gets deactivated. It is not a vector-borne disease. Assertion is true, reason is false.

    Hence, the correct option is (c).

36. Both AIDS and hepatitis B are infectious viral diseases. They are not vector born. Both the diseases are spread through blood and body fluids. Assertion is true, reason is false.

Hence, the correct option is (c).

37. *Plasmodium* is a protozoan parasite which infects the host tissue through a bite of female anopheles mosquito. Initially the parasite multiplies in liver cells and then enters red blood cells. Malaria is the disease caused by this parasite. Assertion is true, reason is false.

Hence, the correct option is (c).

38. Skin provides innate immunity to the body since it obstructs the invasion of pathogens in the body. It does not have any mucous membrane.

Hence, the correct option is (c).

39. Dead or weak disease-causing organisms are injected through vaccination and thus the antibodies are developed in our body in order to fight against diseases. Hence, vaccination is a process of immunization.

Hence, the correct option is (d).

40. Antibiotics are obtained from different moulds and they inhibit the growth of disease-causing organisms. Reason is not the correct explanation of the assertion.

Hence, the correct option is (b).

41. Toxoids are used in vaccines since they help in the development of antibodies.

Hence, the correct option is (a).

42. Innate immunity is provided by sweat, saliva, tears, skin and lymphocytes.

Hence, the correct option is (b).

43. Fever increases the body temperature which is unfavourable for the multiplication of pathogens. Thus, fever prevents the spread of infection by boosting the immune response of the system.

Hence, the correct option is (a).

44. In old people, bones become weak and bone marrow functioning becomes ineffective. Similarly thymus gland functioning also is weakened. As a result, they cannot produce WBC effectively. Therefore, their immune system becomes weak.

Hence, the correct option is (b).

45. Lymphoid organs are organs in which lymphocytes are formed. These organs form a part of the bodies immune system and help in killing pathogens which cause infections. The major lymphoid organs are bone marrow, thymus gland, spleen, lymph nodes, tonsils, etc.

Spleen is a large bean shaped organ which contains lymphocytes and phagocytes. It filters blood by trapping blood-borne microorganisms. Spleen also helps in the formation of RBC and acts as a reservoir of erythrocytes.

Hence, the correct option is (b).

46. Some antibiotics act on the bacterial cells by attacking their cell covering. This results in killing of bacterial cell. The cells of the host tissue also possess plasma membrane. Therefore, the antibiotic works in the same manner on the neighbouring cells. As a result, the cells get damaged partially and the person feels weak.

Hence, the correct option is (c).

47. There are two types of lymphocytes present in our blood, T-lymphocytes and B-lymphocytes. T-lymphocytes do not secrete antibodies but help B-cells produce them. When lymphocytes are damaged immune responses are decreased. Infection of dead pathogens is immunization. Assertion is true, reason is false.

Hence, the correct option is (c).

48. Transplantation of organs or organ transplantation takes place in some patients to save the patient. It is called cell-mediated immune response. Tissue matching and blood matching are essential before organ transplantation. Body is able to differentiate its own cells with other cells and lymphocytes are responsible for graft rejection. Both assertion and reason are correct but reason is not the correct explanation.

Hence, the correct option is (b).

Level 2: Review your Concepts

49. Passive immunity develops naturally when the antibodies enter the body of the foetus from the mother during the developmental stage of the foetus inside the womb of the mother.

50. Skin prevents the entry of the microbes into the body. Oil secreted from the oil glands and the sweat kill the microbes.

51. Through vaccination dead or living, weakened germs are introduced into our body. Then our body recognizes the harmful proteins present in the pathogens and antibodies are spontaneously developed to fight against the disease-causing germs.

52. Chronic disease shows adverse effect on health.

Acute diseases like cough, viral fever, etc., cause certain imbalances and abnormal functioning of body systems which causes temporarily changes in the health for a few days or weeks. Later on, health can be regained.

Chronic diseases like tuberculosis are more harmful and last longer. They show long-term effects.

53. AIDS is acquired immuno deficiency syndrome, caused by human immuno deficiency virus. When a group of symptoms occur together in the existence of a particular disease, it is known as syndrome. Person infected with HIV virus is prone to various pathogens because the immune system becomes weak. There is no particular symptom of the disease in the preliminary period, symptoms occur after many years of attack of virus.

54. Disease which lasts for a short period of time and after treatment patients are recovered completely, and it does not cause long-term effects. Such disease is called acute disease. Cholera is an acute disease. Diseases which last for a long period of time and after treatment patients are not recovered completely, and they cause long-term effects. Such disease is called chronic disease. Arteritis is a chronic disease.

55. The RBCs have a lifespan of 120 days. Once they die, the cells are taken away be WBCs by means of phagocytosis. During this process, the iron-containing pigment haemoglobin gets converted into bilirubin which is a yellow-coloured pigment. This goes into bile secreted by liver and passed out through faeces or urine. When excess of RBCs are damaged resulting in the excess production of bilirubin, it causes disfunctioning of liver. The excess production of this pigment imparts yellow colour to skin, eyes, nails, etc.,

56. When mosquito bites, the parasite enters the blood stream and reaches liver. It multiplies there and enters the RBCs. The symptoms appear only at this stage. The time period between the entry of the parasite and appearance of symptoms is called incubation period.

57. HIV virus is a retro virus. Retro virus is a virus which has the capability of copying RNA into DNA. No other virus discovered so far on Earth has this ability. Therefore, it is the main limiting factor for the development of vaccination for AIDS.

58. The malarial parasite, *Plasmodium* involves two hosts. They are female *Anopheles* mosquito and a vertebrate host usually human. The life cycle of *Plasmodium* involves several different stages both in the insect and man.

The *Plasmodium* parasite enters host's blood stream from the salivary glands of mosquito during its blood meal. The parasite is in the stage of sporozoites. Through blood, the sporozoites enter the liver and multiply there. But, they remain rather dormant in the liver and do not cause any damage to the liver cells. From the liver, they pass into the RBCs (erythrocytes) in the form of merozoites.

The merozoites multiply rapidly and infect the other RBCs. This is the infective stage when symptoms start appearing. They later produce gametocytes and again enter mosquito where it passes through sexual phase to produce sporozoites. Therefore, the parasite causes disease only in humans and does not affect the mosquito in any way.

59. Stagnated water is the main breeding ground for the mosquitoes. Mosquito larvae can thrive well in stagnated water. Therefore, malaria and dengue which are transmitted by mosquitoes are the major infectious diseases which become widespread in the areas with stagnated water.

60. Common cold is a communicable disease. It is an air-borne disease. Microbes causing common cold spread faster through air and are difficult to control.

AIDS is an immuno-deficiency disorder which is a communicable disease. It destroys the immune system of human beings causing multiple disorders. This disease spreads by direct contact through blood and body fluids.

61. Breast-fed babies are less likely to get infections.

Colostrum (breastmilk) is the first pale yellow milk produced after childbirth. It is the baby's first immunization. This provides passive and long lasting active immunity. It contains factors supporting baby's immune system.

When mother comes in contact with microbes, antibodies are produced to fight against these germs.

Such antibodies are passed through breastmilk and when the same microbes infect baby, these antibodies block the areas and prevent infection which causes illness.

62. Persons suffering from AIDS cannot fight small infections. Human immunodeficiency virus causes Acquired immunodeficiency syndrome (AIDS). This virus attacks lymphocytes (a type of white blood cells) and affects the body's immune system. The immune system gets weakened and damaged and ceases to function. So a person cannot fight even a small infection.

63. Tuberculosis is a bacterial disease. When antibiotics are used, they stop the growth of bacterial life cycle and do not allow it to develop further. Common cold is a viral disease. Viruses do not have definite shape and form. It is only a piece of DNA or RNA which can replicate only inside host tissue. Virus does not use common biochemical pathways as used by bacteria, hence antibiotics are ineffective to viral disease.

64. When a host is exposed to living or dead form of microbes called antigens, antibodies are produced in the host body. Such type of immunity is known as active immunity. Microbes infected during vaccination or immunization, induce active immunity in a person. Vaccine against polio virus also induces active immunity.

65. Rheumatoid arthritis is an auto immune disease. Auto immune disease is a disease when the immune system of the body fails to recognize normal body cells with external induced material (self cells with non-self cells). Hence, the immune system mistakenly attacks the body cells or tissue causing damage. In rheumatoid arthritis, the immune system attacks the lining of the joints leading to inflammation of the points. This leads to pain and stiffness in joints.

66. A transplanted cornea of eye is rarely rejected. Cornea of eye has no blood supply. Lymphocytes do not circulate into the anterior chamber of the eye. Hence, this area is considered as immunologically privileged area. As there is no blood supply, antibodies do not circulate into this portion of the eye. Hence, rejection does not occur.

67. Excessive use of antibiotics leads to deficiency disorders. Antibiotics are chemicals which supress the growth of bacteria. Excessive use of antibiotics causes antibiotic-resistance capacity, due to which bacterial infections cannot be treated further. Prolonged use may also kill the useful bacteria present in the intestine which help in synthesizing vitamins. This leads to vitamin deficiency disorders.

68. Skin and mucous membrane help us in covering various organs. They act as physical barriers which provide first line of external defence. These barriers help in preventing the entry of microorganisms like bacteria and virus into the body. Mucous membrane traps the microorganism and does not all so them to move, As skin helps in protection it is called body's first line of defence in immune system.

69. DPT is the vaccine given to infants which saves them from three infectious diseases.

The diseases are: Diphtheria, Pertussis (whooping cough) and Tetanus.

70. Certain antigens present in the environment cause intensifying responses of the immune system.

These responses are called allergies. The substances that produce immune responses are called allergens. Antibodies are produced by these allergens. Common allergens in the environment are dust, pollen grains, drugs etc.

Anti-histamines reduce the symptoms of allergy.

Allergy is due to release of chemicals like histamines and serotonins.

Symptoms of allergitic reactions are sneezing, coughing, watering eye, running rose, itching, etc.

71. HIV virus is a retro virus. Retro virus is a virus which has the capability of copying RNA into DNA. No other virus discovered so far on Earth has this ability. Therefore, it is the main limiting factor for the development of vaccination for AIDS.

72. Chemotherapy is the mode of treatment in which medicines which can kill the cancer cells are administered to the patient. These medicines target the actively dividing cancer cells. At the same time, they may also affect the normal cells in blood, bone marrow, hair, nails, etc. Therefore, during the course of treatment, as the bone marrow gets damaged, it is temporarily less able to produce enough blood cells. Since the WBC count decreases due to this reason, the body becomes more vulnerable to infection.

73. The healthy human body produces lymphocytes (a type of WBCs) which produce antibodies. These antibodies attack and kill the invading pathogens such as bacteria, virus and other parasites. However, the antibodies have a natural ability to recognize the foreign cells and are selective in attacking them without causing any harm to the host tissues.

But, in some persons, the lymphocytes produce some antibodies called auto antibodies which run in the blood stream attack and damage the healthy tissues of the same individual. This may result in some disorder in the functioning of that organ or system. These are called auto immune disorders. For example, rheumatoid arthritis, multiple sclerosis, psoriasis, vasculitis, etc.

74. Our body has a natural immune system. When foreign invaders such as bacteria or viruses enter the body, lymphocytes respond by producing antibodies. These antibodies are protein molecules and they attack the antigens produced by the invading pathogens. This is how the body fights against infections and is protected from the disease.

But, when the body faces a particular invader first time, it takes little longer time to generate the antibody response. In the meantime the antigens rapidly attack the body cells and cause the disease. In case of some diseases such as small pox, polio, etc., the adverse effects of disease are extreme and irreversible. The damage is caused much before the immune system responds.

Vaccines are made of dead or weakened antigens. They do not cause the disease, but make the immune system produce antibodies in response to the particular antigens. Though the antibodies break down after the antigens are killed, the immune cells called memory cells remain in the body. When the pathogen attacks the person again, the memory cells produce antibodies immediately and kill the antigens before they cause the disease.

75.

Pathogen	Disease	Prevention
Rats	Plague	Using zinc phosphide to kill the pathogens
Varicella zoster virus	Chicken pox	Isolation of the patient and the articles used by them.
Trypanosoma brucei	African trypanosomiasis	Prevention of growth of tsetse flies.
Wuchereria bancrofti	Filariasis or Elephantiasis	Eradication of vector culex.

Level 3: Assess Your Concepts

76. Zinc is very important mineral nutrient as it affects multiple aspects of immune system. It enhances the innate immunity. It also enhances the function of neutrophils, macrophages and lymphocytes. As a result, zinc can improve the efficiency of phagocytosis and boost the production of antibodies by lymphocytes

77. Vitamin C is very much required for the functioning of the phagocytes and lymphocytes. When these immune cells interact with the microorganisms and engulf them by means of phagocytosis, certain harmful substances are produced. These are harmful for the immune cells. Vitamin C protects the immune cells from these harmful substances and prevents the early destruction of immune cells.

Vitamin D enhances the absorption of calcium into the bones. This vitamin helps in the mineralization of collagen protein in the bone tissue thereby keeping the bones healthy. Since bone marrow is responsible for the production of WBC more particularly lymphocytes, vitamin D has an indirect impact on the immune system. It also protects our body from autoimmune diseases.

78. The virus responsible for causing AIDS is HIV. It is a retro virus which has the capability of copying RNA into DNA.

The virus is surrounded by a membrane made up of fats and proteins. The virus binds to the lymphocytes and the enzymes present in the lymphocytes remove the membrane of the virus. As a result, the exposed RNA copies into DNA and replicates rapidly infecting the neighbouring lymphocytes. The infected lymphocytes are killed. Since the lymphocytes themselves are killed or damaged, the virus directly affects the immunity of the person.

79. In humans, mammary glands secrete a milk-like liquid during late pregnancy which is called colostrum.

This colostrum is known to contain large number of lymphocytes and many antibodies. This gives incomparable innate immunity to the new born and protects the baby from infections in future.

Colostrum has mild laxative effect which induces the passing of the baby's first stool which is called meconium.

This removes the excess bilurubin which is the waste product of red blood cells and helps prevent jaundice.

80. Antibiotics are a type of antimicrobial drugs used in the treatment of bacterial infections. They may kill or inhibit the growth of bacteria. Antibiotics can work either by killing the bacteria or by inhibiting the growth of bacteria.

The bacteria are prokaryotes with cells possessing a tough cell wall made up of complex sugars. Antibiotics inhibit the synthesis of cell wall which prevents the bacteria from multiplying in the body. Antibiotics also may work by making the plasma membrane lose the ability of semipermeability. Moreover, the ribosomes present in prokaryotic cells are different from the ribosomes present in eukaryotic cells (our body cells). Antibiotics act and inhibit the 30S ribosomes of bacterial cells thereby making the cell incapable of synthesizing proteins. They do not act on the ribosomes of our cells. Hence, antibiotics selectively kill the bacterial cells without causing much harm to the host cells.

81. MMR vaccine is not recommended in pregnancy as matter of caution because it is live attenuated vaccine and may pose threat to foetus.

82. Some vaccines such as those for smallpox or hepatitis B provide long-term immunity. This is because the memory cells in the immune system are capable of generating the antibodies for long periods. The other vaccines can provide only short-term protection. For example, typhoid provides protection for only 2-3 years. This is because the memory cells are capable of generating the antibodies for the antigens for the disease for only short periods. Later on, the memory cells lose their memory.

83. Tetanus is a life-threatening bacterial disease caused by a bacterium *Clostridium tetani*. These bacteria can easily pass into the body through an open wound even a mild cut or scratch. After it enters the skin, it produces a toxin known as tetanospasmin in the blood stream. It then attacks the nervous system which may also lead to death. The incubation period for the bacterium is short that is from 3 to 21 days. The time is not sufficient for the production of antibodies in case the bacterium affects the person. It is very likely that the bacteria may enter the new born through the umbilical cord which is cut at the time of birth. Therefore, pregnant mother should be vaccinated for the disease to protect both mother and baby from the disease.

84. The socio-economic environment plays a pivotal role in shaping health outcomes. Areas with limited access to healthcare, poor sanitation, or low education levels tend to have higher incidences of diseases. Economic hardships can exacerbate health issues, leading to malnutrition, mental health challenges, and inadequate healthcare access. On the other hand, communities with strong socio-economic structures benefit from better healthcare, education, and awareness, leading to enhanced immunity and fewer disease outbreaks. Community awareness and participation are vital. When individuals are informed, they make better health choices, leading to a ripple effect on the broader community. Vaccination drives, health education programs, and community health initiatives can significantly enhance collective immunity and well-being. Hence, while individual health is crucial, the collective socio-economic environment and community actions play an equally, if not more, significant role in determining health outcomes.

NEET SPECIAL WING

Multiple-Answer Type Questions

1. Female mosquitoes are the ones that feed on the blood, they act as a vector and help to transmit the disease from a diseased person to the healthy person's body. Diseases like Chikungunya, Dengue, Malaria, etc are transmitted through them.
2. Endemic disease is confined to a specific area only affecting few people. For example, Rift valley fever is endemic in eastern Africa, goitre is endemic in India (sub-Himalayan region), etc.
3. Protozoans cause a lot od diseases which include sleeping sickness, malaria etc.
4. Symptoms of Hepatitis A infection are like those of jaundice -Nausea, vomiting, weakness, loss of appetite, dark urine.
5. An antibiotic is a chemical substance which can kill as well as inhibit the growth of bacteria. Antibiotics are generally prepared from bacteria or fungi. Functions of antibiotics include - Prevention of further infection, Inhibition of growth of pathogens, Preservation of perishable food like fish and meat, etc.

Comprehension-Based Questions

A.

6. In mammals, foetus is connected to the mother's body via specialised structure called placenta. It through this structure that the foetus receives nutrition as well as preformed antibodies are also passed from the mother's body to the foetus.
7. An antigen can also be introduced to our body through vaccination for the generation of antibodies, which fight against the antigen. This is called artificial active immunity. For example, vaccines of polio and measles.
8. Skin, hair, mucus and secretions are part of our body's first line of defence and is part of innate immunity, something that we are born with.
9. Innate immunity is something that we are born with and forms part of the body's first line of defence.
10. Physical barriers form part of the body's first line of defence.
11. Match the following:

    In case of snake bites the injection, which is given to the patients contain preformed antibodies against snake venom, also known as antivenom.
    (i) (b)

    Antibodies from the mother's body passes on to the foetus via placenta and is an example of natural acquired passive immunity.
    (ii) (e)

    Vaccine against tetanus contains weakened germs which gives us active immunity.
    (iii) (a)

    Attack of chicken pox gives us lifelong active immunity and we are safe guarded against adverse effects of the disease upon subsequent infections.
    (iv) (d)

    Vaccine of polio provides the body artificial active immunity.
    (v) (c)

B.

12. Night blindness is the inability to see well in dark or poor light. It is caused due to deficiency of Vitamin A in diet.
13. Endemic is a disease which is confined to a specific area only affecting few people. For example, Rift valley fever is endemic in eastern Africa, goitre is endemic in India (sub-Himalayan region), etc.
14. Allergies are caused when the body is hypersensitive to certain substances. This causes a reaction in the body which leads to redness, itching and even blisters in severe allergies.
15. Yellow fever is a viral disease which is transmitted to humans by a mosquito named culex. In this case culex acts as a vector.
16. When a patient suffers from tuberculosis, they should be quarantined to stop the disease from spreading further and Anti- Tubercular therapy can be used.

17. Match the following:

Rat flea, a parasite of rats carries the pathogen from the dead rat to human being, this is how the transmission occurs. Thus to prevent plague all measures should be taken to decrease the growth of rats and also to use rat proof bins for storage of cereal grains.

(i) (b)

In yellow fever mosquito acts as a vector. To control the spread of yellow fever, breeding of mosquitoes in shallow water bodies should be prevented. One of the methods is to spray kerosene over the surface of water which prevents dissolution of oxygen in water. This hinders the breeding process in water.

(ii) (c)

Amoebiasis is caused by protozoa which is spread in humans due to house flies. Preventive measure include eating covered food, maintenance of proper sanitation, use of insecticides and safe disposal of garbage.

(iii) (d)

In gastroenteritis, transmission takes place indirectly due to consumption of food items contaminated by cockroaches. The spread of cockroaches can be controlled by spraying insecticides like DDT and maintenance of sewerage system.

(iv) (a)

Hepatitis A is transmitted by contaminated food and water. Immunization by vaccines and interferons is one of the methods of prevention of this disease.

(v) (e)

CHAPTER

6

Improvement in Food Resources

Key Ideas

After completing this chapter, you should be able to:

- Realize the need of improved agricultural practices
- Infer the concept of sustainable agriculture
- Discuss important agricultural practices
- Explain various practices under animal husbandry

Remember

Before beginning this chapter, you should be able to:

- Interpret the importance of food
- Define food preservation methods
- Define storage methods of food grains

Scientific Crypt

A Tribute to Sir Albert Howard (1873–1947)

A British botanist and key figure in the early organic farming movement, is widely recognized for his invaluable contributions to sustainable agriculture and food resource improvement. In the early twentieth century, his work marked a watershed moment in agricultural practises, emphasising the critical role of organic matter and soil health in cultivating resilient, fertile landscapes.

Howard's revolutionary ideas were articulated in his seminal work, '*An Agricultural Testament*' (1940), which emphasized the importance of keeping agriculture and nature in harmony. His composting innovations, particularly the 'Indore Method,' are critical in promoting sustainable food resources and ecological balance. This method converted organic waste into nutrient-rich compost, increasing soil fertility and crop yield while combating food scarcity.

Sir Howard's unwavering pursuit of ecological well-being and natural equilibrium has won him widespread acclaim and continues to influence modern agricultural practices and policies.

Crossword

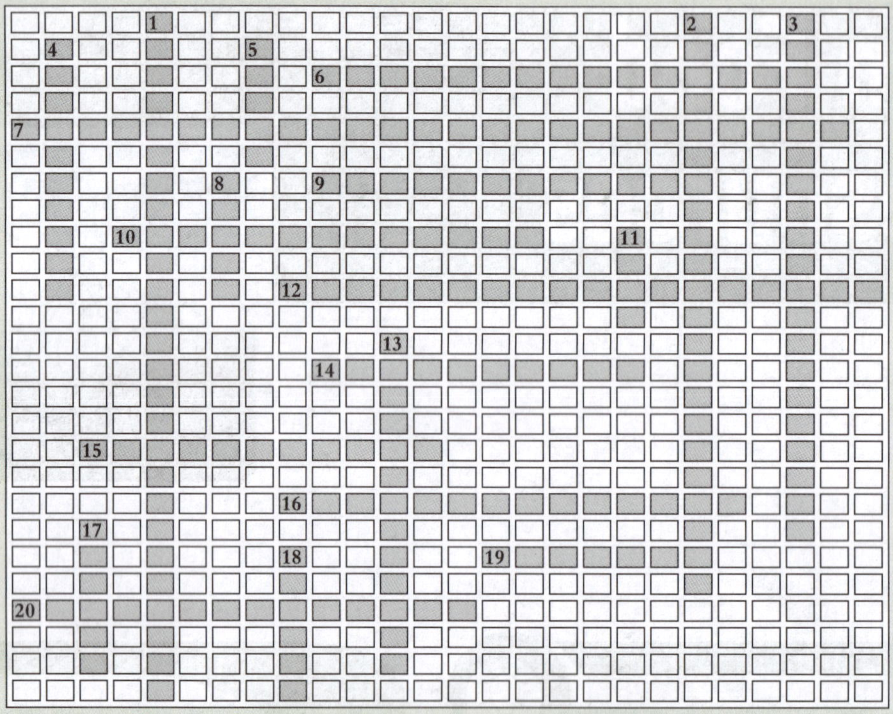

Across

6. Irrigation system where the water is directly drawn from the river with the help of a pump
7. Cross-made between plants of two different genera
9. Systematic cultivation of different crops in a proper sequence in different seasons on the same land
10. Different crops cultivated on one land
12. Method by which crop variety can be improved by genetically modifying them
14. Disease caused by virus in cattle which is accompanied by ulcers in the mouth
15. Culture fishery in marine water is called
16. High-amount plant nutrient
19. Chicken which is reared to obtain meat
20. The practice of raising domestic fowls, such as chicken, turkeys, ducks and goose for meat and eggs

Down

1. Cross-made between plants of two different varieties
2. The practice of development of techniques in agriculture to meet human needs, simultaneously maintaining and improving the ecosystem balance
3. Farming of different types of fish of compatible species having different feeding habits, in the same pond
4. Coffee, coconut, tea and rubber are examples of which typestypes of crops on the basis of their usage
5. Which revolution led to increased potato production
8. Xanthium and parthenium are which kind of plants
11. Cucumbers and melons are examples of which type of crop
13. Different crops grown following specific pattern
17. Organic matter derived from biological wastes like animal faeces and plant wastes which nourishes the soil
18. Crops grown in the rainy season

INTRODUCTION

Food is one of the basic requirements of human beings. The demand for food is continuously increasing with the increase in human population. India is a highly populous country, but the area of cultivable land is limited. Reducing the gap between the demand and supply of food has been a major challenge to us. Worldwide research has brought about a remarkable change in agricultural processes and technologies. This revolutionary change in the field of agriculture is known as green revolution and has increased the production of food grains to a great extent. White revolution, initiated by India's National Dairy Development Board made India the world's largest producer of milk. This has led to the extensive use of chemical fertilizers and pesticides to meet the demand and in return, resulted in environmental threats. Hence, sustainable practices are required to be adopted in agriculture and animal husbandry so as to curb environmental pollution and to maintain the ecological balance.

Sustainable management of natural resources, as well as obtaining a better yield from farms is possible through certain agricultural practices like mixed farming, inter-cropping, integrated farming, etc. Integrated farming is an agricultural practice which combines agriculture with livestock, poultry, fisheries and bee-keeping. This kind of agricultural practice gives rise to a better productivity along with scientific management of the environment. The adoption of an agricultural practice in a region depends on the climatic conditions of that region. In India, different types of crops (Kharif and Rabi) are grown in different seasons since the growth of a crop depends on the temperature and photoperiod (duration of sunlight).

Agricultural Revolutions

Some of the major agricultural revolutions that occurred in India, are listed below:

Table 6.1 List of agricultural revolutions in India

Name	Feature
Green revolution	Food grain production
White revolution	Milk production
Black revolution	Petroleum production
Blue revolution	Fish production
Yellow revolution	Oil seed production
Silver revolution	Poultry production
Round revolution	Potato production
Red revolution	Meat/tomato production

Konnect

Agriculture is the practice of farming, including cultivation of the soil for growing of crops and rearing of animals to provide food and other products.

Sustainable Agriculture

Limited availability of natural resources and unregulated increase in human demands is leading to overexploitation of these resources. In order to meet the demands of humans in order to achieve their development, awareness and attention is now given to development of new methods to get more food. The

Info Bytes!

Mankombu Sambasivan Swaminathan is the 'father of Indian green revolution'.

new methods are being designed in such a way that natural resources are not depleted further and environmental balance is not disturbed. In order to meet this goal, a scheme of sustainable agriculture has been developed.

Sustainable agriculture is the practice of development of techniques in agriculture to meet the human needs, simultaneously maintaining and improving the ecosystem balance and conservation of natural resources. The key principles involved in sustainable agriculture are as follows:

- Merging of biological and ecological processes into agricultural and food production practices.
- Judicious use of non-renewable resources.
- Resolving natural resource issues with cooperation and collaboration.

Types of Crops

Crops can be divided into different types on the basis of seasons they are grown in and also on the basis of their usage.

On the Basis of Seasons

In India, crops which are grown in rainy season from the month of June to October are called the kharif crops. Paddy, soyabean, pigeon pea, maize, cotton, green gram and black gram, etc., are kharif crops. Crops which are grown in the winter season from November to April are called rabi crops. Wheat, gram, peas, mustard, linseed, etc., are rabi crops. Crops which are grown from April to June are called zaid crops. For example, cucumbers, melons, etc. In India, the production of food grains has increased four times from 1952 to 2010, whereas the increase in cultivable land is 1.25 times.

On the Basis of Usage

The major crops can be divided into four main categories depending on their usage, namely

1. Food crops (wheat, maize, rice, millets, pulses, etc.)
2. Cash crops (sugarcane, tobacco, cotton, jute, oilseeds, etc.)
3. Plantation crops (coffee, coconut, tea, rubber, etc.)
4. Horticulture crops (fruits and vegetables)

Agricultural Practices

Improvement in agricultural productivity is possible due to the implementation of sustainable agricultural practices, which can be divided into following three stages:

1. Crop variety improvement
2. Crop production management
3. Crop protection management

Info Bytes!

The history of agriculture dates back over 10,000 years, with ancient civilizations like Mesopotamia cultivating land and domesticating animals for food.

Crop Variety Improvement

Crop variety improvement involves the methods to be adopted to modify the plants genetically for a better yield. Thus, implementation of these methods can fulfil the requirement of food. Plant breeding is a technique performed to produce such varieties of crops. New varieties or strains of crops produced by plant breeding have the following useful characteristics:

- Better yield in terms of both quality and quantity
- Resistance to diseases
- Better response to fertilizers

Info Bytes!

Plant breeding is the production of improved and new crop varieties that are superior to the existing varieties in many characters.

Methods of Crop Variety Improvement

Crop variety improvement is possible by two methods:

1. Hybridization
2. Genetic engineering

Hybridization

Hybridization is a process to produce new varieties of crops by crossing two genetically different parents. Hybridization can be done in three different ways listed as follows:

1. **Intervarietal hybridization:** Crossing of two different varieities of wheat to get progeny having superior charcteristics.
2. **Interspecific hybridization:** Tangelo which is a hybrid of two citrus fruits which is formed by a cross between orange and grapefruit or orange and pomelo.
3. **Intergeneric hybridization:** Peppermint is a hybrid of two diffrent genera Mentha and Piperita

Info Bytes!

The major research institute for agricultural research in India is ICAR (Indian Council of Agricultural Research).

Genetic Engineering

This is a modern technique in the field of crop variety improvement. In this technique, a desired gene possessing a superior character is introduced into a plant and this process results in the development of genetically modified crops. Such improved variety of crops is subjected to a series of tests to ensure high yield, disease resistance, environment tolerance, etc. Seeds possessing such qualities are tolerant to diverse climatic conditions and they can be sown in any variety of soil.

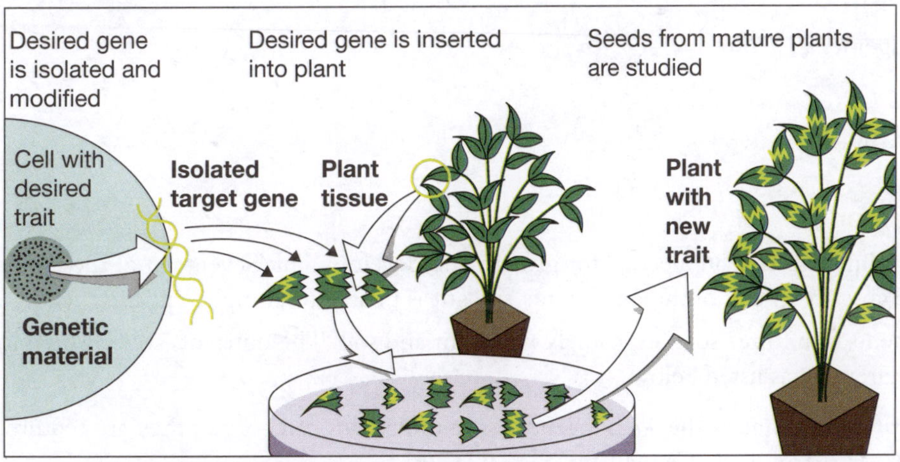

Figure 6.1 Genetic engineering process in plants

Objectives of Crop Variety Improvement

Following are the main applications of crop variety improvement,

- **Increasing** the **yield** of plant products.
- **Improving** the **quality** of food crops like:
  - Baking quality in wheat
  - Protein quality in pulses
  - Oil quality in oil seeds
  - Longer preservation time for fruits and vegetables

Info Bytes!

The history of agriculture dates back over 10,000 years, with ancient civilizations like Mesopotamia cultivating land and domesticating animals for food.

- **Producing biotic-resistant varieties:** Such kind of crops are resistant to fungal and bacterial diseases, insects and pests.
- **Producing abiotic-resistant varieties:** These crops are **resistant to environmental stresses** like drought, salinity, water logging, heat, cold and frost.
- **Changing the duration of maturity:** Reduction in the duration from sowing the seeds to harvesting makes the yield more economical since multiple rounds of crops can be grown in a year. Uniform maturity of crops makes the harvesting process easy and more beneficial.
- **Wide range of adaptability:** Developing the varieties of crops that can be grown in the different climatic conditions in different regions.

Info Bytes!

Wheat is the most widespread crop and is grown everywhere except Antarctica.

- **Imparting desirable characteristics to crops:** Developing varieties with desirable agronomic characteristics for higher productivity. For example,
  - Tallness and profuse branching for fodder crops
  - Dwarfness for cereal crops for reducing the absorption of nutrients

However, high-yielding variety of the crop and introducing it into the field does not ensure high yield. Different farming practices and agricultural technologies are required to be implemented for a better production of crops.

Crop Production Management

Crop production management regulates various areas of crop production to get the best possible yield. The economic conditions of farmers are not uniform throughout the country and due to different conditions of climate and terrains, different agricultural practices are followed. Hence, management of crop production to control these aspects is done using the following four practices:

1. Nutrient management
2. Irrigation
3. Cropping patterns
4. Crop rotation

Nutrient Management

Plants require certain nutrients that are needed for growth and development. Seventeen of these nutrients are classified as essential ones. In the absence of any of these nutrients, a plant is unable to complete its life cycle.

Plants obtain nutrients from three sources, namely water, air and soil. The nutrients are classified into two categories on the basis of their requirement as listed below,

1. **Macronutrients:** Nine out of the 17 nutrients come under this category as they are required in higher amounts. For example, C, H, O, N, P, K, Ca, Mg and S.
2. **Micronutrients:** The remaining nutrients (Fe, Mn, Zn, Cu, Mo, B, Na, Co, Si, Cl and Ni) are required in relatively smaller amounts (but essential for the plant). They are called micronutrients.

Table 6.2 Plant nutrients and their sources

Nutrient	Source
Hydrogen	Water
Carbon	Air
Oxygen	Air and water
Nitrogen	Soil minerals

(Continued)

Table 6.2 *(Continued)*

Nutrient	Source
Phosphorous	Soil minerals
Potassium	Soil minerals
Calcium	Soil minerals
Magnesium	Soil minerals
Iron	Soil minerals
Zinc	Soil minerals
Chlorine	Soil minerals
Molybdenum	Soil minerals
Nickel	Soil minerals
Boron	Soil minerals
Copper	Soil minerals
Manganese	Soil minerals
Sulphur	Soil minerals

Nutrients present in the soil remain dissolved in water. Plants absorb them through the roots. Primary plant nutrients that are absorbed from the soil are nitrogen, phosphorous and potassium. If crops are grown in the same soil repeatedly, then it is highly likely that these primary nutrients decrease in quantity rapidly. These nutrients can be replenished by adding manure and chemical fertilizers into the soil.

Manure

Manure is the organic matter derived from the biological wastes like animal faeces and plant wastes. It replenishes nutrients in the soil and thus renders the soil fertile. Organic matter present in the manure increases the water-holding capacity of sandy soil and avoids water logging in clayey soil. Using manures is environment friendly, because it reduces the excessive use of chemical fertilizers and helps in recycling biological wastes. Manure is classified into two types based on the biological waste material used. These are:

> **Konnect**
>
> Earthworms are called Friends of Farmers as they loosen the soil by burrowing deep into it, thus helping in vermicomposting.

1. Compost and vermicompost
2. Green manure

Compost and vermicompost: Biological waste materials like crop wastes, vegetable wastes, animal excreta, animal refuses, domestic wastes, eradicated weeds, etc., are collected in pits for decomposition. After decomposition, the mass obtained is rich in organic matter and nutrients and is known as compost. If earthworms are used to hasten the process of decomposition, the organic matter obtained is called vermicompost.

Figure 6.2 Earthworm in compost

Green manure: In crop fields, plants, such as sun hemp or gaur are grown and then ploughed to mix with the soil. This activity is carried out prior to the sowing of seeds. These plants get transformed into green manure due to the process of decomposition and enriches the soil with organic matter, nitrogen and phosphorous.

However, manures contain nutrients in small quantities, hence they are needed to be supplied in large quantities to the crop. Manures are not nutrient specific, in other words, they are not much useful if a particular nutrient is needed to be supplied to the plants.

Chemical Fertilizers

Chemical fertilizers are different chemical compounds added to the soil for the replenishment of certain nutrients like phosphorous, nitrogen and potassium. There are different advantages and disadvantages of the usage of chemical fertilizers. Chemical fertilizers are economic and can release nutrients continuously and hence, increase the productivity.

Based on the nutrients available in them, chemical fertilizers are classified into following types,

- Nitrogenous fertilizers: They supply nitrogen. For example, ammonium sulphate.
- Phosphatic fertilizers: They supply phosphorous. For example, single superphosphate.
- Potassic fertilizers: They supply potassium. For example, muriate of potash.
- Complex fertilizers: They supply two or more nutrients. For example, urea ammonium phosphate.

Excessive use of fertilizers affects soil fertility and leads to water pollution. Hence, usage of chemical fertilizers should be optimized.

Organic farming is a process which can reduce the uses of chemical fertilizers. The common practices employed in organic farming are:

- Organic manure: Recycled farm wastes (compost).
- Biofertilizers: Organisms which enrich the soil.
- Biopesticides: Neem leaves and turmeric for storage of grains.

Biofertlizers are used for specific crop plants, such as legumes. They are renewable and non-polluting. Commonly used biofertilizers are

- Blue–green algae
- Mycorrhiza
- Legume

Info Bytes!

Biofertilizers are not substitutes to chemical fertilizers. They play supplementary roles in supplying nitrogen.

Another important aspect of crop production management is irrigation.

Irrigation

Irrigation is the supply of controlled amount of water to the plants. Indian agricultural sector largely depends on monsoon rains. Hence, failure of monsoon leads to crop failure. To overcome this situation, proper irrigation methods have been adopted. Different kinds of irrigation methods are used based on the availability of water and climatic condition of a region. Irrigation system includes following four major methods, namely

1. Wells
2. Canals
3. River lift systems
4. Tanks

Wells for Accessing the Ground Water

There are two types of wells—Dug well and tube well. Dug wells are the simplest means of accessing ground water from water-bearing strata. They become dry when the water table goes down. In tube wells, a suction pump is used to lift water from deeper strata. Tube wells receive water from porous soil strata.

Canals for Irrigation

Canals are widely used in India for irrigation. They collect water from the reservoirs or rivers. Water from the main canals flows to the branches and then to the distributaries. Thus, water from the reservoirs or rivers reaches agricultural lands.

River Lift System

In river lift system, water is directly drawn from the river with the help of a pump and used for irrigation. This method is adopted in those areas where canal irrigation is not possible.

Tanks

Tanks are the reservoirs which store rain water run-off and the collected water is used for irrigation. Rain water harvesting and check dams are the other two ways to make the rain water available for irrigation. Check dams are constructed to prevent the flow of rainwater. Rain water gets collected in check dams and used mainly for irrigation. Rain water harvesting is the process of storing rain water in natural reservoirs for future use. The above methods also increase ground water level and reduce soil erosion.

Info Bytes!

Drip irrigation is drop-by-drop method of water delivery at or near the root area of plants. This is the most water-efficient method.

Figure 6.3 Irrigation canal system

Info Bytes!

Ancient Egyptians practiced crop rotation 4,000 years ago by alternating cereal crops with leguminous crops to improve soil fertility.

Cropping Patterns

Cropping pattern is the selection of varieties of crops and determining the proportion of area for growing them depending on climate, availability of water and nutrients in the soil in a region. Mixed cropping and intercropping are the two methods of cropping patterns.

Mixed Cropping

In mixed cropping, different crops are cultivated simultaneously on the same piece of land. Wheat and gram, wheat and mustard, groundnut and sunflower are some of the examples. In this cropping system, no particular pattern is followed for sowing the seeds. This cropping pattern minimizes the risk of crop failure.

Figure 6.4 Intercropping —Nectarine orchard with tomato plants

Criteria to be taken into consideration while selecting crops for mixed cropping, such as:

- One of the crops should have shallow roots and the another one should have deep roots.
- One of the crops should have high water requirement and the another one should have low water requirement.
- Both plants should require different nutrients.
- One of the crops should mature early and the another should mature late.

Intercropping

In intercropping system, different crops are grown on the same land following a specific pattern. Crops are selected in such a way that their nutrient requirements are different. Specific fertilizers and pesticides are used for each variety. Thus, this cropping pattern increases the productivity and prevents the spreading of diseases among the crops cultivated on one field. Planting soya bean with maize and finger millet with cow pea are examples of intercropping systems.

Crop Rotation

Crop rotation is the systematic cultivation of different crops in a proper sequence in different seasons on the same land. Crop rotation maintains the quantity of nutrients in the soil and thus increases the productivity and prevents diseases. Crop rotation is done for different combinations of crops depending on the duration. For example, leguminous crops are grown in rotation with cereal crops. Leguminous plants are grown with root nodules which contain nitrogen-fixing bacteria. These bacteria fix up the atmospheric nitrogen into nitrates. This thus enriches the soil with nitrates. When in next round, cereal crops are grown, they absorb most of the nitrogen present in the soil. Now when leguminous plants are grown, in next season soil fertility is restored.

Advantages of Crop Rotation

- Restores soil fertility.
- Prevents depletion of nutrients.
- Blocks the building up of pests.

Crop Protection Management

Field crops get affected by large number of weeds, insects, pests and diseases. Weeds are unwanted plants, such as *Xanthium*, *Parthenium* and *Cyperus rotundus*. They consume nutrients and thus prevent the growth of the crops. Insects harm the plants in three different ways. Some insects cut and chew different parts of the plants like root, stem and leaves. Insects having piercing mouth parts, suck the cell sap from different parts of the plant. Some of the insects bore into stem and fruit, enter and feed on the tissues. Different pathogens like virus, bacteria, fungi, etc., present in air, water and soil cause diseases in plants.

Figure 6.5 Chenopodium (weed plant)

Control of Weeds, Insects and Diseases

Weeds can be removed mechanically. There are some preventive methods, like Intercropping and crop rotation which help to prevent the growth of weeds. Preparing the seedbed by tilling it properly and sowing the crops at appropriate time also prevent the growth of weeds. Weedicides can also be used. Insecticides, pesticides, fungicides, etc., protect the crops from insects and diseases. Pest-resistant variety of crops can be used. Summer ploughing exposes the insects and pathogen to the summer heat and thus helps in killing them. This process also destroys the weeds.

Weeds can be controlled by using following methods:

- **Mechanical:** They can be uprooted by hands or using trowel.
- **Chemical:** Weeds can be destroyed by spraying chemicals called weedicides, such as atrazine, 2, 4-D (2, 4-dichlorophenoxy acetic acid), etc.

- **Cultural:** This covers the aspects like intercropping, crop rotation and timely sowing of crops.
- **Biological:** Some insects or other organisms are put into the field which selectively destroy weed plants without harming the plants. For example, millet does not allow growth of weeds. Such crop plants are known as smoother crops.

Insect Pests

Insect pests are those insects which hamper the growth of the plants by attacking them. Following are the types of insect pests:

- **Sucking:** These insect pests puncture the parts of the plant and suck the cell sap with the help of their needle-like beaks. For example, aphids.
- **Chewing:** These insect pests cut the roots, stems or leaves with the help of their chewing mouth parts. They chew and swallow the plant parts in pieces. For example, caterpillars.
- **Internal feeder:** These insect pests bore into stem or fruits. They live inside the plant part and hence, harm the crop field. For example, weevils.

Large white, caterpillars eating leaves — Aphids puncturing the plant — Weevil damaging cotton plant

Figure 6.6 Common insect pests

These pests can be controlled using following methods:
Using pesticides: These are chemicals used to kill pests. For example, insecticides, rodenticides, fungicides and weedicides.
Using natural insecticides: These include neem, nicotine, etc., as they have natural properties of getting rid of insects.
Using biological methods: Some insects are deliberately added to the affected plant crops to attack the pests selectively without harming the main plant. For example, ladybug.

Figure 6.7 Ladybug attacking aphids

Proper Storage of Grains

Increase in grain production creates the problem of proper storage. Inadequate storage measures result in loss of grains. There are two types of factors which cause the loss of grains—Biotic and abiotic factors. The biotic factors are insects, rodents, fungi, mites and bacteria. Inappropriate moisture and temperatures at the warehouses (storage place for grains) are the abiotic factors. These factors lead to some adverse effect on crop protection. The adverse effects of the above factors are:

- Degradation of the quality of grains
- Loss in weight
- Poor germinability
- Decolorization of the grains

The poor quality of grains eventually lead to poor marketability. The following processes are required to be carried out before storing the seeds, such as cleaning the grains thoroughly, Grains to be dried properly first in sunlight and then in shade, Fumigation using chemicals that can kill pests.

Measures to prevent and control damage to the grains are discussed below.

- The storehouses or godowns used for storing grains must be clean and dry. They should not have any dirt, dust or webbing. If there are any holes or cracks in them, they must be sealed properly.
- The grains should be first dried in the sunlight and then in shade. It should be ensured that moisture content of the grains is less than 9%.
- Fumigants (pesticide solution converted into fumes) can be used to kill insect pests. Before storing the grains, storehouses should be fumigated using suitable pesticides.

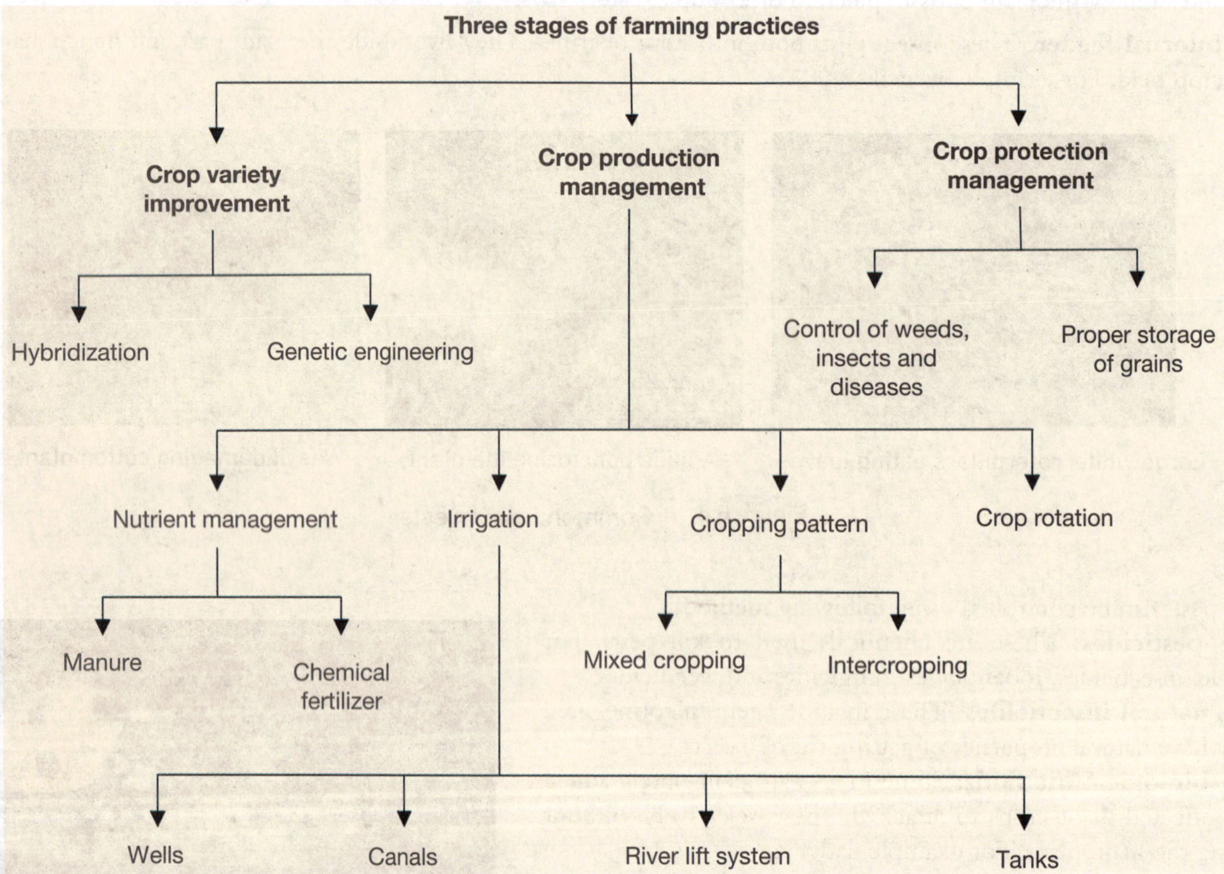

Figure 6.8 Stages of farming practices

Quick Recap

✔ **Compare mixed cropping and intercropping systems.**

Mixed cropping	Intercropping
Two or more crops are grown simultaneously on the same piece of land without following any particular pattern.	More than one crops are grown on the same piece of land following a specific pattern.
Seeds are combined and sown.	Seeds are sown separately.
Same fertilizers and pesticides are used.	Different fertilizers and pesticides are used.
Minimizes the risk of crop failure.	Increases the productivity of the land.
Competition amongst the crop for the nutrients exists.	Competition for nutrients between the crops does not exist.

✔ **How does the absence of competition for nutrients in intercropping lead to increased productivity?**

In intercropping, because crops are grown following a specific pattern, they are chosen such that their nutrient needs complement each other. This means one crop might take up certain nutrients, while another crop utilizes different ones. As a result, crops aren't fighting for the same resources, leading to better growth for both crops and ultimately increased productivity.

✔ **What are the long-term impacts of using chemical fertilizers on soil health compared to manure?**

Prolonged use of chemical fertilizers can lead to soil degradation, making the soil less fertile over time. Chemical fertilizers might increase yield in the short term but can deplete the soil of essential microorganisms and organic matter. Manure, on the other hand, enriches the soil with organic matter, improves soil texture, and promotes the growth of beneficial microorganisms, leading to sustainable agricultural practices and long-term soil health.

Animal Husbandry

Animal husbandry includes proper care, raising and breeding of livestock. Livestock are domesticated animals like buffaloes, cows, pigs, horses, cattle, sheep, camels, goats, etc., which give labour and commodities like meat, egg, milk, fur, wool, leather, etc. Animal husbandry includes the following four practises:

1. Cattle farming
2. Poultry farming
3. Fish production (marine and inland fisheries)
4. Bee keeping

Info Bytes!

Breeds of Cow
Indigenous: Sahiwal, Gir, Red Sindhi
Exotic: Holstein-Friesian, Brown Swiss, Jersey
Cross-breeds: Karan Swiss, Karan Fries

Cattle Farming

Cattle farming involves rearing of two types of animals. One category of animals provides milk and they are called milch or dairy animals. The other category of animals is used for labour and are called draught animals. In India, two different species of cattle are reared—*Bos indicus* (cows) and *Bos bubalis* (buffaloes). Cattle can produce milk during the lactation period after the birth of a calf. Lactation period of a local breed such as Red Sindhi, Sahiwal, etc., can be increased by cross breeding them with an exotic or foreign breed, such as Jersey or Brown Swiss. Thus, the productivity of milk and dairy products can be increased by cross breeding.

Milk Production

Production of good-quality milk depends on the following factors:

- **Breed:** Quantity and quality of milk vary according to the type of breed. For example, exotic cows have long lactation periods and give more amount of milk. On the other hands, indigenous breeds produce low amount of milk per day.
- **Season:** In winter season, quantity of milk produced is higher than in summer season.
- **Health:** If the cattle is suffering from a disease, the quality and quantity of milk produced are hampered.
- **Feed:** Variation in feeds of the cattle also affect the quality of milk temporarily.

Info Bytes!

Lactation period is the duration from the time cow gives birth to a calf till the time it stops to produce milk.

Shelters for Cattle

Roofed sheds are used to shelter the cattle from rain, heat and cold. Cattle shed must be well-ventilated and the floor should have proper slope for proper cleaning and drying.

Figure 6.9 Dairy cows in cattle shed

Food for Cattle

Dairy cattle require feed for growth and milk production. It is important to provide a balanced and sufficient diet to the cattle for the production milk of optimal quantity and good quality. Cattle require two types of food—Roughages, rich in fibre and concentrates, rich in proteins and other nutrients, but low in fibre. Besides these, oil cakes and feed additives rich in micronutrients are also required. Water should also be provided in required quantity.

Cattle Diseases and Prevention

Diseases of cattle lead to the reduction in the production of milk and sometimes lead to even death. Cattle are affected by both internal and external parasites. Internal parasites cause skin diseases. External parasites are worms and flukes. Worms affect stomach and intestine while flukes affect liver. Pathogens like virus and bacteria also cause diseases. Vaccination protects the farm animals from viral and bacterial diseases.

Table 6.3 Common cattle diseases

Disease	Features
Anthrax	It is caused by anthrax bacteria (*Bacillus anthracis*) and is fatal
Foot and mouth disease	It is highly contagious and is caused by a virus. Blisters appear on the mouth and feet of the affected animal
Rinderpest	It is accompanied by ulcers in mouth. It is caused by a virus. It is highly contagious and fatal
Tuberculosis	It is caused by bacteria and is highly contagious. It can also spread to humans through infected milk

Symptoms of a Sick Cattle

Following are the commonly observed symptoms of a sick cattle;

- Cattle remains inactive
- It moves slowly
- It stops taking food
- Milk yield is reduced drastically
- It may have high temperature
- It may pass coloured urine

Poultry Farming

Poultry farming is the practice of raising domestic fowls, such as chicken, turkeys, ducks and goose for meat and egg. Cross-breeding techniques are practiced in poultry farming to produce new varieties with improved qualities.

Poultry products have become choice of staple food for most of the people in many parts of the world.

An egg-laying poultry is called layer and the poultry reared for obtaining meat is called broiler.

Info Bytes!

The word 'poultry' is derived from French word 'poult' that means chicken.

Layers and Broilers

As discussed, there are two main objectives of poultry farming, obtaining eggs and meat. The characteristic features and differences between layers and broilers are discussed in the Table 6.4.

Table 6.4 The characteristic features and differences between layers and broilers in poultry farming

Parameter	Layer	Broiler
Purpose	Obtaining eggs	Obtaining meat
Shelter	Enough space and lighting	Need conditions to grow fast
Feed	Restricted and calculated	Rich in proteins, vitamins A and K
Time period	Kept for longer period as eggs are produced at the age of 20 weeks	Raised up to between 6 and 7 weeks

Shelter and Care of Broiler Chicken

Broiler chicken requires large, dry, clean and hygienic places for their fast growth. Appropriate temperature of their shelter is required to be maintained. Broiler chicken requires protein and vitamin-rich feed for maintaining its carcass quality. Adequate fat is also required for desired growth rate. Poultry feed should be rich in vitamin E and K.

Poultry Diseases

Poultry fowl are susceptible to the pathogens like virus, bacteria, fungi and parasites. Proper sanitation, hygienic shelter, spraying disinfectants at regular interval and appropriate vaccination can prevent the occurrence of infectious diseases.

Info Bytes!

Poultry Breeds
Indigenous: Assel, Chattisgarh, Bursa
Exotic: White leghorn, Australorp, Light sussex

Fish Production

Fish production involves the process of rearing fish in water bodies for the consumption of human being. Raising two categories of fish—Finned true fish and shellfish like prawns and molluscs come under fish production. The process of obtaining fish from natural resources is called fish capturing. Fish can also be cultivated in confined areas like ponds and this process is called culture fishery. The word fishery means the occupation or industry of catching or rearing fish. Fishery can be of two types. They are as follows:

1. Saltwater fishery, also called marine fishery
2. Freshwater fishery, also called inland fishery

Marine Fishery

Resources of marine fishery are 7500 km of coastline and the deep seas. Fish varieties are pomphret, mackerel, tuna, sardines and Bombay duck. Fish capturing takes place using many kinds of fishing nets from fishing boats. Large school of fish are located with the help of satellites and echo-sounders. Fish farming or culture fishery in marine water includes rearing of two types of fish, namely

1. Finned fish like mullets, bhetki and pearl spots
2. Shellfish like prawns, mussels, oyster and seaweed

Pearls are obtained from oysters. Culture fishery in marine water is called mariculture. Mariculture is now in great demand because of delpletion of marine fish stocks.

Info Bytes!

Vegetarian eggs are infertile eggs obtained from hens which are capable of laying eggs without the presence of cock

Inland Fishery

Fresh water resources are canals, ponds, reservoirs and rivers. Brackish water resources (having more salinity than fresh water, but less salinity than sea water) are estuaries and lagoons. The quantity of fish obtained by capturing from fresh water resources is not adequate. Fish production from fresh water mostly involves culture fishery. Culture fishery in fresh water is called aquaculture.

Figure 6.10 Salmon fish, used as source of food

Fish Culture in the Water in Paddy Field

Fish culture is sometimes combined with the cultivation of rice crop since fish feed can be obtained naturally by the amalgamation of fertilizer, soil, water, dung, etc., used for rice crop in the paddy field.

Composite Fish Culture

Composite fish culture is farming of different types of fish of compatible species having different feeding habits, in the same pond. This kind of farming of fish increases the productivity. A combination of 5–6 species, such rohu, catla, mrigal, common carps and grass carps are reared in the same pond. They do not compete for food as different parts of the pond are utilized for their feed.

Different types of compatible fishes with different properties are as follows:

- Catlas are surface feeder.
- Rohus feed in the middle zone of the pond.
- Mrigals and common carps are bottom feeders.
- Grass carp feeds on the weeds.

The major problem of such culture is the lack of pure fish seed for culturing. Most of the fish breed only in monsoon. This has been overcome by breeding fish in ponds by hormonal stimulation which ensures the availability of pure fish seed.

Bee Keeping

Bee keeping is the maintenance of hives of honey bees for the production of honey. Honey is a food of high nutritive value and also finds use in medicine. Beehives are the sources of wax, which is used in preparation of medicines, cosmetics and polishes. Bee keeping can be practiced in any area where sufficient pastures having wild shrubs, fruit orchards and cultivated crops are there. The localities where beehives and honey bees are reared are bee farms or apiaries. Varieties of bees used for commercial honey production are *Apis cerana indica* (Indian bee), *Apis dorsata* (rock bee) and *Apis florea* (little bee). An Italian bee variety, *Apis mellifera* is widely used because of its capacity of producing honey is high. The important factor on which the quality and taste of the honey depend is the nature of the flower from which honeybees collect the nectar.

Info Bytes!

A honey bee has two stomachs.

Castes

Honey bees are social insects. They demonstrate team work and division of labour.

They exist in several morphological forms called castes. Hence, bees are said to polymorphic species. A caste is a collection of individuals within the colony that are morphologically different from other individuals. According to the roles, castes of honey bee are divided into following three types:

1. **Queen:** Size of queen bee is much larger than other castes. Queen is responsible for laying eggs and she lays both fertilized and unfertilized eggs.
2. **Drone:** It is a fertile male. They are larger than workers and are noisy. Their main role is to mate with queen. They are stingless.
3. **Worker:** It is a sterile female and is the smallest in size. They are the most active members of the colony. They have wax glands (to build cells of comb), pollen baskets (for collection of pollen), hypopharangeal glands (to secrete bee milk) and a sting at the tip of abdomen (to defend the colony).

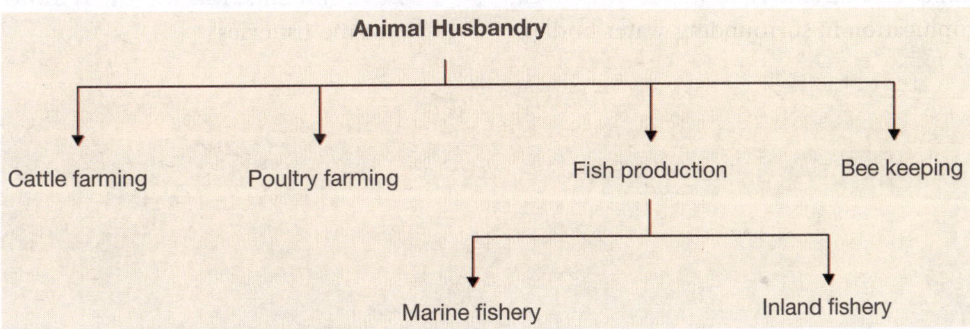

Figure 6.11 Components of animal husbandry

Figure 6.12 Three castes of honey bee: Queen, drone (male) and worker (female)

Quick Recap

✔ Compare **marine fishery and inland fishery.**

Marine fishery	Inland fishery
Carried out in coastal sea coast as well as in deep sea	Carried out in canals, ponds, reservoirs and rivers
Water bodies contain saline water	Water bodies contain fresh water or brakish water (estuaries and lagoons)
Marine fishery includes finned fish like mullet, bhetki, etc., as well as shell fish like prawns, oyster (produce pearls), etc.	Inland fishery includes mostly finned fish like rohu, catla, mrigal, etc.
Fish capturing is more predominant practice	Culture fishery is a more predominant practice
Culture fishery is called mariculture	Culture fishery is called aquaculture

✔ **What are the environmental impacts of mariculture compared to aquaculture?**

Both mariculture and aquaculture have environmental implications. Mariculture can lead to pollution of coastal waters due to waste products, the potential spread of diseases to wild fish populations, and the risk of non-native species escaping and establishing in new areas. Aquaculture, while providing more control over the environment, can lead to overuse of freshwater resources, alteration of local ecosystems, and discharge of nutrient-rich water, which can cause eutrophication in surrounding water bodies.

✔ **Why might shellfish like oysters, which produce pearls, be more predominant in marine fisheries than in inland ones?**

Shellfish like oysters thrive in the saline conditions of marine environments. The production of pearls by certain oyster species is a complex process influenced by their natural habitat. While there are freshwater pearl-producing molluscs, the majority and the most commercially valuable pearl-producing oysters are found in marine environments, making them more predominant in marine fisheries.

POINTS TO REMEMBER

- India is a highly populous country, but the area of cultivable land is limited.
- Sustainable management of natural resources as well as obtaining a better yield from farms is possible through certain agricultural practices like mixed farming, intercropping, integrated farming, etc.
- Crop variety improvement involves the methods to be adopted to modify the plants genetically for a better yield.
- Crop production management regulates various areas of crop production to get the best possible yield.
- Manure is the organic matter derived from the biological wastes like animal faeces and plant wastes.
- Irrigation is the supply of controlled amount of water to the plants.
- Cropping pattern is the selection of varieties of crops and determining the proportion of area for growing them depending on climate, availability of water and nutrients in the soil in a region.
- Crop rotation is the systematic cultivation of different crops in a proper sequence in different seasons on the same land.
- Animal husbandry includes proper care, raising and breeding of livestock.
- Animal husbandry includes cattle rearing, poultry farming, fish production and bee keeping.

DW

CLASSROOM WING

Practice Questions

Very Short Answer Type Questions

Direction for Questions from 1 to 6:
Fill in the blanks.

1. In India, due to the ________ population and limited cultivable land, there's an emphasis on sustainable agricultural practices.
2. To obtain a better yield from farms, ________, intercropping, and integrated farming are some of the practices used.
3. Genetic modifications in plants aim to ensure ______.
4. ________ is a method where different crops are cultivated in a sequence over different seasons on the same piece of land.
5. Apart from cattle rearing, ________, fish production, and beekeeping are parts of animal husbandry.
6. Cattle are both affected by internal and external ________.

Direction for Questions from 7 to 14:
For each of the following questions four choices have been provided. Select the correct alternatives.

7. Why is sustainable management of natural resources crucial for India?
   (a) Due to its large land area
   (b) Because of its large population and limited cultivable land
   (c) Because of its rich mineral resources
   (d) Because of its extensive coastline
8. What is the primary objective of crop variety improvement?
   (a) Increase resistance to pests
   (b) Change the colour of the crops
   (c) To modify plants genetically for better yield
   (d) To increase the size of the crop's leaves
9. Which of the following is derived from animal faeces and plant wastes?
   (a) Pesticides (b) Compost
   (c) Manure (d) Insecticides
10. What is irrigation primarily concerned with?
    (a) Supply of controlled amount of nutrients
    (b) Supply of controlled amount of sunlight
    (c) Supply of controlled amount of water
    (d) Supply of controlled amount of air
11. Crop production management primarily focuses on:
    (a) Genetic modification of crops
    (b) Introducing new crops
    (c) Regulating areas of crop production for best yield
    (d) Ensuring proper irrigation techniques
12. Which practice directly impacts the soil's nutrient content by alternating the type of nutrients absorbed and replenished?
    (a) Crop rotation
    (b) Intercropping
    (c) Mixed farming
    (d) Crop variety improvement
13. The external parasites such as ________ affect the stomach of animals.
    (a) worms (b) flukes
    (c) virus (d) bacteria
14. ________ are used to protect the cattle from rain, heat and cold.
    (a) Roofed sheds
    (b) Open places with no shelter
    (c) Sheds without roof
    (d) Places near to sea

Direction for Questions from 15 to 16:
Match the entries of Column 1 with those of Column 2.

15.

Column 1	Column 2
A. Crop variety improvement	(i) Intercropping
B. Crop production management	(ii) River lift system
C. Crop protection management	(iii) Control of weeds, insects, etc.
D. Irrigation	(iv) Crop rotation
E. Cropping pattern	(v) Hybridization

16.

Column 1	Column 2
A. Finned fish	(i) Estuaries
B. Shell fish	(ii) Canals
C. Fresh water resources	(iii) Prawns
D. Brackish water resources	(iv) Bhetki

Short Answer Type Questions

17. What is the significance of crop rotation in agriculture?

18. Describe the importance of animal husbandry in sustainable agriculture.

19. Name the different methods that are employed in crop variety improvement.

20. What are the different practices that are involved in crop production management?

21. Mention the important objectives of crop variety improvement.

22. What is manure?

23. Distinguish between vermicompost and green manure.

24. We are getting different varieties of rice in the market. All of them resemble each other. Explain.

25. Usage of genetically modified crops has increased to greater extent in recent times. Explain.

26. Replacing chemical fertilizers by organic manure is good for soil more than plants. Explain.

27. What are the advantages of growing wheat with chick pea in mixed cropping?

28. What is the reason behind drying the grains thoroughly after the production?

29. What is cattle farming?

30. What do you mean by animal husbandry and what are its inclusions?

31. What is the breed of chicken which are used only for meat production?

32. What are the different types of fishery?

33. Name the process of capturing fish in the natural resource.

34. What are the different types fish included in marine fishery?

35. Write a short note on composite fish culture?

36. Why is it important to provide balance and sufficient diet for the cattle?

37. Why is it economical to cross-breed Aseel and Leghorn in polutary?

38. What type of food is required by the cattle?

39. What type of combination of fishes are rared in composite fish culture?

Direction for Questions from 40 to 45:
Answer the following questions.

40. What are chemical fertilizers?

41. What is the main use of river lift system?

42. What are the main objectives of crop protection management?

43. What are the different varieties of bees used for honey production?

44. Name the honey bee that is widely used for honey production.

45. Differentiate marine culture from aquaculture.

Essay Type Questions

46. Draw the flow chart involving the different stages of farming and the steps involved in each.

47. Draw a flow chart of different fish production cultures.

48. Identify the type of fish farming which increases the productivity but lacks in pure fish seeding for culture. Also mention its merits.

49. What is the feed required for the following fishes?
    (a) Catlas (b) Rohus
    (c) Mrigals (d) Grass carp

COMPETITION WING

Practice Questions

Level 1: Apply your Concepts

Direction for Questions from 1 to 10:
Fill in the blanks.

1. The crops which are grown from June to October are called ________.

2. ________ refers to the meticulous care, raising, and breeding of animals, and it includes diverse practices from ________ to beekeeping.

3. The process of producing new variety of crops by crossing two genetically different parent crops is known as ________.

4. The modern technique in the field of crop variety improvement is known as ________.

5. The nutrients that are required in large quantities by the plants are known as ________.

6. In _______ cropping, different crops are cultivated at a time.

7. ___________ is a systematic cultivation of different crops in a proper sequence in different seasons on the same land.

8. __________ is the organic matter which is derived from the biological wastes.

9. Indian agricultural sector largely depends upon _____.

10. Cattle can produce milk during __________ period after the birth of a calf.

Direction for Questions from 11 to 17:
For each of the following questions four choices have been provided. Select the correct alternatives.

11. Why might a farmer choose to engage in mixed farming instead of focusing solely on crop cultivation?

(a) To capitalize on the popularity of a single crop.

(b) To ensure continuous and consistent income throughout the year.

(c) Because it requires less land than monoculture.

(d) To minimize water usage.

12. Crop variety improvement primarily aims to:

(a) Increase the size of farmland.

(b) Modify the plants genetically for improved resistance to pests.

(c) Reduce the need for irrigation.

(d) Make crops more colourful for visual appeal.

13. In the context of agriculture, why is understanding the cropping pattern crucial for a region?

(a) It helps in branding and marketing of agricultural products.

(b) It determines which machinery should be imported.

(c) It provides insights into the climate and cultural preferences of the region.

(d) It informs the choice and proportion of crops suitable for optimal yield and sustainable farming.

14. Which statement best illustrates the relationship between manure and soil health?

(a) Manure aerates the soil, making it easier to till.

(b) Manure acts as a pesticide, reducing the need for chemicals.

(c) Manure introduces organic matter, enriching the soil with nutrients.

(d) Manure increases the water-holding capacity of sand.

15. If a farmer wishes to implement a strategy that allows for efficient utilization of resources and also aids in pest control, which method would be most effective?

(a) Crop rotation

(b) Monoculture

(c) Irrigation

(d) Large-scale machinery usage

16. ______ and ______ are examples of shelled fish which come under fish production.

(a) Prawns and molluscs

(b) Mullets and bhetki

(c) Catlas and rohus

(d) Pearl spots and mullets

17. Which among the following is a local Indian breed of cattle?

(a) Jersey (b) Brown Swiss

(c) Red sindhi (d) None of these

Direction for Questions from 18 to 25:
Choose the correct option.

(a) Both A and R are true and R is the correct explanation of A

(b) Both A and R are true, but R is not the correct explanation of A

(c) A is true but R is false

(d) A is false but R is true

18. **Assertion (A):** Paddy is grown in rainy season.
Reason (R): Paddy is a kharif crop.

19. **Assertion (A):** Crop rotation is a part of sustainable agricultural practice.
Reason (R): Crop rotation helps in maintaining the soil fertility.

20. **Assertion (A):** Intercropping increases the productivity of an agricultural land.
Reason (R): Same fertilizers and pesticides can be used for different variety of crops.

21. **Assertion (A):** River lift system is more economical than canal system for irrigation.
Reason (R): In river lift system, a pump is used to lift the water from river.

22. **Assertion (A):** Cross breeding of dairy animals increases the productivity of milk.
Reason (R): Lactation period of dairy animals can be increased by cross breeding.

33. **Assertion (A):** Composite fish culture involves the cultivation of different varieties of fish having same feeding habits.
Reason (R): Different varieties of fish utilize different areas of the same pond for their feed.

24. **Assertion (A):** Protein and fat-rich food should be provided to broiler chicken.
Reason (R): Broiler chicken is grown to provide eggs of good quality.

25. **Assertion (A):** Integrated farming is a part of sustainable agricultural practices.
Reason (R): Sometimes fish is cultured in the paddy field along with the cultivation of rice crop.

Direction for Questions from 26 to 30:
Write the missing corelated terms.

26. Crop Rotation: Cultivation:: Crop Variety Improvement: ________.

27. Mixed Farming: Livestock:: Crop Variety Improvement: ________.

28. Manure: Soil Nutrition:: Irrigation: ________.

29. Crop Production Management: Best Yield:: Cropping Pattern: ________.

30. Animal husbandary : poultry farming :: ________ : Marine fishery.

Direction for Questions from 31 to 35:
Correct the following statements.

31. The new varieties of plants that are produced by plant breeding are not resistant to diseases.

32. Nutrient management to plants comes under crop protection management.

33. Mixed cropping results in crop failure by producing different crops at a time.

34. Genetically modified crops give less yield.

35. Culture fishery in fresh water is known as composite culture.

Level 2: Review your Concepts

36. National office of animal health works to provide the farmers with different range of vaccines to protect the health and welfare of their cattle. Why is it necessary to give vaccine to cattle?

37. Ramesh found that there is difference in production of milk by their cow and the dairy cow. What could be the reason behind this?

38. People in Indonesia practice Paddy fish culture to a greater extent. Explain its advantages.

39. Honey plays a major role in many of ayurvedic medicines. How is it produced?

40. How does animal husbandry complement crop cultivation in the broader spectrum of sustainable agricultural practices?

Level 3: Assess Your Concepts

41. Given the challenges posed by climate change, urbanization, and population growth, how can practices like mixed farming, intercropping, and integrated farming be amalgamated to create a robust framework for sustainable agriculture in densely populated countries with limited cultivable land?

42. Poultry feed should be rich in vitamin E. Give reason.

43. Oilcakes are used as the food for cattles. Why?

AT

NEET SPECIAL WING

Practice Questions

Multiple-Answer Type Questions

Questions number 1 to 5 are multiple-choice questions. Each question has FOUR options (a), (b), (c), and (d). ONE OR MORE THAN ONE of these four option(s) is/are the correct answer(s).

1. Fe, Mn, Zn and Ni are examples of:
   (a) Micronutrients
   (b) Macronutrients
   (c) Both micro and macronutrients
   (d) Essential nutrients

2. Examples of marine fishes include:
   (a) Mullets (b) Prawns
   (c) Mussels (d) Rohu

3. Raising of which kinds of animals is included in the poultry farming?
   (a) Chicken (b) Turkey
   (c) Duck (d) Goose

4. Which of the following are examples of chemical fertilizer?
   (a) Compost
   (b) Urea
   (c) Potassium nitrate
   (d) Ammonium phosphate

5. Which of the following fish are bottom feeders?
   (a) Rohu (b) Catla
   (c) Common carp (d) Mrigals

Comprehension-Based Questions

A. Read the paragraph given below and answer the questions number 6 to 11:

Animal husbandry is the art and science of raising , caring and breeding of livestock. This category involves animals like buffaloes, cows, pigs, horses, cattle, sheep, camels, goats, etc. These animals not only provide meat and eggs but also physical labour. Animal husbandry includes practices such as cattle farming, poultry farming, fish production and bee keeping. Cattle farming involves rearing of milch animals which provide milk or animals which provide physical labour and are called draught animals. Poultry farming is the practice of raising domestic fowls, such as chicken, turkeys, ducks and goose for meat and eggs. An egg-laying poultry is called layer and the poultry reared for obtaining meat is called broiler. Fish production involves the process of rearing fish in water bodies for the consumption of human being. Salt water fishery and fresh water fishery are the two types of fisheries. Bee keeping is the maintenance of hives of honey bees for the production of honey.

6. Worker bees have wax glands
   (a) to make their appendages smooth
   (b) to build cells of comb
   (c) Both a and b
   (d) None of the above

7. Localities where bee hives and honey bees are reared are called as:
   (a) Apiculture (b) Apiaries
   (c) Sericulture (d) Silviculture

8. Broiler chicken are fed:
   (a) Vitamins and minerals
   (b) Proteins and vitamins
   (c) Carbohydrates and proteins
   (d) Carbohydrates and fats

9. A viral disease in cattle which causes blisters on the hand and mouth:
   (a) Anthrax
   (b) Foot and mouth disease
   (c) Rinderpest
   (d) Tuberculosis

10. Milk productivity can be increased by:
   (a) cross breeding
   (b) nutritious diet
   (c) increasing roughage
   (d) exposure to vaccination

11. Match the following:

Column – A	Column – B
(i) Farming of compatible species of fishes	(a) Catlas
(ii) *Apis cerana indica*	(b) Mrigals and common carps
(iii) *Apis dorsata*	(c) Indian bee
(iv) Bottom feeders	(d) Composite fish culture
(v) Surface feeders	(e) Rock bee

B. Read the paragraph given below and answer the questions number 12 to 17:

Implementation of sustainable agriculture and also bringing about an improvement in agricultural productivity go hand in hand. This involves three major stages. The first stage includes crop variety improvement. It involves genetically modifying plants for better yield. This can be done by either hybridization or genetic engineering. The next step is crop production management which regulates the areas of crop production. This involves nutrient management, irrigation, using different cropping patterns and also crop rotation methods to meet optimum crop nutrient requirements. The last step includes crop protection management which endeavours to protect the crops from a host of different things like weeds, insects, pests and diseases.

12. Which of the following is not an advantage of mixed cropping?
   (a) Pest infestation is minimized
   (b) More than one variety of crop can be harvested at the same time
   (c) Both the crops have same maturation time and can be harvested together
   (d) Soil is optimally utilized

13. The correct order of steps for genetic engineering process in plants include:
   (a) Insertion of desired gene into plant, Isolation of targeted gene, study of seeds from mature plants, plants with new traits
   (b) Isolation of targeted gene, Insertion of desired gene into plant, plants with new traits, study of seeds from mature plants
   (c) Plants with new traits, Isolation of targeted gene, Insertion of desired gene into plant, study of seeds from mature plants
   (d) Study of seeds from mature plants, Plants with new traits, Isolation of targeted gene, Insertion of desired gene into plant

14. Which among the following is a complex fertilizer?
   (a) Ammonium sulphate
   (b) Single superphosphate
   (c) Muriate of potash
   (d) Urea ammonium phosphate

15. Which among the following are examples of inter-cropping system?
   (a) Wheat and gram
   (b) Rice and leguminous plants
   (c) Planting soya bean with maize and finger millet
   (d) Wheat and mustard

16. Millet prevent the growth of weeds, earning the name of:
   (a) Nitrogenous crops
   (b) Smoother crops
   (c) Cultural crops
   (d) Chemical weedicide

17. Match the following:

Column – A	Column – B
(i) Biotic factor for loss of grains	(a) Kill insect pests
(ii) Intercropping	(b) Rodents, fungi, mites
(iii) Fumigants	(c) Biofertilizer
(iv) Mycorrhiza	(d) Pump
(v) River lift irrigation	(e) Cropping pattern

Answer Keys

Crossword

Across

6. Riverlift system 7. Inter 9. Croprotation 10. Mixed cropping
12. Genetic engineering 14. Rinderpest 15. Mariculture 16. Macronutrients
19. Broiler 20. Poultry farming

Down

1. Intervarietal Hybridization 2. Sustainable agriculture 3. Composite fish culture
4. Plantation 5. Round 8. Weeds 11. Zaid 13. Inter-cropping
17. Manure 18. Kharif

Classroom Wing

Very Short Answer Type Questions

1. High 2. Mixed farming 3. A better yield 4. Crop rotation
5. Poultry farming 6. Parasites 7. (b) 8. (c) 9. (c)
10. (c) 11. (c) 12. (a) 13. (a) 14. (a)
15. A → (v), B → (iv), C → (iii), D → (ii), E → (i) 16. A → (iv), B → (iii), C → (ii), D → (i).

Competition Wing

Level 1: Apply your Concepts

1. Kharif crops 2. Animal husbandry, poultry farming 3. Hybridization
4. Genetic engineering 5. Major nutrients 6. Mixed 7. Crop rotation
8. Manure 9. Monsoon rains 10. Lactation period 11. (b) 12. (b)
13. (d) 14. (c) 15. (a) 16. (a) 17. (c)
18. (b) 19. (a) 20. (c) 21. (d) 22. (a)
23. (d) 24. (c) 25. (b) 26. Genetic 27. Genetic
28. Water 29. Optimal Land Use 30. Fish production

NEET Special Wing

Multiple-Answer Type Questions

1. (a, d) 2. (a, b, c) 3. (a, b, c, d) 4. (b, c, d) 5. (c, d)

Comprehension-Based Questions

6. (b) 7. (b) 8. (b) 9. (b) 10. (a)

11. (i) → (d); (ii) → (c); (iii) → (e); (iv) → (b); (v) → (a)

12. (c) 13. (b) 14. (d) 15. (c) 16. (b)

17. (i) → (b); (ii) → (e); (iii) → (a); (iv) → (c); (v) → (d)

Hints and Explanations

CLASSROOM WING

Very Short Answer Type Questions

7. India's large population and limited cultivable land which necessitates sustainable management.
8. The aim of crop variety improvement.
9. The manure comes from biological wastes including animal faeces and plant wastes.
10. Irrigation as the supply of a controlled amount of water to plants.
11. The crop production management regulates various areas of production to obtain the best yield.
12. Crop rotation involves planting different crops in succession to balance the nutrients absorbed and replenished in the soil.

Short Answer Type Questions

17. Crop rotation is significant because it helps maintain soil fertility, reduces soil erosion, and helps in the control of pests and diseases. Rotating crops prevents the depletion of soil nutrients and breaks the life cycles of certain pests and diseases.
18. Animal husbandry plays a crucial role in sustainable agriculture by providing a continuous supply of organic manure, aiding in soil fertility, and ensuring a balanced ecosystem. Proper care and breeding of livestock also ensure a steady supply of food products and contribute to the overall economy.
19. There are two methods that are employed in crop variety improvement method, they are,
    (a) Hybridization
    (b) Genetic engineering
20. Following are the different practices that are involved in the crop production management:
    (a) Nutrient management
    (b) Irrigation
    (c) Cropping patterns
    (d) Crop rotation.
21. The major objectives of crop variety improvement are as follows.
    (a) Increasing the yield of plant products
    (b) Improving the quality of food crops
    (c) Producing biotic- and abiotic-resistant varieties
    (d) Changing the duration of maturity
    (e) Wide range of adaptability
    (f) Imparting desirable characteristics to crops.
22. Manure is the organic matter that is derived from the biological wastes which replenishes the nutrients in the soil and thus renders the soil fertility.
23.

Vermicompost	Green manure
The organic manure which is rich in nutrients and obtained by the decomposition of the organic mass with the help earthworms is known as vermicompost	When plants such as Sun hemp and Gaur are grown and ploughed to mix with the soil, they transform into green manure due to the process of decomposition and enrich the soil with organic matter, nitrogen and phosphorus.

24. The different varieties of rice which are found in the market are result of hybridization.

    They are different from each other on the basis of characteristics as they are hybrids formed from different genes.
25. Genetically modified crops are the ones with slight modification in their DNA using genetic engineering methods. Due to these slight modifications, they become resistant to pests, diseases or environmental conditions and finally give a better yield. Due to all these reasons, usage of genetically modified crops has increased to a larger extent.
26. Chemical fertilizers give required nutrients in correct proportion and help in the growth of the plants. But they increase the pH of the soil and make it alkaline in nature and lose its lustre.

    Whereas the organic manure helps maintain the soil fertility and is biodegradable but it breaks down according to nature's rule and releases the nutrients slowly, the nutrients ratio is also unknown. Hence, using organic manure helps to maintain soil health in long run.

27. Following are the advantages of growing wheat with chick pea in mixed cropping.
    (a) Growing leguminous plants like chick pea increases the nitrogen content which can be taken by the cereal plants.
    (b) Increase in high yield.
    (c) Variety of produce which is obtained in a single crop.
    (d) No risk of crop failure.
28. Cleaning of grains thoroughly and drying them in sunlight after that in shade is very important because there are certain factors like biotic and abiotic which result in loss of grains.

    Biotic factors are insects, rodents, fungi mites, etc.

    Abiotic factors are moisture and temperature.
29. Cattle farming is rearing of two types of animalslike:
    (a) One category of animals provide milk and they are called milch or dairy animals.
    (b) Other category of animals are used as labour and are called draught animals.
30. Animal husbandry includes proper care, raising and breeding of live stock. It includes the following:
    - Cattle farming
    - Poultry farming
    - Egg and broiler production
    - Fish production
    - Bee Keeping
31. Broiler chicken is the only breed which is used only for the production of meat.
32. There are two types of fishery listed as follows:
    (a) Saltwater fishery which is also called marine fishery.
    (b) Fresh water fishery is called inland fishery.
33. The process of capturing the fish in the natural resource is known as fish capturing.
34. There are two types of fishes that are included in marine fishery. They are as follows:
    (a) Finned fish like mullets, bhetki and pearl spots.
    (b) Shellfish like prawns, mussels, oyster, seaweed, etc.
35. Composite fish culture: It is farming of different types of fishes of compatible nature having different feeding habits, at the same period. It increases the productivity. Combination of different fishes like rohu, catla, mrigal common carps and grass carps are reared in the same pond. The major problem here is the lack of pure fish seed for culturing. They do not compete for food as different parts of the pond are utilized for their feed. As most of the fish breed in monsoon, segregating the seed of different species becomes difficult.
36. Dairy cattle require feed for growth and milk production. It is important to provide a balanced and sufficient diet to the cattle for the production of milk of optimal quantity and good quality.
37. The hybrid produced by cross breeding Aseel and Leghorn is very economical due to the following reasons:
    - Increased production of eggs
    - It is dwarf and requires less space and food.
    - They are tolerant to high temperature.
    - Requires low maintenance.
    - Fibrous cheaper diets formulated from agricultural by-products can be utilized.
38. Dairy cattle require feed for its growth and milk production.

    We need to provide balanced and sufficient diet to the cattle for the production of optimal quantity and quality of milk.

    Cattle require two types of food such as roughages, rich in fibre and concentrates, also rice rich in proteins but low in fibre. They also need oil cakes, micronutrients and water in sufficient quantity.
39. Different types of fish with compatible species having different feeding habits are cultured in a same pond. They do not compete for food since different parts of pond are utilized for their feed. This also increases the productivity.
40. Chemical fertilizers are the different chemical compounds added to the soil for the replenishment of certain nutrients like phosphorus, nitrogen and potassium.

    They help in the productivity by the continuous release of the nutrients.
41. River lift system is used in the places where canal irrigation is not possible. In this method water is directly drawn from the river with the help of a pump and used for irrigation.
42. The main objectives of crop protection management are:

    (i) Control of weeds, insects and diseases

    (ii) Proper storage of grains

43. There are varieties of bees used for commercial honey production are:

(i) *Apis ceranaindica* (Indian bee)

(ii) *Apis dorsata* (rock bee)

(iii) *Apis florae* (little bee)

44. An Italian bee variety-*Apis mellifera* is widely used for honey production because of its high capacity.

45.

Marine culture	Aquaculture
To culture fishery in marine water is called mariculture.	To culture fishery in fresh water is called aquaculture.

Essay Type Questions

46.

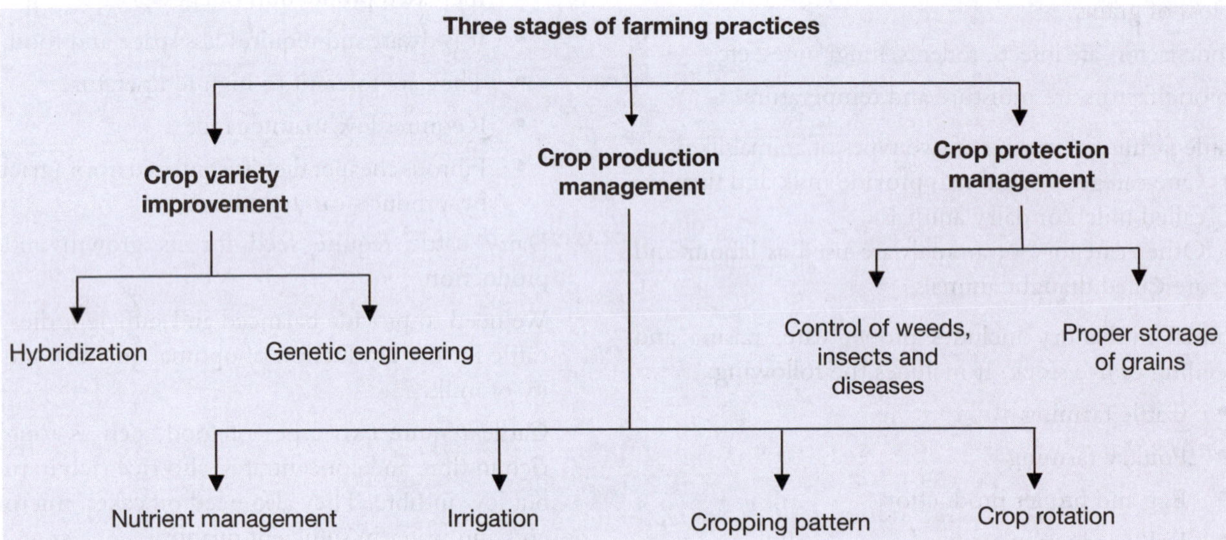

47.

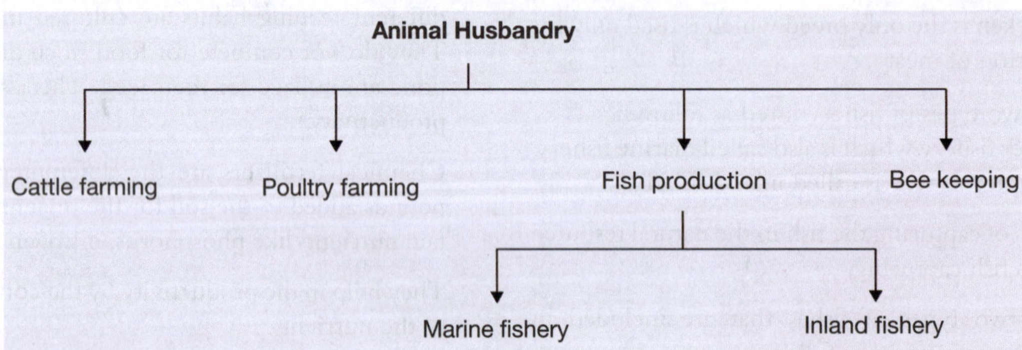

48. Composite fish culture is the farming with increase of productivity due to the following reasons:

- In this type of fishing, different types of fishes of compatible species having different feeding habits are reared in the same pond.
- They do not compete for food as different parts of the pond are utilized for their feed.
- Most of the fish breed in monsoon
- Major problem is the lack of pure fish.

49. Feed for different fish are:

(a) Catlas are surface feeders.

(b) Rohus feed in the middle zone of the pond.

(c) Mrigals are bottom feeders.

(d) Grass craps feed on weeds.

COMPETITION WING

Level 1: Apply your Concepts

11. Mixed farming, which involves the cultivation of crops and the rearing of livestock, can offer diversified sources of income. This can be especially beneficial in mitigating risks associated with crop failure or market fluctuations, ensuring more consistent revenue.

    Hence, the correct option is (b).

12. Crop variety improvement involves genetic modifications to achieve various goals such as higher yields, better resistance to pests and diseases, and improved nutritional content. While increased pest resistance is a primary goal, other benefits may also be sought.

    Hence, the correct option is (b).

13. Cropping patterns are influenced by and give insights into factors like climate, availability of water, and soil nutrients. By understanding this, farmers can select crops that are best suited for the region, maximizing yield while promoting sustainability.

    Hence, the correct option is (d).

14. Manure, being derived from biological wastes like animal faeces and plant residues, is rich in organic matter. When added to soil, it provides essential nutrients that promote plant growth and improve soil health.

    Hence, the correct option is (c).

15. Crop rotation, the practice of growing different crops in succession on the same land, not only ensures that the soil isn't continuously depleted of specific nutrients but can also naturally interrupt the life cycle of pests and diseases, thereby aiding in their control.

    Hence, the correct option is (a).

16. Prawns and molluscs are examples of shelled fishes which come under fish production.

    Hence, the correct option is (a).

17. Red sindhi is a local Indian breed.

    Hence, the correct option is (c).

18. Paddy is a called a kharif crop since it gets cultivated in rainy season. Paddy is cultivated in rainy season because its growth requires retention of water.

    Hence, the correct option is (b).

19. Crop rotation helps in the retention of the nutrient in the soil and thus this process maintains the fertility of the soil. Hence, it reduces the use of chemical fertilizer and becomes a sustainable agricultural practice.

    Hence, the correct option is (a).

20. Intercropping increases the productivity of the soil since same area can be utilized for growing different crops. Different varieties of crops do not compete for food since their requirements for nutrients are different. Different fertilizers and pesticides are used for different varieties.

    Hence, the correct option is (c).

21. In canal irrigation system, water flows to agricultural land due to gravity. But in river lift system electrical energy is used to lift the water from river. Hence, canal irrigation system is more economic than river lift system.

    Hence, the correct option is (d).

22. Cross breeding increases the lactation period of a dairy animal and thus the productivity of milk increases.

    Hence, the correct option is (a).

23. Composite fish culture is the cultivation of different variety of fish, having different feed habits, in the same pond. Different areas of a pond provide different types of food.

    Hence, the correct option is (d).

24. Broiler chicken requires protein and fat rich food for their fast growth rate. They are only used for meat, not for laying eggs.

    Hence, the correct option is (c).

25. Culture of fish in the paddy field is an example of integrated farming and integrated farming is a sustainable agricultural practice since different types of waste materials can be utilized here.

    Hence, the correct option is (b).

26. Just as crop rotation deals with the cultivation practice of rotating crops, crop variety improvement deals with genetic modifications.

27. As mixed farming relates to the incorporation of livestock in cultivation, crop variety improvement pertains to genetic modifications in crops.

28. Just as manure enriches the soil with nutrients, irrigation ensures that plants get the required water.

29. While crop production management aims at obtaining the best yield, cropping patterns focus on using land most effectively based on various factors.

30. Animal husbandry : poultry farming :: Fish production: Marine fishery.

31. The new varieties of plants that are produced by plant breeding are highly resistant to diseases.

32. Nutrient management to plants comes under crop production management.

33. Mixed cropping reduces the risk of crop failure gives a better yield.

34. Due to the improvement in the genes the genetically modified crops result in high yield and are disease resistant.

35. Culture fishery in fresh water is known as aqua culture.

Level 2: Review your Concepts

36. When the cattle are prone to different diseases, it hinders the production of milk and also leads to death at times. Cattle are affected by both internal and external parasites. Internal parasites cause skin disease and external parasites like worms affect the stomach and flukes affect the liver. Hence, giving vaccine in proper time can help protect the cattle.

37. Ramesh's cow is the Indian breed with less lactation period and productivity of milk, whereas the dairy cows are cross-bred with increased productivity of milk.

38. Paddy fish culture has the following advantages:
    - Increase in organic fertilization by fish excreta.
    - Reduction of the harmful insects, whose larvae are eaten by fish.
    - Reduction in rat population due to increased water level.
    - Increase in the productivity of the rice.
    - Control of weeds and increase in aeration of the soil.

    Due to all these advantages paddy fish culture is practiced to a greater extent in Indonesia.

39. Honey is rich in nutrients and finds its application in medicines. Bee keeping is the process of maintaining hives of honey bees for the production of honey. It is practiced in the areas where sufficient pastures having wild shrubs, fruit orchards and cultivated crops are grown.

40. Animal husbandry provides organic manure, aids in pest control, and ensures soil fertility through rotational grazing. It complements crop cultivation by creating a symbiotic cycle where crops benefit livestock through fodder, and animals aid crops through manure and natural tilling, fostering a balanced and sustainable ecosystem.

Level 3: Assess Your Concepts

41. In the face of mounting challenges, an integrated approach is paramount. Mixed farming can ensure food diversity and soil enrichment through animal waste. Intercropping can optimize land use by allowing crops with different nutrient needs to grow simultaneously, promoting soil health. Integrated farming, which combines various practices, can ensure resource optimization, waste reduction, and symbiotic growth. By amalgamating these practices, a sustainable model can be established that not only addresses food security but also promotes biodiversity, soil health, and economic stability. Such a framework would be adaptive to changing climatic conditions, resilient to pests and diseases, and efficient in resource utilization, meeting the demands of densely populated regions with constrained agricultural land.

42. Vitamin E is required for growth and reproduction of poultry fowls. It helps maintain the integrity of the structural tissue. It supports development of the nervous system and contributes to disease resistance. Furthermore, it enhances the nutritional value of meat and eggs.

43. Oilcakes are the residual part of oil seeds after the extraction of the oil. Oilcakes are rich in protein and hence, are used as the food for cattle. Proteinaceous food helps in the growth of the cattle. Other than protein, they are the good source of calcium and vitamin B_{12} and thus, help in the improvement of the quality of milk. Vitamin B_{12} is required for cell growth, maturation and wool growth.

NEET SPECIAL WING

Multiple-Answer Type Questions

1. Plants require certain nutrients that are needed for growth and development. Seventeen of these nutrients are classified as essential ones. In the absence of any of these nutrients, a plant is unable to complete its life cycle. Nutrients like Fe, Mn, Zn, Cu, Mo, Cl and Ni are required in relatively smaller amounts (but essential for the plant). They are called micronutrients.

2. Fish farming or culture fishery in marine water includes rearing of two types of fish, namely- Finned fish like mullets, bhetki and pearl spots. Also, shellfish like prawns, mussels, oyster and seaweed.

3. Poultry farming is the practice of raising domestic fowls, such as chicken, turkeys, ducks and goose for meat and eggs.

4. Chemical fertilizers are different chemical compounds added to the soil for the replenishment of certain nutrients like phosphorous, nitrogen and potassium which include urea, potassium nitrate and ammonium phosphate.

5. Composite fish culture is farming of different types of fish of compatible species having different feeding habits, in the same pond. This kind of farming of fish increases the productivity. A combination of 5–6 species, such rohu, Catla, mrigal, common carps and grass carps are reared in the same pond. Mrigals and common carps are bottom feeders.

Comprehension-Based Questions

A.

6. Honey bees exist in several morphological forms called castes. Hence, bees are said to polymorphic species. One of them is a worker bee which is a sterile female and is the smallest in size. They are the most active members of the colony. They have wax glands which help them to build cells of comb.

7. Bee keeping can be practiced in any area where sufficient pastures having wild shrubs, fruit orchards and cultivated crops are there. The localities where beehives and honey bees are reared are bee farms or apiaries.

8. Broiler chicken requires large, dry, clean and hygienic places for their fast growth. Appropriate temperature of their shelter is required to be maintained. Broiler chicken requires protein and vitamin-rich feed for maintaining its carcass quality.

9. Foot and mouth disease is highly contagious and is caused by a virus. Blisters appear on the mouth and feet of the affected animal.

10. Lactation period of a local breed such as Red Sindhi, Sahiwal, etc., can be increased by cross breeding them with an exotic or foreign breed, such as Jersey or Brown Swiss. Thus, the productivity of milk and dairy products can be increased by cross breeding.

11. Match the following:

    Composite fish culture is farming of different types of fish of compatible species having different feeding habits, in the same pond.
    (i) (d)

    Apis cerana indica is an Indian bee.
    (ii) (c)

    Apis dorsata is commonly known as rock bee.
    (iii) (e)

    Mrigals and common carps are the bottom feeders in a composite fish farming method.
    (iv) (b)

    Catlas are the surface feeders in a composite fish farming method.
    (v) (a)

B.

12. In mixed cropping, different crops are cultivated simultaneously on the same piece of land. In this cropping system, no particular pattern is followed for sowing the seeds. This cropping pattern minimizes the risk of crop failure. One of the crops should mature early and the another should mature late, this is the basic criteria for selecting crops for this cropping pattern.

13. The correct order for genetic engineering process in plants starts with the isolation of targeted gene. This gene is then inserted into plant to get plants with new traits. In the end the seeds acquired from mature plants are studied in details.

14. Complex fertilizers supply two or more nutrients. For example, urea ammonium phosphate.

15. In intercropping system, different crops are grown on the same land following a specific pattern. Planting soya bean with maize and finger millet with cow pea are examples of intercropping systems.

16. Some insects or other organisms are put into the field which selectively destroy weed plants without harming the plants. For example, millet does not allow growth of weeds. Such crop plants are known as smoother crops.

17. Match the following:

Fungi, mites and rodents are biotic factors for loss of grains.
(i) (b)

Intercropping system is a type of cropping pattern in which different crops are grown on the same land following a specific pattern. Crops are selected in such a way that their nutrient requirements are different.
(ii) (e)

Fumigants are pesticide solution converted into fumes which can be used to kill insect pests. Before storing the grains, storehouses should be fumigated using suitable pesticides.
(iii) (a)

Mycorrhiza is a type of commonly used biofertilizer.
(iv) (c)

In river lift system, water is directly drawn from the river with the help of a pump and used for irrigation. This method is adopted in those areas where canal irrigation is not possible.
(v) (d)

CHAPTER

7

Natural Resources

Key Ideas

After completing this chapter, you should be able to:

- Define ecosystem and appreciate the interrelationships among the various living organisms and their environment.
- Classify the different types of natural resources on the basis of their need, availability and sustainability.
- Discuss the causes of water, soil and air pollution and the ways to prevent it with examples.
- Explain biogeochemical cycles with diagram and articulate what will happen if these are disrupted.
- Explain the consequence of ozone depletion and global warming.

Remember

Before beginning this chapter, you should be able to:

- Define interrelationship among various living organisms and their environment
- Define the importance of biodiversity
- List the different layers of earth
- List the difference between biotic and abiotic resources
- Define the importance of atmosphere in our lives

Scientific Crypt

A Tribute to Benjamin Peary Pal (1894–1989)

A renowned Indian botanist and plant breeder, was instrumental in transforming agricultural practices and ensuring food security in post-colonial India. Pal dedicated his life as the founding Director of the Indian Agricultural Research Institute to developing resilient, high-yielding wheat varieties, a staple in Indian cuisine. These innovations played a critical role in alleviating widespread famine and resource scarcity, having a significant impact on agrarian landscapes and livelihoods.

Pal's insights aided in a better understanding of the harmonious interplay between flora and nature's abundant resources, resulting in the sustainable utilization and conservation of these vital assets.

Pal received the prestigious Shanti Swarup Bhatnagar Award in 1958 for his outstanding contributions to agricultural science. His monumental work continues to reverberate in agricultural science, paving the way for future generations to tread and explore. His profound respect for nature and commitment to responsibly harnessing its riches have made him a beacon in the study and management of natural resources.

Crossword

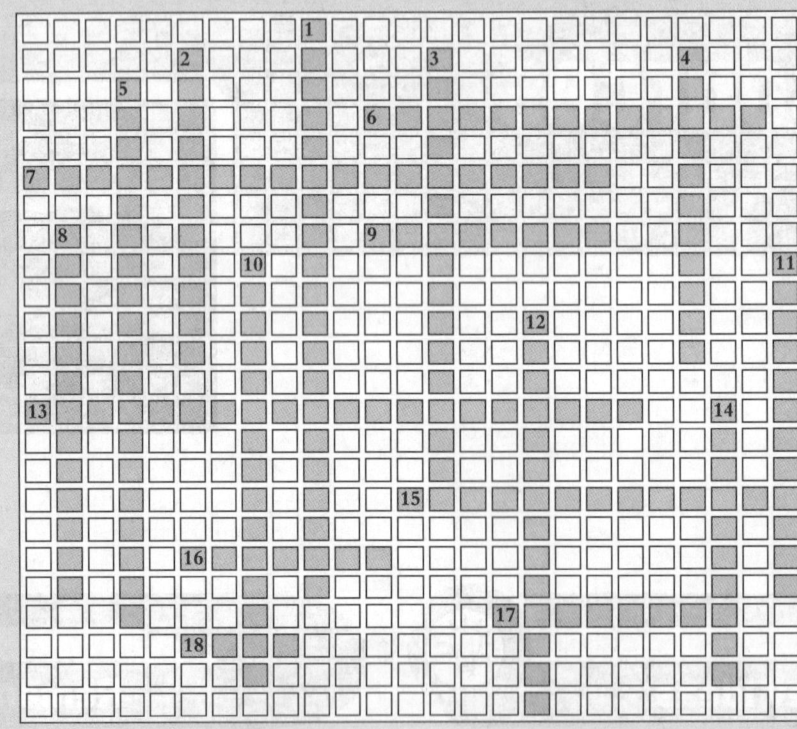

Across

6. The phenomenon of a rise in temperatures due to greenhouse gases
7. Depletion of the ozone layer is caused by
9. Disease caused due to high amounts of mercury in fishes
13. Formation of soil via lichens
15. Natural resources that do not get depleted
16. Soil particles measuring greater than 2 mm
17. Disease caused due to consumption of high amounts of cadmium
18. Dark brown haze produced due to the action of UV rays

Down

1. The constant interaction between both biotic and abiotic components of the biosphere to establish a stable ecosystem
2. Outermost layer of the earth
3. Phenomenon in which organisms at the higher levels of the food chain have higher levels of harmful chemicals
4. Term that represents the vertical section of the crust of the Earth
5. Example of a secondary pollutant
8. Process of conversion of ammonium ions into nitrates
10. Term used for storage of pollutants in the body tissues of humans and animals (fats, kidney, bone, etc.) at a higher concentration than found in the environment
11. Process of soil formation
12. Death of marine animals because of lack of oxygen due to increased organic wastes
14. Process that uses oxygen and releases carbon dioxide

INTRODUCTION

Earth is the only planet where life exists. Everything that encompasses us acting as a life support system is termed as environment. It is the environment that provides us food to eat, air to breathe, water to drink, and fulfil our daily requirements to survive on earth. Life on earth is dependent on a variety of factors, such as ambient temperature, water and food. The resources available on earth and the energy from the sun are the basic needs for survival of life forms on earth. Biodiversity which is the 'Natural Biotic Capital' of the earth is the basic component and life on the planet earth will not continue if we lose this biodiversity. Biodiversity can be regarded as a life insurance for the life itself. Sadly, the human activities have substantially affected the biodiversity by attacking it. The disintegration and degradation of habitats across the globe is resulting in serious loss of biodiversity. There is no possibility of reversing these losses because many of the species have become extinct. India is a mega-diverse country having rich biodiversity and related traditional knowledge.

Resources on the Earth

Living organisms are constantly exploiting the environment or the resources available to them in the environment to sustain their lives and make it more comfortable and meaningful. The various types of ecosystem that may be found in a particular region constitute a biome and several biomes on earth constitute the biosphere. Biosphere refers to the region of earth's crust and atmosphere, which is occupied by the living organisms. It is broadly classified into three physical divisions as follows (Fig. 7.1).

1. **Lithosphere (land):** It refers to the outermost layer of the earth's crust. It is the topmost weathered part, that leads to soil formation.
2. **Hydrosphere (water):** It refers to the water component of the earth. Water covers 75% of the earth's surface.
3. **Atmosphere (air):** It refers to the multi-layered envelope of gases that surrounds the entire earth.

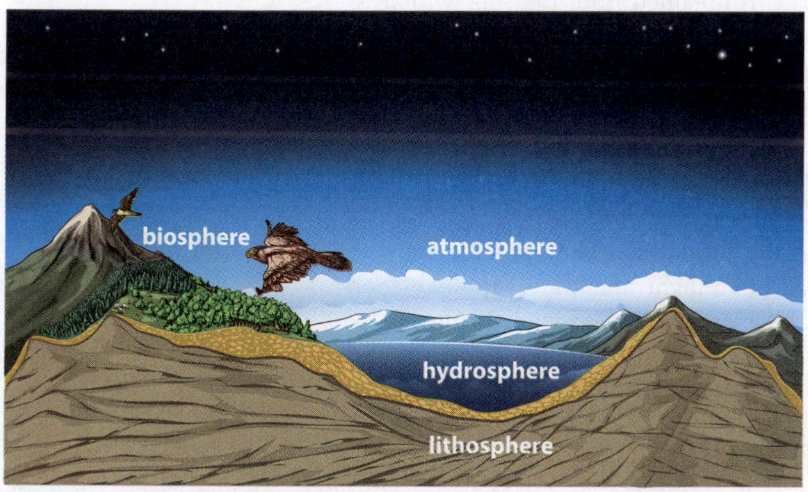

Figure 7.1 Physical divisions of biosphere

Info Bytes!

Only about 2.5% of Earth's water is freshwater, but less than 1% of that is easily accessible to us as it's locked away in glaciers, polar ice caps, atmosphere, and soil.

Info Bytes!

Natural resources are also referred to as earth resources as they are obtained only from the earth.

Types of Natural Resources

The term natural resources is used for all living and non-living components of nature used by humans to fulfil their daily requirements. Natural resources can be divided into two categories (Fig. 7.2).

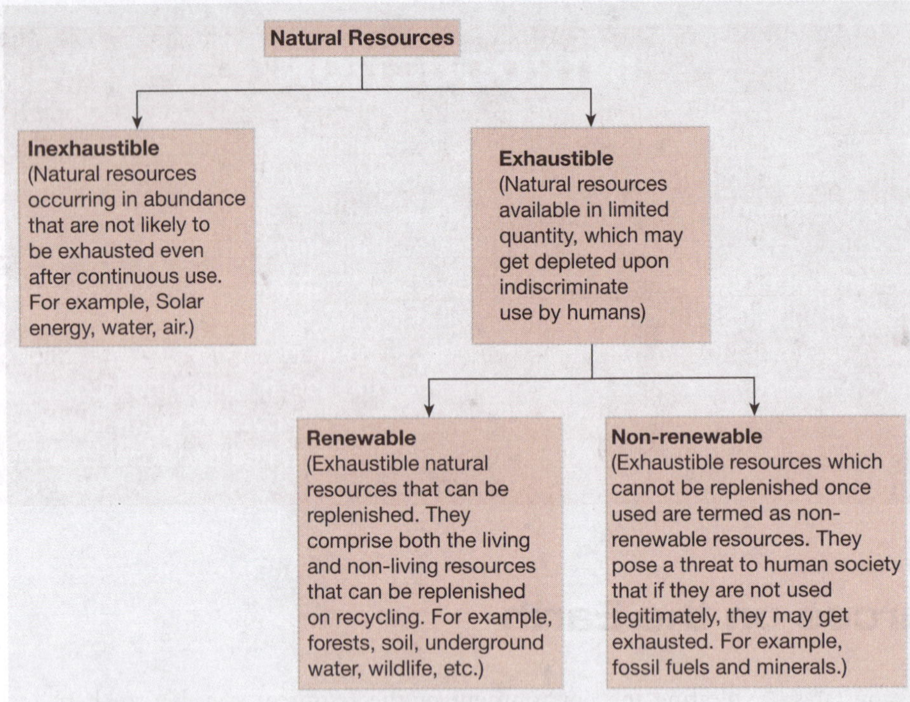

Figure 7.2 Flowchart depicting divisions of natural resources

Components of Biosphere

There are two types of components, namely biotic and abiotic. The **biotic** component constitutes all the living beings. The **abiotic** or non-living component of the biosphere constitutes the air, water and soil (land).

Both the components are essential to meet the basic needs of all the life forms. The energy required to support these life forms is obtained from the sun, which is further used to synthesize food for all living beings. All the abiotic components of the environment form the weather and climate of a particular area.

Konnect

The term '***biosphere***' was coined by the geologist Eduard Suess, in the year 1875. Thus, the concept indicates a geological origin. Evidence was found in the Western Australia revealing the discovery of microbial mat fossils that led the scientists to estimate that the evolution of earth dates back to around 3.48 billion years ago.

Biotic Resources

These include all the living organisms including human beings. It includes producers (green plants, autotrophs) and **consumers** (animals, some bacteria, fungi, viruses).

1. **Plants:** Green plants are referred to as the producers. They provide food to all living beings. Plants in the presence of sunlight and water produce food through a process known as photosynthesis and release oxygen. Plants are of great significance due to the fact that they release oxygen. Therefore, researchers have claimed that 'plants can survive without animals, but survival of animals without plants is difficult'.
2. **Animals:** They are an important constituent of the biotic resources holding an unbreakable relationship with the plants. They are dependent on plants for their survival.

Konnect

The short-term changes in the properties of troposphere, i.e., change in temperature, rain, biometric pressure, humidity and precipitation is termed as **weather**.

The average weather of a particular area, which represents a general pattern of atmospheric weather including extreme and seasonal variations of a particular region over long period of time is termed as **climate**.

Abiotic Resources

Abiotic factors are the non-living parts of the environment that can often have a major influence on living organisms. Abiotic factors include water, sunlight, oxygen, soil and temperature.

1. **Water:** An important abiotic factor – it is often said that 'water is life'. All living organisms need water. Plants must have water to grow. Even plants that live in the desert need a little bit of water to grow. Without water, animals become weak and confused, and they can die if they do not rehydrate.
2. **Sunlight:** The main source of energy on Earth, which makes it an extremely important abiotic factor. Sunlight is necessary for photosynthesis, the process by which plants convert carbon dioxide (CO_2) and water to oxygen (O_2) and sugar – food for the plants that later becomes food for animals.
3. **Oxygen:** Oxygen is another important abiotic factor for many living organisms. Without oxygen, humans would not be able to live. This is true for the many other living organisms that use oxygen. Oxygen is produced by green plants through the process of photosynthesis, and is therefore, directly linked to sunlight.
4. **Soil:** Considered an abiotic factor since it is mostly made up of small particles of rock (sand and clay) mixed with decomposed plants and animals. Plants use their roots to get water and nutrients from the soil.
5. **Temperature:** An abiotic factor that is strongly influenced by sunlight. Temperature plays an important role for animals that cannot regulate their own body temperature, such as reptiles.

The Breath of Life: Air

Air is a mixture of various gases along with water vapour and suspended particles. It contains oxygen, carbon dioxide, nitrogen, water vapour, suspended particles and other gases like argon in minute quantities (Fig. 7.3).

Living beings require oxygen for the breakdown of glucose molecules to produce energy, which leads to the formation of carbon dioxide (Table 7.1). **Combustion** is another process that utilizes oxygen and results in the release of carbon dioxide.

Info Bytes!

The composition of air is the resultant of presence of life on earth.

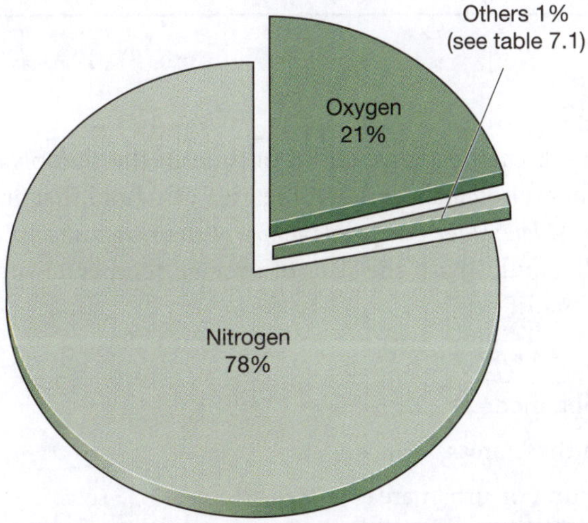

Figure 7.3 Composition of gases in ambient environment

Info Bytes!

The Amazon Rainforest, known as the 'lungs of the Earth,' produces 20% of the world's oxygen.

Table 7.1 Composition of gases in the air

Components of Air	Volume of Gas (%)
Nitrogen (N_2)	78.09
Oxygen (O_2)	20.93
Argon (Ar)	0.93
Carbon dioxide (CO_2)	0.03
Miscellaneous (moisture, dust particles, etc.)	0.02

Importance of Atmosphere

The importance of atmosphere are as follows:

The Role of the Atmosphere in Climate Control

Atmosphere acts as a blanket around the Earth. Air in the atmosphere is inexhaustible and a bad conductor of heat. Thus, it helps to keep the average temperature of the Earth steady during day and night preventing the sudden increase in temperature during day. During night, the escape of heat from the surface of Earth into outer space slows down. Moon lacks Earth-like atmosphere resulting in the variation of temperature during day and night. The average range of temperature on the surface of Moon is as hot as 110°C (during day) and as cool as –190°C (during night). Urban heat island effect refers to the fact that air in urban areas can be 2–3°C warmer than air in the nearby rural areas. Also, it may influence the weather, rate of precipitation, formation of clouds and change in wind patterns.

Info Bytes!

Microclimate refers to the difference in temperature observed over an area of just a few square metres or larger areas covering few kilometres.

The Movement of Air: Winds

Hot summer day followed by cool breeze and monsoon brings relief to a number of people. But, have you ever thought what causes the movement of air? What factors lead to a gentle breeze or transform it to a strong wind or a terrible storm? How does rain occur?

The above mentioned phenomenon takes place as a result of variation in the atmosphere observed due to heating of air and formation of water vapours. The movement of air from one region to another leads to the formation of wind. The sunrays received by Earth are either absorbed or reflected back or reradiated by the land and water bodies. The reflected or reradiated radiations cause the surface of Earth to heat from below, resulting in the formation of convection currents. Due to the fact that land gets heated at a faster rate as compared to water, the air over land also gets heated at a faster rate.

Activity 1

Temperature Variation in Urban Heat Islands

You and your friends can divide into 3–4 groups and ask each group to head outside in the schoolyard on a warm and sunny day. Let the students choose 5–6 areas for their choice and predict the area of school that are warmest and the coldest. Record the temperature data of these areas [*Note: Take care to add a mix of sunny and shaded areas along with a blend of paved, concrete and grass/natural areas*]. You all should mark the data of average temperate of that particular location on direct sunlight and ground covered under shade.

Questions:

- Do the results predicted correlate to the results obtained?
- What are the factors affecting the temperature in these areas?
- Based on the data, which you think, is warmer, rural or urban areas?

Factors Influencing Movement of Air

Factors responsible for diverse types of atmospheric phenomenon, such as breeze, monsoon rains, cyclones, storms, etc., are as follows:

1. Rotation of the Earth
2. Uneven heating of land
3. Difference in the rate of heating and cooling over land and water bodies
4. Condensation and vaporization of water vapour
5. Difference in topography

Konnect

The air in urban areas is 2–3°C warmer than in the nearby rural areas. Why is the difference observed? What makes cities warmer? Can you think of a few factors that result in warmer cities?

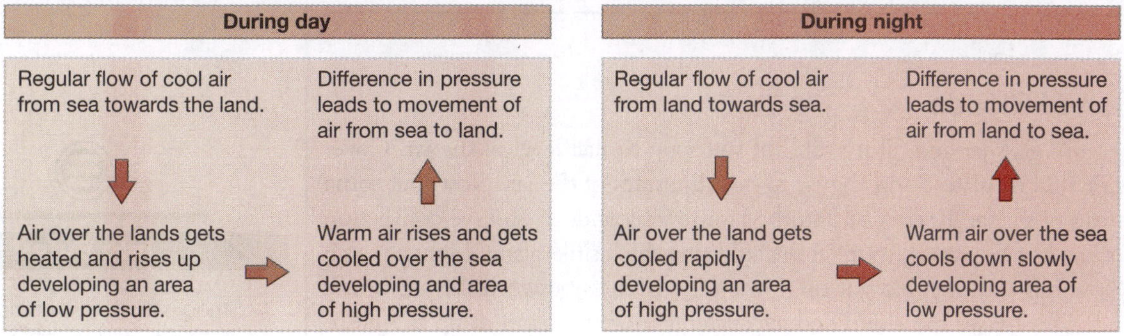

Figure 7.4 Movement of air

Let us perform the following activity to gain knowledge about development of convection currents. The patterns depicted by the direction of smoke reveals the direction in which the hot and cold air moves. It is observed that the air above the burning candle gets heated rapidly and rises up, developing a region of low pressure below. As a result, air from the adjacent cold regions move towards hotter region having low pressure. Let us take an example of coastal areas to illustrate the phenomenon where air above the land gets heated up at a faster rate.

The movement of air follows a spiralling path, outwards from high pressure towards low pressure due to rotation of Earth beneath the moving air. It results in an apparent deflection of wind; right in the Northern Hemisphere and left in the Southern Hemisphere.

Activity 2

Uneven Heating of Air Leads to Air-currents

Take a beaker and place a candle in it. Light the candle. Now, light an incense stick and keep it above different regions on the beaker or a wide-mouthed bottle. Record the variation in the direction of smoke at different regions.

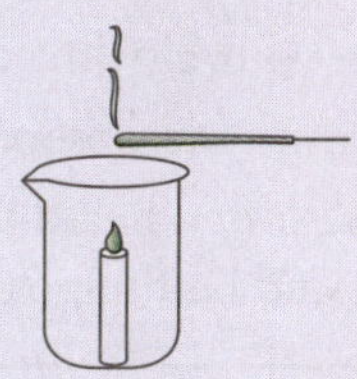

Uneven heating of air leads to air currents

Questions:

- What is the direction of smoke flow when incense stick is placed at the edge of the mouth?
- Did the direction vary when the position was changed from edge to different regions of the beaker?

Rain

During day, the temperature of water bodies rises resulting in the evaporation of water in the form of small droplets of water vapour. A portion of water is also extracted from plants through transpiration, which further enters the atmosphere. The air carrying water vapour gets heated and rises up. This process is followed by **cooling** and **expansion**, which leads to the condensation of water vapour in the presence of dust and other suspended particles.

Once the water droplets are formed, they grow bigger and bigger to form an enormous collection of tiny droplets. These droplets on condensation become heavy and falls down in the form of rain.

Info Bytes!

Coriolis Effect is a force which was first described by Gaspard de Coriolis in the year 1835 to illustrate the circulation of air flow around cyclones. It refers to a force similar to centrifugal force acting on a moving object when observed with reference to an object that itself rotating.

Activity 3

Formation of Clouds

Take an empty glass jar and fill it with hot water up to half level of the jar. Cover the jar with a lid or plate. Swirl the jar to heat the sides of the jar. Now, put some ice on the lid of the jar. Keep it undisturbed for few seconds to observe convection currents as the hot air rises up to meet the cold air, which sinks again. Light a match for a few seconds and then blow it off. Place the match in between the jar mouth and the lid. This makes the cloud and air currents more visible. Lift up the lid to observe a slow release of the clouds. Try it again!

Questions:

- When did the air inside the jar become foggy?
- When is the pressure inside the jar highest?
- What is the role of match in the jar for this experiment?

Info Bytes!

Smog, which is a combination of smoke and fog, is a type of air pollution that reduces visibility and can have harmful health effects.

Activity 4

To Observe Rainfall Patterns Across a Country

Wind patterns decide the rainfall patterns of a specific area. Browse the internet to collect a satellite picture depicting the clouds over India. Also, make a model of rain gauge. With the information collected from internet, answer the questions that follow.

- In your city, maximum amount of rainfall was received in the month of ______.
- Your state observed maximum rainfall in the month of ______.
- It is often heard that the amount of rainfall is decreased in the past few decades. Study the pattern to predict what could be the possible causes for the observed decline.

Air Pollution

The addition of air pollutants such as particulate matter, vapour and gases into the atmosphere causing adverse effect on humans, human assets, vegetation and animals is termed as **air pollution**. It is often heard through press releases that air quality in metro cities is degrading day-by-day due to increased rate of pollution. The question that arises each day is how do we access the air quality? What are the factors leading to air pollution? What is the evidence to prove the presence of air pollution? Let us cover each of them one by one.

The two types of air pollution are discussed below.

1. **Natural:** It includes pollution caused by pollen, forest fire and dust storms, etc.
2. **Man-made:** It includes pollution caused by vehicles, burning of fossil fuels, emission of gases from industries, etc.

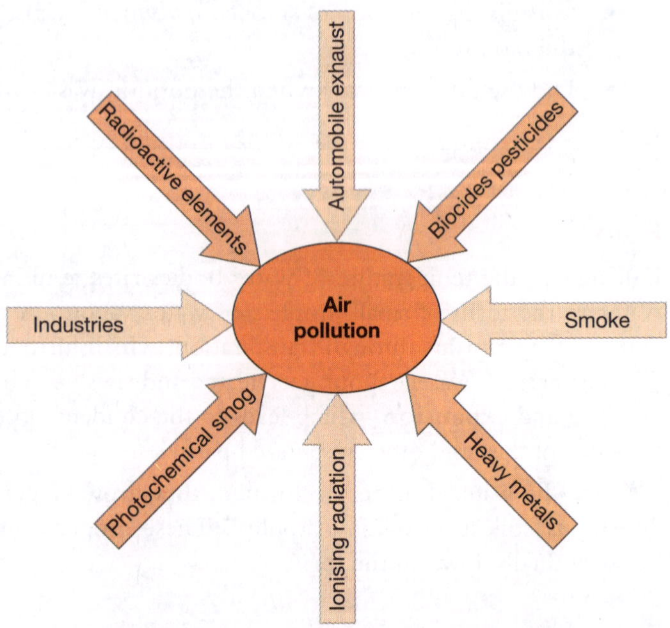

Figure 7.5 Sources of air pollution

The particulate pollutants of the air are also known as suspended particulate matter or SPM, which consists of soot (black powdered substance produced on burning of coal, wood, etc.), smoke, fly ash and dust (Fig. 7.5).

The types of **air pollutants** are as follows.

1. **Gases:** Nitrogen dioxide, hydrogen cyanide, carbon monoxide, sulphur dioxide, hydrogen fluoride, chlorine, methane and ammonia.
2. **Vapours:** Unburnt hydrocarbons (benzene).

Harmful Effects of Air Pollution

1. Asthma, allergic cold and bronchitis are caused by increased concentration of SPM.
2. Irritation in eyes, lungs and throat are caused, which in severe cases may lead to terminal cancer.
3. Damage to internal organs caused by vapours are produced by hydrocarbons.

Info Bytes!

Due to raised levels of carbon dioxide in the atmosphere as a result of human activities, more of it is now entering our oceans, thereby, decreasing the pH of the water bodies which causes acidification.

Smog

It is a dark brown or greyish smoky mist or photochemical haze produced due to the action of ultraviolet radiations. Smog is produced when atmosphere is polluted with the **primary pollutants**, which includes hydrocarbons and oxides of nitrogen released from variable sources including automobile exhaust (Fig. 7.6). It not only leads to reduced visibility, but may result in suffocation.

The atomic oxygen reacts with hydrocarbon to produce radicals, which on combination with O_2, NO_2 and hydrocarbons lead to the formation of secondary pollutants. These secondary pollutants are **aldehydes, formaldehydes** and **peroxyacetyl nitrate (PAN)**. According to the Central Pollution Control Board (CPCB), the Air Quality Index (AQI) touched the figure of 494 in Delhi NCR region since late October 2016.

Figure 7.6 Smog

Activity 5

Activity on Air Pollution

Organize a trip to nearby water bodies, such as lake, pond, river, etc. Observe the number and variety of plant and animal species present. Record the data. Now, select another area, which is comparatively dry. Again count the number and variety of plant species and record the data.

- What do you observe?
- In which region, the number and variety of plant is greater?
- Support your observation with a suitable reason.

Water: A Wonder Liquid

It is evident that 70% of our Earth is covered with an inexhaustible natural resource, water. Then, why should we be concerned about water? Water can be found everywhere in the lakes, rivers, ponds, oceans, soil, underground and even in the atmosphere as water vapours. But, how much of it is actually available for human consumption? A major part of Earth comprises of oceans covering about 97.5% of the total water, 1.9% is occupied as ice-caps, 2.5% is present on the land, while the remaining 0.6% of the total water is available as **fresh water**, which supports life on Earth. Rainfall is the source of freshwater. More than 90% of the fresh water is available as **groundwater** while the remaining 10% is available as either surface water (from rivers, dams, ponds, lakes) or **soil water** or **water vapours**.

> **Activity 6**
>
> Collect water samples from five different source of water. Do the samples contain biotic components?
>
> - Perform chemical tests such as soap test, (Ethylene Diamine Tetra Acetic acid) to test the presence of salts, such as sulphates and chlorides.
> - Record the pH of the sample.
> - Repeat the process during different time periods of the year to check contamination of water.

But why is it so important? Water is essential for the maintenance of all life forms present on Earth. All cellular processes require water as one of the key ingredients for the reactions to take place within cells and also to transport substances from one part of the body to another. Therefore, constant water level is required to be maintained by all organisms to survive. Besides being a key agent in the formation of soil, it is also used by humans for various purposes, such as drinking, washing, irrigation, disposal of wastes and various other purposes.

Water Pollution

It is defined as the undesirable change in the physical, chemical, or biological properties of water due to addition of pollutants that make water unfit for human consumption. The **three types of water pollution** are surface water or inland, underground water and marine water pollution. It is remorseful to state that humans are the major cause of water pollution (Fig. 7.7). However, some part of pollution takes place naturally.

> **Activity 7**
>
> Survey a pond near to your school. Take the help of school authority to find ways taken by municipal authorities to keep the pond clean.

Types of Water Pollutants

Water pollutants are the substances or agents that cause water pollution. It can be broadly classified into three categories as follows (Fig. 7.7).

1. **Physical pollutants:** It includes thermal pollution caused by heat and oil spills.
2. **Chemical pollutants:** It includes organic wastes, such as sewage, fertilizers, pesticides (DDT, DDE, BHC, etc.), PCBs (Polychlorinated biphenyls), detergents, inorganic chemicals (lead, nickel, mercury, arsenic, nitrates, fluorides, cadmium, etc.), inorganic impurities, such as calcium and magnesium and radioactive wastes.
3. **Biological pollutants:** Viruses, protozoa, fungi, nematodes, bacteria, helminthes, etc.

Figure 7.7 Water pollution

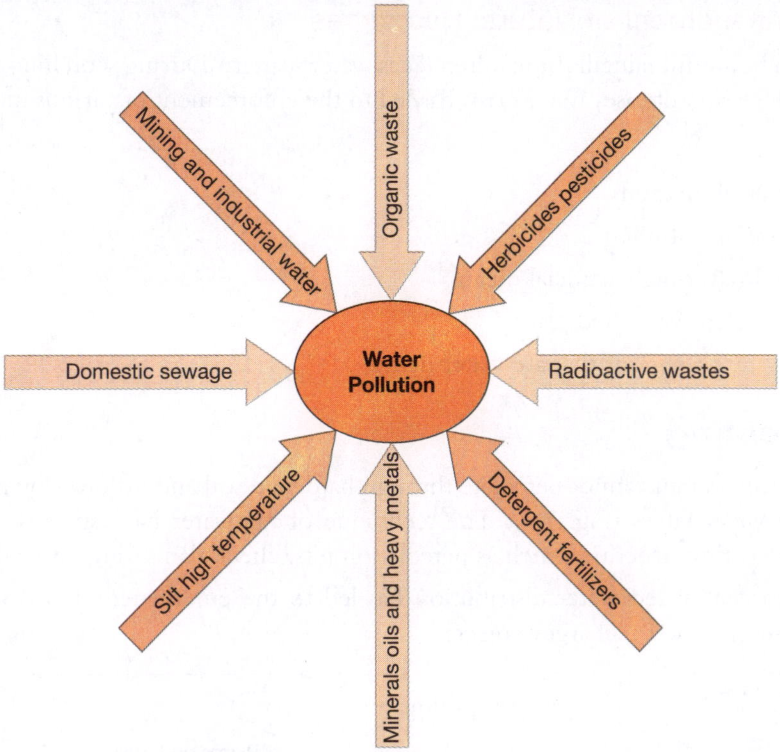

Figure 7.8 Sources of water pollution

Harmful Effects of Water Pollution

1. Biological pollutants such as viruses, bacteria, etc., cause diseases such as cholera, dysentery, jaundice, typhoid and hepatitis.
2. These pollutants may stimulate the growth of some organisms while affecting the others, thereby, disturbing them between different organisms.
3. The increased amount of organic wastes in water bodies promotes the growth of bacteria using up a large proportion of the available oxygen. This leads to the death of the marine animals due to lack of oxygen. This process is termed as **eutrophication**.
4. Industrial waste containing high amount of acids, alkalis and heavy metals cause an adverse effect on the marine life.
5. The decomposition of organic wastes requires oxygen. However, in case of low concentration of oxygen, anaerobic breakdown of organic matter takes place producing pollutants, such as ammonia, methane, organic sulphides, methyl sulphides, hydrogen sulphide. This makes the water turbid and odorous.

Biomagnification

Biomagnification is also known as food chain magnification in a manner that organisms present at the top of the chain contains harmful chemicals, such as DDE, DDT, methyl mercury, etc. They may affect the organisms that feed on them. For example, ***Minimata disease*** in fish-eating population is a result of biomagnification of mercury in fishes.

Bioaccumulation

It is the term used for storage of pollutants in the body tissues of humans and animals (fats, kidney, bone, etc.) at a higher concentration than found in the environment. For example: In Japan, the population eating rice produced from soil containing high concentration of cadmium suffered from a disease called ***Itai Itai***.

Conservation and Management of Natural Resources

Despite being blessed with bountiful rainfall, India often faces water scarcity. During scorching heat of summers, the level of water goes down. In such frequent cases water crisis has led to the enforcement of various means of water conservation and they are as follows.

1. Adoption of food control methods
2. Avoid wastage and overuse of water
3. Groundwater recharging through artificial means
4. Development of integrated watershed plans
5. Transfer of surplus water to regions that are water deficit

Rainwater Harvesting

The amount of water received as rain cannot percolate through hardened soil and it flows down to rivers and sea without replenishing underground water tables (Fig. 7.9). The technique of rainwater harvesting is used to capture, hold and reutilize rainwater by constructing structures, such as percolation pits, check dams, dugout wells and lagoons.

The failure to develop a centralized water distribution has led to the emergence of two new techniques known as rainwater harvesting and groundwater recharge projects.

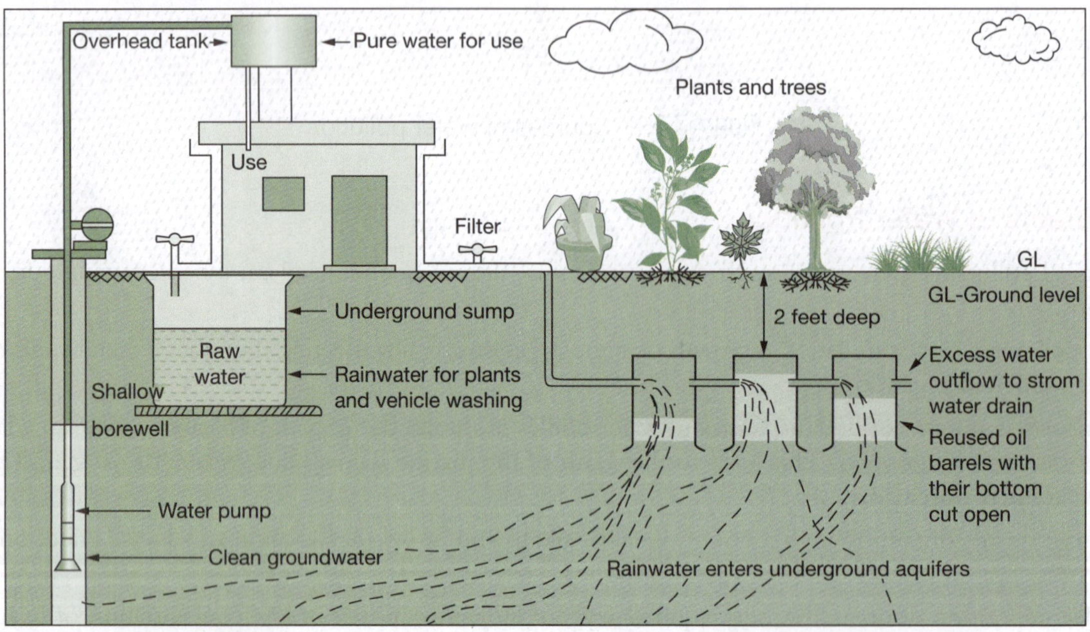

Figure 7.9 Technique of rainwater harvesting to recharge groundwater

Rainwater harvesting is carried out in several steps, which involves the collection of rainwater, its storage, and subsequent use at the time of scarcity. In water stressed areas, the technique is adopted to store meagre quantity of water into huge storage tanks and vessels. This stored water serves to fulfil the demand of population during most of the year.

Advantages of Rainwater Harvesting

1. Checks soil erosion
2. Raise water table level
3. Maintains supply of water during months of the year
4. Control floods
5. Reduce loss of water through surface run-off

Quick Recap

✔ **What is the major source of fresh water in the city/town/village where you live?**
Answer: The major sources of water are as follows.

- Water in the form of snow, ice-covered mountains
- Underground water well
- Surface water like in lakes, rivers, ponds
- Rainfall
- Stored rainwater in tanks and dams

✔ **How can untreated sewage affect aquatic life in freshwater sources?**
Answer: Untreated sewage contains harmful bacteria, viruses, and other pathogens. When released into water bodies, it can lead to waterborne diseases. Additionally, sewage increases the nutrient content in the water, leading to eutrophication, which can cause excessive growth of algae. This depletes oxygen levels, affecting aquatic life and potentially leading to fish kills.

✔ **Can greenhouse gases other than CO_2 contribute significantly to the greenhouse effect? If yes, which ones?**
Answer: Yes, apart from CO_2, other greenhouse gases like methane (CH_4), nitrous oxide (N_2O), and fluorinated gases also significantly contribute to the greenhouse effect. Methane, for instance, is much more effective at trapping heat in the atmosphere than CO_2, making it a potent greenhouse gas, even though it's present in smaller quantities.

✔ **Why is it crucial to manage and reduce suspended particulate matter in urban areas?**
Answer: Urban areas often have high concentrations of suspended particulate matter due to industrial activities, vehicular emissions, and construction. High levels of these particulates reduce air quality, leading to respiratory and cardiovascular issues in residents, lowering the overall quality of life and increasing healthcare costs.

Mineral Riches in the Soil

Soil is regarded as one of the most important resources, which decides the diversity of life in a particular area. But what is it? How is the soil formed? Soil is described as the Earth's portion that comprises the disintegrated rocks and decaying organic material, which supports the life of plants and animals. Its thickness ranges from a few millimetres to 3–4 meters.

Formation of Soil

Soil is formed by two processes, namely weathering and paedogenesis (Fig. 7.10).

Weathering

The process of breakdown of huge rocks into smaller particles is known as weathering. It takes place in three ways as discussed below.

1. **Physical weathering:** Factors that contribute to physical weathering include temperature, rainwater, wind, ice, glaciers, snow and running water. The roots of the plants also play a crucial role in weathering by penetrating into the crevices of the rocks. **Example**: The freezing of water leads to the expansion of water in the rock crevices, which leads to the breakdown of rocks.

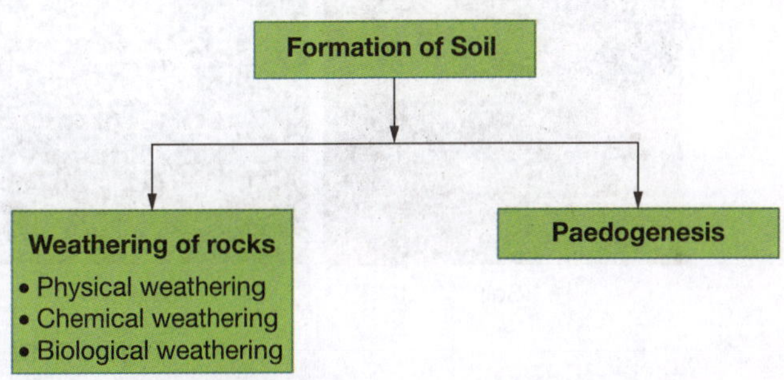

Figure 7.10 Formation of soil

2. **Chemical weathering:** It is carried out by chemical processes, such as hydrolysis, oxidation, reduction and hydration. **Example**: The acidic components derived from decaying of organic matter and carbonic acid present in water leads to the breakdown of complex compounds. The by-product of chemical breakdown includes clay, inorganic salts, silica and hydrated oxides,
3. **Biological weathering:** The breakdown of complex substances by living organisms, such as lichens and bryophytes is termed as biological weathering. **Example**: Lichens grow on the rocks to extract minerals creating crevices at places where a thin layer of soil is formed. Mosses grow over the crevices, thus, created and deepens them leading to the formation of deeper crevices, where roots of herbs pass and become large with the passage of time. This causes fragmentation of rock eventually leading to weathering.

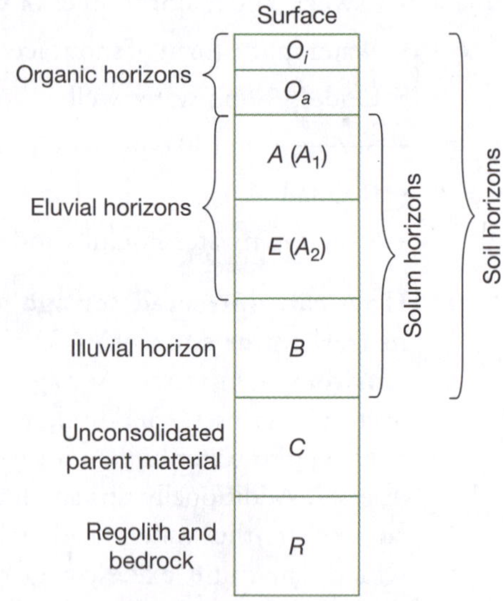

Figure 7.11 Soil profile

Soil Profile

Soil pollution represents the vertical section of the crust of the Earth. It comprises of subsequent horizontal layers known as horizons. These horizons can be distinguished on the basis of colour, texture, thickness, structure, porosity, acidity, consistency and composition (Fig. 7.11).

1. **A-horizon:** It is the top soil comprising of humus and litter.
2. **B-horizon:** It comprises of mineral soil.
3. **C-horizon:** It comprises of unconsolidated parent material.
4. **D-horizon:** It comprises of unmodified parent material or rocks.

Composition of Soil

The top layer of the soil comprises of four different types of rock particles differing in their look, texture and size (Fig. 7.12).

1. **Gravels:** Large particles measuring greater than 2 mm in diameter that can be hand-picked.
2. **Sand particles:** Coarse particles ranging in size of 0.05 mm to 2.00 mm that can be seen by naked eye.
3. **Silt particles:** Soil particles measuring between ranges from 0.005 to 0.05 mm.
4. **Clay particles:** Smallest soil particles measuring less than 0.005 mm.

Figure 7.12 Composition of soil

Types of Soil

Based on the amount and type of particles in the soil, it is divided into three categories and they are as follows.

1. **Sandy soil:** It is found in deserts comprising of large amount of sand particles. It cannot hold much water.
2. **Clayey soil:** It comprises of clay particles with a small amount of silt and humus. It is compact and capable of holding water.
3. **Loamy soil:** It comprises of silt, clay and humus having good water holding capacity. It is porous to provide aeration to the roots.

In India, based on the perspective of agriculture, soil can be divided into the following categories.

1. **Residual soil:** It is found at the place of soil formation and it can be further divided as follows.

Activity 8

Take a 100 ml beaker and fill sand up to 10 ml. Add water at least five times to the amount of sand in the beaker. Now, stir the soil vigorously with the help of stirrer and keep it undisturbed for some time. Observe the beaker after 20 minutes.

What do you observe?

Is soil a mixture? Support you answer with suitable reason.

Can you observe anything floating on the water? What is it?

Table 7.2 Characterstics of residual soil

	Black Soil	Red Soil	Laterite Soil
1. Source	Derived from Basaltic rock, it is porous and contains humus	Red due to the presence of iron oxide Contains clay particles and quartz	Red in colour; Found in regions experiencing heavy rainfall
2. Nutrient	Rich in calcium, iron, aluminium and magnesium	Poor in lime, phosphorous, nitrogen, magnesium and contains less quantity of humus	Rich in nutrients
3. Availability	Found in Maharashtra, Madhya Pradesh, Andhra Pradesh and Gujarat	Found in Tamil Nadu, Kerala, Andhra Pradesh and Orissa	Found in Western Ghats, Andhra Pradesh, Orissa, Assam and parts of Tamil Nadu
4. Benefits	Suitable for cotton and sugarcane	Suitable for castor seed and groundnut	Suitable for tea, coconut and coffee

2. **Transported soil:** It gets displaced and settles in regions away from its origin due to either or a combination of the following causes.
   (i) Flowing water
   (ii) Gravity
   (iii) Wind or glacier

The transported soil is classified into the following three types.

Table 7.3 Characterstics of transported soil

	Alluvial Soil	Desert Soil	Mountainous Soil
1. Description	Layered and contains smooth round particles	It is coarse, porous and sandy.	It comprises of sand, stones, shales, clay and limestones.
2. Nutrient	Rich in humus and comprises of clay, sand and gravel	Rich in minerals	–
3. Availability	Found in plains of Uttar Pradesh, Bihar, Haryana and West Bengal	Found in Gujarat, Ladakh and Rajasthan	Found in Himalayan regions
4. Benefits	Suitable for growing rice, wheat and sugarcane	Produces rich crops when supplied with ample amount of water	–

Soil Erosion

It is defined as the removal and transportation of top layer of the soil through strong winds and running water (Fig 7.13).

Figure 7.13 Soil erosion

Causes of Soil Erosion

The factors responsible for the occurrence of soil erosion are as follows.

- Strong winds
- Heavy rains
- Human activities such as expansion of urban areas
- Dust storms
- Frequent floods
- Improper farming and suspended cultivation

Effects of Soil Erosion

- The displacement of top, fertile layer of the soil from one place to another leads to the reduction in fertility of the soil.
- Landslides as a result of soil erosion results in the destruction of dwellings in the hilly areas.
- Heavy rains leads to rapid movement of the water resulting in floods. This causes enormous loss of life and property.
- The textural changes resulting from soil erosion leads to the removal of top, fertile layer, thereby, reducing water holding capacity of the soil. This makes the soil dry resulting in famines.
- The runaway of top soil clogs drain and other water channels due to deposition of silt. The deposition of silt pollutes water and reduces water level in the reservoirs.

Prevention of Soil Erosion

- To make use of intensive cropping which protects top soil from the exposure of winds or water.
- Sowing grasses on barren lands helps to bind the loose soil.
- Construction of small bunds (embankments) known as contour bunding raises the edges of fields, thereby, preventing soil erosion.
- Practice of reduced or no tillage.
- Constructing proper drainage canals to remove excess of rainwater from the fields.

Soil Pollution

It is known that soil pollution is caused by solid wastes and chemicals (Fig. 7.14). Some sources of soil pollution are discussed as follows.

- Pulp and paper mills.
- Sugar mills
- Oil refineries and power plants
- Domestic wastes (food scraps, cans, rags, ash, broken gadgets, etc.)

Figure 7.14 Soil pollution

Biogeochemical Cycles

There is a constant interaction between both biotic and abiotic components of the biosphere to establish a stable ecosystem. The interaction of components involves transfer of energy between various components of the ecosystem.

The term 'biogeochemical' is described as the uptake of nutrient elements from the surface of the Earth by living organism to perform vital functions such as growth and metabolism (Fig. 7.15). These nutrients are recycled from time to time and the transfer of nutrient element between living and non-living components is termed as biogeochemical cycle of matter. The term is 'biogeochemical cycle' which is made up of three word '*bio*' meaning life, '*geo*' meaning Earth or rocks, soil, air and water of the Earth, and '*cycle*' meaning again and again.

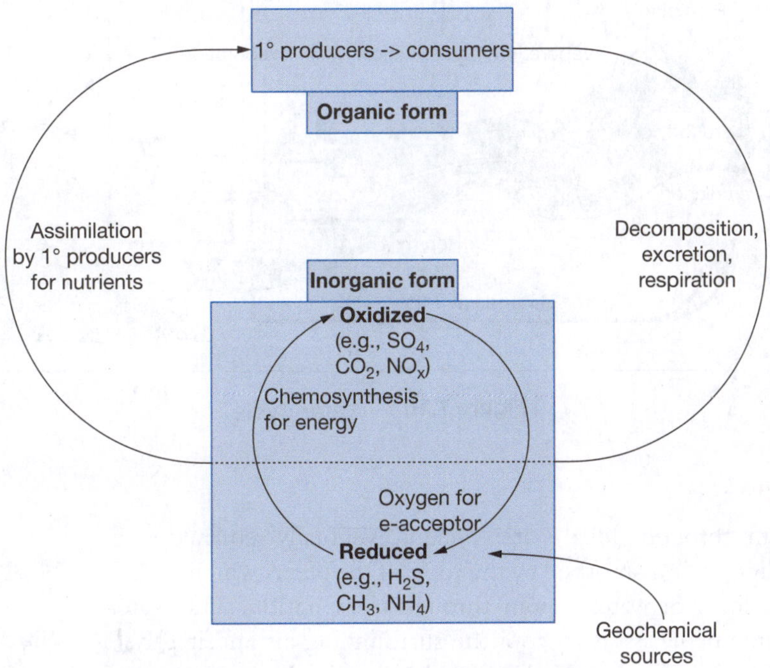

Figure 7.15 Generalized model of nutrient cycle

It is also referred to as 'nutrient cycle'. Each nutrient cycle comprises of two basic divisions and they are as follows:

1. **Reservoir pool:** It comprises of large, slow-moving and mostly non-biological components.
2. **Labile or cycling pool:** It comprises of a smaller yet active proportion of the components that are exchanged between organisms and their immediate environment.

   There are three aspects of the nutrient cycles and they are as follows:

   (a) **Nutrient input:** The nutrients received from external sources are stored for future use.

   (b) **Nutrient output:** The nutrients leaving the ecosystem becomes the input for another ecosystem.

   (c) **Internal nutrient cycling:** Soil acts as a reservoir of nutrients. The nutrients regenerated by decomposers, fungi, actinomycetes through decomposition of dead or partially decomposed plants and animal matters are stored in the soil.

Let us discuss a few nutrient cycles that are involved in maintaining the dynamic state of the system.

Water Cycle

The component that distinguishes Earth from other planets is the availability of water, which supports all life forms on Earth. Water is continuously exchanged between various components of Earth and it consists of two overlapping cycles in the nature: The larger global cycle and the smaller biological water cycle that involves living systems.

Global Water Cycle

Water from water bodies evaporates to form clouds which are blown over the land through winds. On cooling, water falls on the Earth in the form of hail, sleet and snow by a process known as precipitation (Fig. 7.16). Rain may fall either directly into the water bodies or may get soaked into the ground. However, a major portion of water flows in rivers and returns to the seas. The collected water gets evaporated again from the reservoirs or ground to form through evaporation. The repeated cycle completes the **global water cycle.**

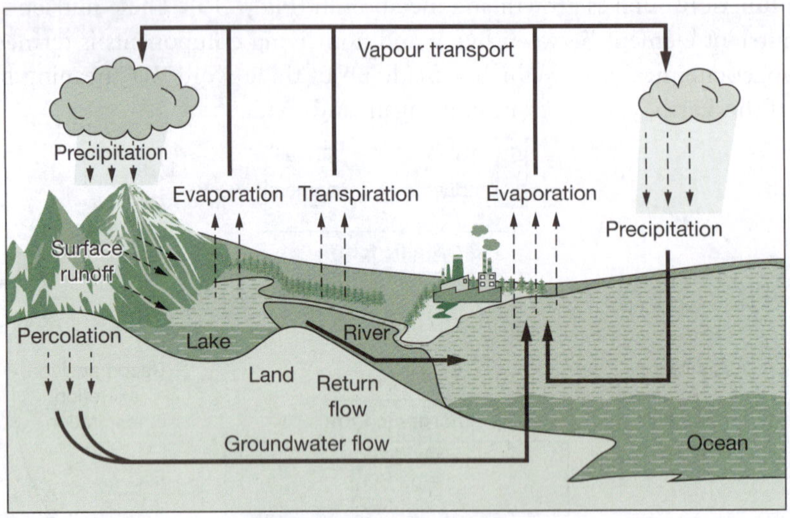

Figure 7.16 Water cycle

Biological Water Cycle

Water received by organisms through global water cycle is eventually returned to it. The water from the soil or reservoir is absorbed by the roots of the plants which returns to the environment in the form of water vapour through transpiration. The water, thus, returned to the environment, assists to cool the surrounding air and it plays a vital role in determining the microclimate. On the other hand, animals consume water from either water bodies or in the form of food, which is returned to the environment as vapours through respiration or to the soil as excreta. Mammals also contribute to this cycle by excreting water as sweat. Water from the above mentioned resources is added to the global water cycle. Rain adds the stored water to the land and reservoir for future use. This completes the biological water cycle.

Water, being a universal solvent is capable to dissolve a variety of substances. As water is transported from place to place and over the rocks, it dissolves essential nutrients, soluble minerals in it, which are deposited at distant places.

There are two aspects of the water cycle that require special emphasis and they are as follows.

1. According to current reports, more water evaporates from the sea than what is returned to it through rainfall. The condition is reversed in case of land.
2. Human activities such as ditching and diking rivers, deforestation, paving over Earth, compact agricultural soil act as an obstruction in recharging groundwater.

Nitrogen Cycle

Nitrogen is an important chemical component of all living organisms. It is present in the form of proteins, amino acids and nucleic acids. Nitrogen exists in both molecular form as (N_2) or as oxides (Fig. 7. 17).

Konnect

Nitrogen is the Perfect Cycle

- It helps to maintain the overall amount of nitrogen steadily in the soil, water and atmosphere.
- It depends upon four different kinds of bacteria referred to as decay causers.
- The key enzyme involved in nitrogen fixation is nitrogenase, which catalyses the splitting of N_2.
- The number of ATP molecules required by bacterium to convert a molecule of nitrogen involved in fixation is 16.
- *Klebsiella pneumoniae*, a soil bacterium consists of 17 genes called nif genes and it plays a vital role in nitrogen fixation.

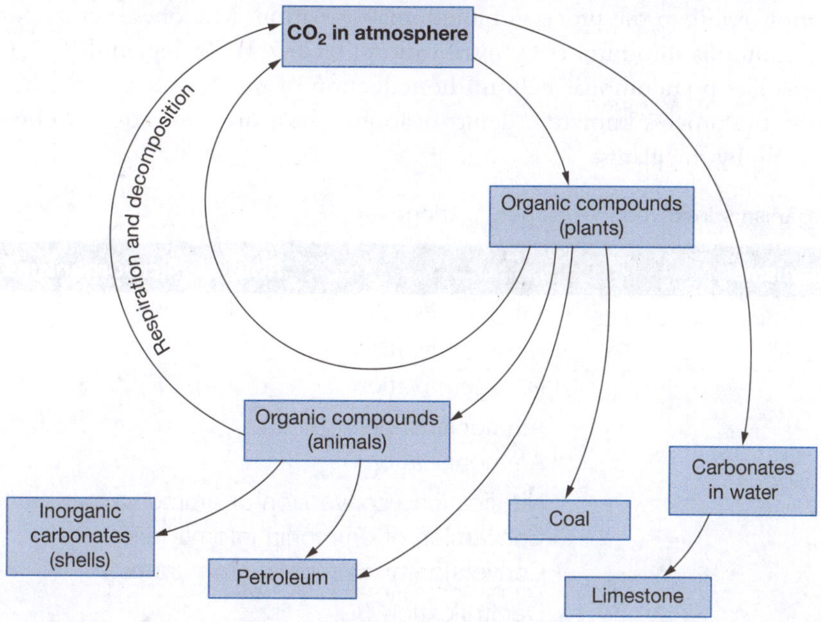

Figure 7.17 A flowchart depicting essential components of the nitrogen cycle

Nitrogen being inert in nature cannot be used in its pure form. Thus, nitrogen needs to be converted into nitrates and nitrites to be used up by the living organisms. However, no living organism except a few bacteria are capable to convert it. The process of conversion is carried out either by industrial nitrogen fixation or nitrogen fixing bacteria like *Azotobacter* and *Rihizobium*. These organisms convert atmospheric nitrogen into nitrates, which is the water soluble form of nitrogen. This process of fixation is termed as nitrogen fixation. At the time of lightning, the atmospheric nitrogen reacts with oxygen to form dilute nitric acid, which is received by Earth in the form of acid rain. Nitrates are absorbed by plants to make organic matter (proteins), which are further consumed by animals. The excreta of animals contain urea or uric acid or when an animal dies, bacteria performs ammonification (production of ammonium ions from nitrogen-containing molecules). The ammonium ion assimilated in the plants is further converted into nitrate by a process known as nitrification (Fig. 7. 18).

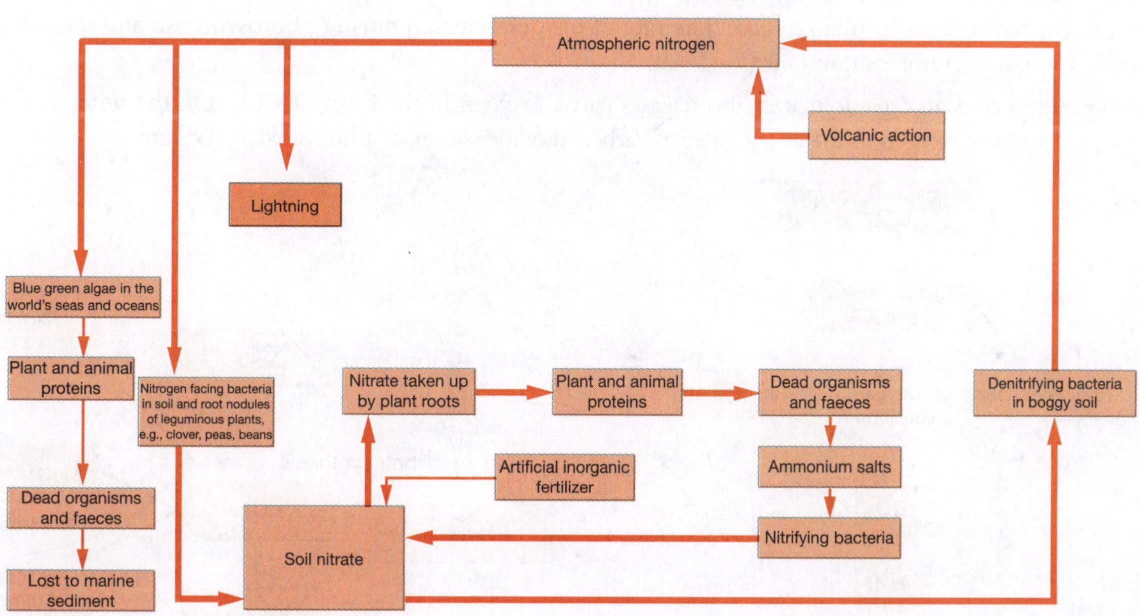

Figure 7.18 Schematic representation of nitrogen cycle

The term 'ammonification' refers to the process of ammonia formation. Microbes such as *Nitrosomonas and Nitrobacter* assist in the conversion of ammonia into nitrates by nitrification (Table 7.4). To replenish the amount of nitrogen in the atmosphere, certain bacteria like pseudomonas help in the reduction of nitrates back to the nitrogen or ammonia form or to some other oxides by the process known as denitrification. Thus, the free nitrogen obtained is returned and the atmospheric pool are taken up by the plants.

Table 7.4 List of organisms involved in nitrogen fixation

Microorganisms	Role of Microorganisms
Rhizobium bacteria (found in root nodules)	Nitrogen fixation
Azotobacter (found in soil)	Nitrogen fixation
Blue-green algae	Nitrogen fixation
Putrefying bacteria	Ammonification
Fungi	Ammonification
Nitrifying bacteria:	Nitrification (Conversion of ammonia into nitrites then into nitrates)
Nitrosomonas	Conversion of ammonia into nitrites.
Nitrobacter	Conversion of ammonia into nitrates.
Denitrifying bacteria	Denitrification
Pseudomonas	(Conversion of nitrate salts into free nitrogen gas)

Oxygen Cycle

Air comprises 21 per cent of oxygen, an important constituent of water. Oxygen enters the system through respiration, which oxidizes food to release carbon dioxide and energy.

$$C_6H_{12}O_6 + 6O_6 \rightarrow 6CO_6 + 6H_2O + \text{Energy}$$

The carbon dioxide released by respiration is utilized by plants to produce food materials through photosynthesis.

$$6CO_2 + 6H_2O + \text{Light Energy} \rightarrow C_6H_{12}O_6 + 6O_2$$

The oxygen released during photosynthesis can be used up again in the process of respiration or it may return to environment in the form of molecular oxygen. The rate of oxygen released during photosynthesis and the rate of oxygen utilized during respiration remains constant (Fig 7.19).

The decomposition of dead organic matter also releases partial oxygen in the form of CO_2. On the other side, burning of fossils also releases a part of oxygen in the atmosphere as carbon dioxide, water, sulphur dioxide and nitrogen oxides (Fig. 7.20).

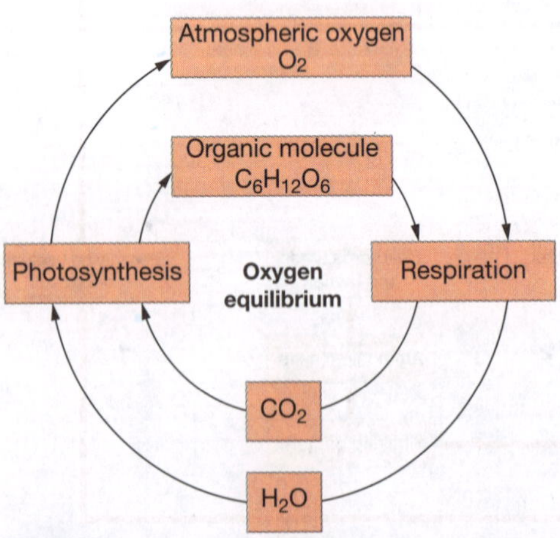

Figure 7.19 The concentration of oxygen in the atmosphere remains constant and it is known as oxygen equilibrium

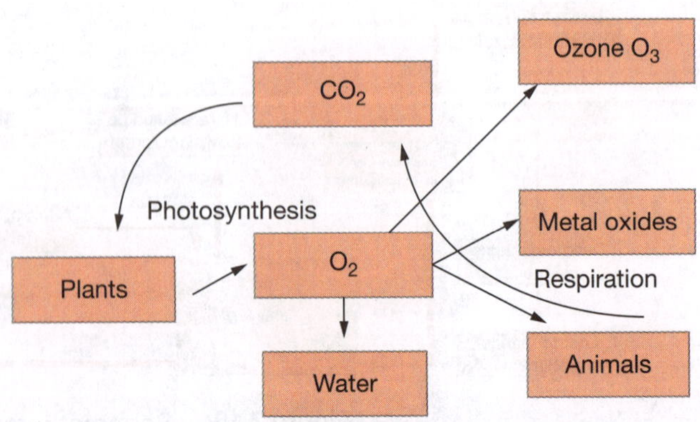

Figure 7.20 Oxygen cycle

Carbon Cycle

Carbon is linked to energy flow because producers, chemosynthetic bacteria require environmental energy to store carbon into sugars. In the carbon cycle, the compounds produced by manufacturers are used up by the consumers. Then, carbon from both consumers and producers is returned to the non-living environment as carbon dioxide through respiration (Fig. 7.21). Carbon accumulates in wood for several years, which is returned to environment by burning of fossils and through respiration by fungi, bacteria and other detrivores. Volcanic eruptions are also an important source of carbon dioxide release in the environment, and therefore, this completes the cycle.

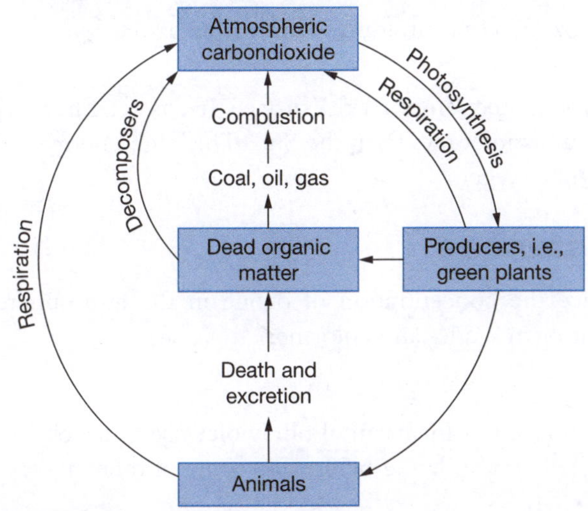

Figure 7.21 Schematic representation of carbon cycle

Carbon sinks: In some cases, cycling materials are stored into reservoirs or sinks and become unavailable to living organisms (Fig. 7.22.). The three reservoirs for the carbon are as follows:

1. Transfer of carbon from organism to deposits of coal, peat and oil.
2. Incorporation of carbon into carbonate rocks.
3. Oceans also act as carbon reservoirs.

Atmosphere also contains two other forms of oxygen, namely as carbon monoxide and methane.

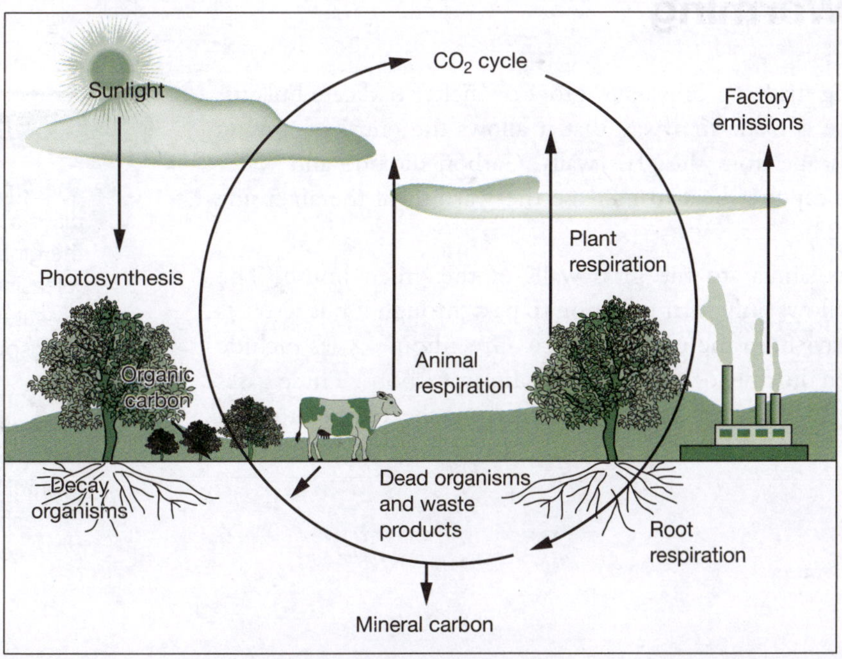

Figure 7.22 Carbon Cycle

Ozone Layer and Its Depletion

Ozone, an allotrope of oxygen is a triatomic blue-coloured gas having pungent odour, which is highly poisonous to living organisms. Ozone is present in the stratosphere of the atmosphere. The density of ozone layer varies from place to place being thickest at the high latitudes in the late summer and comparatively thinner over the tropics.

The part of atmosphere rich in ozone concentration is known as ozone layer, ozonosphere or ozone shield.

Ozone layer holds a vital role in the protection of Earth's surface. It acts as a filter restricting the entry of high energy ultraviolet rays from the Sun. This high energy splits ozone into molecular and atomic oxygen.

Info Bytes!

Find out other factors responsible for ozone layer depletion.

Ozone Depleting Substances

These are the chemicals that reduce the concentration of ozone in the atmosphere. Examples: Chlorofluorocarbons (CFCs), halons, methyl bromide, nitrogen oxides and chlorine.

Effects of Ozone Depletion

The depletion of ozone makes an entry point for harmful ultraviolet rays to reach the surface of Earth causing harmful effects on living beings and some of them are as follows:

- Skin cancer
- Damage to eyes
- Damages immune system
- Decreases crop yield
- Formation of smog

Info Bytes!

The largest recorded ozone hole was in September 2006, spanning over 10.6 million square miles over Antarctica

Global Warming

Greenhouse is a building made up of glass to grow or shelter dedicated plants. The glass of greenhouse is made in a way that it allows the entry of sunrays but restricts them to escape from the glass walls. Carbon dioxide and water vapour inside it further captures heat to increase the warmth of the air inside the greenhouse (Fig. 7.23).

The atmosphere acts similar to the glass walls of the green house. The blanket of atmosphere allows only solar radiation to pass through it but restricts the escape of infrared rays from the earth's surface. Greenhouse gases include carbon dioxide, nitrogen dioxide, ozone and chlorofluorocarbons. These gases trap the heat reflected by the earth, thereby, increasing the temperature of the earth. This phenomenon is referred to as global warming or greenhouse effect.

Info Bytes!

- The Amazon Rainforest plays a critical role in the global water cycle, releasing 20 billion tons of water vapor into the atmosphere daily.
- 2016 was declared the warmest year on record, with global temperatures averaging 1.78 degrees Fahrenheit above the mid-20th-century mean.

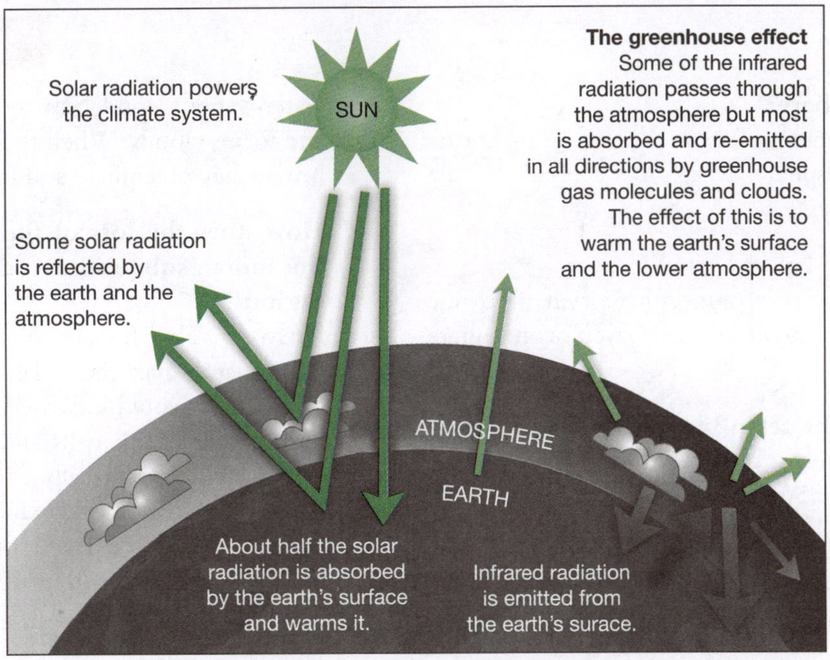

Figure 7.23 Greenhouse effect

Effects of Global Warming

- The rise in temperature has led to the melting of glaciers, thereby, increasing the level of the sea.
- Decrease in the production of crop due to eruption of plant diseases, pests and growth of weeds as a result of increase in the temperature.
- The increase in warmth of the atmosphere has led to the increase in the moisture carrying capacity of the air.

Quick Recap

✔ **What is biosphere?**
Answer: Biosphere refers to the region of Earth's crust and atmosphere, which is occupied by the living organisms.

✔ **What is ozone layer?**
Answer: The part of atmosphere rich in ozone concentration is known as ozone layer, ozonosphere or ozone shield.

✔ **Who coined the term biosphere?**
Answer: The term 'biosphere' was coined by the geologist Eduard Suess.

✔ **What are greenhouse gases?**
Answer: Greenhouse gases include carbon dioxide, nitrogen dioxide, ozone and chlorofluorocarbons.

✔ **What is global water cycle?**
Answer: Water from water bodies evaporates to form clouds which are blown over the land through winds. The collected water gets evaporated again from the reservoirs or ground to form through evaporation. The repeated cycle completes the global water cycle.

✔ **What is nitrogen fixation?**
Answer: The process of conversion is carried out either by industrial nitrogen fixation or nitrogen fixing bacteria like *Azotobacter* and *Rihizobium*. These organisms convert atmospheric nitrogen into nitrates, which is the water soluble form of nitrogen. This process of fixation is termed as nitrogen fixation.

✔ **How are clouds formed?**
Answer: During day time water from different sources like pond, lake, river, sea, well, etc., gets evaporated and this water vapour rises with the hot air. At a specific height, the air cools and the water vapour condenses to form minute droplets and forms clouds. When these water drops become heavy, they precipitate and fall as rain.

✔ **How does the loss of the ozone layer impact the Indian subcontinent differently than polar regions?**
Answer: The Indian subcontinent is closer to the equator than the polar regions. A loss of the ozone layer would increase UV radiation exposure, intensifying health risks and potentially impacting crop yields, especially for a predominantly agricultural country like India. Meanwhile, polar regions would see more drastic effects on their unique ecosystems and further ice melt.

✔ **Considering the diverse flora and fauna of India, how might an increase in greenhouse gases affect biodiversity hotspots like the Western Ghats and the Sundarbans?**
Answer: An increase in greenhouse gases could lead to climate change, affecting the delicate balance of ecosystems in biodiversity hotspots. The Western Ghats might face habitat loss due to changing weather patterns, while the Sundarbans, being a coastal region, could be threatened by rising sea levels, leading to loss of habitat and species.

✔ **With India's high dependence on agriculture, how might nitrogen fixation play a role in sustaining crop yields, and how can its imbalance lead to environmental challenges?**
Answer: Nitrogen fixation is vital for converting atmospheric nitrogen into a form that plants can use. However, excessive reliance on artificial nitrogenous fertilizers can lead to soil degradation, water pollution through runoff, and disruption of natural nitrogen balance, affecting the health of ecosystems and long-term agricultural sustainability.

POINTS TO REMEMBER

- The various types of ecosystem that may be found in a particular region constitute a biome and several biomes on earth constitute the biosphere.
- Natural resources can be divided into two categories-inexhaustible and exhaustible.
- Biotic resources include all the living organisms including human beings. It includes producers (green plants, autotrophs) and consumers (animals, some bacteria, fungi, viruses).
- Abiotic factors include water, sunlight, oxygen, soil and temperature.
- Air is a mixture of various gases along with water vapour and suspended particles.
- The addition of air pollutants such as particulate matter, vapour and gases into the atmosphere causing adverse effect on humans and human assets, vegetation and animals is termed as air pollution.
- Smog is a dark brown or greyish smoky mist or photochemical haze produced due to the action of ultraviolet radiations.
- Water pollution is defined as the undesirable change in the physical, chemical, or biological properties of water due to addition of pollutants that make water unfit for human consumption.
- The technique of rainwater harvesting is used to capture, hold and reutilize rainwater by constructing structures, such as percolation pits, check dams, dugout wells and lagoons.
- Soil is formed by two processes, namely weathering and paedogenesis.
- The process of breakdown of huge rocks into smaller particles is known as weathering.
- Soil profile represents the vertical section of the crust of the earth. It comprises of subsequent horizontal layers known as horizons.
- Based on the amount and type of particles in the soil, it is divided into three categories and they are sandy soil, clayey soil and loamy soil.
- Soil erosion is defined as the removal and transportation of top layer of the soil through strong winds and running water.
- The term 'biogeochemical' is described as the uptake of nutrient elements from the surface of the earth by living organism to perform vital functions such as growth and metabolism.
- The part of atmosphere rich in ozone concentration is known as ozone layer, ozonosphere or ozone shield.
- Greenhouse gases include carbon dioxide, nitrogen dioxide, ozone and chlorofluorocarbons. These gases trap the heat reflected by the earth, thereby, increasing the temperature of the earth.

CLASSROOM WING

Practice Questions

Very Short Answer Type Questions

Directions for Questions 1 to 5
Fill in the blanks.

1. ______ is a type of air pollution that forms a dark brown or greyish mist, created by ultraviolet radiations.
2. The breakdown of huge rocks into smaller particles, which is a fundamental step in the formation of soil, is termed as ______.
3. In an ecological context, the interaction and interdependence between biotic and abiotic factors drive the dynamics of ________ and energy flow.
4. Despite being a minor component in Earth's atmosphere, ________ plays a critical role in regulating global temperatures through the greenhouse effect.
5. The process of paedogenesis plays a critical role in the ______ of soil.

Directions for Questions 6 to 30
Choose the correct option for each questions. There is only one correct response for each question.

6. Which among the following is NOT a component of abiotic factors?
(a) Soil (b) Water
(c) Humans (d) Sunlight
7. What primarily causes soil erosion?
(a) Earthquakes
(b) Strong winds and running water
(c) Tectonic movements
(d) Volcanic eruptions
8. The soil profile comprises of horizontal layers known as:
(a) Strata (b) Beds
(c) Horizons (d) Platforms
9. The harmful concentration of which gas in the atmosphere is responsible for trapping heat and causing the greenhouse effect?
(a) Oxygen (b) Hydrogen
(c) Nitrogen (d) Carbon dioxide
10. Which of the following is NOT a category of soil based on the type of particles?
(a) Sandy soil (b) Marshy soil
(c) Clayey soil (d) Loamy soil
11. Which factor does NOT directly contribute to the formation and quality of soil?
(a) Plant root systems
(b) Atmospheric pressure
(c) Microbial activity
(d) Weathering of rocks
12. Given the rise of greenhouse gases, which of the following is NOT a direct consequence?
(a) Stratospheric cooling
(b) Sea-level rise
(c) Increased photosynthesis
(d) Melting polar ice caps
13. Which of the following step is not involved in the carbon cycle?
(a) Photosynthesis
(b) Transpiration
(c) Respiration
(d) Burning of fossil fuels
14. 'Ozone hole' means
(a) a large sized hole in the ozone layer.
(b) thinning of the ozone layer.
(c) small holes scattered in the ozone layer.
(d) thickening of ozone in the ozone layer.

15. Ozone layer is getting depleted due to

(a) excessive use of automobiles.

(b) excessive formation of industrial units.

(c) excessive use of human-made compounds containing both fluorine and chlorine.

(d) excessive deforestation.

16. Which of the following is a recently originated problem of environment?

(a) Ozone layer depletion

(b) Greenhouse effect

(c) Global warming

(d) All the above

17. When we breathe in air, nitrogen also goes inside along with oxygen. What is the fate of this nitrogen?

(a) It moves along with oxygen into the cells.

(b) It comes out with the CO_2 during exhalation.

(c) It is absorbed only by the nasal cells.

(d) Nitrogen concentration is already more in the cells so it is not at all absorbed.

18. Top soil contains which of the following?

(a) Humus and living organisms only.

(b) Humus and soil particles only.

(c) Humus, living organisms and plants.

(d) Humus, living organisms and soil particles.

19. Choose the correct sequence from the following.

(a) CO_2 in atmosphere → Decomposers → Organic carbon in animals → Organic carbon in plants.

(b) CO_2 in atmosphere → Organic carbon in plants → Organic carbon in animals → Inorganic carbon in soil.

(c) Inorganic carbonates in water → Organic carbon in plants → Organic carbon in animals → Scavengers.

(d) Organic carbon in animals → Decomposers → CO_2 in atmosphere → Organic carbon in plants.

20. The major source of mineral in soil is

(a) parent rock from which soil is formed.

(b) plants

(c) animals

(d) bacteria

21. The total earth's surface covered by water is

(a) 75% (b) 60%

(c) 85% (d) 50%

22. The biotic component of biosphere is not constituted by

(a) producers (b) consumers

(c) decomposer (d) air

23. An increase in carbon dioxide content in the atmosphere would not cause

(a) more heat to be retained by the environment.

(b) increase in photosynthesis in plants.

(c) global warming.

(d) abundance of desert plants.

24. Oxygen is returned to the atmosphere mainly by

(a) burning of fossil fuels (b) respiration

(c) photosynthesis (d) fungi

25. Low visibility during cold weather is due to

(a) formation of fossil fuel.

(b) unburnt carbon particles or hydrocarbons suspended in air.

(c) lack of adequate power supply.

(d) none of these

26. Growth of lichens on barren rocks is followed by the growth of

(a) moss (b) ferns

(c) gymnosperms (d) algae

27. Marked temperature changes in aquatic environment can affect

(a) breeding of animals.

(b) more growth of aquatic plants.

(c) process of digestion in animals.

(d) availability of nutrients.

28. Soil erosion can be prevented by

(a) raising forests.

(b) deforestation.

(c) excessive use of fertilizer.

(d) overgrazing by animals.

29. What happens when rainfall on soil without vegetational cover?
    (a) Rainwater percolates in soil efficiently.
    (b) Rainwater causes loss of surface soil.
    (c) Rainwater leads to fertility of the soil.
    (d) Rainwater does not cause any change in soil.

30. Oxygen is harmful for
    (a) ferns
    (b) nitrogen fixing bacteria
    (c) chara
    (d) mango tree

Short Answer Type Questions

31. What are the effects of global warming?
32. What are the factors that contribute to physical weathering?
33. What are the advantages of rainwater harvesting?
34. What is biomagnification?
35. Explain the term 'biogeochemical' in relation to the ecosystem.
36. Describe the potential implications of a damaged ozonosphere for terrestrial life.

Essay Type Questions

37. Write a note on how forests influence the quality of our air, soil and water resources.
38. Why is water essential for life?
39. Considering the current trajectory of global environmental changes, discuss the potential consequences on both biotic and abiotic components of ecosystems and the subsequent impact on human societies.

COMPETITION WING

Practice Questions

Level 1: Apply your Concepts

Direction for Questions 1 to 70: Choose the correct option for each questions.
There is only one correct response for each question.

1. Which of the following sequences correctly represents the increasing order of particle size in soil types?
   (a) Loamy, Sandy, Clayey
   (b) Clayey, Loamy, Sandy
   (c) Sandy, Loamy, Clayey
   (d) Loamy, Clayey, Sandy
2. Given the increase in harmful ultraviolet radiations reaching the Earth's surface, which layer of the atmosphere is most likely being depleted?
   (a) Troposphere (b) Mesosphere
   (c) Ozonosphere (d) Thermosphere
3. If a region has an abundance of biotic resources with a scarcity of abiotic factors like water and sunlight, what is most likely to occur in the ecosystem?
   (a) Overpopulation of animals and plants
   (b) Balanced ecosystem due to the abundance of biotic resources
   (c) Reduced plant growth and, consequently, a food shortage for herbivores
   (d) Increase in soil quality due to the abundance of biotic resources
4. Considering the term 'biogeochemical', which process does NOT directly relate to it?
   (a) Nutrient cycling within ecosystems
   (b) Formation of ozone in the atmosphere
   (c) Uptake of minerals by plants from the soil
   (d) Decomposition of organic matter releasing nutrients back into the soil
5. Which of the following practices can significantly mitigate soil erosion in a region experiencing heavy rainfall?
   (a) Building more concrete structures to redirect water flow
   (b) Increasing the number of trees and vegetation cover
   (c) Creating more water reservoirs and dams
   (d) Introducing more animal life to graze on the grass
6. Which gas is filled in weather observation balloons?
   (a) Nitrogen (b) Helium
   (c) Argon (d) Oxygen
7. What is the process of seeping water into ground known as?
   (a) Infiltration (b) Irrigation
   (c) Aeration (d) Sublimation
8. Identify which of the following is not a source of groundwater.
   (a) Rainwater (b) Aquifers
   (c) Rivers (d) Seawater
9. Which term is used for the condensation of water vapour in the atmosphere that falls under gravity?
   (a) Transpiration (b) Evaporation
   (c) Precipitation (d) Desalination
10. Which of the given statements is not true for ozone?
    (a) It is a pungent smelling blue gas.
    (b) It can treat gangrene and is used as a disinfectant.
    (c) A molecule of ozone has three oxygen atoms.
    (d) Low level ozone is not harmful.
11. Water and air together constitute what percentage of soil composition?
    (a) Around 10% (b) Around 25%
    (c) Around 50% (d) Around 70%

12. Which layer of the soil is the bedrock?

(a) Horizon O (b) Horizon A

(c) Horizon C (d) Horizon R

13. Which is the most determining factor for soil structure?

(a) Parent rock (b) Humus

(c) Water content (d) Location

14. Water pollution results in the spread of many harmful diseases. Identify which one is not due to water pollution?

(a) Fluorosis (b) Arsenicosis

(c) Lead poisoning (d) Cystic fibrosis

15. Which of the following rocks do not allow seepage of water?

(a) Permeable rocks

(b) Impermeable rocks

(c) Stratified rocks

(d) None of these

16. In which category can fungi be kept?

(a) Consumer (b) Producer

(c) Decomposer (d) None of these

17. Which of the following is not a greenhouse gas?

(a) CO_2 (b) Nitrous oxide

(c) Methane (d) Oxygen

18. What term is given to the process when plants absorb nitrogen through their roots from the soil?

(a) Nitrification

(b) Assimilation

(c) Denitrification

(d) Fixation

19. Living substances that contain carbon are called ________.

(a) organic (b) inorganic

(c) carbonic (d) none of these

20. Which of the given factors is responsible for eutrophication of lakes?

(a) Industrial smoke

(b) Automobile exhaust

(c) Enrichment of water by nutrients

(d) None of these

21. Which of the following is the International Day for 'The Prevention of Ozone Layer'?

(a) September 12 (b) September 16

(c) December 16 (d) December 21

22. Identify the step which is not a part of the carbon cycle.

(a) Transpiration

(b) Respiration

(c) Photosynthesis

(d) Burning of fossil fuels

23. Which of the given facts is true for CFCs?

(a) CFCs have natural sources.

(b) CFCs are soluble in water.

(c) CFCs contain only carbon, chlorine and fluorine.

(d) All the above.

24. Acid rain has high levels of ________.

(a) Nitric and sulphuric acids

(b) Nitric and phosphoric acids

(c) Phosphoric and carbonic acids

(d) Sulphuric and phosphoric acids

25. Which layer of atmosphere is important for telecommunication on earth?

(a) Troposphere (b) Ionosphere

(c) Mesosphere (d) Thermosphere

26. Which of the following is not a cause of soil erosion.

(a) Tilling

(b) Terrace farming

(c) Deforestation

(d) No embankments along the river banks

27. Which of the following is the chief source of minerals in soil?

(a) Plants (b) Animals

(c) Parent rock (d) Bacteria

28. Which of the given sources of water cannot be included in freshwater sources?

(a) Glaciers

(b) Aquifers

(c) Sea

(d) Underground streams

29. Identify the soil formed by intense leaching due to heavy rains.

(a) Laterite soil (b) Alluvial soil
(c) Black soil (d) Mountain soil

30. What are the chief sources of carbon on earth?

(a) Oceans
(b) Atmosphere
(c) Petroleum and its products.
(d) All of these

31. Why nitrogen is an important gas?

(a) It dilutes the activity of oxygen, and thus, combustion of fuel takes place at a moderate rate.
(b) It is used in food preservation.
(c) Only (a)
(d) Both (a) and (b)

32. Read the sentences and choose the correct option.

I. Alluvial soil is formed by the deposition of silt and alluvium brought down by rivers.
II. Its main contents are organic and nitrogenous contents.

Select the correct option.

(a) Only statement I is correct.
(b) Only statement II is correct.
(c) Both are correct.
(d) Both are incorrect.

33. Which of the following is/are part/s of water cycle?

(a) Precipitation (b) Condensation
(c) Evaporation (d) All of the above

34. Which of the following is involved in adding CO_2 back to the atmosphere?

(i) Respiration
(ii) Combustion
(iii) Decay and decomposition of organic remains
(iv) Photosynthesis

Select the correct option.

(a) (i), (ii), (iii) (b) (i), (ii), (iv)
(c) (ii), (iii) (d) (i), (ii)

35. Which of these is/are air pollutants?

(a) Nitrogen oxides (b) Carbon monoxide
(c) Sulphur dioxide (d) All of these

36. Which of these nitrogen fixing bacteria play an important role in the nitrogen cycle?

(a) Rhizobium (b) Azotobacter
(c) Anabaena (d) All of these

37. Which of the given statements are true for renewable sources of energy?

(i) These are derived from natural processes.
(ii) Most energy sources are fossil fuels.
(iii) It is a form of clean energy.

Select the correct option.

(a) All are true.
(b) (i) and (iii) are true.
(c) Only (ii) is true.
(d) (ii) and (iii) are not true.

38. Identify the wrong statement/s from the following.

(a) Increase of CO_2 is due to increased afforestation.
(b) Increase in CO_2 results in the increase of atmospheric temperature at the same rate.
(c) Increase in CO_2 results in melting of glaciers.
(d) All the above

39. Identify how are water vapours formed.

(a) Transpiration from plants
(b) Heating of water bodies
(c) Only (a)
(d) Both (a) and (b)

40. Which of the following makes use of CFCs?

(a) Blowing agents (b) Refrigerators
(c) Both (a) and (b) (d) Only (b)

41. Acid rain is caused by an increase in the atmosphere concentration of

(a) Ozone and dust (b) SO_2 and NO_2
(c) SO_3 and CO (d) CO and CO_2

42. Maximum deposition of DDT will occur in

(a) Phytoplankton (b) Crab
(c) Eel (d) Sea gull

43. A lake with an inflow of domestic sewage rich in organic waste may result in

(a) drying of the lake very soon due to algal bloom
(b) an increased production of fish due to lot of nutrient
(c) death of fish due to lack of oxygen
(d) increased population of aquatic food web organism

44. Which one of the following pair is mismatched?
(a) Fossil fuel burning - release of CO_2
(b) Nuclear power - radioactive waste
(c) Solar energy - greenhouse effect
(d) Biomass burning - release of CO_2

45. Greenhouse effect is the cumulative result of the influences of certain gases. Indentify the gas that is not involved in this influence.
(a) Methane (b) Chloroflurocarbons
(c) Nitrogen (d) Carbon dioxide

46. Soil conservation is a process in which
(a) Soil is aerated
(b) Soil erosion is allowed
(c) Sterile soil is made fertile
(d) Soil is protected against loss

47. Plants die in water-logged soil because of
(a) Nutrient leaching
(b) Dilution of soil nutrient
(c) Stoppage of root respiration
(d) Dilution of cell sap

48. If more trees are grown in the industrial towns
(a) There will be rains
(b) Inhabitants will have more shades
(c) Oxygen will be replenished
(d) They will provide more fuel and food

49. Depletion of forest result in
(a) Less rainfall (b) Soil erosion
(c) Loss of fertility (d) All the above

50. Which one of the following is an example of both organic and inorganic resources?
(a) Metallic ferrous ores (b) Microbes
(c) Soil (d) Air

51. Life supporting part of earth's surface is known as
(a) Lithosphere (b) Stratosphere
(c) Biosphere (d) Ecotone

52. Harmful UV rays of the Sun are absorbed by
(a) Carbon dioxide (b) Ozone
(c) Oxygen (d) Helium

53. One of the important gases that is responsible for greenhouse effect is
(a) CO_2 (b) O_2
(c) N_2 (d) CO

54. Air is a mixture of gases with the following gas in maximum percentage
(a) Oxygen (b) Hydrogen
(c) Nitrogen (d) Carbon dioxide

55. Biosphere includes
(a) Hydrosphere (b) Lithosphere
(c) Atmosphere (d) All of the above

56. Fertility of the soil is reduced by
(a) Decaying organic matter
(b) Crop rotation
(c) Intensive agriculture
(d) None

57. Deforestation causes
(a) Soil erosion (b) Pollution
(c) Both of above (d) None of these

58. The average amount of CO_2 in atmosphere is
(a) 0.3% (b) 0.003%
(c) 3.0% (d) 0.03%

59. The average amount of N_2 in atmosphere is
(a) 78% (b) 0.3%
(c) 7.8% (d) 0.03%

60. Which substance is responsible for depletion of ozone layer?
(a) CO_2 (b) CH_4
(c) CFCs (d) CO

61. Which organism cannot fix atmosphere nitrogen?
(a) *Rhizobium* (b) *Nostoc*
(c) *Azatobacter* (d) *E. coli*

62. Which gas causes 'greenhouse effect' and leads to global warming?
(a) Carbon monoxide (b) Carbon disulphide
(c) Carbon dioxide (d) Oxygen

63. 'Freeing' of N_2 gas from nitrates present in soil and water is known as
(a) Nitrification (b) Ammonification
(c) Denitrification (d) Nitrogen fixation

64. Harmful UV radiations coming from sun to earth are absorbed by
(a) O_2 (b) CO_2
(c) N_2 (d) Ozone

65. What would happen, if all the oxygen present in the environment is covered with ozone?

(a) We will be protected more.
(b) It will become posionous and kill living forms.
(c) Ozone is not stable, hence, it will be toxic.
(d) It will help harmful sun radiations to reach earth and damage many life forms.

66. The two forms of oxygen found in the atmosphere are

(a) Water and ozone
(b) Water and oxygen
(c) Ozone and oxygen
(d) Water and carbon dioxide

67. The process of nitrogen fixation by bacteria does not take place in the presence of

(a) molecular form of hydrogen
(b) elemental form of oxygen
(c) water
(d) elemental form of nitrogen

68. One of the following processes is not a step involved in the water cycle operating in nature

(a) evaporation (b) transpiration
(c) precipitation (d) photosynthesis

69. Which of the following is not a green house gas?

(a) Methane (b) Carbon dioxide
(c) Carbon monoxide (d) Ammonia

70. Which step is not involved in the carbon cycle?

(a) Photosynthesis
(b) Transpiration
(c) Respiration
(d) Burning of fossil fuels

Directions for questions 71 to 75
Match the following.

71.

Column I	Column II
A. Lowermost layer of the atmosphere	(i) Exosphere
B. Known as 'cold layer'	(ii) Thermosphere
C. Space shuttles orbit in this layer	(iii) Troposphere
D. Outermost layer of the atmosphere	(iv) Mesosphere

Select the correct option.

(a) A-iii, B-i, C-ii, D-iv
(b) A-iii, B-iv, C-ii, D-i
(c) A-ii, B-iv, C-iii, D-i
(d) A-i, B-iii, C-iv, D-ii

72.

Column I	Column II
A. Smoke from burning of fossil fuels	(i) Soil pollution
B. Excess use of pesticides	(ii) Air pollution
C. Horning of automobiles	(iii) Water pollution
D. Leakage of crude oil in sea	(iv) Noise pollution

Select the correct option.

(a) A-iii, B-i, C-iv, D-ii
(b) A-ii, B-iv, C-i, D-iii
(c) A-ii, B-i, C-iv, D-iii
(d) A-i, B-iii, C-ii, D-iv

73.

Column I	Column II
A. Alluvial soil	(i) Acidic, porous and coarse
B. Black soil	(ii) Decomposition of metamorphic rocks
C. Red soil	(iii) Very fertile
D. Laterite soil	(iv) Lacks nitrogen and humus

Select the correct option.

(a) A-iii, B-iv, C-ii, D-i
(b) A-iii, B-ii, C-i, D-iv
(c) A-ii, B-iv, C-i, D-iii
(d) A-i, B-iii, C-iv, D-ii

74.

Column I	Column II
A. Change of gas into liquid.	(i) Sleet
B. Falling to earth of any form of water.	(ii) Condense
C. Change into vapour.	(iii) Precipitation
D. Mixture of rain and snow.	(iv) Evaporate

Select the correct option.

(a) A-iii, B-i, C-iv, D-ii
(b) A-ii, B-iii, C-iv, D-i
(c) A-i, B-iii, C-ii, D-iv
(d) A-iv, B-ii, C-i, D-iii

Select the correct option.

(a) A-iii, B-ii, C-iv, D-i
(b) A-ii, B-iii, C-iv, D-i
(c) A-i, B-iv, C-ii, D-iii
(d) A-ii, B-iv, C-i, D-iii

75.

Column I	Column II
A. Wells	(i) Potash alum
B. Chlorination	(ii) Groundwater
C. Water table	(iii) Cleaning water
D. Water of crystallization	(iv) Surface of groundwater

Level 2: Review your Concepts

76. What are the differences between biotic and abiotic components?

77. All the living organisms are basically made up of C, N, S, P, H and O. How do they enter the living forms? Discuss.

78. How are clouds formed?

79. What do you understand by the term microclimate?

80. Why does the percentage of gases like oxygen, nitrogen and carbon dioxide remains almost the same in the atmosphere?

Level 3: Assess Your Concepts

81. How are living organisms dependent on the soil? Are organisms that live in water totally independent of soil as a resource?

82. Discuss the interplay between biotic and abiotic factors in an ecosystem and elucidate how they influence each other's existence and function.

AT

NEET SPECIAL WING

Practice Questions

Multiple-Answer Type Questions

Questions number 1 to 5 are multiple-choice questions. Each question has FOUR options (a), (b), (c), and (d). ONE OR MORE THAN ONE of these four option(s) is/are the correct answer(s).

1. Identify the incorrectly matched pairs.
   (a) Chemical pollutants - DDT, DDE
   (b) Physical pollutants - Oil spills
   (c) Biological pollutants - radioactive wastes
   (d) Biodegradable waste - plastics and metals

2. Which of the following are part of suspended particulate matter?
   (a) Soot
   (b) Smoke
   (c) Fly ash
   (d) Dust

3. Which of the following are secondary pollutants?
   (a) Hydrocarbons
   (b) PAN
   (c) Nitrogen dioxide
   (d) Formaldehyde

4. Identify the correctly matched pairs:
   (a) *Itai Itai* - Cadmium
   (b) Minamata - Mercury
   (c) Blue baby syndrome - excessive chlorides
   (d) Dental caries - excessive fluorides

5. Which of the following factors influence the movement of air?
   (a) Difference in topography
   (b) Different gases
   (c) Rotation of earth
   (d) Uneven heating of land

Comprehension-Based Questions

A. Read the paragraph given below and answer the questions number 6 to 11:

Global warming is a phenomenon which is an increase in global average temperature. It affects the climatic conditions on the planet earth. The current rise in global temperatures is mainly caused by humans. Global warming is caused by burning of fossil fuels, deforestation. Many agricultural and industrial processes add to the greenhouse gases, mainly carbon dioxide and methane. These greenhouse gases absorb the heat that is reradiated back (infrared radiations) from the earth after the sunlight warms the earth. The greenhouse gases are mainly responsible for maintaining the temperature on the earth. But large amount of these gases trap more and more heat and causes global warming.

Global warming causes a host of different problems. The space occupied by desert is expanding, while incidences of heat waves and wildfires are becoming more and more common. Increased temperatures have led to melting of glaciers and rise in the levels of oceans and seas. Higher temperatures are causing storms, droughts and other natural calamities. Rapid climatic changes have resulted in extinction of species. Climate changes also leads to other natural calamities like draughts, floods, etc.

6. Identify which one among the following is not a greenhouse gas.
   (a) Ozone
   (b) Methane
   (c) Hydrogen
   (d) Nitrous oxide

7. Which among the following radiations have higher energy and short wavelength?
   (a) Ultra violet radiations
   (b) Infrared radiations
   (c) Beta radiation
   (d) Alpha radiation

8. Which of the following green house gases is responsible for ozone depletion?
   (a) CH_4
   (b) CFC
   (c) N_2O
   (d) CO_2

9. Which one of the following is incorrect about the greenhouse effect?
   (a) It is a process which naturally maintains the earth's temperature
   (b) Increase in greenhouse gas decreases the global temperatures
   (c) Increase in greenhouse gas increases the global temperature
   (d) Life on earth is possible due to the greenhouse effect

10. Which of the following is not caused due to global warming?
   (a) Increase in UV radiation
   (b) Rise in sea levels
   (c) Melting of glaciers
   (d) Abnormal weather patterns

11. Match the following:

Column – A	Column – B
(i) CFC	(a) Levels increase due to usage of fossil fuels
(ii) CO	(b) Most abundant gas in atmosphere
(iii) N_2	(c) More affinity towards RBC
(iv) CO_2	(d) Ozone depletion
(v) Ozone	(e) Absorbs the UV light

B. Read the paragraph given below and answer the questions number 12 to 17:

Biogeochemical cycles is a constant interaction between the living and non-living components of the biosphere. The matter on the earth is present in the form of atoms. Since matter can neither be created nor destroyed, they are recycled between the living and the non-living components of the ecosystem. The gaseous water cycle includes carbon, oxygen, nitrogen and the water cycle. The sedimentary cycles include sulphur, phosphorous, rock cycles, etc. In water cycle, water is continuously being cycled between the atmosphere and the earth and is important for the survival of living beings. Nitrogen is another important biogeochemical cycle as nitrogen is an important element present in proteins, amino acids and nucleic acids. Oxygen enters the living system vis respiration and is a natural component of air. Carbon is yet another important cycle which is linked to the energy flow in the ecosystem. In carbon cycle, the food produced by the producers is consumed by the consumers The carbon from both the producers and the consumers again enters the abiotic system via respiration.

12. In a nutrient cycle large slow moving non biological components are called:
   (a) Reservoir pool
   (b) Labile pool
   (c) nutrient pool
   (d) source pool

13. Conversion of atmospheric nitrogen into nitrates is called:
   (a) Nitrification
   (b) Denitrification
   (c) Both a and b
   (d) Nitrogen fixation

14. Which of the following bring about nitrification?
   (a) Pseudomonas
   (b) Nitrosomonas
   (c) Azotobacter
   (d) Rhizobium

15. Which among the following is not a carbon sink?
   (a) Deposits of coal, peat and oil
   (b) Carbon in carbonate rocks
   (c) Oceans
   (d) Air

16. The process carried out by bacteria on the dead remains of plants and animals is called:
   (a) Nitrification
   (b) Denitrification
   (c) Ammonification
   (d) Nitrogen fixation

17. Match the following:

Column – A	Column – B
(i) Sedimentary cycle	(a) Water cycle
(ii) Gaseous cycle	(b) Respiration
(iii) Carbon	(c) Ammonia
(iv) Oxygen	(d) Phosphorus
(v) Putrefying bacteria	(e) Fossil fuels

Answer Keys

Crossword

Across

6. Global warming 7. Chlorofluorocarbon 9. Minamata
13. Biological weathering 15. Inexhaustible 16. Gravels 17. Itai-Itai
18. Smog

Down

1. Biogeochemical cycles 2. Lithosphere 3. Biomagnification
4. Soil profile 5. Peroxyacetylnitrate 8. Nitrification 10. Bioaccumulation 11. Paedogenesis
12. Eutrophication 14. Combustion

Classroom Wing

Very Short Answer Type Questions

1. Smog	2. Weathering	3. Nutrient cycling	4. Carbon dioxide	5. Formation
6. (c)	7. (b)	8. (c)	9. (d)	10. (b)
11. (b)	12. (c)	13. (b)	14. (b)	15. (c)
16. (d)	17. (b)	18. (d)	19. (b)	20. (a)
21. (a)	22. (d)	23. (d)	24. (c)	25. (b)
26. (a)	27. (a)	28. (a)	29. (b)	30. (b)

Competition Wing

Level 1: Apply your Concepts

1. (c)	2. (c)	3. (c)	4. (b)	5. (b)
6. (b)	7. (a)	8. (d)	9. (c)	10. (d)
11. (c)	12. (d)	13. (b)	14. (d)	15. (b)
16. (c)	17. (d)	18. (b)	19. (a)	20. (c)
21. (b)	22. (a)	23. (c)	24. (a)	25. (b)
26. (b)	27. (c)	28. (c)	29. (a)	30. (d)
31. (d)	32. (a)	33. (d)	34. (a)	35. (d)
36. (d)	37. (b)	38. (d)	39. (d)	40. (c)
41. (b)	42. (d)	43. (c)	44. (c)	45. (c)
46. (d)	47. (c)	48. (c)	49. (d)	50. (c)
51. (c)	52. (b)	53. (a)	54. (c)	55. (d)
56. (c)	57. (c)	58. (d)	59. (a)	60. (c)
61. (d)	62. (c)	63. (c)	64. (d)	65. (c)
66. (b)	67. (b)	68. (d)	69. (d)	70. (b)
71. (b)	72. (c)	73. (a)	74. (b)	75. (a)

NEET Special Wing

Multiple-Answer Type Questions

1. (c, d) **2.** (a, b, c, d) **3.** (b, d) **4.** (a, b, d) **5.** (a, c, d)

Comprehension-Based Questions

6. (c) **7.** (a) **8.** (b) **9.** (b) **10.** (b)

11. (i) → (d); (ii) → (c); (iii) → (b); (iv) → (a); (v) → (e)

12. (a) **13.** (d) **14.** (b) **15.** (d) **16.** (c)

17. (i) → (d); (ii) → (a); (iii) → (e); (iv) → (b); (v) → (c)

Hints and Explanations

CLASSROOM WING

Very Short Answer Type Questions

6. Abiotic factors pertain to the non-living components of an ecosystem. Humans are biotic in nature.
7. Soil erosion is mainly caused by strong winds and the flow of water, which remove and transport the top layer of the soil.
8. The soil profile is represented by horizontal layers termed as horizons, showing different stages and components of the soil.
9. Among the listed options, carbon dioxide is a primary greenhouse gas responsible for trapping heat and contributing to global warming.
10. Based on particles, soils are categorized into sandy, clayey, and loamy soils. Marshy soil isn't a category based on particle type.
11. Atmospheric pressure doesn't have a direct influence on soil formation or its quality, unlike the other options listed.
12. While increased CO_2 can influence plant growth, the direct consequences of rising greenhouse gases mainly relate to global warming and its impacts.

Short Answer Type Questions

31. The effects of global warming are:
    - The rise in temperature has led to the melting of glaciers, thereby, increasing the level of the sea.
    - Decrease in the production of crop due to eruption of plant diseases, pests and growth of weeds as a result of increase in the temperature.
    - The increase in warmth of the atmosphere has led to the increase in the moisture carrying capacity of the air.
32. Factors that contribute to physical weathering include temperature, rainwater, wind, ice, glaciers, snow and running water. The roots of the plants also play a crucial role in weathering by penetrating into the crevices of the rocks. **Example:** The freezing of water leads to the expansion of water in the rock crevices, which leads to the breakdown of rocks
33. Advantages of rainwater harvesting are:
    - Checks soil erosion
    - Raise water table level
    - Maintains supply of water during months of the year
    - Control floods
    - Reduce loss of water through surface run-off
34. Biomagnification is also known as food chain magnification in a manner that organisms present at the top of the chain contain harmful chemicals, such as DDE, DDT, methyl mercury, etc. They may affect the organisms that feed on them. For example: *Minimata disease* in fish-eating population is a result of biomagnification of mercury in fishes.
35. The term 'biogeochemical' pertains to the uptake of nutrient elements from the earth's surface by living organisms. These nutrients are vital for processes like growth, reproduction, and metabolism, effectively linking biological, geological, and chemical aspects of the ecosystem.
36. A damaged ozonosphere means thinner ozone layers, leading to increased penetration of harmful UV radiations to the Earth's surface. This can result in a higher incidence of skin cancers in humans and animals, disrupt the developmental stages of aquatic life, and reduce the efficiency of photosynthesis in plants, which can impact food chains and overall ecosystem health.

Essay Type Questions

37. **Air:**
    - It helps in purifying the air by absorbing pollutants.
    - It adds oxygen to the air and takes carbon dioxide gas during photosynthesis. Therefore, the greenhouse effect is controlled.
    - Transpiration helps in the formation of clouds, it maintains the temperature of surrounding area and gives cooling effect.

    Soil:

    - Plants in forest hold the soil, thereby, preventing soil erosion.

- It holds the soil which helps in increasing the underground water level.
- Adds nutrients to the soil as lot of vegetation present in forest gets decomposed.

Water:

- Forest helps in bringing rain and increasing the level of water in underground levels.

38. Water is essential for life because:

- About 70% weight of human being is due to water.
- All cellular processes takes place in water as a medium.
- All reactions take place within our body and within the cells occur between substances that are dissolved in water.
- Transportation of substances from one form to another takes place due to water.
- Terrestrial life forms require fresh water for the transportation of substances and also to get rid of high amounts of wastes.

39. The ongoing global environmental changes, primarily driven by anthropogenic activities, promise profound effects on both biotic and abiotic components of ecosystems. Biotic components, including plants and animals, may face habitat loss, altered breeding patterns, and increased vulnerability to diseases. Abiotic components, like soil and water, can witness degradation and scarcity. The interplay between these factors can lead to reduced agricultural yields, compromised water resources, and loss of biodiversity. For human societies, this translates to food and water shortages, economic upheavals, and potential conflicts over resources. Additionally, health threats can rise with increased disease vectors and reduced air and water quality. The overall quality of life could decline, emphasizing the urgency to adopt sustainable practices and ensure a balanced coexistence with nature.

COMPETITION WING

Level 1: Apply your Concepts

1. Sandy soil consists of larger particles, loamy soil has a mixture of particle sizes, and clayey soil is characterized by fine, compact particles.

   Hence, the correct option is (c).

2. The ozonosphere or ozone layer absorbs most of the sun's harmful ultraviolet radiation. Depletion of this layer results in increased harmful ultraviolet radiations reaching the Earth's surface.

   Hence, the correct option is (c).

3. Plants, being primary producers, rely on abiotic factors like water and sunlight for photosynthesis. A scarcity of these factors would result in stunted plant growth, which would impact the food chain starting with herbivores.

   Hence, the correct option is (c).

4. The term 'biogeochemical' pertains to the uptake and cycling of nutrient elements by living organisms from the surface of the earth. The formation of ozone, while vital to the atmosphere, doesn't directly involve the biological component interacting with geological and chemical aspects in the same manner as nutrient cycling.

   Hence, the correct option is (b).

5. Trees and vegetation help in holding the soil together with their roots, reducing runoff, and acting as barriers to wind and water flow, thus significantly reducing soil erosion.

   Hence, the correct option is (b).

Level 2: Review your Concepts

76.

S. No.	Biotic Components	Abiotic Components
1.	Living components of the ecosystem	Non-living components of the ecosystem
2.	It includes living things that either directly or indirectly affects the other organisms in the environment.	They affect reproduction and survival of the organisms.
	Examples: Plants, animals, fungi, bacteria, etc.	**Examples:** Water, light, sound, humidity, minerals, gases, etc.

77. Through photosynthesis and absorption from soil

78. During day time water from different sources like pond, lake, river, sea, well, etc., gets evaporated and this water vapour rises with the hot air. At a specific height, the air cools and the water vapour condenses to form minute droplets and forms clouds. When these water drops become heavy, they precipitate and fall as rain.

79. Microclimate refers to the difference in temperature observed over an area of just a few square metres or larger areas covering few kilometres.

80. Cycling of these gases maintains consistency.

Level 3: Assess Your Concepts

81. All living organisms are directly or indirectly dependent on soil. Plants obtain water and minerals from the soil and prepare food for themselves and animals. Other organisms that live in water are not totally independent of soil because the microbes growing on the soil in water are the primary producers in the soil which starts the food chain and even other microbes that live in soil helps in the decomposition of dead plants and animals in water to return the nutrients and other elements back to the water.

82. Biotic and abiotic factors form the foundation of every ecosystem. Biotic components encompass all living entities, from plants that are primary producers to various levels of consumers and decomposers. Abiotic components, on the other hand, include non-living factors like water, sunlight, soil, and temperature. The presence, abundance, and interactions of biotic factors are profoundly influenced by the abiotic conditions of their environment. For instance, sunlight and temperature dictate photosynthesis rates in plants. Similarly, soil quality affects plant growth, which in turn impacts herbivores relying on those plants. Conversely, biotic factors can modify abiotic factors. For example, plants can influence soil quality and water availability through transpiration and root structures. This intricate interplay ensures the balance, resilience, and health of ecosystems. Disruption in either component can cascade through the system, highlighting their mutual dependence.

NEET SPECIAL WING

Multiple-Answer Type Questions

1. Water pollutants are broadly classified into three categories as-
   i. **Physical pollutants:** It includes thermal pollution caused by heat and oil spills.
   ii. **Chemical pollutants:** It includes organic wastes, such as sewage, fertilizers, pesticides (DDT, DDE, BHC, etc.), PCBs (Polychlorinated biphenyls), detergents, inorganic chemicals (lead, nickel, mercury, arsenic, nitrates, fluorides, cadmium, etc.), inorganic impurities, such as calcium and magnesium and radioactive wastes.
   iii. **Biological pollutants:** Viruses, protozoa, fungi, nematodes, bacteria, helminths, etc.
2. The particulate pollutants of the air are also known as suspended particulate matter or SPM, which consists of soot (black powdered substance produced on burning of coal, wood, etc.), smoke, fly ash and dust, etc.
3. The atomic oxygen reacts with hydrocarbon to produce radicals, which on combination with O_2, NO_2 and hydrocarbons lead to the formation of secondary pollutants. These secondary pollutants are aldehydes, formaldehydes and peroxyacetyl nitrate (PAN).
4. ***Minimata disease*** in fish-eating population is a result of biomagnification of mercury in fishes. In Japan, the population eating rice produced from soil containing high concentration of cadmium suffered from a disease called ***Itai Itai***. Higher concentration of fluorides in water causes cavities of the teeth also known as dental caries. All these conditions are associated with water pollution.
5. Factors responsible for diverse types of atmospheric phenomenon, such as breeze, monsoon rains, cyclones, storms, etc., include-Rotation of the Earth, uneven heating of land, difference in the rate of heating and cooling over land and water bodies, Condensation and vaporization of water vapour and difference in topography

Comprehension-Based Questions

A.

6. Greenhouse is a building made up of glass to grow or shelter dedicated plants. The glass of greenhouse is made in a way that it allows the entry of sunrays but restricts them to escape from the glass walls. Carbon dioxide and water vapour inside it further captures heat to increase the warmth of the air inside the greenhouse. Greenhouse gases include carbon dioxide, nitrogen dioxide, ozone and chlorofluorocarbons.
7. Ultra violet radiations are radiations which have the shortest wavelength and the highest amount of energy associated with them.
8. CFC's being light reach the higher levels of stratosphere and interact with ozone. They react irreversibly and breakdown the ozone molecules, thus depleting the gas and reducing its ability to absorb UV radiations.
9. Some of the effects of global warming include-
   i. The rise in temperature has led to the melting of glaciers, thereby, increasing the level of the sea.
   ii. Decrease in the production of crop due to eruption of plant diseases, pests and growth of weeds as a result of increase in the temperature.
   iii. The increase in warmth of the atmosphere has led to the increase in the moisture carrying capacity of the air. Thus, increase in greenhouse gases leads to more heat being trapped on the earth as a result global temperatures rise.
10. Global warming occurs due to the greenhouse effect and it does not result in increase in UV radiation.
11. Match the following:

    CFC's react irreversibly with ozone molecules and effectively depleting them.
    (i) (d)

    CO has much higher affinity towards RBC then oxygen. Thus, CO is also called as silent killer.
    (ii) (c)

    Nitrogen is the most abundant gas found in earth's atmosphere.
    (iii) (b)

    Increased burning of fossil fuels produces more CO_2 in the atmosphere.
    (iv) (a)

    Ozone layer in the stratosphere is responsible for absorbing and protecting the earth from the harmful UV radiations.
    (v) (e)

B.

12. Reservoir pool comprises of large, slow-moving and mostly non-biological components. It is one of the two divisions of nutrient cycle.

13. Nitrogen being inert in nature cannot be used in its pure form. Thus, nitrogen needs to be converted into nitrates and nitrites to be used up by the living organisms. However, no living organism except a few bacteria are capable to convert it. The process of conversion is carried out either by industrial nitrogen fixation or nitrogen fixing bacteria like ***Azotobacter*** and ***Rihizobium***. These organisms convert atmospheric nitrogen into nitrates, which is the water-soluble form of nitrogen. This process of fixation is termed as nitrogen fixation.

14. The ammonium ion assimilated in the plants is further converted into nitrate by a process known as nitrification. This is brought about by bacteria like Nitrosomonas.

15. In some cases, cycling materials are stored into reservoirs or sinks and become unavailable to living organisms. Examples-transfer of carbon from organism to deposits of coal, peat and oil.

Incorporation of carbon into carbonate rocks and oceans also act as carbon reservoirs.

16. The excreta of animals contain urea or uric acid or when an animal dies, bacteria performs ammonification which is production of ammonium ions from nitrogen-containing molecules. The term 'ammonification' refers to the process of ammonia formation.

17. Match the following:

The sedimentary cycles include sulphur, phosphorous, rock cycles, etc. It consists of a solution phase and a rock phase.
(i) (d)

Water cycle is part of the gaseous cycle.
(ii) (a)

Carbon is stored in the reservoirs of fossil fuels.
(iii) (e)

Air comprises 21 per cent of oxygen, an important constituent of water. Oxygen enters the system through respiration, which oxidizes food to release carbon dioxide and energy.
(iv) (b)

Putrefying bacteria bring about ammonification which is the process of formation of ammonia from dead remains of plants and animals.
(v) (c)

Glossary

Animal husbandry: Branch of agriculture concerned with animals that are raised for meat, fibre, milk, eggs and other products.

Annual rings: Concentric rings formed every year in the stem.

Annual rings: Annual rings are concentric layers of wood produced by trees each year, consisting of a light-coloured springwood and a darker summerwood. The number of rings can determine a tree's age.

Apical meristem: Meristems located at the apices of the plant.

Appendages: Structures which project from the body of an animal used for locomotion and feeding.

Arteriosclerosis: Thickening and hardening of the walls of the arteries.

Bee-keeping: Maintenance of hives of honey bees for the production of honey.

Biconcave: Resembling a flattened disk, a biconcave shape is concave on both sides, with a centre that is thinner than its edges.

Biodiversity: Variety of plant and animal life in the world or in a particular habitat.

Broiler: Poultry reared for obtaining meat.

Canaliculi: Canaliculi are a microscopic network of channels within bone tissue that facilitates both cell-to-cell communication and nutrient exchange.

Castes: Several morphological forms of honey bee.

Cell differentiation: Process by which a cell becomes specialized in order to perform a specific function.

Chitin: Fibrous substance consisting of polysaccharides, present in fungal cell wall.

Chlorenchyma: Type of living tissue (parenchyma) that contains chlorophyll.

Cisternae: Flattened sac-like structures which are parallelly arranged in the ER.

Congenital: Disease which is inherited by an individual at the time of birth.

Cork: Outermost layer of periderm which is outer layer of a plant stem formed in secondary growth.

Craniata: Animals belonging to phylum vertebrata possessing cranium which encloses the brain.

Cristae: Partial partitions in a mitochondrion formed by in folding of the inner membrane.

Cropping pattern: Selection of varieties of crops and determining the proportion of area for growing them depending on climate, availability of water and nutrients in the soil in a region.

Cryptogams: Plants having conspicuous reproductive structures.

Cytology: Branch of biology concerned with the structure and function of cells.

Cytoprocts: Anal opening in a unicellular organism; a special pore in the pellicle of ciliates.

Cytoskeleton: The cytoskeleton is a dynamic framework of protein filaments and tubules inside all cells. It provides structural support, helps maintain the cell's shape, and is essential for cell movement and the transport of organelles.

Dictyosomes: Stacks of flat, membrane-bound cavities (cisternae) that together comprise the Golgi apparatus.

Diploblastic animals: Animals possessing two germ layers in their embryos.

Division of labour: Assignment of specific roles to different organs and organ systems in human body.

Drone: Fertile male stingless honey bees which are larger than workers and their main role is to mate with queen.

Ecdysis: Shedding of the exoskeleton periodically during the life cycle of an animal.

Endocytosis: Taking in of matter by a living cell by invagination of its membrane to form a vacuole.

Epidemic: Widespread occurrence of an infectious disease in a community.

Etiology: Study of causes of a disease.

Exocytosis: Process by which the contents of a cell vacuole are released to the exterior through fusion of the vacuole membrane with the cell membrane.

Exoskeleton: Skeleton present on the surface of the body.

Fibrils: Living organisms contain fibrils, which are fine, protein-based filaments that play a crucial role in providing structural stability and performing various cellular functions.

Fibroblasts: Fibre-forming cells present in rows in between the collagen fibres.

Gametophyte: A gametophyte is the haploid, gamete-producing phase in the life cycle of plants that undergo alternation of generations. This stage is responsible for producing the egg and sperm, which then fuse to form a diploid zygote. This zygote then develops into the sporophyte phase. In plants like mosses (bryophytes), the gametophyte is the most prominent and long-lasting stage of the life cycle.

Green revolution: Revolutionary change in the field of agriculture that has increased the production of food grains to a great extent.

Grit cells: The gritty texture of fruits like pears and guavas comes from stone cells, or grit cells, that are embedded in the pulp.

Haustoria: Haustoria are root-like or hyphal structures that grow into host tissue, acting as a feeding organ for parasitic plants and fungi to obtain water and nutrients.

Hereditary: Passing of traits from parents to offspring (both animal and plants).

Hermaphrodite: Organisms that have both male and female sex organs.

Hierarchy: System in which members of an organization or society are ranked according to relative status or authority.

Histology: Study of tissues.

Homeostasis: Process by which biological systems tend to maintain stability.

Hybridization: Process to produce new varieties of crops by crossing two genetically different parents.

Hypertonic: Solution of lower water concentration than the surrounding environment, having a higher osmotic pressure than a particular fluid.

Hyphae: Branching filaments that make up the mycelium of a fungus.

Hypotonic: Solution of higher water concentration than the surrounding environment, having a lower osmotic pressure than a particular fluid.

Integrated farming: Agricultural practice which combines agriculture with livestock, poultry, fisheries and bee-keeping.

Irrigation: Supply of controlled amount of water to the plants.

Kharif crops: Crops which are grown in rainy season from the month of June to October.

Lactoprotein: The protein component of milk.

Layer: Poultry reared for obtaining eggs.

Lignification: Change in the character of a cell wall, by which it becomes harder.

Lignin: Lignin is a biological polymer found in most plant cell walls that acts as a stiffening agent, giving plants their firm and woody nature.

Lysosomes: Organelle in the cytoplasm of eukaryotic cells containing derivative enzymes enclosed in a membrane.

Manure: Organic matter derived from the biological wastes like animal faeces and plant wastes.

Meristem: A type of tissue in which the cells actively divide.

Metamorphosis: Wide variation in structure, form and functioning of the larval form and the adult.

Microbody: Microbodies are enzyme-filled, membrane-bound organelles in eukaryotic cells that carry out crucial metabolic functions, such as detoxification and fat breakdown.

Microtubule: A microtubule is a vital component of a eukaryotic cell's cytoskeleton, functioning as a hollow, rigid, tube-like structure built from the protein tubulin. These dynamic filaments are essential for providing the cell with structural support, acting as tracks for intracellular transport, and enabling the movement required for cell division.

Morphology: The branch of biology that deals with the form of living organisms.

Mycology: Study of fungi.

Notochord: Long rod-like structure mostly made up of cartilage that separates the digestive tract from the nervous tissue.

Organic farming: Agricultural process which can reduce the use of chemical fertilizers while protecting the environment.

Ornithology: Study of birds.

Pandemic: Disease prevalent over multiple continents or worldwide.

Parenchyma: Tissue that is made up of living cells which are large and unspecialized.

Pathogenicity: Ability of an organism to cause disease.

Pectin: A complex carbohydrate that forms the structural framework of plant cell walls.

Periderm: The "corky outer layer of a plant stem" is known as the periderm. It is a protective tissue that forms in woody plants as they grow and thicken in a process called secondary growth. This specialized tissue also forms as a healing response to injury or infection.

Peroxisomes: Small organelle present in the cytoplasm of many cells, which contains the reducing enzyme catalase and usually some oxidases.

Phanerogamae: Plants having visible reproductive structures.

Phycology: Study of algae.

Placenta: Special structure through which foetus procures nourishment from mother while in the womb.

Plasmodesmata: Narrow thread of cytoplasm that passes through the cell walls of adjacent plant cells and allows communication between them.

Plasmolysis: Contraction of the protoplast of a plant cell as a result of loss of water from the cell.

Pseudocoelom: Body cavity which is not completely lined by peritoneum on the inner and outer sides.

Quarantine: State, period or place of isolation in which people or animals that have been exposed to infectious disease are placed.

Rabi crops: Crops which are grown in the winter season from November to April.

Radial symmetry: Any plane passing through the middle from top to bottom cutting the body into two equal halves.

River Lift System: Irrigation system in which water is directly drawn from the river with the help of a pump.

Saprozoic: Mode of nutrition where nourishment is obtained from dead and decaying organisms.

Sclereids: Composed of very thick-walled, hard and strongly lignified cells called stone cells or grit cells.

Segmentation: Division of the body into distinct portions.

Sieve tubes: Elongated cylindrical, thin-walled cells of phloem with perforated ends.

Slime: Mucus-like substance which exudes from the bodies of certain animals.

Species: Similar group of organisms, which can freely interbreed among themselves and produce fertile offspring.

Sphaerosomes: Small membrane-bound organelles which take part in storage and synthesis of fats.

Sporophyte: In the alternating life cycle of plants, the sporophyte is the diploid, asexual stage that produces spores. For vascular plants, the sporophyte is the most prominent and long-lived form.

Spring wood: Xylem vessels with large cavities.

Stomata: Guard cells along with the openings or pores on leaves.

Suberin: A lipophilic complex polyester biopolymer that occurs in the cell walls.

Sustainable agriculture: Practice of development of techniques in agriculture to meet the human needs, simultaneously maintaining and improving the ecosystem balance and conservation of natural resources.

Symbiosis: Relationship between two organisms who can›t survive without each other.

Tendon: Dense regular connective tissue bundles made of collagen fibres.

Tissues: Group of similar cells that perform certain functions together.

Tonoplast: Membrane which bounds the chief vacuole of a plant cell.

Tracheids: Non-living elongated cells of the xylem.

Translocation: Process to transport of food in plants.

Triploblastic: Triploblastic organisms are all multicellular animals except sponges and cnidarians, and they form from three embryonic cell layers: the ectoderm, mesoderm, and endoderm.

Vascular cambium: As the primary growth tissue for woody plants, the vascular cambium generates wood (secondary xylem) and inner bark (secondary phloem).

Vascular tissue: Complex tissue that carries out the function of conduction of substances through the plant.

Vermicompost: Organic matter obtained when earthworms are used to hasten the process of decomposition.

Photo Credits

CHAPTER 1

Page 1.3—Martin Shields/Alamy Stock Photo; **Page 1.4**—World History Archive/Alamy Stock Photo; **Page 1.4**—Pro3DArtt. Shutterstock; **Page 1.5**—Pro3DArtt. Shutterstock; **Page 1.5**—age fotostock/ Alamy Stock Photo; **Page 1.6**—Mopic. Shutterstock; **Page 1.6**—Artem Povarov/Alamy Stock Phot; **Page 1.6**—Cultura RM/Alamy Stock Photo; **Page 1.8**—KuLouKu. Shutterstock; **Page 1.9**—Sakurra. Shutterstock; **Page 1.9**—Timonina. Shutterstock; **Page 1.9**—tonaquatic19. 123rf.com; **Page 1.9**—eraxion. 123rf.com; **Page 1.11**—Alila Medical Media. Shutterstock; **Page 1.13**—Oxford Designers & Illustrators Ltd. Pearson Education Ltd; **Page 1.17**—Jose Luis Calvo. Shutterstock; **Page 1.17**—HL Studios. Pearson Education Ltd; **Page 1.19**—snapgalleria. Shutterstock; **Page 1.20**—snapgalleria. 123rf.com; **Page 1.21**—Jose Luis Calvo. Shutterstock; **Page 1.22**—alxhar (c) Shutterstock; **Page 1.23**—Art of Science / Shutterstock; **Page 1.24**—Tefi. Shutterstoc; **Page 1.24**—Science History Images/Alamy Stock Photo; **Page 1.24**—Jose Luis Calvo. Shutterstock; **Page 1.24**—mikrostoker. 123rf.com; **Page 1.25**—Designua. Shutterstock; **Page 1.26**—designua. 123rf.com; **Page 1.27**—Amit John. Pearson India Education Services Pvt. Ltd; **Page 1.29**—Alila Medical Media. Shutterstock; **Page 1.29**—blueringmedia. 123rf.com; **Page 1.29**—Art of Science / Shutterstock;

CHAPTER 2

Page 2.5—Mohd Suhail. Pearson India Education Services Pvt. Ltd; **Page 2.6**—Amit John. Pearson India Education Services Pvt. Ltd; **Page 2.6**—Amit John. Pearson India Education Services Pvt. Ltd; **Page 2.7**—Mohd Suhail. Pearson India Education Services Pvt. Ltd; **Page 2.10**—photoiconix. Shutterstock; **Page 2.10**—Gleti. Shutterstock; **Page 2.11**—Biophoto Associates/Science Photo Library; **Page 2.12**—Pearson Education Ltd; **Page 2.13**—Designua. Shutterstock; **Page 2.14**—chiqui. Shutterstock; **Page 2.15**—Blamb. Shuuterstock; **Page 2.18**—Christopher Meade. Shutterstock; **Page 2.19**—Jose Luis Calvo. Shutterstock; **Page 2.19**—Oxford Designers & Illustrators Ltd. Pearson Education Ltd; **Page 2.20**—Jose Luis Calvo. Shutterstock; **Page 2.21**—David Litman. Shutterstock; **Page 2.22**—VasutinSergey. Shutterstock; **Page 2.23**—eraxion. 123rf.com; **Page 2.23**—Sebastian Kaulitzki. Shutterstock; **Page 2.23**—Sebastian Kaulitzki/Alamy Stock Photo; **Page 2.24**—BlueRingMedua. Shutterstock; **Page 2.26**—Designua. Shutterstock; **Page 2.26**—Deco Images II/Alamy Stock Photo;

CHAPTER 3

Page 3.5—BSIP SA/Alamy Stock Photo; **Page 3.5**—BSIP SA/Alamy Stock Photo; **Page 3.8**—Scenics & Science/Alamy Stock Photo; **Page 3.8**—blickwinkel/Alamy Stock Photo; **Page 3.8**—blickwinkel/ Alamy Stock Photo; **Page 3.8**—MELBA PHOTO AGENCY/Alamy Stock Photo; **Page 3.8**—BSIP SA/Alamy Stock Photo; **Page 3.9**—BlueRingMedia. Shutterstock; **Page 3.9**—designua. 123rf.com;

Page 3.9—Emmanuel LATTES/Alamy Stock Photo; **Page 3.10**—Amit John. Pearson India Education Services Pvt. Ltd; **Page 3.14**—Allen McDavid Stoddard. Shutterstock; **Page 3.14**—blickwinkel/Alamy Stock Photo; **Page 3.14**—blickwinkel/Alamy Stock Photo; **Page 3.14**—Wolfilser. Shutterstock; **Page 3.15**—Tunatura. Shutterstock; **Page 3.16**—Marian Uradnik. Shutterstock; **Page 3.17**—BigGabig. Shutterstock; **Page 3.17**—MDWines. Shutterstock; **Page 3.17**—blickwinkel/Alamy Stock Photo; **Page 3.19**—Haydenville, Massachusetts, MA, United States, US USA; **Page 3.22**—peteretchells. 123rf.com; **Page 3.22**—Nigel Cattlin/Alamy Stock Photo; **Page 3.22**—Nigel Cattlin/Alamy Stock Photo; **Page 3.24**—amophoto_au. Shutterstock; **Page 3.24**—Elena Koromysiova. Shutterstock; **Page 3.24**—Cheuk-king Lo. Pearson Education Asia Ltd; **Page 3.24**—photowind. Shutterstock; **Page 3.25**—Monkey Business Images. Shutterstock; **Page 3.25**—frank60. Shutterstock; **Page 3.25**—Kelly Marken. Shutterstock; **Page 3.25**—123rf.com; **Page 3.25**—Julia Pivovarova. Shutterstock; **Page 3.25**—MG photo studio/Alamy Stock Photo; **Page 3.27**—Anne Kitzman. Shutterstock; **Page 3.27**—jeep2499. Shutterstock; **Page 3.27**—220036. Shutterstock; **Page 3.27**—Madlen. Shutterstock; **Page 3.27**—Jan Csernoch/Alamy Stock Photo; **Page 3.27**—Kazakov maksim. Shutterstock; **Page 3.27**—Volodymyr Nikitenko. Shutterstock; **Page 3.28**—F.Neidl. Shutterstock; **Page 3.28**—Manfred Ruckszio. Shutterstock; **Page 3.28**—Steve Lovegrove. Shutterstock; **Page 3.28**—123rf.com; **Page 3.28**—123rf.com; **Page 3.28**—Arto Hakola/Alamy Stock Photo; **Page 3.29**—mlane53. 123rf.com; **Page 3.29**—Egon Zitter. Shutterstock; **Page 3.29**—blickwinkel/Alamy Stock Photo; **Page 3.32**—Alesikka. Shutterstock; **Page 3.32**—kkaplin. Shutterstock; **Page 3.32**—Serp. Shutterstock; **Page 3.32**—Aldona Griskeviciene. Shutterstock; **Page 3.32**—Sozaijiten; **Page 3.40**—ievgen sosnytskyi. Shutterstock;

CHAPTER 4

Page 4.4—Lebendkulturen.de. Shutterstock; **Page 4.4**—WILDLIFE GmbH/Alamy Stock Photo; **Page 4.5**—Andrey Nekrasov/Alamy Stock Photo; **Page 4.5**—Reinhold Leitner. Shutterstock; **Page 4.5**—ellepigrafica. Shutterstock; **Page 4.7**—sciencepics. Shutterstock; **Page 4.11**—WOLF AVNI. Shutterstock; **Page 4.13**—Rattiya Thongdumhyu. Shutterstock; **Page 4.13**—Daniel L. Geiger/SNAP/Alamy Stock Photo; **Page 4.14**—danylyukk1. Shutterstock; **Page 4.15**—Science Picture Co/Alamy Stock Photo; **Page 4.16**—Rattiya Thongdumhyu. Shutterstock; **Page 4.19**—D. Kucharski K. Kucharska. Shutterstock; **Page 4.19**—sydeen. Shutterstock; **Page 4.20**—Vitali Chesnokov. Shutterstock; **Page 4.20**—EcoPrint. Shutterstock; **Page 4.20**—paytai. Shutterstock; **Page 4.20**—Andrew Mackay/Alamy Stock Photo; **Page 4.22**—WILDLIFE GmbH/Alamy Stock Photo; **Page 4.22**—David Litman. Shutterstock; **Page 4.22**—jps. Shutterstock; **Page 4.23**—Mark Boulton/Alamy Stock Photo; **Page 4.23**—Mark Boulton/Alamy Stock Photo; **Page 4.28**—HL Studios. Pearson Education Ltd; **Page 4.33**—Pawel Graczyk. Shutterstock;

CHAPTER 5

Page 5.6—Kletr. Shutterstock; **Page 5.11**—Designua. Shutterstock; **Page 5.11**—alila. 123rf.com; **Page 5.12**—Oxford Designers & Illustrators Ltd. Pearson Education Ltd; **Page 5.13**—Pearson Education Ltd; **Page 5.15**—Peter Probst/Alamy Stock Photo; **Page 5.16**—Moonnoon. Shutterstock;

CHAPTER 6

Page 6.7—D. Kucharski K. Kucharska. Shutterstock; **Page 6.9**—Jim Parkin/Alamy Stock Photo; **Page 6.9**—inga spence/Alamy Stock Photo; **Page 6.10**—Nigel Cattlin/Alamy Stock Photo; **Page 6.11**—PerryÂ´s photography. Shutterstock; **Page 6.11**—891772. Shutterstock; **Page 6.11**—Pavel Mikoska. Shutterstock; **Page 6.11**—Nigel Cattlin/Alamy Stock Photo; **Page 6.14**—John Foxx Collection. Imagestate; **Page 6.16**—Olgysha. Shutterstock; **Page 6.17**—WILDLIFE GmbH/Alamy Stock Photo;

CHAPTER 7

Page 7.3—NoPainNoGain. Shutterstock; **Page 7.9**—Tim Graham / Alamy Stock Photo; **Page 7.10**—Dragan Zivkovic / Alamy Stock Photo; **Page 7.14**—Kachailo / Shutterstock; **Page 7.14**—fabio lamanna / Alamy Stock Photo; **Page 7.14**—Dinodia Photos / Alamy Stock Photo; **Page 7.14**—Scott Nodine / Alamy Stock Photo; **Page 7.16**—Yuri Kravchenko / Alamy Stock Photo; **Page 7.16**—Daniel Dempster Photography / Alamy Stock Photo;